Oxidative Stress and Inflammation as Targets for Novel Preventive and Therapeutic Approches in Non Communicable Diseases

Oxidative Stress and Inflammation as Targets for Novel Preventive and Therapeutic Approches in Non Communicable Diseases

Special Issue Editors

Chiara Nediani
Lisa Giovannelli

MDPI • Basel • Beijing • Wuhan • Barcelona • Belgrade • Manchester • Tokyo • Cluj • Tianjin

Special Issue Editors
Chiara Nediani
University of Florence
Italy

Lisa Giovannelli
University of Florence
Italy

Editorial Office
MDPI
St. Alban-Anlage 66
4052 Basel, Switzerland

This is a reprint of articles from the Special Issue published online in the open access journal *Antioxidants* (ISSN 2076-3921) (available at: https://www.mdpi.com/journal/antioxidants/special_issues/oxidative_stress_inflammation).

For citation purposes, cite each article independently as indicated on the article page online and as indicated below:

LastName, A.A.; LastName, B.B.; LastName, C.C. Article Title. *Journal Name* **Year**, *Article Number*, Page Range.

ISBN 978-3-03928-935-6 (Pbk)
ISBN 978-3-03928-936-3 (PDF)

Cover image courtesy of Chiara Nediani and Lisa Giovannelli.

Contents

About the Special Issue Editors . . . . **vii**

Chiara Nediani and Lisa Giovannelli
Oxidative Stress and Inflammation as Targets for Novel Preventive and Therapeutic Approches
in Non Communicable Diseases
Reprinted from: *Antioxidants* **2020**, *9*, 290, doi:10.3390/polym9040290 . . . . **1**

Tammy D. Kim, Suji Lee and Sujung Yoon
Inflammation in Post-Traumatic Stress Disorder (PTSD): A Review of Potential Correlates of
PTSD with a Neurological Perspective
Reprinted from: *Antioxidants* **2020**, *9*, 107, doi:10.3390/polym9020107 . . . . **7**

**Timon-Orest Trakkides, Nicole Schäfer, Maria Reichenthaler, Konstanze Kühn,
Ricardo J. M. G. E. Brandwijk, Erik J. M. Toonen, Florian Urban, Joachim Wegener,
Volker Enzmann and Diana Pauly**
Oxidative Stress Increases Endogenous Complement-Dependent Inflammatory and
Angiogenic Responses in Retinal Pigment Epithelial Cells Independently of Exogenous
Complement Sources
Reprinted from: *Antioxidants* **2019**, *8*, 548, doi:10.3390/antiox8110548 . . . . **31**

**Cristina Luceri, Elisabetta Bigagli, Sara Agostiniani, Francesco Giudici, Daniela Zambonin,
Stefano Scaringi, Ferdinando Ficari, Maura Lodovici and Cecilia Malentacchi**
Analysis of Oxidative Stress-Related Markers in Crohn's Disease Patients at Surgery and
Correlations with Clinical Findings
Reprinted from: *Antioxidants* **2019**, *8*, 378, doi:10.3390/antiox8090378 . . . . **47**

Hao-Hsiang Chang, Shih-Ping Hsu and Chiang-Ting Chien
Intrarenal Transplantation of Hypoxic Preconditioned Mesenchymal Stem Cells Improves
Glomerulonephritis through Anti-Oxidation, Anti-ER Stress, Anti-Inflammation,
Anti-Apoptosis, and Anti-Autophagy
Reprinted from: *Antioxidants* **2020**, *9*, 2, doi:10.3390/antiox9010002 . . . . **59**

Faisal Nuhu, Anne-Marie Seymour and Sunil Bhandari
Impact of Intravenous Iron on Oxidative Stress and Mitochondrial Function in Experimental
Chronic Kidney Disease
Reprinted from: *Antioxidants* **2019**, *8*, 498, doi:10.3390/antiox8100498 . . . . **77**

Chiara Nediani, Jessica Ruzzolini, Annalisa Romani and Lido Calorini
Oleuropein, a Bioactive Compound from *Olea europaea* L., as a Potential Preventive and
Therapeutic Agent in Non-Communicable Diseases
Reprinted from: *Antioxidants* **2019**, *8*, 578, doi:10.3390/antiox8120578 . . . . **97**

**Jin-Ming Meng, Shi-Yu Cao, Xin-Lin Wei, Ren-You Gan, Yuan-Feng Wang, Shu-Xian Cai,
Xiao-Yu Xu, Pang-Zhen Zhang and Hua-Bin Li**
Effects and Mechanisms of Tea for the Prevention and Management of Diabetes Mellitus and
Diabetic Complications: An Updated Review
Reprinted from: *Antioxidants* **2019**, *8*, 170, doi:10.3390/antiox8060170 . . . . **123**

Ji Eun Park, Heaji Lee, Sun Yeou Kim and Yunsook Lim
Lespedeza bicolor Extract Ameliorated Renal Inflammation by Regulation of NLRP3
Inflammasome-Associated Hyperinflammation in Type 2 Diabetic Mice
Reprinted from: *Antioxidants* **2020**, *9*, 148, doi:10.3390/antiox9020148 . . . . **149**

Zaidatul Akmal Othman, Wan Syaheedah Wan Ghazali, Liza Noordin,
Nurul Aiman Mohd. Yusof and Mahaneem Mohamed
Phenolic Compounds and the Anti-Atherogenic Effect of Bee Bread in High-Fat Diet-Induced
Obese Rats
Reprinted from: *Antioxidants* **2020**, *9*, 33, doi:10.3390/antiox9010033 . . . . **163**

Vladana Domazetovic, Gemma Marcucci, Irene Falsetti, Anna Rita Bilia,
Maria Teresa Vincenzini, Maria Luisa Brandi and Teresa Iantomasi
Blueberry Juice Antioxidants Protect Osteogenic Activity against Oxidative Stress and Improve
Long-Term Activation of the Mineralization Process in Human Osteoblast-Like SaOS-2 Cells:
Involvement of SIRT1
Reprinted from: *Antioxidants* **2020**, *9*, 125, doi:10.3390/antiox9020125 . . . . **175**

Andrea Nieto-Veloza, Zhihong Wang, Qixin Zhong, Hari B. Krishnan and Vermont P. Dia
BG-4 from Bitter Gourd (*Momordica charantia*) Differentially Affects Inflammation In Vitro and
In Vivo
Reprinted from: *Antioxidants* **2019**, *8*, 175, doi:10.3390/antiox8060175 . . . . **195**

Daniela Figueroa Gonzalez and Fiona Young
Gamma Tocopherol Reduced Chemotherapeutic- Induced ROS in an Ovarian Granulosa Cell
Line, But Not in Breast Cancer Cell Lines In Vitro
Reprinted from: *Antioxidants* **2020**, *9*, 51, doi:10.3390/antiox9010051 . . . . **207**

Roberta Fusco, Rosalba Siracusa, Ramona D'Amico, Alessio Filippo Peritore,
Marika Cordaro, Enrico Gugliandolo, Rosalia Crupi, Daniela Impellizzeri,
Salvatore Cuzzocrea and Rosanna Di Paola
Melatonin Plus Folic Acid Treatment Ameliorates Reserpine-Induced Fibromyalgia:
An Evaluation of Pain, Oxidative Stress, and Inflammation
Reprinted from: *Antioxidants* **2019**, *8*, 628, doi:10.3390/antiox8120628 . . . . **227**

Yun-Ho Kim, Min-Kyung Kang, Eun-Jung Lee, Dong Yeon Kim, Hyeongjoo Oh, Soo-Il Kim,
Su Yeon Oh, Kyung-Hee Kim, Sang-Jae Park, Yean-Jung Choi and Young-Hee Kang
Dried Yeast Extracts Curtails Pulmonary Oxidative Stress, Inflammation and Tissue Destruction
in a Model of Experimental Emphysema
Reprinted from: *Antioxidants* **2019**, *8*, 349, doi:10.3390/antiox8090349 . . . . **243**

About the Special Issue Editors

Chiara Nediani studied Biological Sciences at Florence University (Italy). She then completed her studies obtaining her post-graduate diploma in clinical biochemistry. In 2001, she was appointed Researcher of Clinical Biochemistry at the University of Florence and, in 2006, was promoted to Associate Professor. She currently works at the Dipartimento di Scienze Biomediche, Sperimentali e Cliniche "Mario Serio", University of Florence. Her research topics include: regulatory mechanisms of calcium homeostasis in cardiac and skeletal muscle; biochemical aspects and molecular mechanisms of myocardial damage induced by ischemia–reperfusion in cell models and in pigs undergoing volume and pressure overload; and oxidative stress mechanisms in end-stage human failing hearts. Currently, she is working on biochemical aspects and molecular mechanisms induced by oleuropein on amiloid aggregates, neuroblastoma cells, cardiomyocytes, and melanoma cells. She is the scientist responsible and member of various research project units of relevant national interest (PRIN) and private foundations (Telethon and Cassa di Risparmio di Firenze).

Lisa Giovannelli studied biological sciences at Florence University (Italy). She then completed her Ph.D. studies on the role of the cholinergic and purinergic system in the aging brain and the effect of the pharmacological modulation of these pathways, and was awarded her Ph.D. in 1990 from Florence University. In 1996, she was appointed Assistant Professor of Pharmacology at the School of Pharmacy of the University of Florence. She was promoted to Associate Professor (Pharmacology and Toxicology) in 2014. Her main research topics are: DNA damage as a biomarker of the effects of environmental pollutants, degenerative pathologies, and aging in experimental models and in humans; the protective effects of natural antioxidant compounds toward age-related dysfunctions and age-related markers in humans, in laboratory animals and in cell cultures. She has been involved in EU projects on polyphenols and flavonoids (POLYBIND, 1999–2002; FLAVO 2005–2008; NuGO network of Excellence, 2004–2010) and on DNA damage as a marker in human biomonitoring (ESCODD, 1999–2002; EU COST Action hCOMET, 2017–2020).

Editorial

Oxidative Stress and Inflammation as Targets for Novel Preventive and Therapeutic Approches in Non Communicable Diseases

Chiara Nediani [1],* and Lisa Giovannelli [2]

[1] Department of Experimental and Clinical Biomedical Sciences "Mario Serio", viale Morgagni 50, 50134 Florence, Italy

[2] Department of Neurosciences, Psychology, Drug Research and Child Health (NEUROFARBA), Section of Pharmacology and Toxicology, University of Florence, 50139 Florence, Italy; lisa.giovannelli@unifi.it

* Correspondence: chiara.nediani@unifi.it

Received: 25 March 2020; Accepted: 28 March 2020; Published: 31 March 2020

As recently reported by the World Health Organization (WHO), Non-Communicable Diseases (NCDs) has been rising over the last century representing the main cause of death and disability for the general population regardless of age, region, or gender [1,2]. NCDs are chronic diseases characterized by long duration and slow progression that account for most ageing-related diseases including cardiovascular and neurodegenerative diseases, cancer, diabetes mellitus and chronic kidney disease. Inflammation, oxidative stress and dysregulated authophagy are common features in NCDs that participate in the progression of these diseases, and may be key targets for the development of novel preventive and therapeutic strategies [3]. This Special Issue consists of 14 articles related to the establishing of specific biomarkers of the features that detail the pathogenesis of the diseases in order to make the correct diagnosis, to evaluate the evolution of the disease and to open up novel strategies of assessment and intervention for the disorders. Kim et al. [4] summarized in a review the recent evidence on the effect of oxidative stress and inflammation on Post-Traumatic Stress Disorder (PTSD), a chronic debilitating condition resulting from trauma exposition. The authors reported that these may be the causes of the neuroinflammatory responses within the brain. In particular, the over-expression of key inflammatory markers, such as IL-6, may be a result of peripheral cytokines, crossing the blood-brain barrier in response to trauma and psychosocial stress, thus leading to neurodegeneration and to neural tissue loss, followed by dysfunction in the respective brain regions. Indeed neuroimaging-based studies have demonstrated that altered inflammatory markers are associated with structural and functional alterations in brain regions that are responsible for the regulation of stress and emotion. Therefore, the different levels of IL-6 in the serum of individuals exposed to trauma according to the source of oxidative stress, suggest that they may be considered as a peripheral marker for PTSD based on trauma type (the presence of TBI or loss of consciousness, or psychosocial trauma). Oxidative stress and chronic inflammation are also responsible for the damage to retinal pigment epithelium (RPE) that contribute to several retinal degenerative diseases, such as age-related macular degeneration or Stargardt disease. Trakkides et al. [5], for the first time, reported that oxidative stress induced an increased expression of the complement regulators (CFH) and properdin and the central complement protein C3 in RPE cells independent of an external complement source. These increases are, on the other hand, associated with inflammasome activation that, subsequently, enhanced secretion of proinflammatory and proangiogenic factors. The authors concluded that complement proteins and receptors derived from RPE were involved in cell homeostasis following oxidative stress and should be considered as targets for treatment development of retinal degeneration. The finding of peripheral biomarkers of oxidative stress correlated with the clinical status of Crohn's disease (CD) patients, affected by a chronic inflammatory disorder of the intestinal tract, is the aim of the study by Luceri et al. [6]. Indeed these patients are at high risk of post-operative recurrence, so discovering new tools for the assessment of disease activity are needed to prevent long-term complications. In these patients, inflamed bowel tissue and inflammatory cells generate an increase in reactive oxidative species (ROS) that activates a pathogenic cascade, which further exacerbates inflammation and leads to increased oxidative damage to DNA, proteins, and lipids. They found elevated levels of serum advanced oxidation protein product (AOPP), advanced glycated end-products (AGEs), and thiobarbituric acid reactive substances, all markers of oxidative damage, in CD patients with severe relapse, suggesting that these parameters could be evaluated in a prospective as biomarkers for diagnosis or monitoring of CD patients. Therefore, because AOPP and AGEs activate the membrane receptor for advanced glycation end products (RAGE) involved in inflammatory diseases, they hypothesized that AOPP/AGEs activation of RAGE signaling may represent a pathogenic factor in the acute phase of the disease.

Several approaches have been used to prevent damage from oxidative stress and inflammation. In the context of glomerulonephritis (GN), where heterogenous renal conditions lead end stage renal disease (ESRD), many patients are irresponsive towards the standard immunosuppressive therapies, so alternative interventions to cure or prevent GN-related deterioration is very important from both public health and economic points of view. Increased oxidative stress contributes to the pathogenesis of mesangial proliferative GN. Mesenchymal stem cells (MSCs) of various origins, improve kidney injury because they possess an intrinsic anti-oxidative ability. Chang et al. [7] showed that intrarenal transplantation of hypoxic preconditioned MSCs (HMSC), in an anti-Thy1.1-induced rat glomerulonephritis, was a more effective strategy compared with normal MSC, because HMSC, by activating hypoxic inducible factor-1 /VEGF/Nrf2 (HIF-1 /VEGF/Nrf2) signaling, promoted a further intrinsic anti-oxidative defense preserving anti-oxidant proteins and anti-oxidative responsive element proteins, and, subsequently, reduced glomerular apoptosis, autophagy, and inflammation. Another study by Nuhu et al. [8] showed that the use of i.v. iron concomitantly with antioxidant therapy may improve iron deficiency anemia (IDA) in chronic kidney disease (CKD) without significant impact on renal function or oxidant status. It is well known that IDA can exacerbate mitochondrial dysfunction and enhance oxidative stress in patients with CKD. In an experimental-induced rat model of uremia they found that intravenous iron therapy had a modest impact on iron deficiency anemia in uremic animals, but reduced systemic lipid peroxidation and upregulated systemic GPx activity; in addition it increased mitochondrial maximal respiration and respiratory reserve capacity, suggesting a mitochondrial adaptation or upregulation of their numbers or function.

Many epidemiological and clinical trial studies support that many foods commonly consumed in the Mediterranean diet (MD) contain bioactive compounds with helpful activities which are considered to play significant roles in the prevention and treatment of many diseases [9,10]. Among which olive oil, and in particular extra virgin olive oil (EVOO), is well recognized as one of the healthiest foods in the human diet [11]. The beneficial effects of EVOO is the result of the combination of functional components, such as fatty acid composition (with a high content of oleic acid) and wide minor bioactive constituents, among which polyphenols such as oleuropein from *Olea europaea* L. Several biological properties attributed to oleuropein, providing beneficial effects in the prevention of degenerative diseases, are mainly based on its antioxidant potential [12], but a recent review by Nediani et al. [2] describes how oleuropein has multi-target activity including the anti-inflammatory [13], the anti-amyloid aggregation [14], anti-hypertensive [15], hypoglycemic [16], cardioprotective [17], autophagy inducer [18,19] and anticancer [20], also in combination with standard anti-cancer drugs [21]. In this context, the anti-proliferative and pro-apoptosis activity of oleuropein, in addition to its ability to reduce the glycolytic metabolism of different tumor types [22], it might represent an effective tool for complementary cancer therapy. Due to these biological and biomedical effects of oleuropein, special attention is devoted to the recovery, recycling, and upgrading of food waste, leaves and by-products for its use in agronomic, nutraceutical, and biomedical applications [23]. The beneficial effects of olive and tea leaves or different preparations (e.g., infusions, extracts) have been known since ancient times, and have been used as traditional herbal remedies for the treatment of many diseases, such as diabetes mellitus. Diabetes mellitus is the most prevalent metabolic disorder and is becoming a serious worldwide public health threat because it induces serious complications in several organs. In a wide review Meng et al. [24] summarizes and discusses the effect of tea in the prevention and management of diabetes mellitus and its complications, based on findings from epidemiological, experimental, and clinical studies. Tea, in particular green tea, contains many bioactive compounds, such as catechin like epigallocatechin-3-gallate (EGCG), that seems to have a protective effect on type 1 and 2 diabetes mellitus by protecting pancreatic cells, ameliorating insulin resistance and decreasing hyperglycemia. In addition, tea and its bioactive components, due to their anti-inflammatory and antioxidant potentials, may be used in the prevention of diabetic nephropathy, neuropathy, retinopathy and cardiovascular risks. In addition to tea several other medical plants or natural products have been found to have an anti-diabetic effect with an amelioration of kidney dysfunction due to hyperglycemia-induced renal inflammation. Park et al. [25] showed the protective effect against the diabetic complication of *Lespedeza bicolor* extract (LBE) a perennial deciduous shrub belonging to the Leguminosae family that contains antioxidant phenolic components including genistein, quercetin, and naringin, in an *in vivo* animal diabetic model. They found that LBE supplementation, in addition to decreasing serum fasting blood glucose and glycated hemoglobin A1 at a low dose, improved kidney dysfunction, as demonstrated by a lowered urine albumin-creatinine ratio, while at high dose plasma creatinine, blood urea nitrogen and glomerular hypertrophy appeared to have declined. Furthermore, in T2DM mice a high dose of LBE supplementation significantly attenuated renal hyper-inflammation associated with NLRP3 inflammasome and oxidative stress related to nuclear factor erythroid 2-related factor 2. In the same animal model a low dose of LBE supplementation up-regulated energy metabolism through activation of the adenosine monophosphate kinase (AMPK) /Sirtuin (SIRT)-1 pathway. They concluded that LB supplementation might have beneficial effects to prevent and ameliorate hyperglycemia-induced renal inflammation under diabetic conditions.

T2DM is often associated with obesity (Diabesity) to be defined as the XXI Century epidemic. It is a condition linked to many cardiovascular factor risks such as dyslipidemia, hypertension, and coronary artery disease. Obesity, in particular, may be prevented by an adequate lifestyle and treated, at the preclinical stage with a well-balanced diet, sometimes rich in phenolic compounds. The study of Othman et al. [26] showed the anti-atherogenic effect in high-fat diet (HFD)-induced obese rats of a Malaysian bee bread, that contained, in addition to macronutrient sources and essential minerals and vitamins, also phenolic components such as isorhamnetin, apigenin, caffeic acid, ferulic acid, and kaempferol, which have antioxidant properties. They demonstrated that supplementation of bee bread for 6 weeks reduced the Lee obesity index and levels of total cholesterol, low-density lipoprotein, fatty acid synthase activity and of the atherogenic index, an indicator of high risk to develop CVD. Additionally, the markers of the lipid oxidation process such as oxidised-LDL, and malondialdehyde were significantly decreased, probably due to an increase in aortic antioxidant activities, such as those of superoxide dismutase and glutathione peroxidase. The hypocholesterolemic effect may be attributed to the presence of ferulic and caffeic acids, while kaempferol appears to have an anti-inflammatory effect. These results suggest that bee bread has anti-atherogenic property, partly due to the presence of phenolic compounds which have high antioxidant, anti-inflammatory and hypocholesterolemic properties.

Diets rich in antioxidants may be very important in the prevention and treatment of osteoporosis also. In this context it fit the study of Domazetovic et al. [27] that demonstrated how blueberry juice (BJ) containing a high content of polyphenols, in particular anthocyanins, was able to prevent, in human osteoblast-like SaOS-2 cells, a cellular model to study osteoblast functions, the inhibition of osteogenic differentiation and the mineralization process, due to oxidative stress induced by glutathione depletion. The latter is a condition that mimics a metabolic status of oxidative stress that may occur during estrogen deficiency, as well as in aging and inflammatory diseases, where the decrease in antioxidants leads to accelerated bone loss and, thus, to osteoporosis or osteopenia. The polyphenolic content of BJ exerted its antioxidant action and protection from oxidative stress damage, by upregulating alkaline phosphatase and Runt-related transcription factor 2, markers of the osteoblast differentiation process and regulation of bone remodeling. These factors are, in turn, modulated by activation of SIRT1 expression, a possible molecular target for anti-osteoporotic drugs. These data demonstrated the beneficial effects of BJ rich in polyphenols on bone regeneration, and suggest its use as a dietary supplement for osteoporosis prevention and therapies.

As reported above the search for new antioxidants to be used in therapy and prevention of NCDs often relies on plants. Similar to chemically synthesized molecules, plant bioactive compounds often show multiple activities and specificity towards certain cell types. In this respect, the work by Nieto-Veloza et al. [28] investigates the anti-inflammatory effects of a peptide called BG-4, extracted from a plant of the Cucurbitaceae family, Momordica charantia, known as bitter gourd, cultivated in Asia, Africa, and South America. Previous data indicated a possible anticancer activity of the peptide in the colon. Although active *in vitro* in reducing inflammation and oxidative stress markers in lipopolysaccharide (LPS)-activated mouse macrophages, the peptide was not effective in a model of DSS-induced colitis in mice. Indeed, BG-4 administered to mice at a dose supposed to mimic the concentration effective *in vitro*, aggravated the symptoms. Surprisingly, a reduction of inflammatory cytokines was found in serum but not in colon tissue. Thus, this work points out to the fact that mechanisms such as reduction of NO production, that are protective in simple *in vitro* models, like isolated macrophages, can be toxic in complex *in vivo* systems like colon mucosa, where NO production can exert beneficial effects in enterocytes. Another example of cell specificity is provided by the work of Figueroa-Gonzales and Young [29], who investigated the possible beneficial role of γ-tocoferol in ovarian cancer, based on its ability to both reduce ROS and exert cytotoxicity on cancer cells, making it a good candidate to be used as an adjunctive therapy, helping to preserve proliferating non-cancer cells in the granulosa and avoid post-treatment infertility. They showed that γ-tocoferol was indeed able to reduce chemotherapeutic-generated ROS in ovarian cancer cell lines COV434 and OVCAR, but not in breast cancer cell lines.

Combinations of different compounds or complex matrixes of plant origin can often provide additional advantages compared to single molecules. Fusco et al. [30] showed the positive effects of the combination of melatonin, active on chronobiology, but also a sedative, anesthetic and anti-inflammatory molecule, and folic acid, an antioxidant and immunostimulating agent, in a rat model of fibromyalgia. As for many algic pathologies, an oxidative component has been recently proposed for fibromyalgia, and the addition of an antioxidant compound to different therapeutic strategies appears feasible. The results show that the combination increased the pain threshold, improved motility, reduced lipid and protein oxidation and expression of inflammatory markers in the brain more effectively than the single compounds. Asthma and chronic obstructive pulmonary disease are another research field in which the oxidative component plays an important role, and many plant-derived products have shown a potential beneficial role, which can be, at least in part,attributed to their antioxidant activity. As an example of a complex plant-derived matrix, Kim et al. [31] have investigated the effects of an orally administered dried yeast extract in a mouse model of emphysema induced by passive cigarette smoking. Analyses on animal pulmonary tissue and *in vitro* experiments in the human alveolar cell line A549 showed that the extract was able to reduce cigarette smoking-induced inflammation, apoptosis and proteolytic activity in bronchial and pulmonary tissues, thus reducing emphysema. This effect was accompanied by a reduction in ROS production in the tissue.

Conflicts of Interest: The authors declare no conflicts of interest.

References

1. Reddy, K.S. Global Burden of Disease Study 2015 provides GPS for global health 2030. *Lancet* **2016**, *388*, 1448–1449. [CrossRef]
2. Nediani, C.; Ruzzolini, J.; Romani, A.; Calorini, L. Oleuropein, a Bioactive Compound from *Olea europaea* L., as a Potential Preventive and Therapeutic Agent in Non-Communicable Diseases. *Antioxidants* **2019**, *8*, 578. [CrossRef] [PubMed]

3. Peña-Oyarzun, D.; Bravo-Sagua, R.; Diaz-Vega, A.; Aleman, L.; Chiong, M.; Garcia, L.; Bambs, C.; Troncoso, R.; Cifuentes, M.; Morselli, E.; et al. Autophagy and oxidative stress in non-communicable diseases: A matter of the inflammatory state? *Free Radic. Biol. Med.* **2018**, *124*, 61–78. [CrossRef] [PubMed]

4. Kim, T.D.; Lee, S.; Yoon, S. Inflammation in Post-Traumatic Stress Disorder (PTSD): A Review of Potential Correlates of PTSD with a Neurological Perspective. *Antioxidants* **2020**, *9*, 107. [CrossRef]

5. Trakkides, T.O.; Schäfer, N.; Reichenthaler, M.; Kühn, K.; Brandwijk, R.J.; Toonen, E.J.; Urban, F.; Wegener, J.; Enzmann, V.; Pauly, D. Oxidative Stress Increases Endogenous Complement-Dependent Inflammatory and Angiogenic Responses in Retinal Pigment Epithelial Cells Independently of Exogenous Complement Sources. *Antioxidants* **2019**, *8*, 548. [CrossRef] [PubMed]

6. Luceri, C.; Bigagli, E.; Agostiniani, S.; Giudici, F.; Zambonin, D.; Scaringi, S.; Ficari, F.; Lodovici, M.; Malentacchi, C. Analysis of Oxidative Stress-Related Markers in Crohn's Disease Patients at Surgery and Correlations with Clinical Findings. *Antioxidants* **2019**, *8*, 378. [CrossRef]

7. Chang, H.-H.; Hsu, S.-P.; Chien, C.-T. Intrarenal Transplantation of Hypoxic Preconditioned Mesenchymal Stem Cells Improves Glomerulonephritis through Anti-Oxidation, Anti-ER Stress, Anti-Inflammation, Anti-Apoptosis, and Anti-Autophagy. *Antioxidants* **2019**, *9*, 2. [CrossRef]

8. Nuhu, F.; Seymour, A.-M.; Bhandari, S. Impact of Intravenous Iron on Oxidative Stress and Mitochondrial Function in Experimental Chronic Kidney Disease. *Antioxidants* **2019**, *8*, 498. [CrossRef]

9. Grosso, G.; Marventano, S.; Yang, J.; Micek, A.; Pajak, A.; Scalfi, L.; Galvano, F.; Kales, S.N. A comprehensive meta-analysis on evidence of Mediterranean diet and cardiovascular disease: Are individual components equal? *Crit. Rev. Food Sci. Nutr.* **2017**, *57*, 3218–3232. [CrossRef]

10. De Lorenzo, A.; Noce, A.; Bigioni, M.; Calabrese, V.; Della Rocca, D.; Daniele, N.; Tozzo, C.; Renzo, L. The Effects of Italian Mediterranean Organic Diet (IMOD) on Health Status. *CPD* **2010**, *16*, 814–824. [CrossRef]

11. Gaforio, J.J.; Visioli, F.; Alarcón-de-la-Lastra, C.; Castañer, O.; Delgado-Rodríguez, M.; Fitó, M.; Hernández, A.F.; Huertas, J.R.; Martínez-González, M.A.; Menendez, J.A.; et al. Virgin Olive Oil and Health: Summary of the III International Conference on Virgin Olive Oil and Health Consensus Report, JAEN (Spain) 2018. *Nutrients* **2019**, *11*, 2039. [CrossRef] [PubMed]

12. Visioli, F.; Bellomo, G.; Galli, C. Free Radical-Scavenging Properties of Olive Oil Polyphenols. *Biochem. Biophys. Res. Commun.* **1998**, *247*, 60–64. [CrossRef] [PubMed]

13. Margheri, F.; Menicacci, B.; Laurenzana, A.; Del Rosso, M.; Fibbi, G.; Cipolleschi, M.G.; Ruzzolini, J.; Nediani, C.; Mocali, A.; Giovannelli, L. Oleuropein aglycone attenuates the pro-angiogenic phenotype of senescent fibroblasts: A functional study in endothelial cells. *J. Funct. Foods* **2019**, *53*, 219–226. [CrossRef]

14. Rigacci, S.; Guidotti, V.; Bucciantini, M.; Parri, M.; Nediani, C.; Cerbai, E.; Stefani, M.; Berti, A. Oleuropein aglycon prevents cytotoxic amyloid aggregation of human amylin. *J. Nutr. Biochem.* **2010**, *21*, 726–735. [CrossRef]

15. Susalit, E.; Agus, N.; Effendi, I.; Tjandrawinata, R.R.; Nofiarny, D.; Perrinjaquet-Moccetti, T.; Verbruggen, M. Olive (*Olea europaea*) leaf extract effective in patients with stage-1 hypertension: Comparison with Captopril. *Phytomedicine* **2011**, *18*, 251–258. [CrossRef]

16. Murotomi, K.; Umeno, A.; Yasunaga, M.; Shichiri, M.; Ishida, N.; Koike, T.; Matsuo, T.; Abe, H.; Yoshida, Y.; Nakajima, Y. Oleuropein-Rich Diet Attenuates Hyperglycemia and Impaired Glucose Tolerance in Type 2 Diabetes Model Mouse. *J. Agric. Food Chem.* **2015**, *63*, 6715–6722. [CrossRef]

17. Lockyer, S.; Corona, G.; Yaqoob, P.; Spencer, J.P.E.; Rowland, I. Secoiridoids delivered as olive leaf extract induce acute improvements in human vascular function and reduction of an inflammatory cytokine: A randomised, double-blind, placebo-controlled, cross-over trial. *Br. J. Nutr.* **2015**, *114*, 75–83. [CrossRef]

18. Rigacci, S.; Miceli, C.; Nediani, C.; Berti, A.; Cascella, R.; Pantano, D.; Nardiello, P.; Luccarini, I.; Casamenti, F.; Stefani, M. Oleuropein aglycone induces autophagy via the AMPK/mTOR signalling pathway: A mechanistic insight. *Oncotarget* **2015**, *6*, 35344–35357. [CrossRef]

19. Miceli, C.; Santin, Y.; Manzella, N.; Coppini, R.; Berti, A.; Stefani, M.; Parini, A.; Mialet-Perez, J.; Nediani, C. Oleuropein Aglycone Protects against MAO-A-Induced Autophagy Impairment and Cardiomyocyte Death through Activation of TFEB. *Oxid. Med. Cell. Longev.* **2018**, *2018*, 1–13. [CrossRef]

20. Shamshoum, H.; Vlavcheski, F.; Tsiani, E. Anticancer effects of oleuropein: Anticancer effects of oleuropein. *BioFactors* **2017**, *43*, 517–528. [CrossRef]

21. Ruzzolini, J.; Peppicelli, S.; Andreucci, E.; Bianchini, F.; Scardigli, A.; Romani, A.; la Marca, G.; Nediani, C.; Calorini, L. Oleuropein, the Main Polyphenol of *Olea europaea* Leaf Extract, Has an Anti-Cancer Effect on

Human BRAF Melanoma Cells and Potentiates the Cytotoxicity of Current Chemotherapies. *Nutrients* **2018**, *10*, 1950. [CrossRef] [PubMed]

22. Ruzzolini, J.; Peppicelli, S.; Bianchini, F.; Andreucci, E.; Urciuoli, S.; Romani, A.; Tortora, K.; Caderni, G.; Nediani, C.; Calorini, L. Cancer Glycolytic Dependence as a New Target of Olive Leaf Extract. *Cancers* **2020**, *12*, 317. [CrossRef] [PubMed]

23. Romani, A.; Ieri, F.; Urciuoli, S.; Noce, A.; Marrone, G.; Nediani, C.; Bernini, R. Health Effects of Phenolic Compounds Found in Extra-Virgin Olive Oil, By-Products, and Leaf of *Olea europaea* L. *Nutrients* **2019**, *11*, 1776. [CrossRef] [PubMed]

24. Meng, J.-M.; Cao, S.-Y.; Wei, X.-L.; Gan, R.-Y.; Wang, Y.-F.; Cai, S.-X.; Xu, X.-Y.; Zhang, P.-Z.; Li, H.-B. Effects and Mechanisms of Tea for the Prevention and Management of Diabetes Mellitus and Diabetic Complications: An Updated Review. *Antioxidants* **2019**, *8*, 170. [CrossRef]

25. Park, J.E.; Lee, H.; Kim, S.Y.; Lim, Y. Lespedeza bicolor Extract Ameliorated Renal Inflammation by Regulation of NLRP3 Inflammasome-Associated Hyperinflammation in Type 2 Diabetic Mice. *Antioxidants* **2020**, *9*, 148. [CrossRef]

26. Othman, Z.A.; Wan Ghazali, W.S.; Noordin, L.; Mohd. Yusof, N.A.; Mohamed, M. Phenolic Compounds and the Anti-Atherogenic Effect of Bee Bread in High-Fat Diet-Induced Obese Rats. *Antioxidants* **2019**, *9*, 33. [CrossRef]

27. Domazetovic, V.; Marcucci, G.; Falsetti, I.; Bilia, A.R.; Vincenzini, M.T.; Brandi, M.L.; Iantomasi, T. Blueberry Juice Antioxidants Protect Osteogenic Activity against Oxidative Stress and Improve Long-Term Activation of the Mineralization Process in Human Osteoblast-Like SaOS-2 Cells: Involvement of SIRT1. *Antioxidants* **2020**, *9*, 125. [CrossRef]

28. Nieto-Veloza, A.; Wang, Z.; Zhong, Q.; Krishnan, H.B.; Dia, V.P. BG-4 from Bitter Gourd (*Momordica charantia*) Differentially Affects Inflammation In Vitro and In Vivo. *Antioxidants* **2019**, *8*, 175. [CrossRef]

29. Figueroa Gonzalez, D.; Young, F. Gamma Tocopherol Reduced Chemotherapeutic-Induced ROS in an Ovarian Granulosa Cell Line, But Not in Breast Cancer Cell Lines In Vitro. *Antioxidants* **2020**, *9*, 51. [CrossRef]

30. Fusco, R.; Siracusa, R.; D'Amico, R.; Peritore, A.F.; Cordaro, M.; Gugliandolo, E.; Crupi, R.; Impellizzeri, D.; Cuzzocrea, S.; Di Paola, R. Melatonin Plus Folic Acid Treatment Ameliorates Reserpine-Induced Fibromyalgia: An Evaluation of Pain, Oxidative Stress, and Inflammation. *Antioxidants* **2019**, *8*, 628. [CrossRef]

31. Kim, Y.-H.; Kang, M.-K.; Lee, E.-J.; Kim, D.; Oh, H.; Kim, S.-I.; Oh, S.; Kim, K.-H.; Park, S.-J.; Choi, Y.-J.; et al. Dried Yeast Extracts Curtails Pulmonary Oxidative Stress, Inflammation and Tissue Destruction in a Model of Experimental Emphysema. *Antioxidants* **2019**, *8*, 349. [CrossRef] [PubMed]

Review

Inflammation in Post-Traumatic Stress Disorder (PTSD): A Review of Potential Correlates of PTSD with a Neurological Perspective

Tammy D. Kim [1], Suji Lee [1,2] and Sujung Yoon [1,2,*]

[1]   Ewha Brain Institute, Ewha Womans University, Seoul 03770, Korea; damih.m.kim@gmail.com (T.D.K.);
       suji.j.lee@gmail.com (S.L.)
[2]   Department of Brain and Cognitive Sciences, Ewha Womans University, Seoul 03770, Korea
*   Correspondence: sujungjyoon@ewha.ac.kr; Tel.: +82-2-3277-2478

Received: 31 December 2019; Accepted: 22 January 2020; Published: 26 January 2020

Abstract: Post-traumatic stress disorder (PTSD) is a chronic condition characterized by symptoms of physiological and psychosocial burden. While growing research demonstrated signs of inflammation in PTSD, specific biomarkers that may be representative of PTSD such as the detailed neural correlates underlying the inflammatory responses in relation to trauma exposure are seldom discussed. Here, we review recent studies that explored alterations in key inflammatory markers in PTSD, as well as neuroimaging-based studies that further investigated signs of inflammation within the brain in PTSD, as to provide a comprehensive summary of recent literature with a neurological perspective. A search was conducted on studies published from 2009 through 2019 in PubMed and Web of Science. Fifty original articles were selected. Major findings included elevated levels of serum proinflammatory cytokines in individuals with PTSD across various trauma types, as compared with those without PTSD. Furthermore, neuroimaging-based studies demonstrated that altered inflammatory markers are associated with structural and functional alterations in brain regions that are responsible for the regulation of stress and emotion, including the amygdala, hippocampus, and frontal cortex. Future studies that utilize both central and peripheral inflammatory markers are warranted to elucidate the underlying neurological pathway of the pathophysiology of PTSD.

Keywords: inflammation; oxidative stress; post-traumatic stress disorder; cytokines; neuroimaging; magnetic resonance imaging

---

1. Introduction

Post-traumatic stress disorder (PTSD) is a chronic debilitating condition that results from having been exposed to trauma. In the current medical field, the diagnostic criteria of PTSD are largely dependent on the clinical symptomatology that outlines the disorder, including cognitive, behavioral, and affective domains [1]. Specifically, the diagnosis for PTSD includes the presence of symptoms of re-experience, avoidance, negative alterations in cognition and mood, and alterations in arousal and reactivity following the trauma [2]. Clinical symptoms of PTSD have been the sole standard for its diagnosis as acquired through self-report and/or structured clinical interview, and have been demonstrated as reliable predictors of a number of important health outcomes. For instance, previous studies have shown that PTSD symptoms predict the degree of functional recovery from pain [3], depressive symptoms [4], risk of substance abuse [5], and factors related to quality of life such as feeling of dissatisfaction [6]. Furthermore, in addition to the psychobehavioral clinical features, PTSD often involves comorbidities with other health problems such as obesity [7], type 2 diabetes mellitus [8], and cardiovascular complications [9]. Considering that all of the above health concerns involve problems in metabolic syndrome which are then closely related to oxidative stress and inflammation, it may then be presumed that the underlying mechanisms of PTSD involves the dysregulation of the immune system.

While psychobehavioral symptoms are the major factors considered when investigating the pathological state and severity of one's PTSD, understanding the immunological alterations that occur in tandem with these symptoms may be informative. For instance, detailed inflammatory responses to various oxidative stress in PTSD such as physical trauma and psychosocial stress may help identify the potentially distinct or diverging pathways towards the development of PTSD, and further reveal the pathophysiology of the disorder [10]. Growing research on PTSD recommends the development and promotion of early treatment strategies for PTSD prior to any clinical symptom development [11], as trauma-exposed individuals with high PTSD symptom severity demonstrated to have less likelihood of seeking treatment [12], resulting in a higher risk of chronic PTSD. For studies that investigated the biological factors associated with the clinical symptoms of affective or anxiety disorders, findings have shown that clinical symptoms in patients with depression [13] and anxiety disorders [14] are significantly associated with altered profiles of oxidative stress and inflammation, such as altered serum inflammatory markers. Interestingly, these alterations in inflammatory markers remained significant as compared to individuals in their respective control group, even after adjusting for demographic variables and lifestyle, suggesting that inflammatory response within the central nervous system (CNS) may be partly involved in the pathophysiology of PTSD. Furthermore, some studies have indicated that signs of inflammation may not necessarily correlate with the clinical symptoms of PTSD in a direct manner [15,16], and therefore the inclusion of one's immunological state along with the clinical symptom and severity of PTSD may provide further details of one's diagnostic state for PTSD in a more comprehensive manner. Moreover, considering that PTSD also has a late-onset tendency for clinical symptom development [17], incorporating data on the inflammatory state in the acute aftermath of trauma may help promote various strategies of early prevention and intervention for PTSD, as opposed to being solely dependent on the emergence of clinical symptoms as markers of the disorder.

In recent years, a growing number of studies have investigated the immunological alterations in PTSD as to elucidate the detailed biological pathways that underlie the clinical symptoms of the disorder. In particular, in addition to the abundant number of animal model and in vitro studies on the matter, studies using a human cohort have emerged based on the latest version of the Clinician-Administered PTSD Scale as according to the fifth version of the Diagnostic and Statistical Manual (CAPS-5) [18]. Techniques of neurological assessments including magnetic resonance imaging (MRI) and positron emission tomography (PET) have also emerged, which may allow to investigate the inflammatory responses in PTSD from a deeper, neurological perspective. For instance, previous systematic reviews have been done on MRI-based studies that demonstrated significant structural [19] and neurochemical [20] alterations in specific regions of the brain in association with stress or trauma. Further research that investigate these neurological alterations in PTSD in association with inflammatory responses as well as specific clinical symptoms of PTSD using up-to-date methods of clinical assessment may further reveal the underlying pathways of the disorder in a multi-level perspective.

A number of reviews have also been published that discuss the inflammatory changes in a human PTSD model. In particular, articles investigated inflammation as observable through specific serum inflammatory markers that are known to be in association with PTSD [21,22] and conducted meta-analysis and meta-regression [23] as to summarize elevated systemic levels of oxidative stress and inflammation in individuals with PTSD as compared to healthy controls. However, reviews on the topic of inflammation and PTSD have demonstrated inconsistent findings, which have been suggested to be the result of the heterogeneity of the disorder. While controlling for all the factors that make up the heterogeneity of PTSD across the studies reviewed may be difficult to conduct, a targeted and structured review that excludes some of the major contributors to the heterogeneity of PTSD may help reveal some of the detailed underlying pathways of PTSD in relation to inflammation, such as the exclusion of PTSD with comorbid complications, and observing for a potential pattern according to various types of trauma. Moreover, research also indicates that the time between the onset of trauma and the time of assessment may be an important factor that influences the heterogeneity found in inflammatory response in PTSD [24], therefore the distinction between early-onset and later onset of trauma exposure should be considered in addition to recent reviews. A comprehensive and updated review on the growing literature that were recently published on inflammation in PTSD according to various factors that potentially contribute to the heterogeneity may explain for the contrasting findings that were discussed to date. Considering that a few studies in the past have suggested that specific inflammatory markers may play an important role specifically in PTSD [25] and previous articles suggested specific biomarkers as promising for indicating inflammation in PTSD [21], summarizing findings from recent literature on such specified markers may help identify potential biological markers that indicate one's pathophysiology of PTSD.

The current study aims to provide a review of the recent literature on the inflammatory aspect of PTSD in a human model and discuss potential ways to better understand one's state of PTSD through the additional perspective of oxidative stress and inflammation. Specifically, we will review the physiological changes that occur in PTSD as measurable through inflammatory biomarkers, as well as neurological aspects of inflammation in PTSD through neuroimaging methodologies. The summary of the major findings of PTSD with respect to oxidative stress and inflammation may promote further discussion on the potential ways of early detection of those who are at risk for PTSD, as well as early intervention strategies for PTSD.

2. Materials and Methods

2.1. Literature Search Strategy

A literature search was conducted using two major electronic databases: PubMed (https://www.ncbi.nlm.nih.gov/pubmed/) and Web of Science (https://clarivate.com/webofsciencegroup/solutions/web-of-science/). The search was performed under a filter such that studies published from January of 2009 through November of 2019 were included. The following keywords were used as search terms: (1) "inflammation" AND "PTSD", (2) "inflammation" AND "PTSD" AND "magnetic resonance", (3) "oxidative stress" AND "PTSD", (4) "oxidative stress" AND "PTSD" AND "magnetic resonance". Records obtained from the literature search were reviewed such that duplicates of articles identified between the two databases were removed, and the remaining records were assessed for eligibility and excluded accordingly, under the following eligibility criteria.

2.2. Eligibility Criteria

Studies included in the current review were first screened such that they were original research articles using a human cohort, with a target population of PTSD that also explored the alteration in inflammatory state. The following records were to be excluded as part of the screening process: (1) records that are not original research including review papers, conference abstracts, short communications, or commentaries, (2) studies that used animal models, in vitro models, or post-mortem studies, (3) records that were not in English language, or (4) study designs that did not investigate inflammation in a target population of PTSD. After the screening process, the eligibility of the remaining articles was assessed using a full-text review. Articles that met the following criteria were further excluded: (1) studies that investigated PTSD with other comorbid disorders, diseases, or medical conditions (i.e., bipolar disorder, major depressive disorder, cardiovascular disease, myocardial infarction, etc.), or (2) studies that performed clinical trials or other forms of intervention as part of the study design. In addition, studies that investigated the inflammatory state in PTSD from a pediatric sample population were excluded, as well as target population of childhood onset trauma, as previous literature noted that the time lag between the time of trauma and time of assessment or sampling may influence the degree of alteration in inflammatory cytokine levels [24].

2.3. Inflammatory Markers of Interest

For the current review, a select number of inflammatory markers that were previously described as potential biomarkers of PTSD [26,27] were targeted as methods of assessment for inflammation. Studies that investigated the alterations in these selected inflammatory markers were considered eligible, including levels of proinflammatory and anti-inflammatory cytokines. Specifically, cytokines that are most prevalently observed as being altered in relation to PTSD were selected as follows: serum proinflammatory cytokines interleukin (IL)-1β, IL-6, tumor necrosis factor (TNF)-α, and interferon (IFN)-γ as well as C-reactive protein (CRP) which is influenced by proinflammatory cytokines [28], serum anti-inflammatory cytokines IL-4 and IL-10 [29], and PTSD- and oxidative stress-related genes including the brain-derived neurotrophic factor (*BDNF*), arachidonate 12-lipoxygenase (*ALOX12*), arachidonate 15-lipoxygenase (*ALOX15*), and retinoic acid orphan receptor alpha (*RORA*) [30]. Neuroimaging-based studies were also included such as MRI and PET, along with markers of inflammation to examine the moderating role of specific inflammatory markers in the alteration of the brain.

3. Results

3.1. Results from the Literature Search

A total of 572 articles were identified after the literature search conducted under the databases PubMed and Web of Science. Upon the search and identification of records, duplicate records between the two databases were removed, followed by the screening of titles and abstracts of the studies. The screening process excluded a total of 254 studies as according to the eligibility criteria mentioned above in the Materials and Methods section. After careful consideration and full-text review of the remaining records according to the eligibility criteria, 75 studies were removed. After the inclusion of 11 studies through cross-referencing and reviewing of the records, and a total of 50 studies were included in this review. Individuals with PTSD who were participants of studies that were included in this review were exposed to various types of trauma, including accidents such as surviving a car crash, fire, or natural disaster, victims of various crimes including physical assault, sexual violence, or domestic abuse, exposure to combat such as military personnel or police officers, and other forms of trauma that were not specified. Among the 50 articles selected for this review, 43 were studies that explored serum inflammatory cytokine markers as measures of inflammation, 4 were studies exploring PTSD- and oxidative stress-related genes, while the remaining 3 were neuroimaging-based studies that explored the neural correlates of inflammation in PTSD. A detailed summary of the literature search process and the screening and inclusion of the eligible studies for the current review is shown in Figure 1.

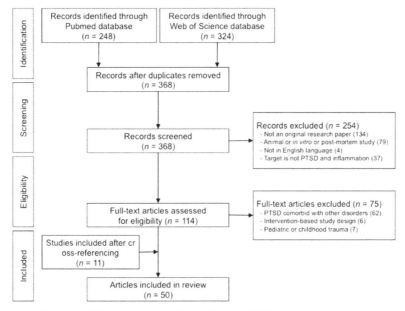

Figure 1. Flowchart of literature search and identification of eligible articles for the current review.

3.2. Alterations of Serum Inflammatory Markers in Association with PTSD

Growing literature emphasizes the importance of regulation of mental health and stress in various disorders including PTSD due to the high prevalence of comorbidity with other chronic metabolic diseases [31]. For instance, the presence of PTSD has been noted to co-occur or associate with risks of chronic medical diseases including cardiovascular diseases and type 2 diabetes mellitus [31]. Considering the significance of cytokines as regulators of immune responses [32], the majority of studies explore the alteration and influence of inflammation in PTSD through the measurement of peripheral cytokine levels. In particular, serum cytokines are often measured and used as peripheral markers of inflammation in various psychiatric disorders including depression [33], panic disorder [34], bipolar disorder [35], and obsessive-compulsive disorder [36].

Cytokines are largely divided into two classes, which are the proinflammatory cytokines and the anti-inflammatory cytokines. As demonstrated via animal models, proinflammatory cytokine levels tend to reflect the promotion and occurrence of inflammation whereas anti-inflammatory cytokine levels are related to the suppressing of inflammation as well as the protection of further damage from inflammation [37]. For studies investigating inflammation in PTSD according to peripheral inflammatory markers, the current review identified and selected 24 studies that explored serum levels of proinflammatory cytokines including one or more of IL-1β, IL-6, TNF-α, and IFN-γ as well as CRP, and 19 studies that explored serum levels of anti-inflammatory cytokines IL-4 and/or IL-10.

3.2.1. Roles of Proinflammatory Cytokines in PTSD: IL-1β, IL-6, TNF-α, IFN-γ and CRP

Proinflammatory cytokines tend to be the more prevalently used outcome variables, as increased proinflammatory cytokines have consistently demonstrated to indicate worsening of the immune system, and may therefore be reliable and direct indicators of disease progression [32]. In addition, despite serum proinflammatory cytokines being peripheral in nature, they have been described as mediators of many pathways underlying the CNS through its important roles in inflammatory response [38], therefore may provide valuable insight with regards to the pathophysiology of PTSD from a CNS perspective. Proinflammatory cytokines increase in concentration with age but also may be elevated with stress as well as secondary symptoms of stress such as sleep and fatigue [24]. The current study summarizes the collective findings from three of the most prevalently explored proinflammatory cytokines in PTSD, which are IL-1β, IL-6, and TNF-α, all of which are often paired as they are all induced by the same endotoxin, lipopolysaccharides (LPS) [39], along with other inflammatory measures. Furthermore, among the 4 proinflammatory cytokines and CRP selected as part of this review, IL-6 downregulates the synthesis of IL-1β and TNF-α [40]. Considering that a distinct regulatory relationship is present among the inflammatory markers of interest of the current review, it may be presumed that alteration in the markers provides implications with regards to the potential direction of alteration in the other remaining cytokines as well.

Through the current literature selection, studies have demonstrated that individuals with PTSD have significantly elevated serum levels of proinflammatory cytokines than the respective control group without PTSD. Specifically, individuals with PTSD demonstrated as having higher levels of serum IL-1β [15,25], IL-6 [15,16,25,41–47], TNF-α [15,16,25,42–44,46–48], IFN-γ [15,47,49], and CRP [42,50] than individuals who have been exposed to trauma but have never developed PTSD. In the current review, IL-6 demonstrated to be the most documented proinflammatory cytokine in human models of PTSD, and the majority of studies demonstrated increased IL-6 levels in the serum sample of individuals diagnosed with PTSD as compared with their respective control group. This may also be in alignment with previous research which noted IL-6 as the most considerable marker for inflammation [21]. Specifically, studies have shown that IL-6 is crucial in the relationship between immune system and CNS in inflammatory states [44]. Furthermore, 4 studies have demonstrated that individuals with PTSD have elevated proinflammatory cytokine levels when compared with healthy individuals who have not been exposed to any trauma [51–54]. In addition, studies have also demonstrated elevated CRP levels which are known to be influenced by proinflammatory cytokines, where individuals with PTSD showed increased CRP levels compared to healthy controls [42], and PTSD symptom severity were positively associated with CRP levels [50,55].

Participants with PTSD resulting from surviving a fire and burn injury were assessed for proinflammatory cytokines including IL-1β, IL-6, IL-8, and TNF-α in a study by Jiang and colleagues [51]. Here, Jiang and colleagues (2018) have also noted that, individuals with severe burn injury and diagnosed with PTSD demonstrated decreased clinical symptoms of PTSD three months after the trauma exposure, while having remained elevated levels of proinflammatory cytokines [51]. In addition, a study by Gill and colleagues (2013) found that women who recover from PTSD have statistically similar IL-6 levels as healthy control individuals who have never been exposed to any trauma [52]. This may then indicate that, for individuals who are able to recover from PTSD, both the normalization of clinical symptoms of PTSD as well as the influences of oxidative stress and inflammation may be possible. Furthermore, the findings from Jiang and colleagues (2018) on the sustained elevation of proinflammatory cytokine levels despite having reduced in clinical symptoms of PTSD [51] may indicate that those who are susceptible or possibly at risk of chronic PTSD may have distinct inflammatory responsiveness, regardless of clinical symptomatology. Therefore, the distinct pattern between inflammatory measures and clinical measures may warrant the incorporation of both physiological data as well as clinical assessments to better understand the pathophysiology of PTSD.

The study by Wang and colleagues (2016) may provide supportive evidence to the potential distinct inflammatory pathways between individuals who are at risk for versus resilient to PTSD [46]. In particular, their findings indicated that the severity of the trauma experienced may not necessarily mediate or influence the relationship between level of serum proinflammatory cytokine IL-1β and post-traumatic stress symptom severity in the case of combat-related PTSD [46]. Among veterans all of whom have been exposed to similar combat, those who are diagnosed with PTSD demonstrated significant imbalance in their inflammatory state as compared to those without PTSD [46], implicating that one's risk or resilience towards PTSD may be largely explained by biological factors and their ability to regulate their inflammatory state, as opposed to the nature or severity of the traumatic event.

Another interesting finding from the studies identified is the supportive evidence of stress influencing proinflammatory cytokine levels even at a younger age group, as well as the potential predictive role of proinflammatory cytokine levels in the comorbidity of PTSD and other chronic metabolic diseases. In particular, Blessing and colleagues (2017) demonstrated increased indicators of systemic inflammation in individuals with PTSD as compared to the respective control group, where the inflammatory markers were also indicators of higher cardiovascular risk as well as insulin resistance [43], which may then provide additional perspective with regards to related diseases such as type 2 diabetes mellitus.

Furthermore, two studies also explored the additional factor of traumatic brain injury (TBI) in PTSD and found significant alteration in proinflammatory cytokine levels in association with PTSD. The first is the study by Devoto and colleagues (2017) who found that TBI may have an additive effect to the alteration of proinflammatory cytokine levels in the case of PTSD, as individuals with PTSD as well as TBI had demonstrated greater elevation in proinflammatory cytokine levels than individuals with PTSD but without TBI [44]. The study also demonstrated that, among individuals with both PTSD and TBI, the levels of proinflammatory cytokines were correlated with post-traumatic stress symptom severity, where serum proinflammatory cytokine levels of IL-6 and TNF-α were higher in individuals with higher post-traumatic symptom severity. The second study is by Kanefsky and colleagues (2019), which further demonstrated that, even within individuals with both PTSD and TBI, the presence of loss of consciousness at the time of the traumatic brain injury may also influence the alteration in proinflammatory cytokine levels of IL-6 [45].

Contrasting findings were also reported in this literature search. For instance, studies have reported that victims of assault who are exposed to trauma and have been diagnosed with PTSD have statistically similar IL-6 cytokine levels as those who have been exposed to trauma but have not developed PTSD [56]. In addition, one study reported insignificant alteration in three of the serum proinflammatory cytokine levels between individuals with PTSD versus those without PTSD [57], and another study reported insignificant alteration in IL-6 in relation to PTSD [58]. Moreover, a study reported small but significant decrease in the levels of IL-6 and IFN-γ in individuals with PTSD as compared to those without PTSD [59]. However, it may be noteworthy that these studies were primarily focused on stress as measured by symptoms of insomnia, respectively, rather than the alteration in the general symptoms PTSD through oxidative stress as measured by the proinflammatory cytokines targeted in this review.

Similarly, McCanlies and colleagues (2011) reported that there was a lack of association between proinflammatory markers of IL-6 and CRP with onset of PTSD symptomatology in urban police officers with high PTSD symptoms [60]. There were also opposite findings reported in one study by Bruenig and colleagues (2018), which reported a positive correlation between post-traumatic stress symptom severity and reduced levels of serum TNF-α [61]. Despite the numerous reports of contrasting findings in terms of levels of proinflammatory cytokines according to the diagnosis of PTSD, however, it is noteworthy that the majority of the literature selected for review upon the screening and assessing for eligibility were largely based on male populations. Considering that between-sex differences in the levels of proinflammatory cytokines IL-6 have been reported [54], where men with PTSD show significantly elevated IL-6 levels as compared to their respective healthy control group while the women did not, this may be an important factor to consider in the summary of the studies selected in this review.

A detailed description of the studies reviewed that investigated alteration in serum proinflammatory cytokine levels in relation to PTSD is provided in Table 1.

Table 1. Studies exploring serum proinflammatory cytokine and C-reactive protein (CRP) level alteration in post-traumatic stress disorder (PTSD).

Trauma Types	Cytokine Markers	N (m/f)	Altered Direction	Main Findings	Ref.
Accident	IL-1β, IL-6, TNF-α	52 (25/27)	Increase	- Individuals with PTSD had higher proinflammatory cytokine concentrations three months after the accident compared to healthy controls, even though clinical symptoms decreased.	[51] †
	IL-1β, IL-6, TNF-α	187 (71/116)	Increase	- Individuals with PTSD had higher IL-1β and TNF-α, and total proinflammatory cytokine scores than those without PTSD. - IL-1β levels in all subjects correlate with self-assessed PTSD symptom severity scores after controlling for trauma exposure severity.	[25]
	CRP	641 (316/325)	Increase	- CRP was positively associated with PTSD severity, particularly with re-experiencing and avoidance symptoms.	[55]
Assault	IL-6	77 (0/77)	Increase	- Individuals with PTSD had higher IL-6 concentrations than trauma-unexposed controls. - Individuals who recover from PTSD had similar IL-6 concentrations as trauma-unexposed controls.	[52] †
	IL-6	68 (0/68)	Increase	- Physical assault history is significantly negatively correlated with phytohemagglutinin A-stimulated IL-6 production.	[41]
	IL-6	60 (10/50)	None	- Individuals with PTSD had statistically similar IL-6 cytokine levels as resilient trauma-exposed individuals.	[56]
Combat	CRP, IL-6, TNF-α	111 (111/0)	Increase	- Individuals with PTSD had lower nitric oxide synthetic capacity and higher CRP levels. - Lower nitric oxide synthetic capacity is associated with higher IL-6, TNF-α, and PTSD symptom severity.	[42]
	IL-6, TNF-α	166 (166/0)	Increase	- Individuals with PTSD had higher levels of IL-6, TNF-α, and other cardiovascular risk markers.	[43]
	IL-6, TNF-α	299 (299/0)	Decrease, Increase	- PTSD symptom severity is correlated with significant decrease in IL-6, increase in TNF-α. - Resilience to PTSD is correlated with increased IL-6.	[61]
	TNF-α	167 (87/80)	Increase	- PTSD symptom severity is positively associated with higher TNF-α levels, and is mediated by attenuated vagal activity, smoking, and alcohol dependence.	[48]
	IL-6, TNF-α	83 (82/1)	Increase	- Individuals with PTSD and TBI had greater increased IL-6 and TNF-α concentrations than individuals with PTSD but without TBI. - IL-6 and TNF-α concentrations were greater in individuals with PTSD and TBI with high PTSD symptom severity than low PTSD symptom severity.	[44]
	IL-1β, IL-6, TNF-α	52 (51/1)	None	- CRP and hair cortisol are correlated with symptoms of depression and PTSD.	[57]

Table 1. *Cont.*

Trauma Types	Cytokine Markers	N (m/f)	Altered Direction	Main Findings	Ref.
	IL-6	66 (64/2)	None	- Individuals with PTSD and recovered insomnia since deployment had decreased CRP concentration than individuals with PTSD and consistent insomnia.	[58]
	IL-6	143 (138/5)	Increase	- Individuals with PTSD and TBI with loss of consciousness had elevated IL-6 compared to individuals with PTSD and TBI without loss of consciousness as well as individuals with PTSD without TBI.	[45]
	IL-1β, IL-6, TNF-α, IFN-γ	104 (104/0)	Increase	- Individuals with PTSD had higher proinflammatory cytokine levels than those without PTSD. - Proinflammatory cytokine levels were not correlated with symptom severity of depression, PTSD diagnosis, or number of traumas.	[15]
	IL-6, TNF-α	61 (61/0)	Increase	- Individuals with PTSD had higher total proinflammatory scores than those without PTSD after controlling for age, BMI, and smoking. - Total proinflammatory score is not correlated with PTSD symptom severity within the PTSD group.	[16]
	IL-6, TNF-α	13 (12/1)	Increase	- Individuals with PTSD had higher IL-6, TNF-α than trauma-exposed individuals without PTSD.	[46]
	IFN-γ	13 (13/0)	Increase	- Individuals with PTSD had higher levels of IL-6, IL-10, IFN-γ, and TNF-α than healthy controls.	[47]
	IFN-γ	299 (299/0)	Decrease	- Individuals with PTSD showed small but significant decrease in levels of IL-6 and IFN-γ.	[59]
	IFN-γ	30 (27/3) [‡]	Increase	- Individuals with PTSD had significantly higher IFN-γ levels compared to healthy controls.	[49]
Police	CRP, IL-6	111 (68/43)	None	- There were no significant association between plasma inflammatory markers including levels of CRP and PTSD symptoms.	[60]
Other	IL-6, TNF-α	44 (22/22)	Increase	- Individuals with PTSD had higher IL-6 and TNF-α levels at sleep onset but not at the end of the sleep cycle. - Men with PTSD show altered levels of TNF-α at the end of the sleep cycle than men without PTSD.	[53] [†]
	IL-6	82 (16/66)	Increase	- Individuals with PTSD had higher IL-6 levels as compared to healthy controls. - Significant sex-differences were present in IL-6 levels compared to healthy individuals, where men showed higher IL-6 levels than the control group, while women did not statistically differ according to PTSD.	[54] [†]
	CRP	2692 (800/1892)	Increase	- PTSD symptoms were positively associated with high CRP levels.	[50]

[†] Indicate studies that included a trauma-unexposed healthy control group. [‡] Depicts the sample size of the PTSD group only, as gender distribution for the control group was not provided. Abbreviations: BMI, body mass index; CRP, c-reactive protein; f, female; IFN, interferon; IL, interleukin; m, male; N, sample size; PTSD, post-traumatic stress disorder; Ref., reference; TBI, traumatic brain injury; TNF, tumor necrosis factor.

3.2.2. Roles of Anti-Inflammatory Cytokines in PTSD: IL-4 and IL-10

In addition to proinflammatory cytokines, anti-inflammatory cytokines also play a pivotal role in the regulatory processes of oxidative stress and inflammation. In contrast to proinflammatory cytokines, which promote and induce inflammatory responses, the primary role of anti-inflammatory cytokines is to inhibit the synthesis of proinflammatory cytokines, and is therefore also described as inhibitors of inflammatory mediators [32].

While numerous anti-inflammatory cytokines are present, the current study reviewed the alteration in levels of IL-4 and IL-10, as it has been previously suggested as an important marker in psychosocial stress [27] as well as other chronic medical diseases including type 2 diabetes mellitus [62] and cardiovascular disease [63], both of which are more often than not closely associated with PTSD. For instance, previous studies have consistently reported that level of serum anti-inflammatory cytokine IL-10 is significantly associated with insulin sensitivity in young individuals, which may later develop towards type 2 diabetes mellitus [64] or chronic pain [65]. In addition, a recent study has also reported that chronic inflammation as observable by altered levels of anti-inflammatory cytokine levels including IL-4 and IL-10 may play a predictive role in disorders such as type 2 diabetes mellitus development [66].

Furthermore, IL-10 enables the suppression of synthesis of TNF-α as well as IL-1β [34], which are proinflammatory cytokines primarily explored in models of PTSD, and may therefore provide a comprehensive overview of the specific inflammatory biomarkers that may represent the pathophysiology of PTSD. Considering that anti-inflammatory cytokines have also been suggested to be potential options of possible treatment of chronic disorders [67], an overview of the alteration in IL-4 and IL-10 may reveal important findings with regards to the distinct role of anti-inflammatory cytokines in PTSD.

A total of 19 studies were selected from the literature search process that explored the alteration in serum levels of IL-4 or IL-10 in PTSD. Contrary to expectations of the opposition roles between proinflammatory and anti-inflammatory cytokine alterations in response to oxidative stress and inflammation, findings from the selected studies have mostly demonstrated statistically similar levels of serum IL-10 between individuals with PTSD and trauma-exposed controls who have never been diagnosed with PTSD [15,16,25,44,45,57,68–70]. Among these studies that demonstrated no alteration in serum IL-10 also included those from Table 1 which demonstrated significant increased proinflammatory cytokine levels in the PTSD group as compared to their respective healthy controls [15,16,25,44,45], indicating that elevated proinflammatory cytokines in association with PTSD may not necessarily reflect reduced anti-inflammatory cytokines. Furthermore, for studies that included a healthy control group who have not been exposed to any type of trauma, consistent results were shown where individuals exposed to trauma – regardless of their diagnosis for PTSD—did not show any between-group differences in IL-10 levels as compared to the control [69,71].

However, it is noteworthy that contrasting findings were reported by de Oliveira and colleagues (2018) as well as Guo and colleagues (2012), where both proinflammatory cytokines including IL-6 and anti-inflammatory cytokines including IL-4 and IL-10 were positively correlated and elevated in individuals with PTSD as compared to the respective healthy control group [54,72]. Dennis and colleagues (2018) also found that PTSD symptom severity is associated with higher IL-10 levels, which are then mediated by vagal activity, smoking, and alcohol dependence [48]. However, this may be partially explained by the well-distributed sex ratio in this particular study of 87 males and 80 female, considering that previous studies have noted significant sex differences in the patterns of inflammatory marker levels. Elevated IL-10 levels in respect to the diagnosis of PTSD were also found in two studies [52,54], although these studies were heavily male-dominant and female-dominant in their populations, respectively. Considering that many studies demonstrated findings of reduced IL-10 levels in association with PTSD diagnosis [46,56,61], this may then suggest that perhaps this anti-inflammatory cytokine are not a suitable marker that provides insight towards the pathophysiology of PTSD or presence of trauma exposure.

A detailed description of the studies reviewed that investigated alteration in serum anti-inflammatory cytokine levels of IL-4 and IL-10 in relation to PTSD is provided in Table 2.

Table 2. Studies exploring serum anti-inflammatory cytokines IL-4 and IL-10 alteration in PTSD.

Trauma Types	N (m/f)	Altered Direction	Main Findings	Ref.
Accident	19 (2/17)	None	- PTSD symptom severity is not significantly associated with IL-10 levels.	[68]
	187 (71/116)	None	- There are no differences in levels of IL-10 between individuals with PTSD and those without PTSD.	[25]
Assault	60 (10/50)	Decrease	- Individuals with PTSD presented lower IL-10 levels than the trauma-exposed individuals without PTSD.	[56]
	30 (10/20)	None	- There are no differences in levels of IL-10 between individuals with PTSD and those without PTSD.	[69] †,‡
Combat	167 (87/80)	Increase	- PTSD symptom severity is positively associated with higher IL-10 levels, and is mediated by attenuated vagal activity, smoking, and alcohol dependence.	[48]
	83 (82/1)	None	- There were no anti-inflammatory cytokine level alterations between individuals with PTSD and TBI versus those with PTSD without TBI.	[44]
	64 (60/4)	Increase	- PTSD individuals with mTBI had elevated IL-10 levels compared to individuals with PTSD but without mTBI. - IL-10 concentration is positively correlated with PTSD symptom severity.	[52]
	299 (299/0)	Decrease	- PTSD symptom severity had a trend-line negative correlation with IL-10 levels.	[61]
	52 (51/1)	None	- CRP and hair cortisol are correlated with symptoms of depression and PTSD.	[57]
	143 (138/5)	None	- There are no between-group differences in IL-10 levels among individuals with PTSD and TBI with loss of consciousness versus individuals with PTSD and TBI without loss of consciousness, as well as individuals with PTSD but no TBI. - PTSD symptom severity is not significantly associated with IL-10 levels.	[45]
	61 (61/0)	None	- There are no significant differences in IL-10 levels between individuals with PTSD and those without PTSD.	[16]
	104 (104/0)	None	- Concentrations of IL-10 are not significantly altered in PTSD subjects.	[15]
	13 (12/1)	Decrease	- Plasma and salivary levels of IL-10 are lower in veterans with PTSD compared to veterans without PTSD.	[46]
Refugee	60 (27/33)	None	- IL-10 levels are not significantly different between individuals with PTSD and healthy controls.	[71] †

Table 2. *Cont.*

Trauma Types	N (m/f)	Altered Direction	Main Findings	Ref.
Other	273 (141/132)	None	- Anti-inflammatory cytokine levels are not different in the chronic PTSD group compared with those in the recovery and resilient group.	[70]
	104 (64/40)	Decrease	- Individuals with PTSD showed increased global DNA methylation and decreased IL-4 than to healthy controls.	[73]
	100 (47/53)	Increase	- Individuals with PTSD showed increased cytokine levels compared to healthy controls in 6 cytokines including IL-2, IL-4, IL-6, IL-8, IL-10, and TNF-α.	[72]
	30 (27/3) §	None	- There are no significant difference in IL-4 levels between individuals with PTSD and healthy controls.	[49]
	82 (16/66)	Increase	- Individuals with PTSD had a significant increase in the serum levels of IL-6 and IL-10 than the control group.	[54] †

† Indicate studies that included a trauma-unexposed healthy control group. ‡ Trauma types of the individuals in the PTSD group of this study were described as *other* for two individuals, *car accident* for five individuals, and miscellaneous forms of assault for the remaining individuals. § Depicts the sample size of the PTSD group only, as gender distribution for the control group was not provided. Abbreviations: CRP, c-reactive protein; f, female; IFN, interferon; IL, interleukin; m, male; mTBI, mild traumatic brain injury; N, sample size; PTSD, post-traumatic stress disorder; Ref., reference; TBI, traumatic brain injury; TNF, tumor necrosis factor.

3.3. Roles of PTSD- and Oxidative Stress-Related Genetic Markers in PTSD

Five studies explored specific genes that have been previously suggested to be of significance in PTSD and oxidative stress, which included the investigation of the *ALOX12* and *ALOX15* [74], *BDNF* [75,76], and *RORA* [77,78]. In summary, studies based on individuals who were exposed to combat-related trauma demonstrated inconsistent findings, where one reported that veterans with PTSD have higher frequencies of the Met/Met and 66Met alleles as compared with veterans without PTSD [75], while another demonstrated that the frequencies of the two alelles were similar between the veteran groups [76]. While the findings from the two studies are contrasting, it is noteworthy that both studies strictly included trauma-exposed veterans without the inclusion of a healthy control group that has not been exposed to trauma, and the studies vary in sex distribution. Furthermore, Bruenig and colleagues (2016) have noted that the low Met/Met genotype frequencies in their sample may have influenced the results also [76].

Two other studies have explored the association between single nucleotide polymorphism (SNP) in the *RORA* gene with PTSD, where both studies found the same SNP within the *RORA* gene (rs8042149) to be significantly associated with the presence of PTSD [77,78]. Considering that the *RORA* gene is expressed in neurons and brain structures as to serve neuroprotective roles within the brain such as in response to oxidative stress [77], these findings indicate that *RORA* may be a marker for assessing one's capability in neuroprotection towards oxidative stress or inflammation, therefore a potential marker for an individual's risk or resilience towards developing PTSD. The two genes *ALOX12* and *ALOX15* were also assessed in one study [74], which demonstrated that the *ALOX12* locus (rs1042357 and rs10852889) significantly moderated the association between PTSD diagnosis and reduced cortical thickness in the brain, whereas the *ALOX15* locus did not moderate in this association.

A detailed description of the studies exploring PTSD- and oxidative stress-related genetic markers in relation to PTSD is provided in Tables 3 and 4.

Table 3. Studies exploring PTSD- and oxidative stress-related genetic markers in PTSD.

Trauma Types	Genetic Marker	N (m/f)	Altered Direction	Main Findings	Ref.
Combat	*BDNF* Val66Met (rs6265)	461 (413/48)	Increase	- Individuals with PTSD had higher frequencies of Met/Met and 66Met allele than individuals without PTSD.	[75]
	BDNF Val66Met (rs6265)	257 (257/0)	None	- Individuals had similar frequencies of Met/Met and 66Met allele as resilience trauma-exposed individuals.	[76]
Other	*RORA* SNPs	435 (260/175)	N/A	- A significant association was reported between a *RORA* SNP (rs8042149) and PTSD diagnosis.	[77]
	RORA SNPs	551 (193/358)	N/A	- A significant association was reported between a *RORA* SNP (rs8042149) and PTSD diagnosis.	[78]

Abbreviations: BDNF, brain-derived neurotrophic factor; m, male; N, sample size; N/A, not applicable; PTSD, post-traumatic stress disorder; Ref., reference; SNP, single nucleotide polymorphism.

3.4. Brain Alterations in Relation to Inflammation and Oxidative Stress in PTSD

Another growing field of interest within the study of inflammation and oxidative stress in PTSD is the neuroinflammatory responses within the brain. Neuroinflammation refers to the physiological reactivity of the brain in response to various types of inflammation or oxidative stress, including but not limited to external injury or trauma [79,80], and is often observed in individuals with chronic diseases during their early stages of the disease as part of a coping mechanism [81]. Considering that investigating neuroinflammatory responses are often invasive in nature [79], the utilization of neuroimaging techniques to target inflammatory responses within the brain may potentially bridge the association between altered levels of peripheral biomarkers such as proinflammatory and anti-inflammatory cytokines and the clinical symptoms that arise in PTSD.

In the case of proinflammatory cytokine, previous literature have noted that IL-1β and IL-6 are secreted at stress-induced states and take part in the catecholaminergic pathways [82]. Considering that the catecholaminergic pathway has been demonstrated to play an important role in specific regions of the brain including the hippocampus and amygdala [82], it has then been suggested that these peripheral inflammatory markers may represent alteration in the function or activity of the hippocampus and amygdala, influencing symptoms including but not limited to emotion lability [83], fear reactivity, and retrieval of traumatic memories [82], all of which are crucial factors in PTSD. Previous studies have also shown that IL-1β is known to be consistently increased in major depression after psychosocial stress [84].

Over the years, emergence of novel technologies in neuroimaging have allowed the indirect correlative investigation of neuroinflammation without the invasive nature of directly measuring neuroinflammatory responses, as neuroimaging methods allow the direct measurement of the structure and functional state of the brain. In particular, neuroimaging techniques including MRI and PET have been largely utilized as they can obtain detailed information with regards to the structure of the brain such as cortical thickness, subcortical volume, or the metabolism of targeted brain regions as measured by glucose uptake. The current search included 3 neuroimaging-based studies on oxidative stress and inflammation in PTSD. The selected studies all reported findings that were consistent with previous literature, where markers of oxidative stress or inflammation are significantly associated with alterations of the brain.

The first study is by Miller and colleagues (2015), which explored the influence of the gene *ALOX12* on the association between PTSD and cortical thickness of the brain [74]. This study takes on an approach that is distinct from peripheral measures of proinflammatory cytokines, in that it investigated the *ALOX12* locus and its potential moderating roles, based on previous knowledge that the *ALOX12* enzyme plays a key role in an oxidative-related neuronal death program [85,86]. Findings from this study first indicated that the *ALOX12* locus—through two single nucleotide polymorphisms rs1042357 and rs10852889—plays a significant moderating role in the association between PTSD and reduced cortical thickness of the brain. Specifically, brain areas with reduced cortical thickness included the middle frontal gyrus, superior frontal gyrus, rostral anterior cortex and medial orbitofrontal cortex, all of which were close in proximity and part of the frontal cortex of the brain.

The second study is by O'Donovan and colleagues (2015), which provided findings that are consistent to previous literature, where elevated proinflammatory cytokine levels of soluble receptor II for tumor necrosis factor (sTNF-RII) were significantly associated with PTSD [87]. The study also explored the influence of inflammation from a neurological perspective, and found that elevated levels of sTNF-RII is associated with reduced hippocampal subcortical volume in the case of veterans who have been exposed to combat and are diagnosed with PTSD, while this association was not present in veterans without PTSD [87]. Here, it is noteworthy that while the study also explored the potential roles of IL-6 by observing for alterations in serum IL-6 level, findings reported that IL-6 was not statistically associated with the reduced hippocampal volume in PTSD. In fact, findings indicated that higher post-traumatic stress symptom severity is associated with increased sTNF-RII and reduced IL-6 levels, which may contrast to previous literature as shown in Table 1, where the majority of individuals with PTSD were characterized with elevated serum levels of IL-6. This contrasting finding may be explained by the fact that, while IL-6 is often described as a proinflammatory cytokine marker of inflammation, it also does have anti-inflammatory properties [88,89]. Specifically, the primary roles of IL-6 are largely coupled with the regulation of the other two proinflammatory cytokines IL-1β and TNF-α, and studies have reported that IL-6 often inhibits the expression of IL-1β and TNF-α while promoting IL-10 [90]. This has been suggested to be especially so when in an anti-inflammatory environment, where the integrity of the blood-brain barrier needs to be regulated [91], such as during the occurrence of neuroinflammatory responses.

The last of the neuroimaging-based studies reviewed is a pilot study using 18F-fluorodeoxyglucose (FDG)-PET by Toczek and colleagues (2019), which investigated the association between the levels of proinflammatory cytokines and the amygdala of the brain as to explore the relationship between oxidative stress and inflammation measurable by peripheral markers and the alteration of the amygdala [92]. The study reported that there were no significant associations between levels of IL-1β, IL-6, and TNF-α with FDG signal of the amygdala. The FDG signal has been used as a tool to detect vascular inflammation in specific regions [93] and FDG signal within a brain region may provide important contextual information such as the metabolism and glucose intake within the region [94,95], ultimately enabling the inference regarding the functional activity of the respective brain region. Although there had been no associations found between levels of IL-1β, IL-6, and TNF-α and amygdala activity as measured by FDG signal, findings from the study by Toczek and colleagues (2019) reported a significant correlation among FDG signal in the amygdala, spleen and bone marrow [92]. The spleen and bone marrow are closely related organs that are also described as lymphoid organs [96,97] and have been previously described as key factors in the immune system as immune cells migrate across the spleen [97], while the bone marrow is the production site for lymphocytes [98]. As such, while proinflammatory cytokine levels did not alter in association with FDG signal of the amygdala in this study, correlation between FDG signals within lymphoid organs and the amygdala in individuals with PTSD may implicate inflammatory responses within the brain that results from trauma. Considering that FDG signal within the spleen and bone marrow have been suggested as potential approaches to measuring systemic inflammation in other chronic metabolic diseases [99], this finding may reflect a link between amygdala activity and systemic inflammation in PTSD. The findings by Toczek et al. (2019) are also consistent with a portion of previous literature, which provided evidence for brain alterations in specific regions including the amygdala, hippocampus, and prefrontal cortex in patients diagnosed with PTSD [100,101]. In particular, previous literature suggested that the amygdala, hippocampus, and prefrontal cortex each has a high density of glucocorticoid receptors, which are then related with the activation of the hypothalamic-pituitary-adrenal (HPA) axis [102]. Considering that the HPA axis is a significant contributor in responsiveness towards psychosocial stress [103] and various forms of trauma exposure [104], studies that bridge the relationship among alteration in inflammatory markers from a genetic or peripheral level, structural and functional alterations of brain regions associated with PTSD, and the clinical symptoms of PTSD, may provide a more comprehensive overview of the pathophysiology of PTSD as a non-communicable disease.

A detailed description of the neuroimaging-based studies reviewed that investigated the relationship between inflammatory and oxidative stress markers and alteration within the brain in PTSD is provided in Table 4.

Table 4. Neuroimaging-based studies exploring oxidative stress and inflammation in PTSD.

Trauma Types	Inflammatory and Oxidative Stress Marker	Outcome Measure (Modality)	N (m/f)	Main Findings	Ref.
Combat	*ALOX12* SNPs, *ALOX15* SNPs	Cortical thickness (sMRI)	218 (194/24)	- The *ALOX12* locus (rs1042357, rs10852889) moderated the association between PTSD and reduced cortical thickness in the middle frontal gyrus, superior frontal gyrus, rostral anterior cortex and medial orbitofrontal cortex. - There were no associations between *ALOX15* locus and cortical thickness in PTSD.	[74]
	IL-6, sTNF-RII	Hippocampal volume (sMRI)	206 (170/36)	- Increased sTNF-RII is associated with reduced hippocampal volume. - There were no associations between levels of IL-6 and hippocampal volume. - Higher PTSD severity is associated with elevated sTNF-RII and reduced IL-6 levels.	[87]
Unspecified	IL-1β, IL-6, TNF-α, FDG signal in spleen and bone marrow	FDG signal in amygdala (FDG-PET/CT)	16(10/6)	- There were no associations between IL-1β, IL-6 and TNF-α levels and FDG signal in the amygdala, spleen and bone marrow. - Positive correlations among FDG signals in the amygdala, spleen and bone marrow.	[92]

Abbreviations: CT, computed tomography; f, female; FDG, 18F-fluorodeoxyglucose; IL, interleukin; m, male; N, sample size; PET, positron emission tomography; PTSD, post-traumatic stress disorder; Ref, reference; sMRI, structural magnetic resonance imaging; SNP, single nucleotide polymosphism; sTNF-RII, soluble receptor II for tumor necrosis factor; TNF, tumor necrosis factor.

4. Conclusions

The current structured review provides an overview of the recent evidence presented on the influence of oxidative stress and inflammation in PTSD. The studies reviewed here demonstrate the alterations of specific peripheral inflammatory markers that may potentially be implemented as correlates of PTSD, including the elevated levels of serum proinflammatory cytokines IL-1β, IL-6, and TNF-α. Among these, IL-6 has been shown to be elevated or reduced in the serum of individuals exposed to trauma according to the source of oxidative stress, such as whether the trauma is physical in nature, includes the presence of TBI or loss of consciousness, or entails psychosocial trauma. This may in turn suggest the potential of serum IL-6 level as a peripheral marker for PTSD based on trauma type. This review also discussed the three neuroimaging-based studies on the inflammatory response associated with PTSD within the brain, from which can be concluded that particular brain regions may be identifiable as neural correlates of PTSD, including the prefrontal cortex, hippocampus, and amygdala of the brain. Specifically, the evidence from the studies reviewed revealed reduction in cortical thickness among regions of the prefrontal cortex and hippocampal volume, as well as a potential link between amygdala activity and systemic inflammation in PTSD.

Given the current findings summarized, a potential pathway underlying inflammation in PTSD may be suggested. A major collective finding from this review was elevated serum IL-6 levels in all but one study [48] among the studies reviewed for alteration in proinflammatory cytokines in association with PTSD across various trauma types. Considering that IL-6 has been known to cross the blood-brain barrier (BBB) as an immune mediator [105], it may then be that psychosocial stress as a result of trauma induces elevated peripheral IL-6 concentrations, which then influences the inflammatory cytokines within the brain via crossing of the BBB. This potential pathway may also be in alignment with previous animal model study findings which reported increased proinflammatory cytokines within specific regions of the brain associated with PTSD including the hippocampus, amygdala, and prefrontal cortex [106], all of which are in alignment with the three neuroimaging-based studies reviewed in the current article also (Table 4). Moreover, the same study also reported reduced anti-inflammatory cytokines within the three brain regions [106], suggesting a similar pathway in the case of anti-inflammatory cytokines with respect to psychosocial stress in PTSD as well. The over-expression of IL-6 and other proinflammatory cytokines within the brain as a result of peripheral cytokines crossing the BBB in response to trauma and psychosocial stress may then lead to neurodegeneration as previously described [107], and thus leading to neural tissue loss followed by dysfunction in the respective brain regions. Dysfunction in the regions of the prefrontal cortex, amygdala, and hippocampus are then responsible for functions of executive control, emotional lability, fear reactivity, and retrieval of traumatic memories as demonstrated in PTSD. The dysfunction of the three brain regions according to inflammation may further be explored through detailed clinical assessments according to function, such as neurocognitive tests and PTSD symptom severity as measurable by CAPS-5. Here, the alteration in glucocorticoid receptor regulation in the three brain regions may also influence the neurochemical profile of the respective brain regions. For instance, alteration in proinflammatory cytokines including IL-6 as a result of psychosocial stress may disrupt the relationship between proinflammatory cytokines and glucocorticoid receptors, whose function is to inhibit and regulate proinflammatory cytokines [108]. Considering that disruption in glucocorticoid receptor signaling affects immune function as well as hypothalamus-pituitary axis including levels of cortisol [109], these alterations may further reinforce the related clinical symptoms of PTSD such as sustained fear and anxiety.

It is also important to note that, among trauma-exposed individuals, many individuals were found resilient and did not develop PTSD. The distinct pathways between trauma-exposed individuals who are diagnosed with PTSD versus trauma-exposed individuals who are resilient to PTSD may be broken down to two possibilities, one of which is having a preexisting proinflammatory state that distinguishes between individuals who are at risk or resilient to PTSD as described in previous studies [110,111]. Here, the premise is that individuals who are at risk for PTSD have a distinct proinflammatory state prior to any exposure to trauma as compared with resilient individuals. Another perspective is the distinct responsiveness towards trauma that may vary according to genetic factors [21], such as the *ALOX12* locus as described in Table 4 [74]. Since the activation of many genes including *ALOX12*, *ALOX15*, and *RORA* have shown to alter according to oxidative stress in a PTSD model [108], a targeted approach that observes for the relationship between inflammation and trauma exposure according to genetic variants may identify the risk or resilience factors of PTSD.

A few limitations should be noted. First of all, the current review provided an overview of some of the major peripheral inflammatory markers that are targeted in the field of PTSD research. As such, a large portion of inflammatory cytokines including chemokines have been excluded in this review in order to take a targeted, narrow approach to identifying the potential biomarkers of PTSD. In addition, considering previous literature which emphasized the significance of particular genes in relation to PTSD and inflammation beyond the currently reviewed genes, future reviews that include a wider scope of methodological approaches in this topic are warranted for a more supportive mechanistic interpretation of the findings. Furthermore, despite previous studies which suggested that immune mediators such as the proinflammatory cytokines discussed in this review are able to directly influence the CNS including the hippocampus of the brain through the crossing of the BBB [105], the current structured review included a small number of neuroimaging-based studies as supportive evidence. Future directions in the study of inflammatory responses within the brain in PTSD as well as other non-communicable diseases may benefit in further exploring the detailed alteration of the brain in response to stress through the review of various neuroimaging techniques, such as magnetic resonance spectroscopy (MRS), diffusion tensor imaging (DTI), functional MRI (fMRI), and perfusion MRI. It is also noteworthy that current literature in this topic of interest largely consist of male participants, due to the nature of conditions that are most prevalent in the exposure of traumatic events. In order to better distinguish the sex differences that had been discussed in some of the studies reviewed, future research that consider a wider distribution of target populations according to trauma type is warranted. Lastly, the literature selection criteria of the current review excluded a number of studies that provided significant evidence with regards to the pathophysiology of PTSD due to its comorbid sample population. As PTSD has a prevalence of comorbidity with a vast number of other chronic diseases [7–9,31,112,113], the segregation between PTSD with other medical conditions may limit our understanding of its pathophysiology if observed independently. Further research that investigate the pathogenesis of PTSD through a multi-level approach of inflammatory responses, clinical symptoms, and brain structural and functional changes, may help determine the detailed underlying pathway of PTSD, and open up novel strategies of assessment and intervention for the disorder.

Author Contributions: Conceptualization, S.Y.; writing—original draft preparation, S.Y., T.D.K., and S.L.; writing—review and editing, S.Y.; supervision, S.Y.; funding acquisition, S.Y. All authors proofread the manuscript. All authors have read and agreed to the published version of the manuscript.

Funding: This work was supported by the Brain Research Program through the National Research Foundation of Korea (NRF) funded by the Ministry of Science and ICT (2015M3C7A1028373) and the ICT R&D program of Institute for Information & Communications Technology Promotion (B0132-15-1001).

Acknowledgments: The authors thank Shinhye Kim for her technical support and contribution towards the preparation of the tables and figures.

Conflicts of Interest: The authors declare no conflict of interest.

References

1. Kowalik, J.; Weller, J.; Venter, J.; Drachman, D. Cognitive behavioral therapy for the treatment of pediatric posttraumatic stress disorder: A review and meta-analysis. *J. Behav. Ther. Exp. Psychiatry* **2011**, *42*, 405–413. [CrossRef] [PubMed]
2. American Psychiatric Association. *Diagnostic and Statistical Manual of Mental Disorders*, 5th ed.; American Psychiatric Publishing: Arlington, VA, USA, 2013; pp. 133–137.
3. Sterling, M.; Hendrikz, J.; Kenardy, J. Similar factors predict disability and posttraumatic stress disorder trajectories after whiplash injury. *Pain* **2011**, *152*, 1272–1278. [CrossRef] [PubMed]
4. Roley, M.E.; Claycomb, M.A.; Contractor, A.A.; Dranger, P.; Armour, C.; Elhai, J.D. The relationship between rumination, PTSD, and depression symptoms. *J. Affect Disord.* **2015**, *180*, 116–121. [CrossRef] [PubMed]
5. Simpson, T.L.; Stappenbeck, C.A.; Varra, A.A.; Moore, S.A.; Kaysen, D. Symptoms of posttraumatic stress predict craving among alcohol treatment seekers: Results of a daily monitoring study. *Psychol. Addict. Behav.* **2012**, *26*, 724–733. [CrossRef] [PubMed]
6. Sautter, F.J.; Armelie, A.P.; Glynn, S.M.; Wielt, D.B. The development of a couple-based treatment for PTSD in returning veterans. *Prof. Psychol. Res. Pr.* **2011**, *42*, 63–69. [CrossRef]
7. Bartoli, F.; Crocamo, C.; Alamia, A.; Amidani, F.; Paggi, E.; Pini, E.; Clerici, M.; Carrà, G. Posttraumatic stress disorder and risk of obesity: Systematic review and meta-analysis. *J. Clin. Psychiatry* **2015**, *76*, 1253–1261. [CrossRef]
8. Vancampfort, D.; Rosenbaum, S.; Ward, P.B.; Steel, Z.; Lederman, O.; Lamwaka, A.V.; Richards, J.W.; Stubbs, B. Type 2 diabetes among people with posttraumatic stress disorder: Systematic review and meta-analysis. *Psychosom. Med.* **2016**, *78*, 465–473. [CrossRef]

9. Edmondson, D.; Kronish, I.M.; Shaffer, J.A.; Falzon, L.; Burg, M.M. Posttraumatic stress disorder and risk for coronary heart disease: A meta-analytic review. *Am. Heart J.* **2013**, *166*, 806–814. [CrossRef]

10. Kim, Y.K.; Amidfar, M.; Won, E. A review on inflammatory cytokine-induced alterations of the brain as potential neural biomarkers in post-traumatic stress disorder. *Prog. Neuropsychopharmacol. Biol. Psychiatry* **2019**, *91*, 103–112. [CrossRef]

11. Palmer, C. A theory of risk and resilience factors in military families. *Mil. Psychol.* **2008**, *20*, 205–217. [CrossRef]

12. Kim, J.E.; Dager, S.R.; Jeong, H.S.; Ma, J.; Park, S.; Kim, J.; Yera, C.; Suji, L.L.; Kang, I.; Ha, E.; et al. Firefighters, posttraumatic stress disorder, and barriers to treatment: Results from a nationwide total population survey. *PLoS ONE* **2018**, *13*, e0190630. [CrossRef] [PubMed]

13. Howren, M.B.; Lamkin, D.M.; Suls, J. Associations of depression with C-reactive protein, IL-1, and IL-6: A meta-analysis. *Psychosom Med.* **2009**, *71*, 171–186. [CrossRef] [PubMed]

14. Vogelzangs, N.; Beekman, A.T.F.; De Jonge, P.; Penninx, B.W.J.H. Anxiety disorders and inflammation in a large adult cohort. *Transl. Psychiatry* **2013**, *3*, e249. [CrossRef] [PubMed]

15. Lindqvist, D.; Wolkowitz, O.M.; Mellon, S.; Yehuda, R.; Flory, J.D.; Henn-Haase, C.; Bierer, L.M.; Abu-Amara, D.; Coy, M.; Neylan, T.C.; et al. Proinflammatory milieu in combat-related PTSD is independent of depression and early life stress. *Brain Behav. Immun.* **2014**, *42*, 81–88. [CrossRef] [PubMed]

16. Lindqvist, D.; Mellon, S.H.; Dhabhar, F.S.; Yehuda, R.; Grenon, S.M.; Flory, J.D.; Bierer, L.M.; Abu-Amara, D.; Coy, M.; Makotkine, I.; et al. Increased circulating blood cell counts in combat-related PTSD: Associations with inflammation and PTSD severity. *Psychiatry Res.* **2017**, *258*, 330–336. [CrossRef]

17. McFarlane, A.C.; Williamson, P.; Barton, C.A. The impact of traumatic stressors in civilian occupational settings. *J. Public Health Policy* **2009**, *30*, 311–327. [CrossRef]

18. Weathers, F.W.; Bovin, M.J.; Lee, D.J.; Sloan, D.M.; Schnurr, P.P.; Kaloupek, D.G.; Keane, T.M.; Marx, B.P. The Clinician-Administered PTSD Scale for DSM–5 (CAPS-5): Development and initial psychometric evaluation in military veterans. *Psychol. Assess* **2018**, *30*, 383–395. [CrossRef]

19. Ahmed-Leitao, F.; Spies, G.; van den Heuvel, L.; Seedat, S. Hippocampal and amygdala volumes in adults with posttraumatic stress disorder secondary to childhood abuse or maltreatment: A systematic review. *Psychiatry Res. Neuroimaging* **2016**, *256*, 33–43. [CrossRef]

20. Karl, A.; Werner, A. The use of proton magnetic resonance spectroscopy in PTSD research—meta-analyses of findings and methodological review. *Neurosci. Biobehav. Rev.* **2010**, *34*, 7–22. [CrossRef]

21. Hori, H.; Kim, Y. Inflammation and post-traumatic stress disorder. *Psychiatry Clin. Neurosci.* **2019**, *73*, 143–153. [CrossRef]

22. Speer, K.; Upton, D.; Semple, S.; McKune, A. Systemic low-grade inflammation in post-traumatic stress disorder: A systematic review. *J. Inflamm. Res.* **2018**, *11*, 111–121. [CrossRef] [PubMed]

23. Passos, I.C.; Vasconcelos-Moreno, M.P.; Costa, L.G.; Kunz, M.; Brietzke, E.; Quevedo, J.; Salum, G.; Magalhães, P.V.; Kapczinski, F.; Kauer-Sant'Anna, M. Inflammatory markers in post-traumatic stress disorder: A systematic review, meta-analysis, and meta-regression. *Lancet Psychiatry* **2015**, *2*, 1002–1012. [CrossRef]

24. Rohleder, N.; Aringer, M.; Boentert, M. Role of interleukin-6 in stress, sleep, and fatigue. *Ann. N. Y. Acad. Sci.* **2012**, *1261*, 88–96. [CrossRef] [PubMed]

25. Wang, W.; Wang, L.; Xu, H.; Cao, C.; Liu, P.; Luo, S.; Duan, Q.; Ellenbroek, B.; Zhang, X. Characteristics of pro-and anti-inflammatory cytokines alteration in PTSD patients exposed to a deadly earthquake. *J. Affect Disord.* **2019**, *248*, 52–58. [CrossRef] [PubMed]

26. Walker, F.R.; Pfingst, K.; Carnevali, L.; Sgoifo, A.; Nalivaiko, E. In the search for integrative biomarker of resilience to psychological stress. *Neurosci. Biobehav. Rev.* **2017**, *74*, 310–320. [CrossRef] [PubMed]

27. Kamezaki, Y.; Katsuura, S.; Kuwano, Y.; Tanahashi, T.; Rokutan, K. Circulating cytokine signatures in healthy medical students exposed to academic examination stress. *Psychophysiology* **2012**, *49*, 991–997. [CrossRef]

28. Jones, K.A.; Thomsen, C. The role of the innate immune system in psychiatric disorders. *Mol. Cell. Neurosci.* **2013**, *53*, 52–62. [CrossRef]

29. Marsland, A.L.; Walsh, C.; Lockwood, K.; John-Henderson, N.A. The effects of acute psychological stress on circulating and stimulated inflammatory markers: A systematic review and meta-analysis. *Brain Behav. Immun.* **2017**, *64*, 208–219. [CrossRef]

30. Miller, M.W.; Lin, A.P.; Wolf, E.J.; Miller, D.R. Oxidative Stress, Inflammation, and Neuroprogression in Chronic PTSD. *Harvard Rev. Psychiatry* **2018**, *26*, 57–69. [CrossRef]

31. Stein, D.J.; Benjet, C.; Gureje, O.; Lund, C.; Scott, K.M.; Poznyak, V.; van Ommeren, M. Integrating mental health with other non-communicable diseases. *BMJ* **2019**, *364*, l295. [CrossRef]

32. Dinarello, C.A. Proinflammatory cytokines. *Chest* **2000**, *118*, 503–508. [CrossRef] [PubMed]

33. Valkanova, V.; Ebmeier, K.P.; Allan, C.L. CRP, IL-6 and depression: A systematic review and meta-analysis of longitudinal studies. *J. Affect Disord.* **2013**, *150*, 736–744. [CrossRef] [PubMed]

34. Quagliato, L.A.; Nardi, A.E. Cytokine alterations in panic disorder: A systematic review. *J. Affect Disord.* **2018**, *228*, 91–96. [CrossRef]

35. Goldstein, B.I.; Kemp, D.E.; Soczynska, J.K.; McIntyre, R.S. Inflammation and the phenomenology, pathophysiology, comorbidity, and treatment of bipolar disorder: A systematic review of the literature. *J. Clin. Psychiatry* **2009**, *70*, 1078–1090. [CrossRef]

36. Gray, S.M.; Bloch, M.H. Systematic review of proinflammatory cytokines in obsessive-compulsive disorder. *Curr. Psychiatry Rep.* **2012**, *14*, 220–228. [CrossRef] [PubMed]

37. You, Z.; Luo, C.; Zhang, W.; Chen, Y.; He, J.; Zhao, Q.; Zuo, R.; Wu, Y. Pro-and anti-inflammatory cytokines expression in rat's brain and spleen exposed to chronic mild stress: Involvement in depression. *Behav. Brain Res.* **2011**, *225*, 135–141. [CrossRef]

38. Karavelioğlu, E.; Gönül, Y.; Kokulu, S.; Hazman, Ö.; Bozkurt, F.; Koçak, A.; Eser, O. Anti-inflammatory and antiapoptotic effect of interleukine-18 binding protein on the spinal cord ischemia-reperfusion injury. *Inflammation* **2014**, *37*, 917–923. [CrossRef]

39. Abbas, A.K.; Lichtman, A.H.; Pillai, S. *Basic immunology: Functions and disorders of the immune system*; Elsevier Health Sciences: Philadelphia PA, USA, 2014; pp. 68–69.

40. Raeburn, C.D.; Sheppard, F.; Barsness, K.A.; Arya, J.; Harken, A.H. Cytokines for surgeons. *Am. J. Surg.* **2002**, *183*, 268–273. [CrossRef]

41. Newton, T.L.; Fernandez-Botran, R.; Miller, J.J.; Lorenz, D.J.; Burns, V.E.; Fleming, K.N. Markers of inflammation in midlife women with intimate partner violence histories. *J. Womens Health (Larchmt)* **2011**, *20*, 1871–1880. [CrossRef]

42. Bersani, F.S.; Wolkowitz, O.M.; Lindqvist, D.; Yehuda, R.; Flory, J.; Bierer, L.M.; Makotine, I.; Abu-Amara, D.; Coy, M.; Reus, V.I.; et al. Global arginine bioavailability, a marker of nitric oxide synthetic capacity, is decreased in PTSD and correlated with symptom severity and markers of inflammation. *Brain Behav. Immun.* **2016**, *52*, 153–160. [CrossRef]

43. Blessing, E.M.; Reus, V.; Mellon, S.H.; Wolkowitz, O.M.; Flory, J.D.; Bierer, L.; Lindqvist, D.; Dhabhar, F.; Li, M.; Qian, M.; et al. Biological predictors of insulin resistance associated with posttraumatic stress disorder in young military veterans. *Psychoneuroendocrinology* **2017**, *82*, 91–97. [CrossRef] [PubMed]

44. Devoto, C.; Arcurio, L.; Fetta, J.; Ley, M.; Rodney, T.; Kanefsky, R.; Gill, J. Inflammation relates to chronic behavioral and neurological symptoms in military personnel with traumatic brain injuries. *Cell Transplant.* **2017**, *26*, 1169–1177. [CrossRef] [PubMed]

45. Kanefsky, R.; Motamedi, V.; Mithani, S.; Mysliwiec, V.; Gill, J.M.; Pattinson, C.L. Mild traumatic brain injuries with loss of consciousness are associated with increased inflammation and pain in military personnel. *Psychiatry Res.* **2019**, *279*, 34–39. [CrossRef] [PubMed]

46. Wang, Z.; Mandel, H.; Levingston, C.A.; Young, M.R.I. An exploratory approach demonstrating immune skewing and a loss of coordination among cytokines in plasma and saliva of Veterans with combat-related PTSD. *Hum. Immunol.* **2016**, *77*, 652–657. [CrossRef]

47. Hammad, S.M.; Truman, J.P.; Al Gadban, M.M.; Smith, K.J.; Twal, W.O.; Hamner, M.B. Altered blood sphingolipidomics and elevated plasma inflammatory cytokines in combat veterans with post-traumatic stress disorder. *Neurobiol. Lipids* **2012**, *10*, 2.

48. Dennis, P.A.; Weinberg, J.B.; Calhoun, P.S.; Watkins, L.L.; Sherwood, A.; Dennis, M.F.; Beckham, J.C. An investigation of vago-regulatory and health-behavior accounts for increased inflammation in posttraumatic stress disorder. *J Psychosom Res.* **2016**, *83*, 33–39. [CrossRef]

49. Zhou, J.; Nagarkatti, P.; Zhong, Y.; Ginsberg, J.P.; Singh, N.P.; Zhang, J.; Nagarkatti, M. Dysregulation in microRNA expression is associated with alterations in immune functions in combat veterans with post-traumatic stress disorder. *PLoS ONE* **2014**, *9*, e94075. [CrossRef]

50. Michopoulos, V.; Rothbaum, A.O.; Jovanovic, T.; Almli, L.M.; Bradley, B.; Rothbaum, B.O.; Gillespie, C.F.; Ressler, K.J. CRP genetic variation and CRP levels are associated with increased PTSD symptoms and physiological responses in a highly traumatized civilian population. *JAMA Psychiatry* **2015**, *172*, 353.

51. Jiang, D.; Jiang, S.; Gong, F.; Yuan, F.; Zhao, P.; He, X.; Lv, G.; Chu, X. Correlation between depression, posttraumatic stress disorder, and inflammatory factors in patients with severe burn injury. *Am. Surg.* **2018**, *84*, 1350–1354.

52. Gill, J.M.; Saligan, L.; Lee, H.; Rotolo, S.; Szanton, S. Women in recovery from PTSD have similar inflammation and quality of life as non-traumatized controls. *J. Psychosom Res.* **2013**, *74*, 301–306. [CrossRef]

53. Küffer, A.; Straus, L.D.; Prather, A.A.; Inslicht, S.S.; Richards, A.; Shigenaga, J.K.; Madden, E.; Metzler, T.J.; Neylan, T.C.; O'Donovan, A. Altered overnight levels of pro-inflammatory cytokines in men and women with posttraumatic stress disorder. *Psychoneuroendocrinology* **2019**, *102*, 114–120. [CrossRef] [PubMed]

54. de Oliveira, J.F.; Wiener, C.D.; Jansen, K.; Portela, L.V.; Lara, D.R.; de Mattos Souza, L.D.; da Silva, R.A.; Moreira, F.P.; Oses, J.P. Serum levels of interleukins IL-6 and IL-10 in individuals with posttraumatic stress disorder in a population-based sample. *Psychiatry Res.* **2018**, *260*, 111–115. [CrossRef] [PubMed]

55. Rosen, R.L.; Levy-Carrick, N.; Reibman, J.; Xu, N.; Shao, Y.; Liu, M.; Ferri, L.; Kazeros, A.; Caplan-Shaw, C.E.; Pradhan, D.R.; et al. Elevated C-reactive protein and posttraumatic stress pathology among survivors of the 9/11 World Trade Center attacks. *J. Psychiatr Res.* **2017**, *89*, 14–21. [CrossRef]

56. Teche, S.P.; Rovaris, D.L.; Aguiar, B.W.; Hauck, S.; Vitola, E.S.; Bau, C.H.; Freitas, L.H.; Grevet, E.H. Resilience to traumatic events related to urban violence and increased IL10 serum levels. *Psychiatry Res.* **2017**, *250*, 136–140. [CrossRef] [PubMed]

57. Groer, M.W.; Kane, B.; Williams, S.N.; Duffy, A. Relationship of PTSD symptoms with combat exposure, stress, and inflammation in American soldiers. *Biol. Res. Nurs.* **2015**, *17*, 303–310. [CrossRef] [PubMed]

58. Heinzelmann, M.; Lee, H.; Rak, H.; Livingston, W.; Barr, T.; Baxter, T.; Scattergood-Keepper, L.; Mysliwiec, V.; Gill, J. Sleep restoration is associated with reduced plasma C-reactive protein and depression symptoms in military personnel with sleep disturbance after deployment. *Sleep Med.* **2014**, *15*, 1565–1570. [CrossRef]

59. Bruenig, D.; Mehta, D.; Morris, C.P.; Lawford, B.; Harvey, W.; Young, R.M.; Voisey, J. Correlation between interferon γ and interleukin 6 with PTSD and resilience. *Psychiatry Res.* **2018**, *260*, 193–198. [CrossRef]

60. McCanlies, E.C.; Araia, S.K.; Joseph, P.N.; Mnatsakanova, A.; Andrew, M.E.; Burchfiel, C.M.; Violanti, J.M. C-reactive protein, interleukin-6, and posttraumatic stress disorder symptomology in urban police officers. *Cytokine* **2011**, *55*, 74–78. [CrossRef]

61. Bruenig, D.; Mehta, D.; Morris, C.P.; Harvey, W.; Lawford, B.; Young, R.M.; Voisey, J. Genetic and serum biomarker evidence for a relationship between TNFα and PTSD in Vietnam war combat veterans. *Compr. Psychiatry* **2017**, *74*, 125–133. [CrossRef]

62. Van Exel, E.; Gussekloo, J.; de Craen, A.J.; Frölich, M.; Bootsma-van der Wiel, A.; Westendorp, R.G. Low production capacity of interleukin-10 associates with the metabolic syndrome and type 2 diabetes: The Leiden 85-Plus Study. *Diabetes* **2002**, *51*, 1088–1092. [CrossRef]

63. Lio, D.; Candore, G.; Crivello, A.; Scola, L.; Colonna-Romano, G.; Cavallone, L.; Hoffman, E.; Caruso, M.; Licastro, F.; Caldarera, C.M.; et al. Opposite effects of interleukin 10 common gene polymorphisms in cardiovascular diseases and in successful ageing: Genetic background of male centenarians is protective against coronary heart disease. *J. Med. Genet.* **2004**, *41*, 790–794. [CrossRef] [PubMed]

64. Straczkowski, M.; Kowalska, I.; Nikolajuk, A.; Krukowska, A.; Gorska, M. Plasma interleukin-10 concentration is positively related to insulin sensitivity in young healthy individuals. *Diabetes Care* **2005**, *28*, 2036–2037. [CrossRef] [PubMed]

65. Uceyler, N.; Valenza, R.; Stock, M.; Schedel, R.; Sprotte, G.; Sommer, C. Reduced levels of antiinflammatory cytokines in patients with chronic widespread pain. *Arthritis Rheum.* **2006**, *54*, 2656–2664. [CrossRef] [PubMed]

66. Gupta, R.; Soni, S. An Overview on Inflammatory Biomarkers for Diabetes Mellitus. *Madridge J. Diabetes* **2019**, *3*, 64–66. [CrossRef]

67. Zhang, J.M.; Jianxiong, A. Cytokines, Inflammation and Pain. *Int. Anesthesiol. Clin.* **2009**, *45*, 27–37. [CrossRef]

68. An, K.; Salyer, J.; Kao, H.F.S. Psychological strains, salivary biomarkers, and risks for coronary heart disease among hurricane survivors. *Biol. Res. Nurs.* **2015**, *17*, 311–320. [CrossRef]

69. Dalgard, C.; Eidelman, O.; Jozwik, C.; Olsen, C.H.; Srivastava, M.; Biswas, R.; Eudy, Y.; Rothwell, S.W.; Mueller, G.P.; Yuan, P.; et al. The MCP-4/MCP-1 ratio in plasma is a candidate circadian biomarker for chronic post-traumatic stress disorder. *Transl. Psychiatry* **2017**, *7*, e1025. [CrossRef]

70. Michopoulos, V.; Beurel, E.; Gould, F.; Dhabhar, F.S.; Schultebraucks, K.; Galatzer-Levy, I.; Rothbaum, B.O.; Ressler, K.J.; Nemeroff, C.B. Association of prospective risk for chronic PTSD symptoms with low TNFα and IFNγ concentrations in the immediate aftermath of trauma exposure. *Am. J. Psychiatry* **2020**, *177*, 58–65. [CrossRef]

71. Gola, H.; Engler, H.; Sommershof, A.; Adenauer, H.; Kolassa, S.; Schedlowski, M.; Groettrup, M.; Elbert, T.; Kolassa, I.T. Posttraumatic stress disorder is associated with an enhanced spontaneous production of pro-inflammatory cytokines by peripheral blood mononuclear cells. *BMC Psychiatry* **2013**, *13*, 40. [CrossRef]

72. Guo, M.; Liu, T.; Guo, J.C.; Jiang, X.L.; Chen, F.; Gao, Y.S. Study on serum cytokine levels in posttraumatic stress disorder patients. *Asian Pac. J. Trop Med.* **2012**, *5*, 323–325. [CrossRef]

73. Smith, A.K.; Conneely, K.N.; Kilaru, V.; Mercer, K.B.; Weiss, T.E.; Bradley, B.; Tang, Y.; Gillespie, C.F.; Cubells, J.F.; Ressler, K.J. Differential immune system DNA methylation and cytokine regulation in post-traumatic stress disorder. *Am. J. Med. Genet. B Neuropsychiatr. Genet.* **2011**, *156*, 700–708. [CrossRef] [PubMed]

74. Miller, M.W.; Wolf, E.J.; Sadeh, N.; Logue, M.; Spielberg, J.M.; Hayes, J.P.; Sperbeck, E.; Schichman, S.A.; Stone, A.; Carter, W.C.; et al. A novel locus in the oxidative stress-related gene ALOX12 moderates the association between PTSD and thickness of the prefrontal cortex. *Psychoneuroendocrinology* **2015**, *62*, 359–365. [CrossRef] [PubMed]

75. Zhang, L.; Benedek, D.M.; Fullerton, C.S.; Forsten, R.D.; Naifeh, J.A.; Li, X.X.; Hu, X.Z.; Li, H.; Jia, M.; Xing, G.Q.; et al. PTSD risk is associated with BDNF Val66Met and BDNF overexpression. *Mol. Psychiatry* **2014**, *19*, 8. [CrossRef]

76. Bruenig, D.; Lurie, J.; Morris, C.P.; Harvey, W.; Lawford, B.; Young, R.M.; Voisey, J. A case-control study and meta-analysis reveal BDNF Val66Met is a possible risk factor for PTSD. *Neural Plast.* **2016**, *6979435*, 1–10. [CrossRef] [PubMed]

77. Logue, M.W.; Baldwin, C.; Guffanti, G.; Melista, E.; Wolf, E.J.; Reardon, A.F.; Wildman, D.; Galea, S.; Koenen, K.C.; Miller, M.W. A genome-wide association study of post-traumatic stress disorder identifies the retinoid-related orphan receptor alpha (RORA) gene as a significant risk locus. *Mol. Psychiatry* **2013**, *18*, 937. [CrossRef] [PubMed]

78. Amstadter, A.B.; Sumner, J.A.; Acierno, R.; Ruggiero, K.J.; Koenen, K.C.; Kilpatrick, D.G.; Galea, S.; Gelernter, J. Support for association of RORA variant and post traumatic stress symptoms in a population-based study of hurricane exposed adults. *Mol. Psychiatry* **2013**, *18*, 1148. [CrossRef]

79. Van der Kolk, B.; Greenberg, M.; Boyd, H.; Krystal, J. Inescapable shock, neurotransmitters, and addiction to trauma: Toward a psychobiology of post traumatic stress. *Biol. Psychiatry* **1985**, *20*, 314–325. [CrossRef]

80. Zunszain, P.A.; Anacker, C.; Cattaneo, A.; Choudhury, S.; Musaelyan, K.; Myint, A.M.; Thuret, S.; Price, J.; Pariante, C.M. Interleukin-1β: A new regulator of the kynurenine pathway affecting human hippocampal neurogenesis. *Neuropsychopharmacology* **2012**, *37*, 939–949. [CrossRef]

81. Camps, J. *Oxidative Stress and Inflammation in Non-Communicable Diseases-Molecular Mechanisms and Perspectives in Therapeutics*; Springer International Publishing AG: Cham, Switzerland, 2014.

82. Maes, M.; Lin, A.H.; Delmeire, L.; van Gastel, A.; Kenis, G.; De Jongh, R.; Bosmans, E. Elevated serum interleukin-6 (IL-6) and IL-6 receptor concentrations in posttraumatic stress disorder following accidental man-made traumatic events. *Biol. Psychiatry* **1999**, *45*, 833–839. [CrossRef]

83. Ouchi, Y.; Yagi, S.; Yokokura, M.; Sakamoto, M. Neuroinflammation in the living brain of Parkinson's disease. *Parkinsonism Relat. Disord.* **2009**, *15*, S200–S204. [CrossRef]

84. Beurel, E.; Michalek, S.M.; Jope, R.S. Innate and adaptive immune responses regulated by glycogen synthase kinase-3 (GSK3). *Trends Immunol.* **2010**, *31*, 24–31. [CrossRef] [PubMed]

85. Pallast, S.; Arai, K.; Ziaoying, W.; Lo, E.H.; Leyen, K. 12/15-Lipoxygenasetargets neuronal mitochondria under oxidative stress. *J. Neurochem.* **2009**, *111*, 882–889. [CrossRef] [PubMed]

86. Porro, B.; Songia, P.; Squellerio, I.; Tremoli, E.; Cavalca, V. Analysis, physiological and clinical significance of 12-HETE: A neglected platelet-derived 12-lipoxygenase product. *J. Chromatogr. B* **2014**, *964*, 26–40. [CrossRef] [PubMed]

87. O'Donovan, A.; Chao, L.L.; Paulson, J.; Samuelson, K.W.; Shigenaga, J.K.; Grunfeld, C.; Weiner, M.W.; Neylan, T.C. Altered inflammatory activity associated with reduced hippocampal volume and more severe posttraumatic stress symptoms in Gulf War veterans. *Psychoneuroendocrinology* **2015**, *51*, 557–566. [CrossRef] [PubMed]

88. Opal, S.M.; DePalo, V.A. Anti-inflammatory cytokines. *Chest* **2000**, *117*, 1162–1172. [CrossRef] [PubMed]
89. Nichols, D.; Chmiel, J.; Berger, M. Chronic inflammation in the cystic fibrosis lung: Alterations in inter-and intracellular signaling. *Clin. Rev. Allergy Immunol.* **2008**, *34*, 146–162. [CrossRef] [PubMed]
90. Grandner, M.A.; Seixas, A.; Shetty, S.; Shenoy, S. Sleep duration and diabetes risk: Population trends and potential mechanisms. *Curr. Diab. Rep.* **2016**, *16*, 106. [CrossRef]
91. Novak, P.; Cente, M.; Kosikova, N.; Augustin, T.; Kvetnansky, R.; Novak, M.; Filipcik, P. Stress-induced alterations of immune profile in animals suffering by Tau protein-driven neurodegeneration. *Cell. Mol. Neurobiol.* **2018**, *38*, 243–259. [CrossRef]
92. Toczek, J.; Hillmer, A.T.; Han, J.; Liu, C.; Peters, D.; Emami, H.; Wu, J.; Esterlis, I.; Cosgrove, K.P.; Sadeghi, M.M. FDG PET imaging of vascular inflammation in post-traumatic stress disorder: A pilot case–control study. *J. Nucl. Cardiol.* **2019**, *25*, 392–397. [CrossRef]
93. Sadeghi, M.M. 18F-FDG PET and vascular inflammation: Time to refine the paradigm? *J. Nucl. Cardiol.* **2015**, *22*, 319–324. [CrossRef]
94. McColl, B.W.; Allan, S.M.; Rothwell, N.J. Systemic infection, inflammation and acute ischemic stroke. *Neuroscience* **2009**, *158*, 1049–1061. [CrossRef] [PubMed]
95. Villien, M.; Wey, H.Y.; Mandeville, J.B.; Catana, C.; Polimeni, J.R.; Sander, C.Y.; Zürcher, N.R.; Chonde, D.B.; Fowler, J.S.; Rosen, B.R.; et al. Dynamic functional imaging of brain glucose utilization using fPET-FDG. *Neuroimage* **2014**, *100*, 192–199. [CrossRef] [PubMed]
96. Olszewski, W.L. Anatomy of the lymphatic system and its disorders. In *Lymphedema*; Springer: London, UK, 2011; pp. 49–56.
97. Khalili, S.; Liu, Y.; Kornete, M.; Roescher, N.; Kodama, S.; Peterson, A.; Piccirillo, C.A.; Tran, S.D. Mesenchymal stromal cells improve salivary function and reduce lymphocytic infiltrates in mice with Sjögren's-like disease. *PLoS ONE* **2012**, *7*, e38615. [CrossRef] [PubMed]
98. Ueda, Y.; Kondo, M.; Kelsoe, G. Inflammation and the reciprocal production of granulocytes and lymphocytes in bone marrow. *J. Exp. Med.* **2005**, *201*, 1771–1780. [CrossRef]
99. Heymsfield, S.B.; Hu, H.H.; Shen, W.; Carmichael, O. Emerging technologies and their applications in lipid compartment measurement. *Trends Endocrinol. Metab.* **2015**, *26*, 688–698. [CrossRef]
100. Shin, L.M.; Rauch, S.L.; Pitman, R.K. Amygdala, medial prefrontal cortex, and hippocampal function in PTSD. *Ann. N. Y. Acad. Sci.* **2006**, *1071*, 67–79. [CrossRef]
101. Henigsberg, N.; Kalember, P.; Petrović, Z.K.; Šečić, A. Neuroimaging research in posttraumatic stress disorder–focus on amygdala, hippocampus and prefrontal cortex. *Prog. Neuropsychopharmacol. Biol. Psychiatry* **2019**, *90*, 37–42. [CrossRef]
102. Greenberg, M.S.; Tanev, K.; Marin, M.F.; Pitman, R.K. Stress, PTSD, and dementia. *Alzheimers Dement.* **2014**, *10*, S155–S165. [CrossRef]
103. Kudielka, B.M.; Buske-Kirschbaum, A.; Hellhammer, D.H.; Kirschbaum, C. HPA axis responses to laboratory psychosocial stress in healthy elderly adults, younger adults, and children: Impact of age and gender. *Psychoneuroendocrinology* **2004**, *29*, 83–98. [CrossRef]
104. Shalev, A.Y.; Videlock, E.J.; Peleg, T.; Segman, R.; Pitman, R.K.; Yehuda, R. Stress hormones and post-traumatic stress disorder in civilian trauma victims: A longitudinal study. Part I: HPA axis responses. *Int. J. Neuropsychopharmacol.* **2008**, *11*, 365–372. [CrossRef]
105. Banks, W.A.; Kastin, A.J.; Broadwell, R.D. Passage of cytokines across the blood-brain barrier. *Neuroimmunomodulation* **1995**, *2*, 241–248. [CrossRef] [PubMed]
106. Wilson, C.B.; Ebenezer, P.J.; McLaughlin, L.D.; Francis, J. Predator exposure/psychosocial stress animal model of post-traumatic stress disorder modulates neurotransmitters in the rat hippocampus and prefrontal cortex. *PLoS ONE* **2014**, *9*, e89104. [CrossRef] [PubMed]
107. Rothaug, M.; Becker-Pauly, C.; Rose-John, S. The role of interleukin-6 signaling in nervous tissue. *Biochim. Biophys. Acta Mol. Cell Res.* **2016**, *1863*, 1218–1227. [CrossRef] [PubMed]
108. Miller, G.E.; Chen, E.; Sze, J.; Marin, T.; Arevalo, J.M.; Doll, R.; Ma, R.; Cole, S.W. A functional genomic fingerprint of chronic stress in humans: Blunted glucocorticoid and increased NF-κB signaling. *Biol. Psychiatry* **2008**, *64*, 266–272. [CrossRef] [PubMed]
109. Marques, A.H.; Silverman, M.N.; Sternberg, E.M. Glucocorticoid dysregulations and their clinical correlates: From receptors to therapeutics. *Ann. N. Y. Acad. Sci.* **2009**, *1179*, 1–18. [CrossRef] [PubMed]

110. Pace, T.W.; Heim, C.M. A short review on the psychoneuroimmunology of posttraumatic stress disorder: From risk factors to medical comorbidities. *Brain Behav. Immun.* **2011**, *25*, 6–13. [CrossRef] [PubMed]
111. Olff, M.; van Zuiden, M. Neuroendocrine and neuroimmune markers in PTSD: Pre-, peri-and post-trauma glucocorticoid and inflammatory dysregulation. *Curr. Opin. Psychol.* **2017**, *14*, 132–137. [CrossRef]
112. Morrison, F.G.; Miller, M.W.; Wolf, E.J.; Logue, M.W.; Maniates, H.; Kwasnik, D.; Cherry, J.D.; Svirsky, S.; Restaino, A.; Hilderbrandt, A.; et al. Reduced interleukin 1A gene expression in the dorsolateral prefrontal cortex of individuals with PTSD and depression. *Neurosci. Lett.* **2019**, *692*, 204–209. [CrossRef]
113. Ogłodek, E.A.; Just, M.J.; Szromek, A.R.; Araszkiewicz, A. Assessing the serum concentration levels of NT-4/5, GPX-1, TNF-α, and l-arginine as biomediators of depression severity in first depressive episode patients with and without posttraumatic stress disorder. *Pharmacol. Rep.* **2017**, *69*, 1049–1058. [CrossRef]

Article

Oxidative Stress Increases Endogenous Complement-Dependent Inflammatory and Angiogenic Responses in Retinal Pigment Epithelial Cells Independently of Exogenous Complement Sources

Timon-Orest Trakkides [1], Nicole Schäfer [1], Maria Reichenthaler [1], Konstanze Kühn [1], Ricardo J. M. G. E. Brandwijk [2], Erik J. M. Toonen [2], Florian Urban [3], Joachim Wegener [3], Volker Enzmann [4] and Diana Pauly [1,*]

[1] Experimental Ophthalmology, Eye clinic, University Hospital Regensburg, 93053 Regensburg, Germany; timon-orest.trakkides@stud.uni-regensburg.de (T.-O.T.); nicole.schaefer@ukr.de (N.S.); maria.reichenthaler@googlemail.com (M.R.); konstanze_kuehn@t-online.de (K.K.)

[2] R&D Department, Hycult Biotech, 5405 PD Uden, The Netherlands; r.brandwijk@hycultbiotech.com (R.J.M.G.E.B.); e.toonen@hycultbiotech.com (E.J.M.T.)

[3] Institute of Analytical Chemistry, Chemo- and Biosensors, University of Regensburg, 93053 Regensburg, Germany; florian.urban@ur.de (F.U.); joachim.wegener@ur.de (J.W.)

[4] Department of Ophthalmology, University Hospital of Bern and Department of Biomedical Research, University of Bern, 3010 Bern, Switzerland; volker.enzmann@insel.ch

* Correspondence: diana.pauly@ukr.de; Tel.: +49-941-944-9228

Received: 24 September 2019; Accepted: 11 November 2019; Published: 13 November 2019

Abstract: Oxidative stress-induced damage of the retinal pigment epithelium (RPE) and chronic inflammation have been suggested as major contributors to a range of retinal diseases. Here, we examined the effects of oxidative stress on endogenous complement components and proinflammatory and angiogenic responses in RPE cells. ARPE-19 cells exposed for 1–48 h to H_2O_2 had reduced cell–cell contact and increased markers for epithelial–mesenchymal transition but showed insignificant cell death. Stressed ARPE-19 cells increased the expression of complement receptors CR3 (subunit CD11b) and C5aR1. CD11b was colocalized with cell-derived complement protein C3, which was present in its activated form in ARPE-19 cells. C3, as well as its regulators complement factor H (CFH) and properdin, accumulated in the ARPE-19 cells after oxidative stress independently of external complement sources. This cell-associated complement accumulation was accompanied by increased *nlrp3* and *foxp3* expression and the subsequently enhanced secretion of proinflammatory and proangiogenic factors. The complement-associated ARPE-19 reaction to oxidative stress, which was independent of exogenous complement sources, was further augmented by the poly(ADP-ribose) polymerase (PARP) inhibitor olaparib. Our results indicate that ARPE-19 cell-derived complement proteins and receptors are involved in ARPE-19 cell homeostasis following oxidative stress and should be considered as targets for treatment development for retinal degeneration.

Keywords: oxidative stress; retinal pigment epithelial cells; complement system; inflammasome; foxp3; olaparib

1. Introduction

One of the most oxidative environments in the body is the retinal pigment epithelium (RPE) [1], which is in close contact with the photoreceptors and maintains visual function [2]. Low levels of reactive oxygen species are required to maintain physiological functions [3], but the combination of visible light exposure, elevated metabolic activity, the accumulation of oxidized lipoproteins, and decreased antioxidant functions during aging make the retinal tissue vulnerable to oxidative stress [4,5]. Oxidative damage to the RPE has therefore been identified as a contributing factor to different retinal degenerative diseases, such as age-related macular degeneration or Stargardt disease [6–11].

Consistent with these observations, constant oxidative stress can trigger chronic inflammation, subsequently leading to cellular damage in the RPE/retina [6,12]. On the basis of genetic polymorphisms in genes of the complement system, systemic complement activation, and local complement deposition in degenerative retinal tissue, a contribution of the complement system to oxidative stress-related retinal degeneration has been hypothesized [7,13,14]. The complement system is composed of over 40 proteins, which bridge the innate and adaptive immune defense [15]. The main functions are (I) the removal of damaged cells, (II) protection against invading pathogens, and (III) the attraction of immune cells.

Besides the traditional view, evidence is accumulating that complement components are also involved in physiological processes, such as responses to oxidative stress and cellular maintenance [6]. The complement system comprises several soluble and membrane-bound proteins and receptors, which can be produced by a number of cells (including nonimmune cells and extrahepatic tissue) and contribute to autocrine cell physiology [16]. The role of endogenous complement-dependent regulation of cellular homeostasis has recently been extensively studied [17]. T-cells, B-cells, and human airway epithelial cells contain intracellular stores of C3, which is endogenously cleaved into its active forms, C3a and C3b, by intracellular proteases [18–20]. Activated C3 is correlated with the activation of the NLR family pyrin domain containing 3 (NLRP3) inflammasome in T-effector cells [18], which leads to proinflammatory cytokine release. An antagonizing complement modulation has been described for regulatory T-cells, where C3aR and C5aR1 activation resulted in the activation of the forkhead box P3 (FOXP3) transcription factor [18,21]. The FOXP3 transcription factor acts in multimodal fashion and stimulates the release of anti-inflammatory cytokines and proangiogenic factors [21–23].

Oxidative stress and inflammasome activation have previously been correlated with external complement activity in RPE cells [6,24]. FOXP3 activation in RPE cells also depends on extracellularly added complement components [25]. However, an RPE-derived complement has not been discussed as a source for NLRP3 or FOXP3 modulation. Complement components can be produced by RPE cells [26], and their expression is changed under oxidative stress [27–31]. Further activated forms of C3 (C3a), independently of extracellular complement sources, are also secreted by RPE cells, suggesting a similar function of the complement system in RPE cells compared to T-cells [32–35].

In this study, we report that H_2O_2 stimulated the accumulation of complement proteins C3, complement factor H (CFH), and properdin in RPE cells and increased the expression of complement receptors C5aR1 and CR3 (subunit CD11b). This was accompanied by increased *nlrp3* inflammasome expression and the FOXP3-associated release of proangiogenic factors. Our results indicate a cell homeostatic function of cell-derived complement components that is independent of external complement receptor ligands.

2. Materials and Methods

2.1. Cell Culture and Treatment

Human male adult retinal pigment epithelium cells (ARPE-19 cells, passage 39; American Type Culture Collection, #CRL-2302) were cultivated for 6 days in cell culture flasks with Dulbecco's modified eagle medium (DMEM/F12; Sigma-Aldrich, Darmstadt, Germany), 10% fetal calf serum (FCS; PanBiotech, Aidenbach, Germany), and 1% penicillin/streptomycin (37 °C, 5% CO_2). Cells were trypsinized (0.05% trypsin/0.02% ethylenediaminetetraacetic acid (EDTA)) and seeded in a concentration of 1.6×10^5 cells/cm^2 (passage 39) on mouse laminin-coated (5 µg/cm^2, Sigma-Aldrich, Darmstadt, Germany) 0.4-µm-pore polyester membrane inserts (Corning, Corning, NY, USA). Cells were cultivated for 4 weeks with apical and basal media exchanges (first-day medium with 10% FCS), remaining time medium with 5% FCS). Before treatment, the FCS concentration was reduced to 0% within 3 days (5%–2.5%–1.25%). ARPE-19 cells were treated with either 0.5 mM H_2O_2 for 1, 4, 24, and 48 h or with 0.5 mM H_2O_2 and 0.01 mM olaparib (Biomol, Hamburg, Germany) for 4 h.

2.2. Immunohistochemistry and Terminal Deoxynucleotidyl Transferase dUTP Nick End Labeling (TUNEL) Assay

Phosphate buffered saline (PBS)-washed, paraformaldehyde-fixated (4%, 20 min; Merck, Darmstadt, Germany) ARPE-19 cells were permeabilized (PBS/0.2% Tween20 (PBS-T), 45 min), and unspecific bindings were blocked (3% bovine serum albumin (BSA) (Carl Roth, Karlsruhe, Germany)/PBS-T, 1 h). Antigens were detected using a primary antibody (Supplementary Materials, Table S1, overnight, 3% BSA/PBS-T) and a fluorescence-conjugated antispecies antibody (Supplementary Materials, Table S1, 45 min, 3% BSA/PBS). The fluorochrome HOECHST 33342 (1:1000) was used to stain DNA. Cells were covered with fluorescence mounting medium (Dako, Agilent Technologies, Santa Clara, CA, USA). Images were taken with a confocal microscope (Zeiss, Jena, Germany).

The TUNEL assay was performed with a DeadEnd™ Fluorometric TUNEL System (Promega, Madison, WI, USA) on paraformaldehyde-fixated, washed, and permeabilized (0.2% Triton X-100 in PBS) cells. Images were taken with a confocal microscope (Zeiss, Jena, Germany).

2.3. Transepithelial Resistance (TER) and Cellular Capacitance

TER and cell layer capacitance were recorded online using the established cellZscope device (nanoAnalytics, Münster, Germany), as previously described [36]. The dielectric properties of empty filter inserts were determined independently and were included in the equivalent circuit used for analysis. Fitting the parameters of the equivalent circuit to the experimental data was achieved via nonlinear least-squares optimization according to the Levenberg–Marquardt algorithm.

2.4. Real-Time, Quantitative Polymerase Chain Reaction (RT-qPCR)

Here, mRNA was isolated using a NucleoSpin® RNA/Protein kit (Macherey-Nagel, Düren, Germany). Purified mRNA was transcribed into cDNA with a QuantiTect® Reverse Transcription Kit (Qiagen, Hilden, Germany). Transcripts of complement components, receptors, and inflammation-associated markers were analyzed using a Rotor-Gene SYBR® Green PCR Kit either with QuantiTect Primer Assays (Supplementary Materials, Table S2) or in-house-designed primer pairs (Metabion, Planegg, Germany) (described in the Supplementary Materials, Table S3) in a Rotor Gene Q 2plex cycler (Qiagen, Hilden, Germany). Data were analyzed using the delta delta Ct (ddCt) method. Values were depicted on a linear scale using log-transformed scores to equally visualize increases and decreases in expression levels.

2.5. Western Blot

Proteins were dissolved in RIPA buffer (Sigma-Aldrich, Darmstadt, Germany) with protease and phosphatase inhibitors (1:100, Sigma-Aldrich, Darmstadt, Germany). Samples were diluted in reducing Laemmli sample buffer and denatured (95 °C, 10 min). Following sample separation in a 12% SDS-PAGE, proteins were transferred onto an activated polyvinylidene difluoride membrane using a wet-blotting system. Membranes were blocked (1 h, 5% BSA/PBS-T) and incubated with the primary antibody (Supplementary Materials, Table S1, overnight, 5% BSA/PBS-T). Peroxidase-conjugated antispecies antibodies were used for detection (Supplementary Materials, Table S1, 1 h, PBS-T). WesternSure PREMIUM Chemiluminescent Substrate (LI-COR biosciences, Lincoln, NE, USA) visualized the antigen in a Fluor Chem FC2 Imaging System (Alpha Innotech, San Leandro, CA, USA).

2.6. Protein Secretion Assays

Properdin levels in cell culture supernatants were determined using a sandwich ELISA, as previously described [37]. C3 quantification was performed using a newly developed C3 ELISA (cat# HK366-01; Hycult Biotech, Uden, Netherlands) according to the manufacturer's protocol. CFH was quantified in an in-house ELISA with mouse anti-CFH monoclonal antibody (BioRad, Feldkirchen, Germany) as a capture antibody and goat anti-CFH polyclonal antibody (Merck, Darmstadt, Germany) as a detection antibody (Supplementary Materials, Table S1). A comparison of properdin, C3, and CFH levels in supernatants of lower and higher ARPE-19 passages was performed using a MILLIPLEX MAP Human Complement Panel (Merck, Darmstadt, Germany). Interleukin (IL)-1β und IL-6 concentrations were determined according to the protocol of a custom ProcartaPlex® multiplex immunoassay kit (ThermoFisher, Waltham, MA, USA). IL-8 was analyzed using xMAP technology, anti-IL-8 beads (cat# 171-BK31MR2; BioRad, Feldkirchen, Germany), and anti-IL-8 biotin (cat# 171-BK31MR2; BioRad, Feldkirchen, Germany) according to the manufacturer's protocol. The readout of the multiplex assays (IL-1β, IL-6, and IL-8) was performed using a Magpix instrument (Luminex, Austin, TX, USA). Vascular endothelial growth factor (VEGF)-α concentrations were determined using a human VEGF Quantikine ELISA Kit (R&D system, Minneapolis, MN, USA).

2.7. Statistics

Expression statistical analyses for the mRNA were performed using a nonparametric, unpaired Kruskal–Wallis test with Dunn's multiple comparison correction, and protein secretion was statistically analyzed using an ordinary two-way analysis of variance ANOVA with Bonferroni's multiple comparisons test (GraphPad Prism 7; GraphPad Software Inc., San Diego, CA, USA).

3. Results

3.1. Stressed, In Vivo-Like Cultivation of ARPE-19 Cells

We investigated cellular stress response and cell-specific complement expression in a cell line of human RPE cells, the ARPE-19 cell line. Aged ARPE-19 cells of passage 39 were cultivated under in vivo-like, unstressed conditions. This was visualized by staining zonula occludens 1 (ZO-1), an important protein for cell–cell contact, and this showed the formation of stable tight junctions and mainly mononuclear, polarized cell growth on transwell filters (Figure 1A,D). Stable transepithelial resistance (TER), a measure of the cell layer's barrier function, and the cell layer's capacitance, which is indicative of the expression of membrane protrusions such as microvilli and other membrane folding, were characteristics of the in vivo-like cultivated ARPE-19 cells (Supplementary Materials, Figure S1A,B). H_2O_2 treatment resulted in cellular stress, which was indicated by reduced cell–cell contact after 4 h (Figure 1B) and a time-dependent translocation of ZO-1 from the cell membrane to the cytoplasm after 24 h (Figure 1E). Evidence of induced cellular stress by H_2O_2 was also observed in the increased mRNA expression of vimentin (*vim*) and α-smooth muscle actin (*α-sma*), a typical mesenchymal marker indicating an epithelial–mesenchymal transition (Supplementary Materials, Figure S1C,D) [38–40]. However, the majority of the ARPE-19 cells did not undergo apoptosis under these nonlethal oxidative stress conditions, as shown by a low number of TUNEL-positive cells (Figure 1C,F), and H_2O_2-treated cells maintained the cell layer's barrier function as well as the cell layer's capacitance (Supplementary Materials, Figure S1E,F).

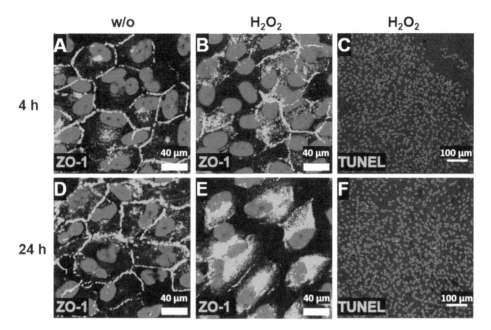

Figure 1. ARPE-19 cells reduced tight junctions and circumvented apoptosis under oxidative stress. (**A,D**) ARPE-19 cells untreated (without (w/o)) and stressed with H_2O_2 for (**B,C**) 4 h or (**E,F**) 24 h translocated the zonula occludens protein 1 (ZO-1, green) time-dependently from the (**A,D**) cell membrane to the (**B,E**) cytoplasm. (**C,F**) ARPE-19 cells treated with oxidative stress showed a minimal TUNEL-positive (light blue) apoptotic reaction after (**F**) 24 h.

3.2. ARPE-19 Cells Increased Complement Receptor Expression under Oxidative Stress

ARPE-19 cells express cellular receptors, sense the cellular environment, and can react to complement activation products. Complement receptor 3 (CR3) is a heterodimer integrin consisting of two noncovalently linked subunits (CD11b and CD18) on leukocytes/microglia, and it is activated by C3 cleavage products (iC3b, C3d, and C3dg). We detected CD11b with low expression in mRNA and low protein levels in ARPE-19 cells (Figure 2A,B). Oxidative stress increased *cd11b* mRNA expression after 4 h, which was also shown in protein levels with immunostaining (Figure 2A,C).

The activation of complement protein C5 was detected by complement receptor C5aR1, which was expressed by ARPE-19 cells (Figure 2D). H_2O_2 treatment increased *c5ar1* expression comparably to *cd11b* expression (Figure 2D-F). C5aR1 protein accumulation was observed after 4 h in the cell nuclei (Figure 2F), which was more distributed in/on the cell after 24 h (Figure 2G). Increased C5aR1 protein levels were also confirmed in Western blots (Figure 2H,I).

The transcription levels of complement receptor *c3aR* were not significantly changed in H_2O_2-treated ARPE-19 cells (Supplementary Materials, Figure S2A).

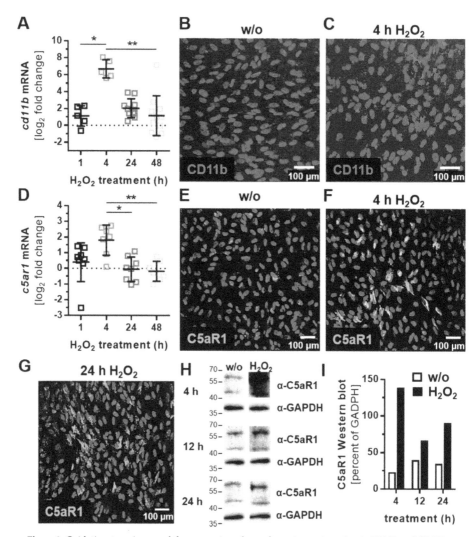

Figure 2. Oxidative stress increased the expression of complement receptor subunit CD11b and C5aR1 in ARPE-19 cells. (**A**) *Cd11b* mRNA expression was increased 4 h after H_2O_2 treatment. This effect was confirmed on a protein level by immunohistochemistry using (**B,C**) anti-CD11b (red) antibodies. (**D**) *C5ar1* mRNA also increased on (**D**) mRNA and (**E–G**) protein level (anti-C5aR1, green) in H_2O_2 treated cells. (**H**) Western blots of ARPE-19 cell lysates detected C5aR1 between 40 and 60 kDa after 4–24 h H_2O_2 treatment (full immunoblots are shown in the Supplementary Materials, Figure S3A,B; $n = 1$) (**I**) Quantitatively, C5aR1 expression was increased in H_2O_2-treated cells in the Western blots. (**A,D**) Mean with standard deviation is shown, * $p \leq 0.05$, ** $p \leq 0.01$. The dotted line depicts the untreated control; (**B,E,H,I**) w/o untreated control.

3.3. Complement Proteins Accumulated in ARPE-19 Cells under Oxidative Stress

Complement proteins, which can modulate the activity of complement receptors at the RPE, are locally produced in the retina [26,41] and by ARPE-19 cells (Figure 3; Supplementary Materials, Figure S2B–I). The mRNA expression and cellular protein levels of the stabilizing complement regulator, properdin, were increased after 24 h of H_2O_2 treatment (Figure 3A,C–E), but properdin secretion was not detected (Figure 3B, Supplementary Materials, Figure S4G). This indicated properdin storage in the stressed ARPE-19 cells (Figure 3C–E).

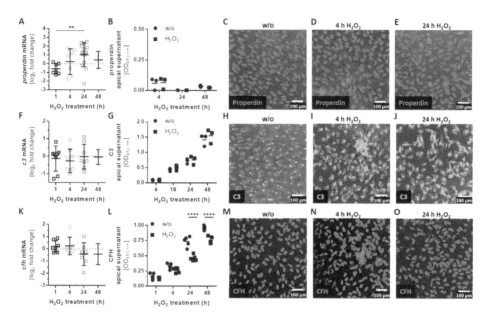

Figure 3. Oxidative stress induced complement component accumulation in ARPE-19 cells. (**A**) *Properdin* mRNA levels were increased 24 h following H_2O_2 treatment. This did not affect (**B**) apical properdin secretion, but was confirmed in the protein level by immunohistochemistry using an (**C–E**) anti-properdin (red) antibody. (**F**) C3 mRNA and (**G**) apical C3 protein secretion were not altered in stressed ARPE-19 cells. Immunohistochemistry using (**H–J**) anti-C3 (green) antibodies showed an increase of cell-associated (**I,J**) C3 after oxidative stress treatment. (**K**) *Cfh* mRNA and (**L**) CFH apical protein concentration were decreased following H_2O_2 treatment. (**M–O**) Immunohistochemistry using anti-complement factor H (CFH, purple) antibodies showed an increase in cell-associated (**N,O**) CFH after oxidative stress treatment. Mean with standard deviation is shown, ** $p \leq 0.01$, **** $p \leq 0.0001$; dotted line depicts untreated control (**A,F,K**); w/o untreated control (**G,G,L**); ELISA control standard curves and protein concentrations in the basal supernatants are shown in the Supplementary Materials, Figure S4D–I.

The transcription levels of additional complement components (*c3, c4a, c4b, cfb, cfd,* and *c5*) and soluble (*cfh, cfi*) and membrane-bound complement regulators (*cd46, cd59*) did not significantly change under oxidative stress conditions (Figure 3F,K; Supplementary Materials, Figure S2B–I).

However, we observed a change in cellular accumulation and the modulated secretion of complement components in the protein level through oxidative stress (Figure 3H–J,L–O). Central complement component *c3* was not regulated in mRNA and the protein secretion level by oxidative stress (Figure 3F,G; Supplementary Materials, Figure S4H), but we detected an increase in cellular C3 in immunostainings of ARPE-19 cells (Figure 3H–J). The secretion of C3 was more observable in younger compared to older ARPE-19 cells treated with H_2O_2 (Supplementary Materials, Figure S4B). A similar effect of cellular complement component accumulation and associated reduced secretion was detectable for complement regulator CFH (Figure 3L–O; Supplementary Materials, Figure S4I). However, *cfh* mRNA expression was not changed under oxidative stress (Figure 3K).

3.4. Autocrine Complement Receptor Activation Following Oxidative Stress Was Correlated with the Release of Proinflammatory and Proangiogenic Factors

Intracellular complement proteins and cellular complement receptors have previously been associated with the autocrine regulation of cell differentiation and cell physiology in T-cells as well as lung epithelial cells [20,42]. In line with this, we found a colocalization of CD11b and C3 in ARPE-19 cells (Figure 4A,B) and activated C3 fragments (C3b α', C3d) in the ARPE-19 cells (Figure 4C), without adding any exogenous complement source.

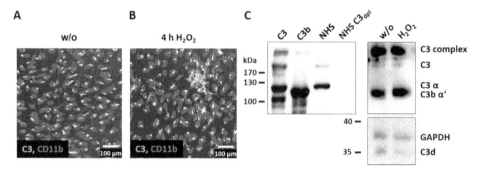

Figure 4. C3 and complement receptor CD11b were colocalized in ARPE-19. (**A**) Unstressed (w/o) and (**B**) H_2O_2-treated ARPE-19 cells were stained with anti-C3 (green) and anti-CD11b (red) antibodies. Overlapping staining signals (yellow) suggested a colocalization of C3 and CD11b. (**C**) C3 and activation products (C3b α' and C3d) were detected in untreated and H_2O_2-treated ARPE-19 cells using a Western blot under reducing conditions (controls: native C3, C3b, human serum (NHS), and C3-depleted human serum (NHS C3$_{dpl}$)). Full immunoblots are shown in the Supplementary Materials, Figure S3C,D; immunoblots were repeated twice.

The intracellular cleavage of complement proteins into active fragments (independently of the systemic complement cascade) can be mediated by intracellular proteases such as cathepsin B (CTSB) and cathepsin L (CTSL) [17,18]. Both proteases were expressed by ARPE-19 cells, and they were upregulated following oxidative stress (Figure 5). The mRNA expression of *ctsb* and *ctsl* was increased after 24 h of H_2O_2 treatment (Figure 5A,B). We confirmed a higher concentration of CTSL in ARPE-19 cells under stress conditions also on the protein level (Figure 5C,D).

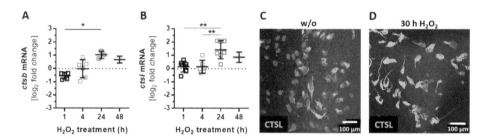

Figure 5. The expression of intracellular proteases was increased by oxidative stress in ARPE-19. (**A**) *Ctsb* and (**B**) *ctsl* mRNA expression increased 24 h after H_2O_2 treatment. This effect was confirmed on the protein level in immunostainings using an (**C,D**) anti-CTSL (green) antibody. (**A,B**) Mean with standard deviation is shown, * $p \leq 0.05$, ** $p \leq 0.01$, dotted line depicts untreated control; (**C**) w/o untreated control.

The activation of complement receptor signaling regulates the pro- and anti-inflammatory response in T- and RPE cells [24,43]. This can induce inflammasome activation and regulate the mammalian target of rapamycin (mTOR)-pathway, involving the FOXP3 transcription factor [24,25,44]. After the detection of H_2O_2-dependent regulation of complement receptors (Figure 2), cellular complement protein accumulation (Figure 3), cell-derived C3 colocalized with CD11b, and C3 activation products C3b and C3d in ARPE-19 cells (Figure 4), we hypothesized that the NLRP3 inflammasome and FOXP3 also play an autocrine, complement-dependent role in ARPE-19 cells treated with H_2O_2. This regulation would be independent of blood-derived complement components and would involve the release of cytokines and growth factors in stressed ARPE-19 cells (Figure 6).

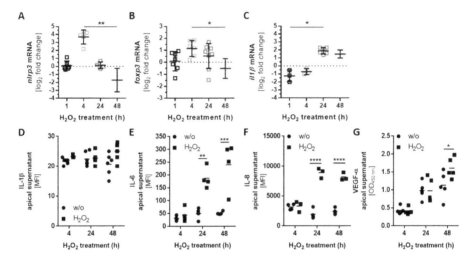

Figure 6. Increased *nlrp3* and *foxp3* mRNA expression correlated with proinflammatory and proangiogenic factor secretion. (**A**) *Nlrp3*, (**B**) *foxp3*, and (**C**) *il1β* mRNA levels increased either (**A,B**) 4 h or (**C**) 24 h and 48 h following H_2O_2 treatment. The proinflammatory cytokine release of (**D**) Interleukin (IL)-1β and (**E**) IL-6 was detected in stressed ARPE-19 cells. This was correlated with an enhanced secretion of the proangiogenic factors (**F**) IL-8 and (**G**) vascular endothelial growth factor (VEGF)-α in H_2O_2-treated cells. MFI: mean fluorescence intensity. Mean with standard deviation is shown, * $p \leq 0.05$, ** $p \leq 0.01$, *** $p \leq 0.001$, **** $p \leq 0.0001$; (**A,B,C**) dotted line depicts untreated control; (**D–G**) w/o untreated control; protein concentrations in the basal supernatants are shown in the Supplementary Materials, Figure S4J–L.

Indeed, we detected an increased expression of *nlrp3* and *foxp3* mRNA after 4 h of H_2O_2 treatment (Figure 6A,B). Subsequent enhanced expression of *il1β* mRNA after 24 h and 48 h was associated with increased *nlrp3* levels in stressed ARPE-19 cells (Figure 6C). However, the mRNA expression of *il18* was not changed (Supplementary Materials, Figure S2J). Further, we found higher proinflammatory cytokine levels in the H_2O_2-treated ARPE-19 cell supernatants compared to the untreated controls (Figure 6D,E). IL-1β was slightly increased after treatment, while IL-6 was significantly elevated in the supernatant of stressed ARPE-19 cells.

Increased *foxp3* expression is an attribute of anti-inflammatory regulatory T-cells, which secrete mainly transforming growth factor (TGF)-β and IL-10. We did not detect a change in *tgf-β* expression (Supplementary Materials, Figure S2K) or IL-10 secretion in H_2O_2-treated ARPE-19 cells. Therefore, we assumed a proangiogenic function of *foxp3* in the cells, as previously reported [22,23]. In line with this, we observed an increase in IL-8 and VEGF-α concentration in the apical supernatant of stressed ARPE-19 cells (Figure 6F,G). This correlation between complement components, *foxp3* expression, and proangiogenic reactions in RPE cells needs to be further investigated.

As a side note, IL-17, interferon (IFN)-γ, IL-18, IL-2, and tumor necrosis factor (TNF)-α were not detected in the apical or basal supernatant of 4-, 24-, and 48-h untreated and H_2O_2-treated ARPE-19 cells (data not shown).

3.5. Olaparib Boosted the Proinflammatory Response of ARPE-19 Cells to Oxidative Stimuli

Oxidative stress-induced cellular reactions have been previously ameliorated by an approved anticancer drug, olaparib, which is an inhibitor of poly(ADP-ribose) polymerase (PARP) [45–47]. We investigated the effects of olaparib on H_2O_2-dependent mRNA expression changes of complement receptors, components, and inflammation-related transcripts (Figure 7, Supplementary Materials, Figure S5). Oxidative stress increased the expression of *cd11b*, *c5ar1*, and *nlrp3* after 4 h of H_2O_2 treatment. This was further enhanced by olaparib treatment (Figure 7A–C). An increase in *properdin* and *ctsb* transcripts was observed after 24 h following oxidative stress alone (Figures 3A and 5A). A combination of H_2O_2 and olaparib accelerated this reaction, with a significant increase in *properdin* and *ctsb* mRNA expression after only 4 h (Figure 7D,E). The expression of *cfd* (Supplementary Materials, Figure S2E) was not altered under oxidative stress; however, H_2O_2 and olaparib together increased *cfd* transcript levels (Figure 7F). Olaparib did not interfere with the transcription of *foxp3* (Figure 7G) and other transcripts (*c3*, *c4a*, *c5*, *cfb*, *cfh*, *cfi*, *c3ar*, and *ctsl*) (Supplementary Materials, Figure S5) in ARPE-19 cells treated with H_2O_2.

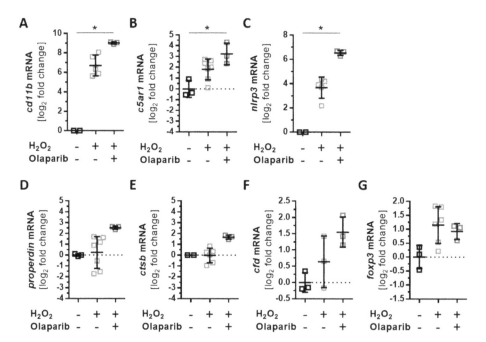

Figure 7. Olaparib enhanced oxidative stress-dependent expression changes in ARPE-19 cells. ARPE-19 cells were treated for 4 h with H_2O_2, and the effect of simultaneously added olaparib on transcription was investigated. (**A**) *Cd11b*, (**B**) *c5aR1*, and (**C**) *nlrp3* transcripts were significantly increased in olaparib-treated, stressed cells compared to unstressed cells. Olaparib also increased the expression of (**D**) *properdin*, (**E**) *ctsb*, and (**F**) *cfd*. (**G**) *Foxp3* mRNA levels were not changed in stressed ARPE-19 cells following olaparib addition. Mean with standard deviation is shown, * $p \leq 0.05$; dotted line depicts untreated control.

4. Discussion

The RPE is exposed to high-energy light, and it conducts the phagocytosis of oxidized photoreceptor outer segments. Both of these processes are accompanied by a rapid release of reactive oxygen species [6,48,49]. Reactive oxygen species, including H_2O_2, are on the one hand major cellular stressors [6,50] and on the other hand cellular survival factors [3,51]. Antioxidants are decreased in light-exposed retinae, allowing the intraocular accumulation of H_2O_2 [52]. We used H_2O_2 treatment to mimic physiological oxidative stress in serum-free cultivated ARPE-19 cells to investigate the endogenous complement response in ARPE-19 cells independent of external complement sources [53,54].

Oxidative stress increased the concentration of the complement regulators CFH and properdin and the central complement protein C3 in ARPE-19 cells in a time-dependent manner, without access to any extracellular complement source. Previous studies have mostly reported a reduced expression of *cfh* mRNA in RPE cells exposed to oxidative stress [28–31], but these studies did not include further CFH protein analysis. Our reported CFH protein accumulation after H_2O_2 treatment in polarized, monolayer ARPE-19 cells (using immunohistochemistry) is in contrast to reduced CFH protein detection results in Western blots of non-in vivo-like cultivated ARPE-19 cells following H_2O_2 treatment [30].

However, it is known that intracellular CFH can enhance the cleavage of endogenously expressed C3 through a cathepsin L (CTSL)-mediated mechanism [55]. The concentrations of lysosomal protease CTSL and the central complement protein C3 were both enhanced under oxidative stress conditions in ARPE-19 cells. Previous studies of RPE cell-derived complement components only focused on *c3* mRNA expression, which was not changed under low H_2O_2 concentrations [56]. We went a step further and showed that C3 was accumulated in the ARPE-19 cells following oxidative stress. This ARPE-19 cell-dependent local accumulation of C3 was also shown for ARPE-19 cells treated with cigarette smoke [27].

If C3 is activated in the blood, CFH serves as a negative regulator and properdin as a positive regulator. We showed for the first time that oxidative stress increased *properdin* mRNA expression in ARPE-19 cells. This resulted in a higher properdin protein concentration in these cells, which may promote cellular C3 cleavage. In summary, our data described a local production of complement proteins in ARPE-19 cells and an enhanced cellular storage of complement proteins in the cells after H_2O_2 treatment. This cellular accumulation suggests an autocrine, cellular function of complement proteins in ARPE-19 cells following oxidative stress that is independent of external complement protein sources.

Our studies revealed a colocalization of accumulated, endogenous C3 with complement receptor 3 (CR3, subunit CD11b) in ARPE-19 cells exposed to oxidative stress and an increase in CD11b after 4 h. CR3 expression has been associated with inflammasome activation as a reaction to complement components and/or oxidative stress in white blood cells and RPE cells [57,58]. In agreement with this association, the addition of H_2O_2 to ARPE-19 cells increased the time-dependent expression of *nlrp3* and *il-1β* mRNA and subsequently enhanced the secretion of proinflammatory cytokines.

Inflammasome activation can be triggered by reactive oxygen species and has been associated with lipid peroxidation end products and phototoxicity in RPE cells [59,60]. The involvement of the complement components in this oxidative stress response of RPE cells has only been described in relation to extracellularly added anaphylatoxins so far [24], but an endogenous complement of RPE cells has not been suggested as a potential priming factor for the inflammasome. We detected activated C3 cleavage products in ARPE-19 cells, and previous studies have shown that activated C3a can be intracellularly generated in RPE cells independent of the systemic canonical complement system [32–35]. Further, C3 receptors were expressed (CR3, C3aR) and regulated (CR3) under oxidative stress in ARPE-19 cells, indicating a role for endogenous complement components in stressed ARPE-19 cells.

Cellular C3 is cleaved by lysosomal CTSL [18,55], and NLRP3 inflammasome activation depends on this CTSL activity [60]. It has been reported that CTSL inhibition reduces inflammasome activity in ARPE-19 cells exposed to oxidative stress [61]. These findings show the interaction between cell-specific complement component cleavage and inflammasome activity. It is already known that endogenous

C3-driven complement activation is required for IL-1β and IL-6 secretion, as well as for inflammasome activation in immune cells [62]. Our data suggest that proinflammatory cytokine secretion may also be an autocrine mechanism in ARPE-19 cells associated with complement components and receptors.

In addition to C3, C5 has been identified as a key player in cell homeostasis [24]. The *c5aR1* receptor is expressed in RPE cells [63,64] and was increased after oxidative stress treatment. *C5* mRNA expression was not changed, and the biologically highly active C5a fragment, a ligand for C5aR1 with a very low biological half-life (approximately 1 min [65,66]), was not detected in our study. The rapid C5a–C5aR interaction might have interfered with our detection schedule. However, C5aR1 stimulation is associated with IL-8 and VEGF-α secretion in ARPE-19 cells [63,64]. The increased secretion of these proangiogenic factors was also observed following the H_2O_2 stimuli. The signaling pathway is not exactly known so far, but exclusive C5aR1 activation by non-ARPE-19 cell components can be excluded. In regulatory T-cells, the transcription factor FOXP3 promotes the expression of IL-8 [22], and in bladder cancer cells, a knock-down of *foxp3* has resulted in the reduced expression of *vegf-α* [23]. *Foxp3* mRNA was expressed in ARPE-19 cells and increased under oxidative stress conditions. Previous studies have shown that extracellular C5a can activate FOXP3 in ARPE-19 cells, which is associated with increased IL-8 secretion [25]. We showed that this could also be due to the endogenous activation of C5aR1 following oxidative stress in RPE cells.

These changes in expression and cellular complement protein accumulation following oxidative stress were time-dependent (Supplementary Materials, Figure S6). The first changes in complement receptor (CD11b, C5aR1) and component (CFH, C3) levels in the ARPE-19 cells occurred after 4 h and were accompanied by changes in *nlrp3* and *foxp3* mRNA expression. Downstream alterations in properdin expression, intracellular proteases, and an increase in the epithelial–mesenchymal transition marker as well as a loss of tight junctions were described. This indicates that complement receptor signaling may be involved in the early response of ARPE-19 cells to H_2O_2 treatment.

Oxidative stress-related cell damage in ARPE-19 cells and retinal degeneration in mouse models of RPE degeneration, as well as hereditary retinal degeneration, were successfully ameliorated using olaparib in previous studies [45–47]. Olaparib is a clinically developed poly(ADP-ribose) polymerase inhibitor that was developed for cancer treatment by blocking the DNA repair mechanism. ARPE-19 cells were resistant to H_2O_2-induced mitochondrial dysfunction and to energy failure when olaparib was added [45]. We asked the following question: can olaparib also normalize complement-associated proinflammatory expression profiles in H_2O_2-treated cells? Surprisingly, olaparib accelerated the effect of oxidative stress in ARPE-19 cells and enhanced the expression of complement receptors, complement components, and *nlrp3* mRNA. This shows that the endogenous complement-related, proinflammatory response of ARPE-19 cells could be correlated with defective DNA repair mechanisms.

Finally, it needs to be pointed out that this analysis of endogenous complement components and oxidative stress reaction was primarily set up to generate the first data describing an RPE cell-dependent complement reaction. We took advantage of the most commonly used in vitro RPE model (the ARPE-19 cell line), which expresses well-characterized RPE-specific markers [67,68] and provides an unlimited genetic and environmentally identical availability without any risk of contamination with other or undifferentiated cell types. However, it needs to be considered that this model system bears a higher risk of undergoing an epithelial–mesenchymal transition because of long-term cultivation, showing limitations in measuring transepithelial resistance and less expressed RPE-specific markers compared to primary or stem-cell-derived RPE cells [68]. To follow up with this intriguing line of thinking, future studies are needed to verify these cell-associated complement functions in primary or stem-cell-derived RPE cells with different genetic and environmental backgrounds.

5. Conclusions

Oxidative stress and activation of the complement system cause retinal degeneration, but the mechanism behind this is still a matter of investigation. We showed for the first time that oxidative stress can increase endogenous ARPE-19 cell complement components and receptors and that the process was associated with the release of proinflammatory and proangiogenic factors.

Our data offer a steppingstone for numerous further investigations regarding the function of a cell-associated complement system in primary human RPE. Many questions were raised during this project: How are the complement components activated? Independent of external complement sources, what is (are) the signaling pathway(s) of the complement receptors? How are inflammasome regulation and FOXP3 activity modulated by endogenous complement components in RPE cells? Can endogenous complement factors be targeted to affect cell-associated signaling pathways? These new perspectives will hopefully help to decipher the function of intracellular complement components in retinal health and disease and offer new strategies for the treatment of retinal degeneration.

Supplementary Materials: The following are available online at http://www.mdpi.com/2076-3921/8/11/548/s1, Figure S1: ARPE-19 cells showed a stable, confluent monolayer, and H_2O_2 treatment increased the expression of epithelial–mesenchymal transition markers; Figure S2: H_2O_2 treatment did not influence the transcription levels of several genes in ARPE-19 cells; Figure S3: The secretome of ARPE-19 cells was influenced by cell passages and H_2O_2 addition; Figure S4: The stable expression of complement components and related genes after Olaparib and oxidative stress treatment in ARPE-19 cells; Figure S5: Full immunoblots for Figures 2H and 4C; Figure S6: Time-dependent changes of H_2O_2 treatment in ARPE-19 cells; Table S1: Primary and secondary antibodies; Table S2: QuantiTec PrimerAssays; Table S3: In-house-designed RT-qPCR primers.

Author Contributions: Conceptualization, T.-O.T., J.W., V.E., and D.P.; methodology, T.-O.T., N.S., M.R., K.K., R.J.M.G.E.B., E.J.M.T., F.U., and D.P.; validation, J.W., D.P.; investigation, T.-O.T, N.S., M.R., K.K., R.J.M.G.E.B., E.J.M.T., F.U., and D.P.; data curation, T.-O.T., F.U., J.W., V.E., and D.P.; writing—original draft preparation, D.P.; writing—review and editing, T.-O.T., N.S., K.K., R.J.M.G.E.B., E.J.M.T., F.U., J.W., and V.E.; visualization, F.U. and D.P.; supervision, J.W., V.E., and D.P.; project administration, V.E. and D.P.; funding acquisition, V.E. and D.P.

Funding: This research was funded by the Velux Foundation, grant #1103, to V.E. and D.P.

Acknowledgments: We thank Renate Foeckler, Andrea Dannullis, and Elfriede Eckert for excellent technical support.

Conflicts of Interest: The authors declare no competing interests.

References

1. Yu, D.-Y.; Cringle, S.J. Retinal degeneration and local oxygen metabolism. *Exp. Eye Res.* **2015**, *80*, 745–751. [CrossRef] [PubMed]

2. Strauss, O. The retinal pigment epithelium in visual function. *Physiol. Rev.* **2005**, *85*, 845–881. [CrossRef] [PubMed]

3. Dröge, W. Free radicals in the physiological control of cell function. *Physiol. Rev.* **2002**, *82*, 47–95. [CrossRef] [PubMed]

4. Sachdeva, M.M.; Cano, M.; Handa, J.T. Nrf2 signaling is impaired in the aging RPE given an oxidative insult. *Exp. Eye Res.* **2014**, *119*, 111–114. [CrossRef]

5. Cai, J.; Nelson, K.C.; Wu, M.; Sternberg, P.; Jones, D.P. Oxidative damage and protection of the RPE. *Prog. Retin. Eye Res.* **2000**, *19*, 205–221. [CrossRef]

6. Datta, S.; Cano, M.; Ebrahimi, K.; Wang, L.; Handa, J.T. The impact of oxidative stress and inflammation on RPE degeneration in non-neovascular AMD. *Prog. Retin. Eye Res.* **2017**, *60*, 201–218. [CrossRef]

7. Radu, R.A.; Hu, J.; Yuan, Q.; Welch, D.L.; Makshanoff, J.; Lloyd, M.; McMullen, S.; Travis, G.H.; Bok, D. Complement system dysregulation and inflammation in the retinal pigment epithelium of a mouse model for Stargardt macular degeneration. *J. Biol. Chem.* **2011**, *286*, 18593–18601. [CrossRef]

8. Teussink, M.M.; Lambertus, S.; de Mul, F.F.; Rozanowska, M.B.; Hoyng, C.B.; Klevering, B.J.; Theelen, T. Lipofuscin-associated photo-oxidative stress during fundus autofluorescence imaging. *PLoS ONE* **2017**, *12*, e0172635. [CrossRef]

9. Kaarniranta, K.; Koskela, A.; Felszeghy, S.; Kivinen, N.; Salminen, A.; Kauppinen, A. Fatty acids and oxidized lipoproteins contribute to autophagy and innate immunity responses upon the degeneration of retinal pigment epithelium and development of age-related macular degeneration. *Biochimie* **2019**, *159*, 49–54. [CrossRef]

10. Jun, S.; Datta, S.; Wang, L.; Pegany, R.; Cano, M.; Handa, J.T. The impact of lipids, lipid oxidation, and inflammation on AMD, and the potential role of miRNAs on lipid metabolism in the RPE. *Exp. Eye Res.* **2019**, *181*, 346–355. [CrossRef]

11. Yumnamcha, T.; Devi, T.S.; Singh, L.P. Auranofin Mediates Mitochondrial Dysregulation and Inflammatory Cell Death in Human Retinal Pigment Epithelial Cells: Implications of Retinal Neurodegenerative Diseases. *Front. Neurosci.* **2019**, *13*, 1065. [CrossRef] [PubMed]

12. Xu, H.; Chen, M.; Forrester, J.V. Para-inflammation in the aging retina. *Prog. Retin. Eye Res.* **2009**, *28*, 348–368. [CrossRef] [PubMed]

13. Pujol-Lereis, L.M.; Schäfer, N.; Kuhn, L.B.; Rohrer, B.; Pauly, D. Interrelation Between Oxidative Stress and Complement Activation in Models of Age-Related Macular Degeneration. *Adv. Exp. Med. Biol.* **2016**, *854*, 87–93. [PubMed]

14. Weber, B.H.F.; Charbel Issa, P.; Pauly, D.; Herrmann, P.; Grassmann, F.; Holz, F.G. The role of the complement system in age-related macular degeneration. *Dtsch. Arztebl. Int.* **2014**, *111*, 133–138. [CrossRef]

15. Merle, N.S.; Church, S.E.; Fremeaux-Bacchi, V.; Roumenina, L.T. Complement System Part I—Molecular Mechanisms of Activation and Regulation. *Front. Immunol.* **2015**, *6*, 262. [CrossRef]

16. Lubbers, R.; van Essen, M.F.; van Kooten, C.; Trouw, L.A. Production of complement components by cells of the immune system. *Clin. Exp. Immunol.* **2017**, *188*, 183–194. [CrossRef]

17. Jiménez-Reinoso, A.; Marin, A.V.; Regueiro, J.R. Complement in basic processes of the cell. *Mol. Immunol.* **2017**, *84*, 10–16. [CrossRef]

18. Liszewski, M.K.; Kolev, M.; Le Friec, G.; Leung, M.; Bertram, P.G.; Fara, A.F.; Subias, M.; Pickering, M.C.; Drouet, C.; Meri, S.; et al. Intracellular complement activation sustains T cell homeostasis and mediates effector differentiation. *Immunity* **2013**, *39*, 1143–1157. [CrossRef]

19. Kremlitzka, M.; Nowacka, A.A.; Mohlin, F.C.; Bompada, P.; De Marinis, Y.; Blom, A.M. Interaction of Serum-Derived and Internalized C3 With DNA in Human B Cells-A Potential Involvement in Regulation of Gene Transcription. *Front. Immunol.* **2019**, *10*, 493. [CrossRef]

20. Kulkarni, H.S.; Elvington, M.L.; Perng, Y.-C.; Liszewski, M.K.; Byers, D.E.; Farkouh, C.; Yusen, R.D.; Lenschow, D.J.; Brody, S.L.; Atkinson, J.P. Intracellular C3 Protects Human Airway Epithelial Cells from Stress-associated Cell Death. *Am. J. Respir. Cell Mol. Biol.* **2019**, *60*, 144–157. [CrossRef]

21. Strainic, M.G.; Shevach, E.M.; An, F.; Lin, F.; Medof, M.E. Absence of signaling into CD4$^+$ cells via C3aR and C5aR enables autoinductive TGF-β1 signaling and induction of Foxp3$^+$ regulatory T cells. *Nat. Immunol.* **2013**, *14*, 162–171. [CrossRef] [PubMed]

22. Himmel, M.E.; Crome, S.Q.; Ivison, S.; Piccirillo, C.; Steiner, T.S.; Levings, M.K. Human CD4+ FOXP3+ regulatory T cells produce CXCL8 and recruit neutrophils. *Eur. J. Immunol.* **2011**, *41*, 306–312. [CrossRef] [PubMed]

23. Jou, Y.-C.; Tsai, Y.-S.; Lin, C.-T.; Tung, C.-L.; Shen, C.-H.; Tsai, H.-T.; Yang, W.H.; Chang, H.I.; Chen, S.Y.; Tzai, T.S. Foxp3 enhances HIF-1α target gene expression in human bladder cancer through decreasing its ubiquitin-proteasomal degradation. *Oncotarget* **2016**, *7*, 65403–65417. [CrossRef] [PubMed]

24. Brandstetter, C.; Holz, F.G.; Krohne, T.U. Complement Component C5a Primes Retinal Pigment Epithelial Cells for Inflammasome Activation by Lipofuscin-mediated Photooxidative Damage. *J. Biol. Chem.* **2015**, *290*, 31189–31198. [CrossRef]

25. Busch, C.; Annamalai, B.; Abdusalamova, K.; Reichhart, N.; Huber, C.; Lin, Y.; Jo, E.A.H.; Zipfel, P.F.; Skerka, C.; Wildner, G.; et al. Anaphylatoxins Activate Ca2+, Akt/PI3-Kinase, and FOXO1/FoxP3 in the Retinal Pigment Epithelium. *Front. Immunol.* **2017**, *8*, 703. [CrossRef]

26. Anderson, D.H.; Radeke, M.J.; Gallo, N.B.; Chapin, E.A.; Johnson, P.T.; Curletti, C.R.; Hancox, L.S.; Hu, J.; Ebright, J.N.; Malek, G.; et al. The pivotal role of the complement system in aging and age-related macular degeneration: Hypothesis re-visited. *Prog. Retin. Eye Res.* **2010**, *29*, 95–112. [CrossRef]

27. Kunchithapautham, K.; Atkinson, C.; Rohrer, B. Smoke exposure causes endoplasmic reticulum stress and lipid accumulation in retinal pigment epithelium through oxidative stress and complement activation. *J. Biol. Chem.* **2014**, *289*, 14534–14546. [CrossRef]

28. Wu, Z.; Lauer, T.W.; Sick, A.; Hackett, S.F.; Campochiaro, P.A. Oxidative stress modulates complement factor H expression in retinal pigmented epithelial cells by acetylation of FOXO3. *J. Biol. Chem.* **2007**, *282*, 22414–22425. [CrossRef]

29. Bian, Q.; Gao, S.; Zhou, J.; Qin, J.; Taylor, A.; Johnson, E.J.; Tang, G.; Sparrow, J.R.; Gierhart, D.; Shang, F. Lutein and zeaxanthin supplementation reduces photooxidative damage and modulates the expression of inflammation-related genes in retinal pigment epithelial cells. *Free Radic. Biol. Med.* **2012**, *53*, 1298–1307. [CrossRef]

30. Zhang, Y.; Huang, Q.; Tang, M.; Zhang, J.; Fan, W. Complement Factor H Expressed by Retinal Pigment Epithelium Cells Can Suppress Neovascularization of Human Umbilical Vein Endothelial Cells: An in vitro Study. *PLoS ONE* **2015**, *10*, e0129945. [CrossRef]

31. Marazita, M.C.; Dugour, A.; Marquioni-Ramella, M.D.; Figueroa, J.M.; Suburo, A.M. Oxidative stress-induced premature senescence dysregulates VEGF and CFH expression in retinal pigment epithelial cells: Implications for Age-related Macular Degeneration. *Redox Biol.* **2016**, *7*, 78–87. [CrossRef]

32. Fields, M.A.; Bowrey, H.E.; Gong, J.; Moreira, E.F.; Cai, H.; Del Priore, L.V. Extracellular matrix nitration alters growth factor release and activates bioactive complement in human retinal pigment epithelial cells. *PLoS ONE* **2017**, *12*, e0177763. [CrossRef] [PubMed]

33. Kaur, G.; Tan, L.X.; Rathnasamy, G.; La Cunza, N.; Germer, C.J.; Toops, K.A.; Fernandes, M.; Blenkinsop, T.A.; Lakkaraju, A. Aberrant early endosome biogenesis mediates complement activation in the retinal pigment epithelium in models of macular degeneration. *Proc. Natl. Acad. Sci. USA* **2018**, *115*, 9014–9019. [CrossRef]

34. Wu, L.; Tan, X.; Liang, L.; Yu, H.; Wang, C.; Zhang, D.; Kijlstra, A.; Yang, P. The Role of Mitochondria-Associated Reactive Oxygen Species in the Amyloid β Induced Production of Angiogenic Factors by ARPE-19 Cells. *Curr. Mol. Med.* **2017**, *17*, 140–148. [CrossRef]

35. Fernandez-Godino, R.; Garland, D.L.; Pierce, E.A. A local complement response by RPE causes early-stage macular degeneration. *Hum. Mol. Genet.* **2015**, *24*, 5555–5569. [CrossRef] [PubMed]

36. Wegener, J.; Abrams, D.; Willenbrink, W.; Galla, H.-J.; Janshoff, A. Automated multi-well device to measure transepithelial electrical resistances under physiological conditions. *Biotechniques* **2004**, *37*, 590–597. [CrossRef]

37. Pauly, D.; Nagel, B.M.; Reinders, J.; Killian, T.; Wulf, M.; Ackermann, S.; Ehrenstein, B.; Zipfel, P.F.; Skerka, C.; Weber, B.H. A novel antibody against human properdin inhibits the alternative complement system and specifically detects properdin from blood samples. *PLoS ONE* **2014**, *9*, e96371. [CrossRef] [PubMed]

38. Kalluri, R.; Weinberg, R.A. The basics of epithelial-mesenchymal transition. *J. Clin. Investig.* **2009**, *119*, 1420–1428. [CrossRef]

39. Grisanti, S.; Guidry, C. Transdifferentiation of retinal pigment epithelial cells from epithelial to mesenchymal phenotype. *Invest. Ophthalmol. Vis. Sci.* **1995**, *36*, 391–405.

40. Bataille, F.; Rohrmeier, C.; Bates, R.; Weber, A.; Rieder, F.; Brenmoehl, J.; Strauch, U.; Farkas, S.; Fürst, A.; Hofstädter, F.; et al. Evidence for a role of epithelial mesenchymal transition during pathogenesis of fistulae in Crohn's disease. *Inflamm. Bowel Dis.* **2008**, *14*, 1514–1527. [CrossRef]

41. Schäfer, N.; Grosche, A.; Schmitt, S.I.; Braunger, B.M.; Pauly, D. Complement Components Showed a Time-Dependent Local Expression Pattern in Constant and Acute White Light-Induced Photoreceptor Damage. *Front. Mol. Neurosci.* **2017**, *10*, 197. [CrossRef]

42. Reichhardt, M.P.; Meri, S. Intracellular complement activation-An alarm raising mechanism? *Semin. Immunol.* **2018**, *38*, 54–62. [CrossRef]

43. Hess, C.; Kemper, C. Complement-Mediated Regulation of Metabolism and Basic Cellular Processes. *Immunity* **2016**, *45*, 240–254. [CrossRef] [PubMed]

44. Arbore, G.; West, E.E.; Spolski, R.; Robertson, A.A.B.; Klos, A.; Rheinheimer, C.; Dutow, P.; Woodruff, T.M.; Yu, Z.X.; O'Neill, L.A.; et al. T helper 1 immunity requires complement-driven NLRP3 inflammasome activity in CD4+ T cells. *Science* **2016**, *352*, aad1210. [CrossRef] [PubMed]

45. Jang, K.-H.; Do, Y.-J.; Son, D.; Son, E.; Choi, J.-S.; Kim, E. AIF-independent parthanatos in the pathogenesis of dry age-related macular degeneration. *Cell Death Dis.* **2017**, *8*, e2526. [CrossRef] [PubMed]

46. Sahaboglu, A.; Barth, M.; Secer, E.; Amo EMDel Urtti, A.; Arsenijevic, Y.; Zrenner, E.; Paquet-Durand, F. Olaparib significantly delays photoreceptor loss in a model for hereditary retinal degeneration. *Sci. Rep.* **2016**, *6*, 39537. [CrossRef]

47. Kovacs, K.; Vaczy, A.; Fekete, K.; Kovari, P.; Atlasz, T.; Reglodi, D.; Gabriel, R.; Gallyas, F.; Sumegi, B. PARP Inhibitor Protects Against Chronic Hypoxia/Reoxygenation-Induced Retinal Injury by Regulation of MAPKs, HIF1α, Nrf2, and NFκB. *Investig. Ophthalmol. Vis. Sci.* **2019**, *60*, 1478–1490. [CrossRef]

48. Schmidt, M.; Giessl, A.; Laufs, T.; Hankeln, T.; Wolfrum, U.; Burmester, T. How does the eye breathe? Evidence for neuroglobin-mediated oxygen supply in the mammalian retina. *J. Biol. Chem.* **2003**, *278*, 1932–1935. [CrossRef]

49. Nita, M.; Grzybowski, A. The Role of the Reactive Oxygen Species and Oxidative Stress in the Pathomechanism of the Age-Related Ocular Diseases and Other Pathologies of the Anterior and Posterior Eye Segments in Adults. *Oxid. Med. Cell. Longev.* **2016**, *2016*, 3164734. [CrossRef]

50. Tokarz, P.; Kaarniranta, K.; Blasiak, J. Role of antioxidant enzymes and small molecular weight antioxidants in the pathogenesis of age-related macular degeneration (AMD). *Biogerontology* **2013**, *14*, 461–482. [CrossRef]

51. Finkel, T. Signal transduction by reactive oxygen species. *J. Cell. Biol.* **2011**, *194*, 7–15. [CrossRef] [PubMed]

52. Yamashita, H.; Horie, K.; Yamamoto, T.; Nagano, T.; Hirano, T. Light-induced retinal damage in mice. Hydrogen peroxide production and superoxide dismutase activity in retina. *Retina* **1992**, *12*, 59–66. [CrossRef] [PubMed]

53. Kaczara, P.; Sarna, T.; Burke, J.M. Dynamics of H2O2 availability to ARPE-19 cultures in models of oxidative stress. *Free Radic. Biol. Med.* **2010**, *48*, 1064–1070. [CrossRef] [PubMed]

54. Spector, A.; Ma, W.; Wang, R.R. The aqueous humor is capable of generating and degrading H2O2. *Investig. Ophthalmol. Vis. Sci.* **1998**, *39*, 1188–1197.

55. Martin, M.; Leffler, J.; Smolag, K.I.; Mytych, J.; Björk, A.; Chaves, L.D.; Alexander, J.J.; Quigg, R.J.; Blom, A.M. Factor H uptake regulates intracellular C3 activation during apoptosis and decreases the inflammatory potential of nucleosomes. *Cell Death Differ.* **2016**, *23*, 903–911. [CrossRef] [PubMed]

56. Hollborn, M.; Ackmann, C.; Kuhrt, H.; Doktor, F.; Kohen, L.; Wiedemann, P.; Bringmann, A. Osmotic and hypoxic induction of the complement factor C9 in cultured human retinal pigment epithelial cells: Regulation of VEGF and NLRP3 expression. *Mol. Vis.* **2018**, *24*, 518–535.

57. Samstad, E.O.; Niyonzima, N.; Nymo, S.; Aune, M.H.; Ryan, L.; Bakke, S.S.; Lappegård, K.T.; Brekke, O.L.; Lambris, J.D.; Damås, J.K.; et al. Cholesterol crystals induce complement-dependent inflammasome activation and cytokine release. *J. Immunol.* **2014**, *192*, 2837–2845. [CrossRef]

58. Bian, Z.-M.; Field, M.G.; Elner, S.G.; Kahlenberg, J.M.; Elner, V.M. Distinct CD40L receptors mediate inflammasome activation and secretion of IL-1β and MCP-1 in cultured human retinal pigment epithelial cells. *Exp. Eye Res.* **2018**, *170*, 29–39. [CrossRef]

59. Kauppinen, A.; Niskanen, H.; Suuronen, T.; Kinnunen, K.; Salminen, A.; Kaarniranta, K. Oxidative stress activates NLRP3 inflammasomes in ARPE-19 cells–implications for age-related macular degeneration (AMD). *Immunol. Lett.* **2012**, *147*, 29–33. [CrossRef]

60. Brandstetter, C.; Mohr, L.K.M.; Latz, E.; Holz, F.G.; Krohne, T.U. Light induces NLRP3 inflammasome activation in retinal pigment epithelial cells via lipofuscin-mediated photooxidative damage. *J. Mol. Med.* **2015**, *93*, 905–916. [CrossRef]

61. Brandstetter, C.; Patt, J.; Holz, F.G.; Krohne, T.U. Inflammasome priming increases retinal pigment epithelial cell susceptibility to lipofuscin phototoxicity by changing the cell death mechanism from apoptosis to pyroptosis. *J. Photochem. Photobiol. B* **2016**, *161*, 177–183. [CrossRef] [PubMed]

62. Asgari, E.; Le Friec, G.; Yamamoto, H.; Perucha, E.; Sacks, S.S.; Köhl, J.; Cook, H.T.; Kemper, C. C3a modulates IL-1β secretion in human monocytes by regulating ATP efflux and subsequent NLRP3 inflammasome activation. *Blood* **2013**, *122*, 3473–3481. [CrossRef] [PubMed]

63. Fukuoka, Y.; Medof, E.M. C5a receptor-mediated production of IL-8 by the human retinal pigment epithelial cell line, ARPE-19. *Curr. Eye Res.* **2001**, *23*, 320–325. [CrossRef] [PubMed]

64. Cortright, D.N.; Meade, R.; Waters, S.M.; Chenard, B.L.; Krause, J.E. C5a, but not C3a, increases VEGF secretion in ARPE-19 human retinal pigment epithelial cells. *Curr. Eye Res.* **2009**, *34*, 57–61. [CrossRef] [PubMed]

65. Wagner, J.L.; Hugli, T.E. Radioimmunoassay for anaphylatoxins: A sensitive method for determining complement activation products in biological fluids. *Anal. Biochem.* **1984**, *136*, 75–88. [CrossRef]

66. Oppermann, M.; Götze, O. Plasma clearance of the human C5a anaphylatoxin by binding to leucocyte C5a receptors. *Immunology* **1994**, *82*, 516–521.

67. Dunn, K.C.; Aotaki-Keen, A.E.; Putkey, F.R.; Hjelmeland, L.M. ARPE-19, a human retinal pigment epithelial cell line with differentiated properties. *Exp. Eye Res.* **1996**, *62*, 155–169. [CrossRef]

68. Ablonczy, Z.; Dahrouj, M.; Tang, P.H.; Liu, Y.; Sambamurti, K.; Marmorstein, A.D.; Crosson, C.E. Human retinal pigment epithelium cells as functional models for the RPE in vivo. *Investig. Ophthalmol. Vis. Sci.* **2011**, *52*, 8614–8620. [CrossRef]

Article

Analysis of Oxidative Stress-Related Markers in Crohn's Disease Patients at Surgery and Correlations with Clinical Findings

Cristina Luceri [1,*], **Elisabetta Bigagli** [1,*], **Sara Agostiniani** [1], **Francesco Giudici** [2], **Daniela Zambonin** [2], **Stefano Scaringi** [3], **Ferdinando Ficari** [2], **Maura Lodovici** [1,†] and **Cecilia Malentacchi** [4,†]

[1] Department of Neurosciences, Psychology, Drug Research and Child Health (NEUROFARBA), Section of Pharmacology and Toxicology, University of Florence, 50139 Florence, Italy

[2] Department of Experimental and Clinical Medicine, University of Florence, 50134 Florence, Italy

[3] Department of Experimental and Clinical Medicine, Surgery Unit IBD, Careggi-University Hospital (AOUC), 50139 Florence, Italy

[4] Department of Biomedical Experimental and Clinical Sciences "Mario Serio", University of Florence, 50134 Florence, Italy

* Correspondence: cristina.luceri@unifi.it (C.L.); elisabetta.bigagli@unifi.it (E.B.)

† Co-last authors contributed equally to this work.

Received: 16 July 2019; Accepted: 4 September 2019; Published: 6 September 2019

Abstract: Crohn' disease (CD) patients are at high risk of postoperative recurrence and new tools for the assessment of disease activity are needed to prevent long-term complications. In these patients, the over-production of ROS generated by inflamed bowel tissue and inflammatory cells activates a pathogenic cascade that further exacerbates inflammation and leads to increased oxidative damage to DNA, proteins, and lipids. We measured the products of protein/lipid oxidation and the total antioxidant capacity (ferric reducing ability of plasma, FRAP) in the serum of CD patients with severe disease activity requiring surgery with the aim to characterize their redox status and identify associations between oxidative stress-related markers and their clinical characteristics. At the systemic level, CD was associated with increased levels of protein and lipid oxidation products when compared to healthy volunteers, even though the FRAP values were similar. Advanced oxidation protein product (AOPP) levels showed the highest difference between patients and the controls (11.25, 5.02–15.15, vs. 1.36, 0.75–2.70, median, interquartile range; $p < 0.0001$) and the analysis of receiver operating characteristic (ROC) curves, indicated for AOPP, the best area under the curve (AUC) value for CD prediction. Advanced glycated end-products (AGEs) were also significantly higher in CD patients ($p < 0.01$), which is of interest since AOPP and AGEs are both able to activate the membrane receptor for advanced glycation end products (RAGE) involved in inflammatory diseases. Thiobarbituric acid reactive substance (TBARS) levels were significantly higher in CD patients with ileal localization and aggressive disease behavior, in smokers, and in patients suffering from allergies. In conclusion, our data indicate that circulating oxidative stress biomarkers may be attractive candidates as disease predictors as well as for clinical or therapeutic monitoring of CD. Our results also suggest that AOPP/AGEs and RAGE signaling may represent a pathogenic factor and a potential therapeutic target in CD.

Keywords: Crohn' disease; biomarkers; oxidative stress

---

1. Introduction

Crohn's disease (CD) is a chronic inflammatory disorder of the intestinal tract, with increasing prevalence worldwide [1,2]. It is generally accepted that CD as well as ulcerative colitis (UC) are the result of complex interactions among environmental factors, dysregulated immune system, gut microbiota, and disease susceptibility genes [3]. Accumulating data suggest that oxidative stress is at the crossroad between these multiple mechanisms [4–6].

Both chronic inflammation and immune system hyperactivation are accompanied by abnormally high levels of reactive oxygen species (ROS) and decreased antioxidant defenses, resulting in oxidative stress. Oxidative stress leads to mucosal layer damage and bacterial invasion, which in turn further stimulate the immune response and contribute to disease progression [7]. One of the main advantages of oxidative modifications of cellular proteins, lipids, and nucleic acids is that they can be measured not only in the affected intestinal tract, but also at the systemic level; several studies have in fact reported increased levels of oxidative stress biomarkers in the serum/plasma of inflammatory bowel disease (IBD) patients [8]. This is of interest at least for two reasons: on one hand, circulating biomarkers of oxidative stress offer the advantage of easy collection, low costs, and the possibility to be used on a large scale; on the other hand, the systemic oxidative stress observed in CD may likely contribute to the development of extra-intestinal manifestations such as perianal fistulas, dermatologic diseases, and arthritis, which are very common in these patients [9].

Circulating antioxidant capacity also seems to be correlated with the clinical status of the patients. Plasma free thiols were recently reported to be associated with favorable outcome in CD, being negatively correlated with biomarkers of inflammation [10], and serum free thiols and uric acid were significantly lower in active CD patients with anemia [11]. Furthermore, a very strong positive correlation was found between the endoscopic activity index and the serum total oxidant status in CD patients under regular follow-up [12]. These data suggest that the measure of circulating oxidative stress markers might be clinically useful both for early diagnosis as well for clinical monitoring. Clinical diagnosis of CD can be complex and it is often delayed. Moreover, CD patients need an adequate assessment of disease activity either to guide clinical treatment, prevent long-term complications, or induce a long-term remission after surgery.

On these bases, the aim of the present study was to explore the association between several peripheral biomarkers of oxidative stress and the clinical characteristics of a cohort of CD patients characterized by therapeutic failure and a complicated disease requiring surgery.

2. Methods

2.1. Study Population

The study protocol was approved by the Ethical Review Committee of the Hospital of Careggi, Florence, Italy. Written informed consent was obtained from all eligible participants. A total of 71 subjects (54 patients with CD and 17 controls) were included in this observational study. Patients were recruited between January 2015 to January 2017 at the Digestive Surgery Unit of the Careggi Hospital, where all had severe relapse (CD activity index scores of >200) requiring surgery. The healthy volunteers were recruited among the personnel of the Careggi Hospital. Serum was obtained from blood samples, taken at surgery for CD patients or at enrolment for the control subjects, collected in Vacutainer ®collection tubes, coagulated at room temperature, and centrifuged at 1800× *g* for 10 min before the distribution of the supernatant in cryo-tubes, and stored at −20 °C until analysis.

Information on gender, age, disease duration, diagnostic delay, smoking habits, location, disease behavior, extra-intestinal manifestation, perianal disease, recurrence, number of operations, immunological comorbidity, familiarity IBD, and therapy were collected. Demographic and clinical characteristics of CD patients and healthy controls are reported in Table 1.

Table 1. Demographic and clinical characteristics of Crohn's patients and healthy volunteers enrolled in the study.

Demographic and Clinical Characteristics	Crohn's Patients	Controls
n	*54*	*17*
Gender		
-male	28 (51.9%)	7 (41.2%)
-female	26 (48.1%)	10 (58.8%)
Age (years)	42.12 ± 2.055	42.41 ± 3.73
Disease duration (years)	12.86 ± 1.37	
Diagnostic delay (months)	78.89 ± 16.32	
Smoke habit		
no	19 (38.0%)	8 (47.1%)
yes	16 (32.0%)	5 (29.4%)
former	15 (30.0%)	4 (23.5%)
CDAI	233.6 ± 5.66	
Disease location		
-Ileum	28 (53.8%)	
-Colon	18 (34.6%)	
-Ileo-colon	6 (11.5%)	
Disease behavior		
-Inflammatory	4 (7.5%)	
-Stricturing	28 (52.8%)	
-Fistulizing	3 (5.7%)	
-Stricturing and Fistulizing	18 (34.0%)	
Extra-intestinal disease		
-Skin	7/46 (15.21%)	
-Arthritis	12/46 (26.1%)	
Perianal disease yes/no	23/28 (45.10%)	
Recurrence		
-yes	30 (57.69%)	
-no	22 (42.31%)	
Multiple operations		
1	22 (42.31%)	
2	15 (28.85%)	
3	15 (28.85%)	
Allergies yes/no	19/25 (43.2%)	
Familial IBD yes/no	15/34 (30.6%)	

CDAI = Crohn disease activity index. Data are means ± SE or absolute and relative frequencies.

2.2. Ethics Approval and Consent to Participate

This study was approved by the Ethical Committee of Careggi-University Hospital (AOUC), Florence, Italy, on May 2, 2011, protocol no. 2011/0016888, rif. 95/10, authorization Gen Dir 17/572011 protocol no. 2011/0018055, and written informed consent was obtained from all study subjects.

2.3. Ferric Reducing Activity of Plasma (FRAP)

A FRAP reagent solution was freshly prepared by mixing 300 mM acetate buffer, pH 3.6, TPTZ solution (10 mM 2,4,6-tripyridyl-s-triazine (TPTZ) in 40 mM HCl), and 20 mM FeCl3·6H$_2$O in a volume ratio of 10:1:1. To perform the assay, 0.9 mL of FRAP reagent, 90 μL of distilled water, and 30 μL of serum were mixed and incubated at 37 °C for 30 min. The absorbance was measured at 595 nm. The antioxidant potential of samples was determined from a standard curve plotted using the FeSO4·7H$_2$O [13].

2.4. Advanced Oxidation Protein Product (AOPP)

For AOPP determination, 20 μL of serum and 980 μL of PBS were mixed to 50 μL of KI 1.16 M and 100 μL of acetic acid. The absorbance of the reaction mixture was immediately read at 340 nm. AOPP were quantified in μmol/mg of proteins using Chloramine-T (Sigma-Aldrich, Milan, Italy) as the standard for the calibration curve [14].

2.5. Carbonyl Residues (CO)

Carbonyl residues were determined following the method of Correa-Salde and Albesa [15] with a few modifications. Serum samples (100 μL) were treated for 1 h at room temperature with 900 μL of 0.1% dinitrophenylhydrazine in 2 M HCl and precipitated with 400 μL of 10% trichloroacetic acid (TCA) before being centrifuged for 20 min at 4 °C at 10,000× g. The pellets were extracted with 500 μL of ethanol:ethyl acetate mixture (1:1) and centrifuged for 3 min at 4 °C at 10,000× g, three times and then dissolved in 15 mL of 6 M guanidine HCl in 20 mM potassium phosphate buffer (PBS), pH 7.5. The solutions were incubated at 37 °C for 30 min and insoluble debris was removed by centrifugation. The absorbance was measured at 370 nm.

Carbonyl content was calculated using a molar absorption coefficient of 22,000 M^{-1} cm^{-1} and expressed as nmol/mg of proteins. Protein content was estimated by using the Bio-Rad DC protein assay kit (Bio-Rad, Segrate, Milan, Italy).

2.6. Thiobarbituric Acid Reactive Substances (TBARS)

TBARS were evaluated as an index of lipid peroxidation according the method by Dietrich-Muszalska et al. [16]. A total of 100 μL of serum was first deproteinized by adding 100 μL of TCA, then 160 μL was added to 32 μL of 0.12 M thiobarbituric acid (Sigma-Aldrich, Milan, Italy) in TRIS 0.26 M, and heated for 15 min at 100 °C. The reaction was stopped by placing the vials in an ice bath for 10 min and after centrifugation (at 1600× g at 4 °C for 10 min), the absorbance of the supernatant was measured at 532 nm (Perkin Elmer Wallac 1420 Victor3 Multilabel Counter).

TBARS content was calculated using a molar absorption coefficient of 1.56×10^{-5} M^{-1} cm^{-1} and expressed as μM.

2.7. Advanced Glycated End-Products (AGEs)

AGEs were determined by exploiting the characteristic autofluorescence of the large part of AGEs as described by Cournot and Burillo [17]. A total of 100 μL of 1:5 diluted in PBS serum, were placed in a 96-well plate and the fluorescence intensity was read at 460 nm, after excitation at 355 nm. Results were expressed as arbitrary units (AU).

2.8. Statistical Analyses

Statistical analyses were performed using Statgraphics Centurion XVI software and Graph-Pad Prism 7.00. *p*-values less than 0.05 were considered statistically significant. Normality was verified with the Kolmogorov–Smirnov test. Normally distributed and continuous variables were expressed as means ± standard deviation (SD). Non-normally distributed variables were expressed as median and interquartile range. Comparison of continuous variables between the two groups were performed using the Student's t-test (normally distributed) or Mann–Whitney test (non-normally distributed). Differences between proportions were assessed using the chi-square or Fisher exact test.

The area-under-curve (AUC) of the receiver operating characteristic (ROC) curves for each oxidative stress biomarker were used to characterize their utility for discriminating CD patients from healthy subjects.

A stepwise multiple linear regression analysis with backward selection was performed with oxidative stress markers as the dependent variables and the following factors as independent variables: age at surgery, gender, diagnostic delay, smoke habit, CDAI, disease location, disease behavior, disease duration, extra-intestinal disease, perianal disease, first clinical presentation, recurrence, number of surgeries, allergies, and family history of IBD.

An oxidative score was calculated and consisted of four components. For oxidative markers (TBARS, CO, AGEs, and AOPP) values below the median value were assigned 0 point and those above the median value, 1 point. For FRAP values, the point assignment was the reverse (0 below the median and −1 above the median value). According to the sum of the four components, patients were allocated to three oxidative score categories: low, medium, and high.

3. Results

3.1. Baseline Characteristics

No significant differences in age, gender, and smoke habit distribution were observed between CD patients and the control group.

At the time of surgery for CD, 16 patients were smokers, 15 former smokers, and 19 had never smoked. In about 54% of the patients, the disease was localized in the ileum, in 34.6% in the colon and only 6 (11.5%) patients had a disease involving both segments. Many of the patients (41%) presented extra-intestinal diseases (skin and arthritis), 45.10% perianal disease, 55.5% had already undergone surgery, and in 30.6% of the cases, familial IBD was observed.

3.2. Oxidative Damage and Antioxidant Capacity

All of the oxidative damage parameters measured were significantly higher in the serum of CD patients when compared to the controls (Table 2). In particular, the difference between the AOPP levels in the serum of CD patients was very high when compared to healthy volunteers with a median value of 11.25 (5.02–15.15) vs. 1.36 (0.75–2.70) μmol/g of proteins, respectively (Table 2 and Figure 1A).

Based on the analysis of ROC curves, we assessed the diagnostic utility of the oxidative damage biomarkers as predictors of CD. The area under the ROC curve (AUC) was 0.6938 for TBARS, 0.7412 for CO, 0.7195 for AGEs, and 0.5765 for FRAP. The AOPP determination resulted in a much higher AUC value of 0.9306 for the prediction of Crohn's disease (Figure 1B).

The antioxidant capacity, measured as FRAP values, in the CD patients and controls was similar (Table 2).

Through univariate analysis, we observed that CD patients treated with azathioprine ($n = 24$) presented FRAP levels significantly higher ($p < 0.05$) than those untreated ($n = 18$). Moreover, serum AOPP levels were significantly reduced in patients treated with mesalazine ($p < 0.01$), but the number of untreated patients was very low (6 vs. 41).

Table 2. Mean values of oxidative markers in serum samples from Crohn's patients or healthy volunteers.

Oxidative Markers	Crohn's Patients	Controls	
n	*54*	*17*	
FRAP, μM Fe^{2+}	368.2 ± 90.72	343.8 ± 100.30	NS
TBARS, μM	4.00 ± 1.35	3.11 ± 0.45	$p < 0.01$
AGEs, AU	293.3 ± 108.80	216.0 ± 35.03	$p < 0.01$
AOPP, μmol/g of proteins	11.25 (5.02–15.15)	1.36 (0.75–2.70)	$p < 0.0001$
CO, nmol/mg of proteins	0.122 (0.095–0.146)	0.074 (0.061–0.12)	$p < 0.01$

Means ± SD or median (interquartile range 25–75); *p*-values by t test or by Mann–Whitney test. AU: Arbitrary Units.

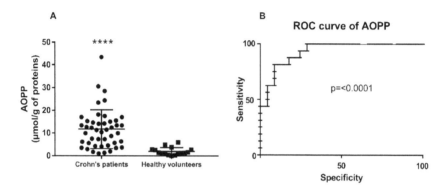

Figure 1. (**A**) Scatter dot plot of the advanced oxidation protein products (AOPP) levels in the serum of Crohn' patients and healthy volunteers. **** $p < 0.0001$ by Mann–Whitney test. (**B**) ROC curve for AOPP.

Positive correlations existed among almost all of the different markers of oxidative stress, both in the CD patients and in the controls (Tables S1 and S2). Figure 2 shows the correlation between circulating AOPP and TBARS levels in CD patients. No correlation between CDAI and oxidative-stress parameters was observed.

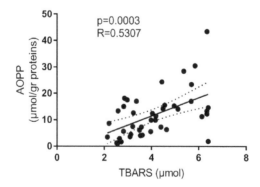

Figure 2. Correlation between AOPP and TBARS levels in the serum of Crohn's patients.

3.3. Multiple Regression Analysis

Multiple regression analysis identified five independent variables associated with circulating TBARS in CD patients; in contrast, the other oxidative stress biomarkers did not show significant associations with clinical parameters. By backward stepwise regression, TBARS were associated to the disease site, behavior, and first clinical presentation, being higher in patients with an ileal localization of the disease, with a fistulizing and stricturing behavior and with the severity of the first clinical presentation (combination of occlusion, anemia, and weight loss or the presence of perianal fistulas). Moreover, TBARS were also associated with the smoke habit and with the presence of allergies (Table 3). The oxidative score was associated with smoke habit ($p = 0.013$) and with the presence of a skin extension of the disease ($p = 0.0245$) (Table 4).

Table 3. Multiple regression analysis of factors associated with circulating TBARS in Crohn's patients.

Parameter	Estimate Coefficient	*p*-Value
CONSTANT	1.89611	0.0113
Disease Location	−0.63005	0.0185
First Clinical Presentation	0.270233	0.0089
Smoking	0.865863	0.0005
Disease Behavior	0.383783	0.0275
Allergies	0.997169	0.0001

Table 4. Multiple regression analysis of factors associated with the oxidative score in Crohn's patients.

Parameter	Estimate Coefficient	*p*-Value
CONSTANT	0.490099	0.0159
Smoking	0.420792	0.0113
Skin Extension	0.782178	0.0245

4. Discussion

Accumulating evidence indicates that oxidative stress is not only merely a consequence of chronic inflammation, but may have an essential role in the development and maintenance of inflammation and aberrant immune response in CD. In this regard, our results demonstrate an overall increase in oxidative stress biomarkers in CD patients at surgery when compared to the controls, highlighting that severe clinical activity is reflected by systemic oxidative stress. Among the markers analyzed, AOPP demonstrated the greatest diagnostic ability in differentiating CD patients from the controls. AOPPs are di-tyrosine-containing and cross-linking products, formed by the reaction of plasma proteins, mainly albumin, with chlorinated compounds resulting from the activity of myeloperoxidase (MPO) [14,18]. For this reason, AOPP are recognized as both oxidative protein damage markers and mediators of inflammation.

Increased plasma AOPP levels in patients with chronic diseases including active CD patients have been reported by others [19–21]. In our study, CD patients had very high levels of AOPP in their serum, much higher when compared to the study by Krzystek-Korpacka and co-workers [20], who measured a mean level of 1.87 µmol/g of albumin in the plasma of active CD patients. We measured AOPP levels in the serum of CD patients at surgery, therefore with severe clinical conditions, and these high levels can be a consequence of their clinical status.

Interestingly, some mechanistic studies have demonstrated the role of AOPP in the pathogenesis and progression of CD. There is in fact in vitro and in vivo evidence that AOPPs induced depletion of intestinal epithelial cells and inflammatory changes that alter the structural integrity of the intestinal mucosa [22–24]. These compounds are also able to modulate cell cycle arrest [25]; Shi and co-worker recently demonstrated that AOPPs exhibit their negative regulatory function on intestinal epithelial cell cycle progression by activating the RAGE/CD36-c-jun N-terminal kinase (JNK)-p27kip1 signaling pathway [21]. By interacting with RAGE and CD36 receptors, AOPP activate protein kinase C and nicotinamide adenine dinucleotide phosphate (NADPH) oxidase as well as the NF-κB-dependent inflammatory pathway [26]. Xu et al. [27] also found that the deposition of AOPPs in fibrotic lesions from CD patients promoted epithelial–mesenchymal transition, a fundamental mechanism in complications of CD such as intestinal fibrosis through the oxidative and inflammatory pathway.

Other than AOPP, the first identified ligands of RAGE were AGEs. Although RAGE/AGE signaling has mainly been studied in diabetes, there is also evidence of its activation in neurodegenerative diseases, cancer, and in various inflammatory diseases including CD [28–30]. Mice lacking RAGE receptors are in fact protected from chemically-induced intestinal inflammation and treatment with a RAGE-specific inhibitor protects mice from indomethacin-induced enteritis and dextran sulfate sodium-induced colitis, suggesting that the RAGE signaling pathway could be a promising therapeutic target for IBD patients [30]. On the contrary, there are no reports available in the literature on the serum level of AGEs in patients with CD. AGEs are heterogeneous compounds mainly generated through the non-enzymatic glycation of protein, lipids, and nucleic acid driven by hyperglycemia and oxidative stress, but increased serum levels were associated with hypercholesterolemia [31] and cigarette smoking [32]. In addition, humans are exposed to dietary sources of AGEs through animal-derived foods and cooking processes that result in the formation of new AGEs [33]. Moreover, AGEs such as glycol aldehyde and 2-hydroxy-propanal may be generated by activated neutrophils, even in the absence of sugars [34].

Lipid peroxidation products are also implicated in the pathogenesis of IBD. For instance, it has been reported that 4-hydroxynonenal treatment suppressed colonic expression of tight junction proteins, enhanced bacterial translocation from the gut into the systemic circulation, and increased activation of Toll-like receptor 4 signaling [35].

In our cases, circulating TBARS were significantly higher when compared to the controls and these results are in line with those obtained by others who measured elevated lipid peroxidation markers malondialdehyde (MDA)/TBARS in CD patients [35–38]. In the study by Sampietro and co-workers, CD patients at surgery showed a significantly higher basal peroxidative state when compared to the controls, but while the inflammatory and oxidative indices were significantly reduced, two months later, and maintained low one year after surgery, TBARS did not reach levels comparable to those in the control subjects, indicating that in quiescent CD, there is an upregulated level of plasma peroxidation [39].

Szczeklik and co-workers recently described the presence of an upward trend in the serum (and saliva) MDA levels, depending on the severity of CD and a correlation between the MDA levels and the visible symptoms of inflammation [40]. Our results showed a significant correlation among lipid peroxidation, disease location, and behavior and with the severity of the first clinical presentation of CD. All these data suggest the role of TBARS as a potential marker of the severity of the disease.

Serum TBARS levels were also correlated with smoking habit being higher in smokers and to a lesser extent, in former smokers when compared to non-smokers. Cigarette smoke is a well-known source of ROS and one of the most powerful oxidative stress inducers. It is considered both an etiological risk factor for CD as well as for its recurrence; smokers have a higher risk when compared to non-smokers of developing a postoperative recurrence and the risk increases in relation to the number of cigarettes smoked [41,42].

We also defined an oxidative score to take into account the overall oxidative–antioxidant status of each patient and identified positive correlations with smoking habit and the presence of cutaneous manifestation of the disease, a well-recognized complication of IBD that frequently occurs in CD and is associated with a worse prognosis [43,44]. The pathogenic mechanism underlying the development of cutaneous manifestations in CD patients is still not known, but our results suggest that oxidative stress may have a role.

Despite the high degree of oxidative stress observed in CD patients, witnessed by the increase in all oxidative markers measured, all correlated to each other, we did not observe differences in their antioxidant status, measured as FRAP, when compared to controls. On the contrary, several studies reported a reduced antioxidant capacity in CD patients, measured both as plasma carotenoids and other vitamin content [45,46], or as total antioxidant capacity [12,47,48], or as plasma free thiols [10]. In particular, Bourgonje and coworkers reported strong and negative correlations among albumin-adjusted plasma free thiols and a number of pro-inflammatory markers of disease activity [10]. In this study, a more favorable redox status was also observed in CD patients with ileal disease compared to patients with colonic localization; in contrast, in our study, the ileal localization was significantly associated with increased serum TBARS levels. We previously reported that disease located in the upper part of the intestine is a risk factor for recurrence when compared to diseases located in the distal ileum and colon [49].

The serum/plasma total antioxidant activity is the sum of the contribution of endogenous (uric acid, bilirubin, albumin) and exogenous (medications and food-derived) antioxidants, thus this disagreement may be due, not only to the complexity of the disease, but also to the variability in patient medications and dietary habits or supplement use. In this context, we noted differences in AOPP values associated with the treatment with mesalazine, known to exert anti-inflammatory and antioxidant effects, and in the FRAP levels that were significantly higher in patients under azathioprine treatment, which may be related to its contribution to oxidative stress [50].

Moreover, the lack of an association between circulating markers of oxidative damage and total antioxidant capacity suggests that in CD, oxidative stress is not just the result of an imbalance between oxidants and antioxidants, but may prime, at least in the acute phase of the disease, pro-inflammatory mechanisms through RAGE activation.

The main limitations of this study are the relatively small sample size, the cross-sectional design, the lack of follow-up, and of recurrent measurements during the course of the disease, which are necessary to validate the relevance of using oxidative stress markers in the clinical setting.

5. Conclusions

Despite these limitations, our data provide evidence that circulating AOPP and TBARS levels are significantly elevated in CD patients with severe relapse, suggesting that these parameters could be evaluated in a prospective, larger study on the progression of CD disease, as biomarkers for diagnosis or monitoring of CD patients. Moreover, our results indicate that AOPP/AGEs activation of RAGE signaling should be explored for diagnostic or therapeutic purposes in immune-mediated diseases such as CD.

Supplementary Materials: The following are available online at http://www.mdpi.com/2076-3921/8/9/378/s1. Table S1: Correlations among markers of oxidative stress in Crohn's patients, Table S2: Correlations among markers of oxidative stress in healthy volunteers.

Author Contributions: Conceptualization, M.L. and C.M.; data curation, C.M.; formal analysis, C.L.; investigation, S.A.; methodology, M.L. and E.B.; original draft preparation, C.L.; writing—review and editing, C.L. and E.B.; patient qualification for the study and clinical material collection F.G., F.F., S.S. and D.Z.; project administration, M.L. and C.M.; funding acquisition, M.L., C.M. and F.G.

Funding: This research was supported by grants from Ente Cassa di Risparmio di Firenze (2016.0842 and 2017. 0841) and by the University of Florence (Fondi di Ateneo).

Acknowledgments: We thank all the patients and the healthy volunteers who participated in this study.

Conflicts of Interest: The authors declare that they have no conflicts of interest.

References

1. Molodecky, N.A.; Soon, I.N.G.S.; Rabi, D.M.; Ghali, W.A.; Ferris, M.; Chernoff, G.; Benchimol, E.I.; Panaccione, R.; Ghosh, S.; Barkema, H.W. Increasing incidence and prevalence of the Inflammatory Bowel Diseases. *YGAST* **2012**, *142*, 46–54.

2. Ng, S.C.; Shi, H.Y.; Hamidi, N.; Underwood, F.E.; Tang, W.; Benchimol, E.I.; Panaccione, R.; Ghosh, S.; Wu, J.C.Y.; Chan, F.K.L.; et al. Articles worldwide incidence and prevalence of Inflammatory Bowel Disease in the 21st century: A systematic review of population-based studies. *Lancet* **2017**, *390*, 2769–2778. [CrossRef]

3. Torres, J.; Mehandru, S.; Colombel, J.F.; Peyrin-Biroulet, L. Crohn's disease. *Lancet* **2017**, *389*, 1741–1755. [CrossRef]

4. Pereira, C.; Gracio, D.; Teixeira, J.P.; Magro, F. Oxidative stress and DNA damage: Implications in Inflammatory Bowel Disease. *Inflamm. Bowel Dis.* **2015**, *21*, 16–19. [CrossRef] [PubMed]

5. Patlevic, P.; Vascova, J.; Svork, P., Jr.; Vasko, L.; Svork, P. Reactive oxygen species and antioxidant defense in human gastrointestinal diseases. *Integr. Med. Res.* **2016**, *5*, 250–258. [CrossRef] [PubMed]

6. Tian, T.; Wang, Z.; Zhang, J. Review article pathomechanisms of oxidative stress in Inflammatory Bowel Disease and potential antioxidant therapies. *Oxid. Med. Cell Longev.* **2017**, *2017*. [CrossRef] [PubMed]

7. Heidemann, J.; Domschke, W.; Kucharzik, T.; Maaser, C. Intestinal microvascular endothelium and innate immunity in Inflammatory Bowel Disease: A second line of defense? *Infect. Immun.* **2006**, *74*, 5425–5432. [CrossRef] [PubMed]

8. Rezaie, A.; Parker, R.D.; Abdollahi, M. Oxidative stress and pathogenesis of Inflammatory Bowel Disease: An epiphenomenon or the cause? *Dig. Dis. Sci.* **2007**, *52*, 2015–2021. [CrossRef]

9. Ardizzone, S.; Sarzi Puttini, P.; Cassinotti, A.; Bianchi Porro, G. Extraintestinal manifestations of Inflammatory Bowel Disease. *Dig. Liver Dis.* **2008**, *40*, S253–S259. [CrossRef]

10. Bourgonje, A.R.; von Martels, J.Z.H.; Bulthuis, M.L.C.; van Londen, M.; Faber, K.N.; Dijkstra, G.; van Goor, H. Crohn's disease in clinical remission is marked by systemic oxidative stress. *Front. Physiol.* **2019**, *10*, 1–10. [CrossRef]

11. Neubauer, K.; Kempinski, R.; Matusiewicz, M. Nonenzymatic serum antioxidant capacity in IBD and its association with the severity of bowel inflammation and corticosteroids treatment. *Medicina* **2019**, *55*, 88. [CrossRef] [PubMed]

12. Yuksel, M.; Ates, I.; Kaplan, M.; Arikan, M.; Ozin, Y.O.; Kilic, Z.M.Y.; Topcuoglu, C.; Kayacetin, E. Is oxidative stress associated with activation and pathogenesis of Inflammatory Bowel Disease? *J. Med. Biochem.* **2017**, *36*, 341–348. [CrossRef] [PubMed]

13. Benzie, I.; Strain, J. The ferric reducing ability of plasma as a measure of antioxodant. *Anal. Biochem.* **1996**, *239*, 70–76. [CrossRef] [PubMed]

14. Witko-Sarsat, V.; Friedlander, M.; Capeillère-Blandin, C.; Nguyen-Khoa, T.; Nguyen, A.T.; Zingraff, J.; Jungers, P.; Descamps-Latscha, B. Advanced oxidation protein products as a novel marker of oxidative stress in uremia. *Kidney Int.* **1996**, *49*, 1304–1313. [CrossRef] [PubMed]

15. Correa-Salde, V.; Albesa, I. Reactive oxidant species and oxidation of protein and heamoglobin as biomarkers of susceptibility to stress caused by chloramphenicol. *Biomed. Pharmacother.* **2009**, *63*, 100–104. [CrossRef] [PubMed]

16. Dietrich-Muszalska, A.; Kolińska-Łukaszuk, J. Comparative effects of aripiprazole and selected antipsychotic drugs on lipid peroxidation in plasma. *Psychiatry Clin. Neurosci.* **2018**, *72*, 329–336. [CrossRef] [PubMed]

17. Cournot, M.; Burillo, E.; Saulnier, P.; Planesse, C.; Gand, E.; Rehman, M.; Rondeau, P.; Gonthier, M.; Feigerlova, E.; Meilhac, O.; et al. Circulating concentrations of redox biomarkers do not improve the prediction of adverse cardiovascular events in patients with type 2 diabetes mellitus. *J. Am. Hearth Assoc.* **2018**, *7*, e00007397. [CrossRef]

18. Capeillère-Blandin, C.; Gausson, V.; Descamps-Latscha, B.; Witko-Sarsat, V. Biochemical and spectrophotometric significance of advanced oxidized protein products. *Biochim. Biophys. Acta Mol. Basis Dis.* **2004**, *1689*, 91–102. [CrossRef]

19. Dalle-Donne, I.; Giustarini, D.; Colombo, R.; Rossi, R.; Milzani, A. Protein carbonylation in human diseases. *Trends Mol. Med.* **2003**, *9*, 169–176. [CrossRef]

20. Krzystek-Korpacka, M.; Neubauer, K.; Berdowska, I.; Boehm, D.; Zielinski, B.; Petryszyn, P.; Terlecki, G.; Paradowski, L.; Gamian, A. Enhanced formation of advanced oxidation protein products in IBD. *Inflamm. Bowel Dis.* **2008**, *14*, 794–802. [CrossRef]

21. Shi, J.; Sun, S.; Liao, Y.; Tang, J.; Xu, X.; Qin, B.; Qin, C.; Peng, L.; Luo, M.; Bai, L.; et al. Redox biology advanced oxidation protein products induce G1 phase arrest in intestinal epithelial cells via a RAGE/CD36-JNK-p27kip1 mediated pathway. *Redox Biol.* **2019**, 101196. [CrossRef] [PubMed]

22. Xie, F.; Sun, S.; Xu, A.; Zheng, S.; Xue, M.; Wu, P.; Zeng, J.H.; Bai, L. Advanced oxidation protein products induce intestine epithelial cell death through a redox-dependent, c-jun N-terminal kinase and poly (ADP-ribose) polymerase-1-mediated pathway. *Cell Death Dis.* **2014**, *5*, e1006. [CrossRef]

23. Fasano, A. Intestinal permeability and its regulation by Zonulin: Diagnostic and therapeutic implications. *Clin. Gastroenterol. Hepatol.* **2012**, *10*, 1096–1100. [CrossRef] [PubMed]

24. Libertucci, J.; Dutta, U.; Kaur, S.; Jury, J.; Rossi, L.; Fontes, M.E.; Shajib, M.S.; Khan, W.I.; Surette, M.G.; Verdu, E.F.; et al. Inflammation-related differences in mucosa-associated microbiota and intestinal barrier function in colonic Crohn's disease. *Am. J. Physiol. Liver Physiol.* **2018**, *315*, G420–G431. [CrossRef] [PubMed]

25. Sun, S.; Xie, F.; Xu, X.; Cai, Q.; Zhang, Q.; Cui, Z.; Zheng, Y.; Zhou, J. Advanced oxidation protein products induce S-phase arrest of hepatocytes via the ROS-dependent, β-catenin-CDK2-mediated pathway. *Redox Biol.* **2018**, *14*, 338–353. [CrossRef] [PubMed]

26. Guo, Z.J.; Niu, H.X.; Hou, F.F.; Zhang, L.; Fu, N.; Nagai, R.; Lu, X.; Chen, B.H.; Shan, Y.X.; Tian, J.W.; et al. Advanced Oxidation Protein Products Activate Vascular Endothelial cells via a RAGE-mediated signaling pathway. *Antioxid. Redox Signal.* **2008**, *10*, 1699–1712. [CrossRef] [PubMed]

27. Xu, X.; Sun, S.; Xie, F.; Ma, J.; Tang, J.; He, S.; Bai, L. Advanced oxidation protein products induce epithelial-mesenchymal transition of intestinal epithelial cells via a PKC δ-mediated, redox-dependent signaling pathway. *Antioxid Redox Signal.* **2017**, *27*, 37–56. [CrossRef] [PubMed]

28. Ciccocioppo, R.; Vanoli, A.; Klersy, C.; Imbesi, V.; Boccaccio, V.; Manca, R.; Betti, E.; Cangemi, G.C.; Strada, E.; Besio, R.; et al. Role of the advanced glycation end products receptor in Crohn's disease inflammation. *World J. Gastroenterol.* **2013**, *19*, 8269–8281. [CrossRef]

29. Ramasamy, R.; Shekhtman, A.; Schmidt, A.M. The multiple faces of RAGE–opportunities for therapeutic intervention in aging and chronic disease. *Expert Opin. Ther. Targets* **2016**, *20*, 431–446. [CrossRef]

30. Body-Malapel, M.; Djouina, M.; Waxin, C.; Langlois, A.; Gower-Rousseau, C.; Zerbib, P.; Schmidt, A.M.; Desreumaux, P.; Boulanger, E.; Vignal, C. The RAGE signaling pathway is involved in intestinal inflammation and represents a promising therapeutic target for Inflammatory Bowel Diseases. *Mucosal Immunol.* **2019**, *12*, 468–478. [CrossRef]

31. McNair, E.; Qureshi, M.; Prasad, K.; Pearce, C. Atherosclerosis and the hypercholesterolemic AGE-RAGE axis. *Int. J. Angiol.* **2016**, *25*, 110–116. [PubMed]

32. Prasad, K.; Hons, M. Role of advanced glycation end products and its receptors in the pathogenesis of cigarette smoke-induced cardiovascular disease. *Int. J. Angiol.* **2015**, *24*, 75–80. [PubMed]

33. Uribarri, J.; Woodruff, S.; Goodman, S.; Cai, W.; Chen, X.; Pyzik, R.; Yong, A.; Striker, G.E.; Vlassara, H. Advanced glycation end products in foods and a practical guide to their reduction in the diet. *J. Am. Diet Assoc.* **2010**, *110*, 911–916. [CrossRef]

34. Anderson, M.M.; Hazen, S.L.; Hsu, F.F.; Heinecke, J.W. Human neutrophils employ the myeloperoxidase–hydrogen peroxide–chloride system to convert hydroxy-amino acids into glycolaldehyde, 2-hydroxypropanal, and acrolein. A mechanism for the generation of highly reactive alpha-hydroxy and α,β-unsaturated aldehydes by phagocytes at sites of inflammation. *J. Clin. Investig.* **1997**, *99*, 424–432. [PubMed]

35. Wang, Y.; Wang, W.; Yang, H.; Shao, D.; Zhao, X. Free radical biology and medicine intraperitoneal injection of 4-hydroxynonenal (4-HNE), a lipid peroxidation product, exacerbates colonic inflammation through activation of Toll-like receptor 4 signaling. *Free Radic. Biol. Med.* **2019**, *131*, 237–242. [CrossRef] [PubMed]

36. Levy, E.; Rizwan, Y.; Thibault, L.; Lepage, G.; Brunet, S.; Bouthillier, L.; Seidman, E. Altered lipid profile, lipoprotein composition, and oxidant and antioxidant status in pediatric Crohn disease. *Am. J. Clin. Nutr.* **2000**, *71*, 807–815. [CrossRef] [PubMed]

37. Alzoghaibi, M.A.; Al, I.A.; Al-Jebreen, A.M. Lipid peroxides in patients with Inflammatory Bowel Disease. *Saudi J. Gastroenterol.* **2007**, *13*, 187–190. [CrossRef] [PubMed]

38. Boehm, D.; Krzystek-korpacka, M.; Neubauer, K.; Matusiewicz, M.; Paradowski, L.; Gamian, A. Lipid peroxidation markers in Crohn's disease: The associations and diagnostic value. *Clin. Chem. Lab. Med.* **2012**, *50*, 1359–1366. [CrossRef]

39. Sampietro, G.M.; Cristaldi, M.; Cervato, G.; Maconi, G.; Danelli, P.; Cervellione, R.; Rovati, M.; Bianchi Porro, G.; Cestaro, B.; Taschieri, A.M. Oxidative stress, vitamin A and vitamin E behaviour in patients submitted to conservative surgery for complicated Crohn's disease. *Dig. Liver Dis.* **2002**, *34*, 696–701. [CrossRef]

40. Szczeklik, K.; Krzyściak, W.; Cibor, D.; Rodacka, R.D.; Polończyk, J.P.; Mach, T.; Owczarek, D. Markers of lipid peroxidation and antioxidant status in the serum and saliva of patients with active Crohn disease. *Pol. Arch. Intern. Med.* **2018**, *128*, 362–370.

41. Reese, G.E.; Nanidis, T.; Borysiewicz, C.; Yamamoto, T.; Orchard, T.; Tekkis, P.P. The effect of smoking after surgery for Crohn's disease: A meta-analysis of observational studies. *Int. J. Colorectal Dis.* **2008**, *23*, 1213–1221. [CrossRef]

42. To, N.; Ford, A.C.; Gracie, D.J. Systematic review with meta-analysis: The effect of tobacco smoking on the natural history of ulcerative colitis. *Aliment. Pharmacol. Ther.* **2016**, *44*, 117–126. [CrossRef] [PubMed]

43. Tromm, A.; May, D.; Almus, E.; Voigt, E.; Greving, I.; Schwegler, U.; Griga, T. Cutaneous manifestations in inflammatory bowel disease. *Z. Gastroenterol.* **2001**, *39*, 137–144. [CrossRef] [PubMed]

44. Horaist, C.; De Parades, V.; Abramowitz, L.; Benfredj, P.; Bonnaud, G.; Bouchard, D.; Fathallah, N.; Sénéjoux, A.; Siproudhis, L.; Staumont, G.; et al. Elaboration and validation of Crohn's disease anoperineal lesions consensual definitions. *World J. Gastroenterol.* **2017**, *23*, 5371–5378. [CrossRef] [PubMed]

45. Maor, I.; Rainis, T.; Lanir, A.; Lavy, A. Oxidative stress, inflammation and neutrophil superoxide release in patients with Crohn's disease: Distinction between active and non-active disease. *Dig. Dis. Sci.* **2008**, *53*, 2208–2214. [CrossRef] [PubMed]

46. Geerling, B.J.; Badart-Smook, A.; Stockbrugger, R.W.; Brummer, R.M. Comprehensive nutritional status in patients with long-standing Crohn disease currently in remission. *Am. J. Clin. Nutr.* **1998**, *67*, 919–926. [CrossRef] [PubMed]

47. Koutroubakis, I.E.; Malliaraki, N.; Dimoulios, P.D. Decreased total and corrected antioxidant capacity in patients with Inflammatory Bowel Disease. *Dig. Dis. Sci.* **2004**, *49*, 1433–1437. [CrossRef]

48. Pereira, C.; Coelho, R.; Grácio, D.; Dias, C.; Silva, M.; Peixoto, A.; Lopes, P.; Costa, C.; Teixeira, J.P.; Macedo, G.; et al. DNA damage and oxidative DNA damage in Inflammatory Bowel Disease. *J. Crohn's Colitis* **2016**, *10*, 1316–1323. [CrossRef]

49. Fazi, M.; Giudici, F.; Luceri, C.; Pronestì, M.; Tonelli, F. Long-term results and recurrence-related risk factors for Crohn disease in patients undergoing side-to-side isoperistaltic strictureplasty. *JAMA Surg.* **2016**, *151*, 452–460. [CrossRef]

50. Pelin, M.; De Ludicibus, S.; Londero, M.; Spizzo, R.; Dei Rossi, S.; Martelossi, S.; Ventura, A.; Decorti, G.; Stocco, G. Thiopurine biotransformation and pharmacological effects: Contribution of oxidative stress. *Curr. Drug Metab.* **2016**, *17*, 542–549. [CrossRef]

Article

Intrarenal Transplantation of Hypoxic Preconditioned Mesenchymal Stem Cells Improves Glomerulonephritis through Anti-Oxidation, Anti-ER Stress, Anti-Inflammation, Anti-Apoptosis, and Anti-Autophagy

Hao-Hsiang Chang [1,2], Shih-Ping Hsu [1,3,*,†] and Chiang-Ting Chien [1,*,†]

1   School of Life Science, National Taiwan Normal University, Taipei 116, Taiwan; allanchanghs@gmail.com
2   Department of Family Medicine, National Taiwan University Hospital and College of Medicine,
    Taipei 100, Taiwan
3   Department of Internal Medicine, Far Eastern Memorial Hospital, New Taipei City 220, Taiwan
*   Correspondence: shihping999@yahoo.com.tw (S.-P.H.); ctchien@ntnu.edu.tw or
    hopefinny169@gmail.com (C.T.-C.)
†   These authors contribute equally to this work.

Received: 23 November 2019; Accepted: 16 December 2019; Published: 18 December 2019

Abstract: To confer further therapeutic potential and prevent some adverse effects by the mesenchymal stem cells (MSCs) transplantation, we explored the effects of locally intrarenal arterial administration of hypoxic preconditioned MSCs in the anti-Thy1.1 induced rat glomerulonephritis. Proteinuria, histochemical staining, and western blotting were used to explore the therapeutic effects and mechanisms. Locally intrarenal arterial MSCs transplantation successfully implanted the fluorescent or CD44 labeled MSCs in the nephritic glomeruli, ameliorated proteinuria, and glomerulosclerosis in nephritic rats. Hypoxic preconditioning significantly upregulated hypoxic inducible factor-1α/VEGF (HIF-1α/VEGF) in the MSCs and was more efficient than normoxic MSCs in reducing the degree of urinary protein, glomerulosclerosis, fibrosis, macrophage/monocyte infiltration, GRP78 mediated endoplasmic reticulum stress, Beclin-1/LC3-II mediated autophagy, and Bax/Bcl-2/caspase 3 mediated apoptosis. Hypoxic MSCs could further promote intranuclear nuclear factor (erythroid-derived 2, Nrf2) and reduce nuclear factor kappa B expression in nephritic kidneys. As compared to normoxic MSCs, hypoxic MSCs transplantation significantly upregulated the renal expression of anti-oxidative response elements/enzymes including glutamate-cysteine ligase catalytic subunit, glutamate-cysteine ligase modifier subunit, glutathione peroxidase, catalase, Mn, and Cu/Zn superoxide dismutase. In summary, intrarenal hypoxic preconditioning MSCs transplantation was more effective to activate hypoxic inducible factor-1α/VEGF/Nrf2 (HIF-1α/VEGF/Nrf2) signaling, preserve anti-oxidant proteins and anti-oxidative responsive element proteins, and subsequently reduce glomerular apoptosis, autophagy, and inflammation.

Keywords: apoptosis; autophagy; hypoxic preconditioning; mesenchymal stem cell; Nrf2; inflammation

1. Introduction

Glomerulonephritis (GN) is a constellation of heterogenous renal diseases featured as a shared pathophysiology of immune mediated glomerular inflammation [1,2]. Some GN patients may benefit from specific immunosuppressive therapies and many others who are irresponsive to this type of management eventually develop end stage renal disease (ESRD) [3–6]. Glomerulonephritis is one of the leading causes of ESRD and remains a medical challenge [7]. Implementation of interventions to cure or prevent GN related deterioration is very important from both public health and economic aspects. Stem cells have the potential of self-renewal and the ability of immune modulation and as such, provide a potential therapeutic option to the unmet need of GN sufferers [8].

Mesenchymal stem cells (MSCs) have been shown to improve renal functions in animal GN models [8], and in some refractory human lupus nephritis studies [9–11]. In these studies, MSCs cross-talked with target organs by secreting growth factors, cytokines, and prostaglandins, which regulate anti-inflammation, anti-apoptosis, and anti-fibrosis effects and enhance cell proliferation, survival, and angiogenesis to repair injured tissue. These paracrine effects play a major role in MSC's therapeutic effect to the damaged kidney [2,8,12]. Additionally, increased oxidative stress contributes to the pathogenesis of mesangial proliferative GN and leads to renal dysfunction [13]. MSCs have been shown to possess anti-oxidative effects which help in the treatment of GN [14]. Strategies to enhance their anti-oxidative ability could promote the therapeutic efficacy of MSCs [15]. However, compared with the anti-inflammatory and immune-modulatory effects, the mechanisms underlying the anti-oxidative effects are relatively unknown. Hypoxic preconditioning is a promising strategy to improve the efficacy and stemness of MSC therapy, through preventing senescence, increasing differentiation efficiency [16], and enhancing MSC homing [17]. There is surprisingly little knowledge about how hypoxic preconditioning affects the anti-oxidative therapeutic effects of MSCs. The present study aimed to investigate the anti-oxidative stress mechanisms involved in the use of locally intrarenal transplantation, for reduction of possible adverse effect, of normoxic MSCs and hypoxic-preconditioned mesenchymal stem cells (HMSCs) in the anti-thy1.1 GN rat model.

2. Materials and Methods

2.1. Animals

Female Wistar rats weighing 220–250 g were purchased from BioLASCO Taiwan Co. Ltd. (Taipei, Taiwan) and housed in the Experimental Animal Center, National Taiwan University. All the surgical and experimental procedures were approved by the ethics committee "Institutional Animal Care and Use Committee of the National Taiwan University College of Science" (identification code of approval: 20100244 and date of approval: 02/11/2011) and were in accordance with the guidelines of the National Science Council of Republic of China (NSC 1997). To monitor fecal and urinary excretion, the rats were placed into the metabolic cage. The feces and urine samples were collected and recorded every 12 h before surgical experiments. During the experiment, the rats were given free access to food and water.

2.2. Cell Preparations (MSCS Isolation, Characterization, and Culture)

Femora from Wistar rats (BioLASCO Taiwan Co Ltd., Taipei, Taiwan), 8 to 10 weeks of age, were removed, and soft tissues were detached aseptically. Bone marrow was extruded by inserting a 23-gauge needle into the shaft of the bone and was flushed out with basal medium (α-minimal essential medium [α-MEM], Gibco-BRL, Gaithersburg, MD, USA). Isolation of MSCs was performed according to similar procedures as described previously [18]. Briefly, mononuclear cells were isolated from the bone marrow aspirates by a density gradient centrifugation method were suspended in complete culture medium (α-MEM supplemented with 16.6% fetal bovine serum, 100 U/mL penicillin, 100 μg/mL streptomycin, and 2 mM L-glutamine) and seeded in plastic dishes. After 24 h of the initial culture, nonadherent cells were removed by a change of medium and irrigation of the culture. The culture typically reaches 65% to 70% confluency within 6 to 8 days and reached subconfluency at 9 days, when the cells (passage 0) were harvested for further subculturing. Starting from passage 1, the cells were seeded at 100 cells/cm^2 and were grown in complete culture medium with a medium change twice per week. For hypoxic MSC cultures, cells were cultured in a gas mixture composed of 94% N_2, 5% CO_2, and 1% O_2 [19], whereas in normoxic MSC cultures, cells were cultured in 95% air and 5% CO_2. For maintenance of the hypoxic gas mixture, an incubator with two air sensors, one for CO_2 and the other for O_2, was used. O_2 concentration was achieved and maintained using delivery of

N_2 gas from a tank containing pure N_2. If the O_2 concentration rose above the desired level, N_2 gas was automatically injected into the system to displace the excess O_2.

2.3. HIF-1α Determination and Growth Factors Array Assay

The hypoxic inducible factor-1α (HIF-1α) concentration and multiple growth factors assay from cultured condition medium and MSCs or HMSCs were determined with HIF-1α ELISA kit (MBS2702491, MyBioSource, San Diego, CA, USA) and RayBio® rat growth factor array (AAR-GF-1-2, RayBiotech, Peachtree Corners, GA, USA) according to the manufacturer's instructions.

2.4. Experimental Model and Design

Anti-thy1.1 GN was induced by injection of 0.2 mL of phosphate-buffered saline containing 250 µg anti-thy1.1 monoclonal antibody (Cedarlane, Burlington, ON, Canada) into rats via a jugular vein under sodium pentobarbital anesthesia (50 mg/kg, i.p.) at day 0, and 0.2 mL of saline injection into the jugular vein as a control group. This method for induction of acute GN had been reported previously [20]. Under avertin anesthesia (400 mg/kg, Acros Organics, Morris Plains, NJ, USA), one PE10 tubing was introduced into the left renal artery from the left femoral artery via the aorta for direct MSCs or HMSCs delivery (Figure 1A). Varied numbers of MSCs or HMSCs including 1, 2, and 5×10^5 cells were administered via this catheter in the therapeutic groups, and saline was administration in control groups. The grouping and experimental design are shown in Figure 1B.

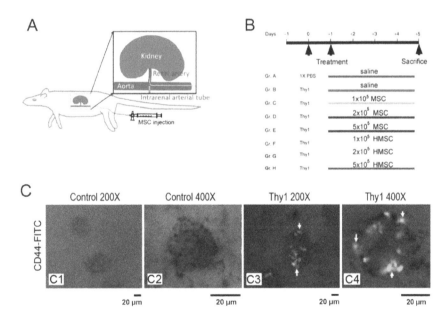

Figure 1. The technique for locally intra-renal arterial administration of mesenchymal stem cells (MSCs) was displayed in (**A**). The experimental grouping and design are displayed in the eight groups (**B**). High levels of green fluorescence were visualized under UV light in the glomeruli of nephritic kidney sections (**C3–4**) but not in the normal kidney sections (**C1–2**). C1, C3 magnification 200×; C2, C4 magnification 400×.

2.5. Tracking of Intrarenal Arterial Injected MSCs in Rat Kidneys

To ascertain the MSC expression in the kidney, we infused MSCs containing a green fluorescent protein (GFP) into the left kidney and examined the GFP expression in rat kidneys one hour later.

The sections were examined under UV light for the detection of fluorescence around the glomeruli, arterial lining cells and tubular cells. Immunochemical stains with primary antibodies against MSC CD44 (MCA643GA, Serotec, Kidlington, UK) were also performed for identification of MSCs in kidneys.

2.6. Measurements of Proteinuria and Hydroxyproline Degree

Twenty four hours urine samples were collected (on day 5 after anti-Thy1.1 infusion) from all experimental rats with free access to water. Urinary protein concentration was determined by a Bio-Rad protein assay (Bio-Rad Laboratories, München, Germany). Hydroxyproline content was measured with Hydroxyproline Assay Kit (STA-675, Cell Biolabs, Inc., San Diego, CA, USA).

2.7. Renal Morphology

For assessing the morphological change, renal histology was evaluated using H&E, periodic acid-Schiff (PAS) and Masson stained 5-µm paraffin sections based on at least 50 glomeruli per kidney section. PAS-stained sections were examined for glomerulosclerosis. One hundred glomeruli per section were randomly selected for assessing the degree of glomerular damage using a semi-quantitative scoring method: grade 0, normal glomeruli; grade 1, sclerotic area up to 25% (minimal sclerosis); grade 2, sclerotic area 25 to 50% (moderate sclerosis); grade 3, sclerotic area 50 to 75% (moderate-severe sclerosis); grade 4, sclerotic area 75 to 100% (severe sclerosis), as described previously [21].

2.8. Immunohistochemistry

Immunohistochemical staining was performed on formalin fixed, paraffin-embedded kidney sections with ED-1 (clone ED-1, Serotec, Oxford, UK), primary antibodies against MSC CD44 (MCA643GA, Serotec, Kidlington, UK), GRP78 (1:500; Santa Cruz Biotechnology, Dallas, TX, USA), LC3-II (1:1000; MBLI Corporation, Woburn, MA, USA), caspase 3 (Epitomics, Burlingame, CA, USA), terminal deoxynucleotidyl transferase-mediated digoxigenin-deoxyuridine nick-end labeling (TUNEL, BioVision, Milpitas, CA, USA), collagen IV (Abcam, Cambridge, UK) and 4-hydroxynonenal (4HNE, Bioss, Woburn, MA, USA). Briefly, paraffin sections were deparaffinized with xylene and rehydrated in an alcohol series and water. Kidney sections were subjected to antigen retrieval and were blocked with a peroxidase-blocking reagent. Sections were incubated with the primary antibody overnight at 4 °C. After washing, the kidney sections were incubated with Envision system-horseradish peroxidase-labeled polymer (Dako, Glostrup, Denmark) for 1 h at room temperature. The sections were visualized with 3,3′-diaminobenzidine tetrahydrochloride (Dako, Glostrup, Denmark) and counterstained with hematoxylin. Apoptotic cells in the kidney were identified by TUNEL staining. The TUNEL method for the in situ apoptotic assay was performed according to the method of Gavrieli et al. with minor modifications [22]. The number of positive ED1 and TUNEL stained cells was evaluated by counting stained cells per high power field (×400) in at least 20 randomly selected fields. The percentage of positive stained area in the GRP-78, LC3-II, caspase 3 and collagen VI assays was analyzed by Adobe Photoshop 7.0.1 imaging software (San Jose, CA, USA) analysis.

2.9. Western Blot and Nuclear Extraction

Western blot analysis was performed on isolated glomeruli to detect the levels of renal anti-oxidant responsive element proteins, and nuclear extractions were done to detect nuclear factor (erythroid-derived 2)-like 2 (Nrf2), nuclear factor kappa B (NF-kB) expressions. Briefly, tissues were grinded to powder in liquid nitrogen. Then the tissue powder was lysed in RIPA Buffer (Bio Basic, Amherst, NY, USA) supplemented with a protease inhibitor (Roche, Basel, Switzerland) for 10 min at 4 °C. The concentration of protein was measured by a BCA protein assay kit (Thermo Scientific, Waltham, MA, USA). A protein sample (80 µg) was mixed with 1× sample buffer and was boiled for 3 min. Protein samples were resolved in 10% SDS-polyacrylamide gel electrophoresis (SDS-PAGE) and transferred to PVDF membrane (Millipore, Billerica, MA, USA). The blot was blocked with Hyblock (Hycell, Taipei, Taiwan) for 1 min, and incubated with primary antibodies overnight at 4

°C. Detection of signals was performed by Western Lightning plus-ECL (PerkinElmer, Waltham, MA, USA). Nuclear extracts were obtained using the NE-PER nuclear and cytoplasmic extraction reagents (Thermo Scientific, Waltham, MA, USA) according to the manufacturer's instructions.

Primary antibodies included Mn-superoxide dismutase (MnSOD, 1:1000; Enzo Life Sciences, Farmingdale, NY, USA), Cu/Zn-SOD (1:500; Millipore, Billerica, MA, USA), catalase (Assay Designs, Ann Arbor, MI, USA), heme oxygenase 1(BioVision, Milpitas, CA, USA), Nrf2 (Cayman, Ann Arbor, MI, USA), NFkB (Santa Cruz, Dallas, TX, USA), glutamate-cysteine ligase catalytic subunit (GCLC, Abcam, Cambridge, UK), glutamate-cysteine ligase modifier subunit (GCLM, Abcam, Cambridge, UK), glutathione peroxidase 1(GPX1, Abcam, Cambridge, UK), β-actin (1:5000; Sigma-Aldrich, St. Louis, MO, USA), γ-tubulin (Abcam, Cambridge, UK) and Lamin A/C (Abcam, Cambridge, UK) as a control for nuclear extraction. Secondary antibodies included HRP-conjugated goat anti-mouse IgG, HRP-conjugated rabbit anti-goat IgG, and HRP-conjugated goat anti-rabbit IgG (all at 1:10,000; all from Southern Biotech Laboratories, Birmingham, AL, USA).

2.10. Statistical Analysis

We used the soft Scion Image β3b Scion Corporation, Frederick, MD software to quantify western blot density. We used a one-way ANOVA and Bonferroni SPSS/Windows (SPSS Inc., Chicago, IL, USA) to analyze experimental data (the difference from the experimental was assessed by a one way ANOVA). We used GraphPad PRISM® 3.0 (GraphPad Software Inc., San Diego, CA, USA) and Sigma Plot 10.0 (San Jose, CA, USA) for figure preparation.

3. Results

3.1. Recruitment of MSCs and HMSCs into Nephritic Not Normal Kidneys

Detection of fluorescence in the kidneys after intrarenal arterial administration of fluorescent MSCs is illustrated in Figure 1C. High levels of GFP were visualized under UV light and the fluorescence was found in the nephritic kidneys (Figure 1C3,4) but not in the normal kidney (Figure 1C1,2). Fluorescence cells were found at glomeruli in the MSC treated groups. CD44 positive cells were found in glomeruli of MSC or HMSC treated kidneys, but not in the control kidney (Figure 2A). These results confirm the recruitment of MSCs and HMSCs in injured kidneys. There was no significant difference in trafficking CD44 positive cell numbers between the MSC and HMSC groups.

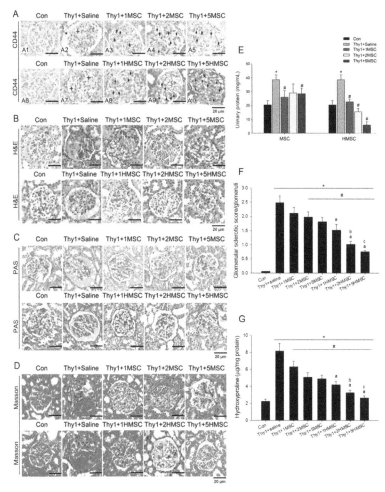

Figure 2. Representative pictures of immunohistochemical stained sections for CD44, a marker for MSC, in ten groups of rats show CD44 positive stains in the glomeruli indicated by arrows in MSCs or HMSCs treated kidneys compared to control kidney (**A1–10**). Anti-Thy1.1 evoked mesangial lysis (indicated by +) and the mesangial matrix accumulation (indicated with *) in the nephritic rats. Intrarenal MSCs transplantation ameliorated anti-Thy1.1-induced nephritis in the rat model. Normoxic (MSC) and hypoxic MSCs (HMSC) markedly reduced the inflammatory cell infiltration in the glomeruli in H&E stains (**B**). The severity of glomerulosclerosis was explored in both normoxic MSC and HMSC treated rats in PAS stains (**C**) and in Masson stains (**D**). Thy1-induced nephritis significantly elevated urinary protein level and the elevated urinary protein level was significantly reduced by intrarenal MSC or HMSC treatment (**E**). Glomerular sclerotic index calculated by the PAS sections among the experimental groups are presented in (**F**). Thy1-induced nephritis significantly increased glomerular sclerosis in all nephritis treated groups as compared to Con group. MSC at cell number $(2–5) \times 10^5$ level and HMSC at cell number $(1–5) \times 10^5$ level significantly reduced sclerosis degree. Glomerular fibrosis determined by the hydroxyproline contents among all groups of animals are presented in (**G**). Thy1-induced nephritis significantly increased renal hydroxyproline content in all nephritis treated groups as compared to Con group. MSC and HMSC significantly reduced renal fibrotic degree. Each graph is amplified at 400×. The scale bar (20 μm) is indicated in each graph. * $p < 0.05$ vs. Con group. # $p < 0.05$ vs. Thy1 group. a $p < 0.05$ vs. Thy1 + 1MSC group. b $p < 0.05$ vs. Thy1 + 2MSC group. c $p < 0.05$ vs. Thy1 + 5MSC group.

3.2. MSC or HMSC Ameliorates Nephritic Severity in the Rat GN Model

The success of glomerulonephritis induction in our model was confirmed by the elevated urine protein concentrations and typical characteristics in the histopathologic examination, including mesangial cell proliferation, mesangialysis, and sclerosis appearance 5 days after injury. In H&E stains of both MSC and HMSC treated kidneys, the severity of glomerulosclerosis was attenuated and decreased numbers of inflammatory cells in glomeruli were found (Figure 2B). The glomerulosclerosis index by PAS stains sections (Figure 2C) are 0.01 for the control, 0.5 for anti-Thy1 with placebo, 0.19 for 1×10^5 MSC treated group, 0.16 for 2×10^5 MSC treated group, 0.03 for 5×10^5 MSC treated group, 0.03 for 1×10^5 HMSC treated group, and 0 for both 2 and 5×10^5 MSC treated groups (Figure 2F). Both normoxic and hypoxic MSC reduced the severity of proteinuria in GN rats. The level of proteinuria reduction did not differ among 1, 2, 5×10^5 MSC infusion, but there exists a trend in HMSCs with a higher cell number having a lower proteinuria (Figure 2E). The severity of glomeruli fibrosis was also ameliorated by MSC and HMSC administration, which is shown in the Masson stains (Figure 2D) and in the hydroxyproline content (Figure 2H).

3.3. Hypoxic Preconditioning Upregulated HIF-1α and VEGF Expression

Hypoxic preconditioning significantly upregulated HIF-1α concentration (Figure 3A) and VEGF (Figure 3D) expression in the MSCs but downregulated several growth factors with growth factors array assay (Figure 3B) in the conditioned medium (Figure 3C).

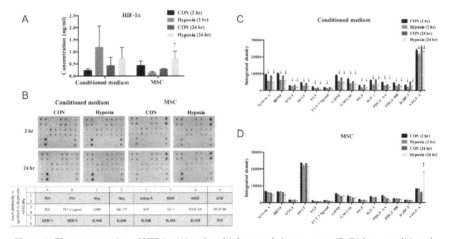

Figure 3. The concentration of HIF-1α (**A**) and multiple growth factors array (**B–D**) from conditioned medium and MSC were determined. The upregulation and downregulation were denoted with the arrows.

3.4. MSCs or HMSCs Reduce ED1, ER Stress, Autophagy, and Apoptosis with Western Blot

The oxidative stress index of renal ED-1 (Figure 4A), GRP78 (Figure 4B), Beclin-1 (Figure 4C), LC3-II (Figure 4D), Bax/Bcl-2 ratio (Figure 4E), Caspase-3 (Figure 4F), PARP (Figure 4G) was significantly elevated in anti-Thy1.1 treated glomeruli. MSCs with three dosages did not significantly reduce these oxidative parameters in the anti-thy1.1 treated kidneys. However, HMSCs treated anti-thy1.1 kidneys with the number of 5×10^5 significantly reduced these parameters as compared to anti-thy1.1 treated group.

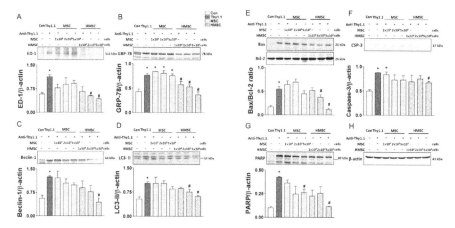

Figure 4. The oxidative stress index of renal ED-1 (**A**), GRP78 (**B**), Beclin-1 (**C**), LC3-II (**D**), Bax/Bcl-2 ratio (**E**), Caspase-3 (**F**), PARP (**G**) and β-actin (**H**) is determined with western blot among eight groups of rats. The quantitative data showed that anti-Thy1.1 significantly enhanced ED-1, GRP78, Beclin-1, LC3-II, Bax/Bcl-2 ratio, Caspase 3, and PARP in the damaged kidneys. MSCs with three amounts did not significantly reduce these oxidative parameters in the anti-thy1.1 treated kidneys. HMSCs treated anti-thy1.1 kidneys with the number of 5×10^5 significantly reduced these parameters as compared to anti-thy1.1 treated group. * $p < 0.05$ vs. Con group. # $p < 0.05$ vs. Thy1.1 group.

3.5. MSCs or HMSCs Reduce ED-1 Infiltration, ER Stress, Autophagy, and Apoptosis by IHC

The representative pictures of immunohistochemical stained sections and semi-quantitative analyses of ED-1, GRP78, LC3-II, caspase 3, TUNEL and collagen IV in the study groups are presented in Figure 5. With the semi-quantitative analysis of the histochemical stained kidney sections for ED-1, anti-Thy1.1 administration markedly increased the numbers of ED-1positive cells in the glomeruli. Infusion of MSCs reduced the number of ED-1 positive cells that infiltrated in the kidneys, and infusion of HMSCs had a better reduction of the ED1 positive cell number (Figure 5A1–5) than MSCs. Similar results were found for GRP78, LC3-II, caspase 3, TUNEL, and collagen IV. These sections show that anti-Thy1.1 administration increased stress index protein (GRP78) accumulation (Figure 5B1–5), autophagy index protein (LC3-II) detection (Figure 5C1–5), caspase 3 positive cells (Figure 5D1–5), apoptotic (TUNEL+) cells (Figure 5E1–5), and collagen IV accumulation (Figure 5F1–5). MSC infusion ameliorated the increase in GRP78, LC3-II, caspase 3, TUNEL, and collagen IV in kidneys after anti-Thy1.1 infusion. HMSC infusion had a greater effect on ameliorating inflammatory cell infiltration, stress protein accumulation, apoptotic cells and autophagy in glomeuli vs. MSC treatment.

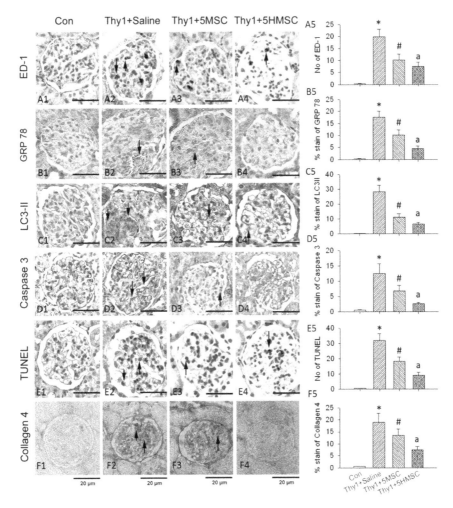

Figure 5. Immunohistochemical stains for ED1, GRP78, LC3-II, Caspase1, TUNEL, and Collagen IV in the study groups. Detection of ED1+ cell in the study groups are demonstrated in (**A1–4**). Semiquantitative assessment revealed infusion of MSCs and showed a reduction in numbers of macrophage/monocyte infiltration (ED1+ cell). HMSCs possessed a better reduction effect (**A5**). Representative pictures of sections for stress index protein acculumation (**B1–4**), autophagy by LC3-II (**C1–4**), apoptotic cells by caspase 1(**D1–4**) and TUNEL (**E1–4**) and collagen deposition (**F1–4**) in glomeruli. The semiquantitative assessment of these sections revealed anti-Thy1.1 administration increased stress index protein (GRP78) accumulation, autophagy index protein (LC3II) detection, apoptotic (TUNEL, caspase 1) cells, and collagen IV accumulation. MSC infusion ameliorated the increase in GRP78, LC3 II, caspase 1, TUNEL, and collagen IV in kidneys after anti-Thy1.1 infusion. HMSC infusion had greater therapeutic reduction effects. Each graph is amplified at 400×. The scale bar (20 μm) is indicated in the Figure. * $p < 0.05$ vs. Con group. # $p < 0.05$ vs. Thy1 group. a $p < 0.05$ vs. Thy1 + 5MSC group.

3.6. HMSCs Promote Nuclear Nrf2 Expression, Reduce NF-kB Expression, Rescue ROS Enzymatic Scavengers and Elevate Anti-Oxidative Response Element Proteins

Figure 6 demonstrates the reactive oxygen species (ROS) injury index and the intrinsic anti-oxidative mechanisms expression among the experimental groups. The accumulation of ROS by 4 HNE histochemical stain among the groups are demonstrated in Figure 6A1–4, the semi-quantitative analyses of these sections revealed that anti-Thy1.1 infusion greatly increased ROS. In the treatment groups, only a higher HMSC cell number ameliorated the ROS accumulation (Figure 6A5). ROS enzymatic scavenger expressions including MnSOD, Cu/ZnSOD, and catalase were significantly reduced by antiThy-1.1 infusion. These enzymes were rescued by HMSC transplantation, but not by MSCs (Figure 6B1–3). As for Nrf2 signaling, the master regulator of ROS injury, the results showed that nuclear Nrf2 expression was not changed, while NF-kB expression was elevated by anti-Thy1.1 infusion. Infusion of HMSCs significantly increased nuclear Nrf2 and reduced NF-kB expressions in anti-Thy1.1 treated rat kidneys. Infusion of MSCs had a lesser effect on nuclear Nrf2 elevation and NF-kB expression. However, the effect did not reach statistical significance (Figure 6C1–3). Semi-quantitative detection of anti-oxidative response element (ARE) protein expression (GCLC, GCLM and GPX) by Western blotting in the kidneys are shown (Figure 6D1–3). These proteins had a consistent expression trend in the experimental groups. Briefly, the anti-Thy1.1 antibody infusion reduced ARE protein expressions, and hypoxic preconditioning MSCs rescued these protein expressions. Administration of MSCs did not significantly increase protein expression, though it tended to increase their levels. Figure 6E demonstrated a summary diagram of this study.

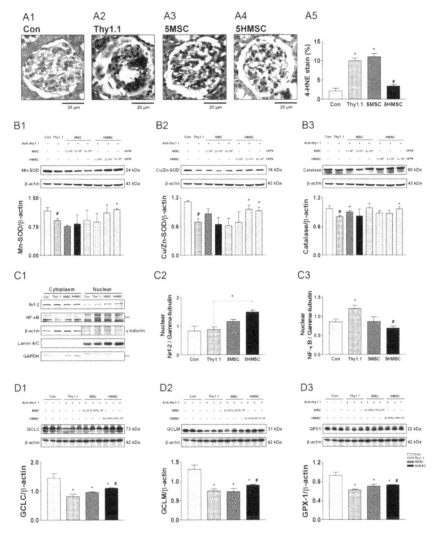

Figure 6. The index of ROS, ROS enzymatic scavenger expression, master anti-oxidative injury regulator Nrf2 expression, and anti-oxidative response protein expressions among the experimental groups. The accumulation of ROS by 4 HNE stain among the groups are demonstrated from the amplified graph at 400× (scale bar = 20 μm, **A1–4**). The semi-quantitative analyses of these sections revealed that anti-Thy1.1 infusion greatly increased ROS, and HMSCs ameliorated the ROS accumulation (**A5**). ROS enzymatic scavengers including MnSOD, Cu/ZnSOD and catalase were significantly reduced by antiThy-1 infusion. These enzymes were rescued by HMSCs (**B1–3**). The nuclear Nrf2 expression is not triggered by anti-Thy 1.1 infusion and is enhanced in the HMSC treated group. Significantly elevated nuclear NFkB expression is noted in anti-Thy1.1 group, which is efficiently suppressed in HMSCs treated group (**C1–3**). Downstream antioxidative response element protein expression including GCLC, GCLM, GPX are suppressed by anti-Thy 1.1 infusion. These proteins are rescued by HMSC transplantation (**D1–3**). * $p < 0.05$ vs. Con group. # $p < 0.05$ vs. Thy1.1 group.

4. Discussion

Hypoxic preconditioning significantly upregulated HIF-1α/VEGF expression in the MSCs, however, it downregulated several growth factors in the hypoxic conditioned medium implicating an enhanced HIF-1α/VEGF signaling. As far as we know, there is no in vivo data to confirm that HMSCs transplantation can upregulate HIF-1α and VEGF in the rat GN model. However, HMSCs transplantation increased expression of pro-survival and pro-angiogenic factors including HIF-1 and VEGF in the rat model of myocardial infarction [23] or ischemic/reperfusion kidney [24]. Our present data displayed that intrarenal arterial administration of either MSCs or HMSCs ameliorates the severity of glomerulosclerosis and levels of proteinuria in the anti-Thy-1.1 induced rat GN model. HMSCs showed a better therapeutic effect than MSCs on the amelioration of glomerulosclerosis, inflammatory cell infiltration, ER stress, apoptosis, and autophagy. In addition, hypoxic preconditioning enabled MSCs to activate nuclear Nrf2 expression and rescued ROS scavengers in kidneys after Thy-1.1 lesion. Our results indicate that hypoxic preconditioning further enhances the therapeutic effects of MSCs through multiple mechanisms including increasing intra-nuclear Nrf2 expression in the target organ.

Several studies have demonstrated that stem cells derived from various origins ameliorate kidney injury in GN animal models [2,25–29]. MSCs have the ability to cause anti-inflammation, anti-fibrosis, and inhibition of cell death and this is the basis for cell therapies [2,25,26,29,30]. In this study, both MSCs and HMSCs showed anti-inflammatory effects by decreasing macrophage/monocyte infiltration in glomeruli of treated kidneys and by inhibiting NF-κB translocation into nucleus. A significant further decrease in numbers was found in the HMSC treated group, indicating that hypoxic preconditioning is an effective strategy to promote the anti-inflammatory effect. The results of Masson stains confirm the therapeutic effect of MSCs on anti-fibrosis, and this effect was further enhanced by hypoxic preconditioning. We also demonstrated that intra-glomerular cell apoptosis and autophagy were decreased by MSC infusion, and a further reduction was noted in the HMSC treat group. The therapeutic anti-inflammation, anti-fibrosis, anti-apoptosis, and anti-autophagy mechanisms of MSCs are compatible to previous studies [31,32]. Hypoxic preconditioning showed a consistent enhancement of these therapeutic mechanisms seen in MSCs.

Another important finding in this study is that hypoxic preconditioning enabled MSCs to increase nuclear Nrf2 and decrease NF-κB expression. Oxidative stress generated by the immune reaction is believed to be one of the crucial mechanisms that cause injuries to glomeruli in the GN. The Keap1–Nrf2 pathway signaling and the anti-oxidant responsive elements play a central role in protection against oxidative stresses. In this study, anti-Thy1.1 lesion was found to suppress the antioxidant activity by decreasing ROS scavenger expression and elevating nuclear NF-κB, which contributed to inflammatory cytokine cascades. The nuclear Nrf2 expression remained unchanged after anti-Thy1.1 lesion, indicating that the master intrinsic anti-oxidative regulator, Nrf2/Keap1 pathway, was not triggered. Nrf2 expression levels increased with MSCs transplantation to GN rats. However, it failed to reach a significant difference. At the same time, ROS enzymatic scavengers and other ARE proteins were not rescued. With HMSC transplantation, nuclear Nrf2 expression increased and ROS scavengers and ARE proteins were rescued in diseased kidneys. From these results it seems that conventional MSC transplantation may not trigger enough Nrf2 pathway signaling activity to enhance ARE protein expressions. Therefore, hypoxic preconditioning enabled MSCs to activate the Nrf2 pathway signaling and to rescue the ROS scavengers in kidneys which were suppressed by the anti-Thy1.1 infusion. Our findings provide evidence supporting the viewpoint of Ezquer et al.'s study [33], in which MSCs were believed to possess the main enzymatic mechanisms to detoxify the reactive oxygen species and to prevent oxidative damage in rat nephritis based on some in vitro cellular studies [34,35].

The major challenges that underlie the application of stem cell therapy to GN patients are safety concerns and efficacy issues. Enhancing the anti-oxidative effect of stem cells is one promising strategy to promote their efficacy for inflammatory or oxidative stress related disease such as GN. Nrf2 is a crucial regulator of the antioxidant defense system and governs the expression of genes associated with redox homeostasis. The beneficial effects of targeting the Nrf2 pathway for nephritis have been demonstrated in animal studies through tranduction of the OR1 gene to enhance antioxidation [36] or via Keap-1 gene knockout to activate the Nrf2 system [37]. Bardoxolone, an Nrf2 activator, has been shown to improve renal functions in type 2 diabetic patients with chronic kidney disease in a human phase 2 trial [38], though it had cardiovascular safety issues [39]. The current study shows that HMSC transplantation is an effective measure to enhance Nrf2 pathway signaling and therapeutic effects in damaged kidneys. Hypoxic preconditioning, i.e., stem cell cultured in an ischemic condition which mimics the bone marrow niche environment, is a common way to preserve stemness, enhance homing, and increase efficacy of stem cell therapy. In cellular studies, hypoxic preconditioning has enhanced stemness and expanded cell numbers [40]. Hypoxic mimetic preconditioning enhances MSC migration and prolongs kidney retention through promoting CXCR4 expression [24]. The results of this study link hypoxic preconditioning to anti-oxidative injury. We demonstrated that HMSCs promote Nrf2 signaling and resultant ARE protein elevation. The cytokines involved in the Nrf2 pathway signaling activation promoted by HMSCs need to be further investigated.

MSC homing to injured tissue is the first step and crucial because the therapeutic application of stem cell therapy is predicated on the transplanted cells migrating and participating in tissue repair. Enhancing the homing capabilities and the self-defense potential of stem cells can promote their therapeutic efficacy. As shown in Figure 1C, the MSCs indeed transplanted to the damaged glomeruli implicating its efficient homing to the damaged site. Hypoxic preconditioning enhanced stem cells with several possible defense mechanisms including antioxidant, ant-apoptosis, anti-ER stress, and anti-inflammatory potential and the homing HMSC may protect itself and the adjacent cells against oxidative stress through the possible autocrine and/or paracrine effect to release growth factors and other protective mediators. This hypothesis requires further experiments to confirm. In future, we will perform the in vitro and in vivo experiments to determine the released protective molecules from the homing HMSCs and to explore the exact mechanism for attenuating glomerular injury in the GN model. In the present study, intrarenal arterial administrations of MSCs or HMSCs lead to positive CD44 staining existence in the glomeruli. The advantage of intrarenal arterial administration can demonstrate the direct delivery and location of stem cells to the kidney and prevent the risk of stem cells trapping in the lung or other non-target tissue/organ by systemically intravenous administration. The average stem cell numbers trafficked in glomeruli increased with hypoxic preconditioning and higher infused cell numbers. In previous studies, hypoxic precondition has been associated with increased CXCR4, CX3CR1 expression in a cellular study [17]. CXCR4 and CX3CR1 respond to SDF-1α, activate the Akt signal pathway [41] and elevate matrix metalloproteinases [42] contributing to transmigration. Our findings confirm that hypoxic preconditioning is an effective strategy to enhance the homing effect of MSCs in the rat GN model.

The mesangial cell proliferation peaks at about 1 week, and the nephritis spontaneously repairs after 2–3 weeks in the anti-Thy1.1 nephritic model. To prevent the possible spontaneous repair effect, we demonstrated the clinically available HMSCs transplantation on reducing glomerular matrix accumulation, attenuating proteinuria, and ameliorating glomerular sclerosis in rats with anti-Thy1 disease at the early stage within 1 week (sacrificed on day 5). These results suggest that renal arterial administration of HMSCs in vivo may have promise as an anti-inflammatory, anti-proliferative, and anti-fibrotic strategy in the treatment of acute phases or relapses of mesangial proliferative glomerulonephritis. There are some limitations to the current study. First, we only investigated the Nrf2 pathway and ARE expressions in the regulation of MSCs antioxidant status. Functions of other oxidative stress-related pathways, such as PI3K/Akt and FoxO/TXNIP need further elucidation. Secondly, mechanisms that influence the enhanced repairing efficacy of MSCs after transplantation were not fully elucidated. Further studies focusing on the cytokines involved in the anti-oxidant enhancement are needed. Third, we used an acute GN model in this study. Whether these results can be applied to chronic GN, mandates further investigations.

5. Conclusions

Our experimental data can be summarized as Figure 7. As well as enhancing the anti-inflammatory, anti-ER stress, anti-fibrosis, anti-apoptosis, and anti-autophagy properties, anti-oxidative mechanisms also play a role in the therapeutic effect of hypoxic preconditioned MSCs on glomerulonephritis. Hypoxic preconditioning is one effective strategy to activate further intrinsic anti-oxidative defense systems by promoting the HIF-1α/VEGF signaling, Nrf2 pathway, rescue antioxidant enzymes, and increase anti-oxidative responsive element proteins.

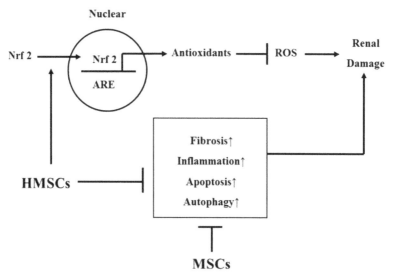

Figure 7. The summary diagram is demonstrated. HMSCs prevent renal damage by suppression of pathological signals (including fibrosis, inflammation, apoptosis, and autophagy) and increase antioxidant status against oxidative stress. HMSCs reduce renal damage majorly through suppression of pathological signals.

Author Contributions: H.-H.C., S.-P.H., and C.-T.C. conceived the hypothesis; H.-H.C. and C.-T.C. conducted the statistical analyses for this manuscript; H.-H.C., S.-P.H., and C.-T.C. drafted the manuscript; H.-H.C., S.-P.H., and C.-T.C. contributed to discussion of the results; H.-H.C., S.-P.H., and C.-T.C. contributed to the design and conduction of the study. All the authors critically revised the drafted manuscript. All authors have read and agreed to the published version of the manuscript.

Funding: This work was supported by grants from the Ministry of Science and Technology (MOST 102-2320-B-003-001-MY3), National Taiwan University Hospital (Grant No. 103-N2562) and Taipei Veteran General Hospital (Grant No. VN100-02).

Acknowledgments: The authors would like to thank Yi-Huei Li and Jun-Tzao Huang for their dedication to the study.

Conflicts of Interest: All the authors declare no conflict of interest.

Abbreviations

ED-1	macrophage/monocyte
ER stress	endoplasmic reticulum stress
ESRD	end stage renal disease
GN	glomerulonephritis
HIF-1α	hypoxia induced factor-1α
HMSCs	hypoxic-preconditioned mesenchymal stem cells

MSCs	mesenchymal stem cells
NF kB	nuclear factor kappa B
Nrf2	nuclear factor (erythroid-derived 2)
ROS	reactive oxygen species
VEGF	vascular endothelial growth factor
TUNEL	terminal deoxynucleotidyl transferase–mediated digoxigenin-deoxyuridine nick-end labeling

References

1. Couser, W.G. Glomerulonephritis. *Lancet* **1999**, *353*, 1509–1515. [CrossRef]
2. Kunter, U.; Rong, S.; Djuric, Z.; Boor, P.; Müller-Newen, G.; Yu, D.; Floege, J. Transplanted mesenchymal stem cells accelerate glomerular healing in experimental glomerulonephritis. *J. Am. Soc. Nephrol.* **2006**, *17*, 2202–2212. [CrossRef] [PubMed]
3. D'Amico, G. Influence of clinical and histological features on actuarial renal survival in adult patients with idiopathic IgA nephropathy, membranous nephropathy, and membranoproliferative glomerulonephritis: Survey of the recent literature. *Am. J. Kidney Dis.* **1992**, *20*, 315–323. [CrossRef]
4. Deegens, J.K.; Wetzels, J.F. Diagnosis and treatment of primary glomerular diseases. Membranous nephropathy, focal segmental glomerulosclerosis and IgA nephropathy. *Minerva Urol. Nefrol.* **2005**, *57*, 211–236.
5. Heaf, J.; Lokkegaard, H.; Larsen, S. The epidemiology and prognosis of glomerulonephritis in Denmark 1985–1997. *Nephrol. Dial. Transpl.* **1999**, *14*, 1889–1897. [CrossRef]
6. Moranne, O.; Watier, L.; Rossert, J.; Stengel, B. N-Progress Study Group. Primary glomerulonephritis: An update on renal survival and determinants of progression. *QJM* **2008**, *101*, 215–224. [CrossRef]
7. Pippias, M.; Jager, K.J.; Kramer, A.; Leivestad, T.; Sanchez, M.B.; Caskey, F.J.; Collart, F.; Couchoud, C.; Dekker, F.W.; Finne, P.; et al. The changing trends and outcomes in renal replacement therapy: Data from the ERA-EDTA Registry. *Nephrol. Dial. Transpl.* **2015**, *31*, 831–841. [CrossRef]
8. Jin, M.; Xie, Y.; Li, Q.; Chen, X. Stem cell-based cell therapy for glomerulonephritis. *Biomed. Res. Int.* **2014**, *2014*, 124730. [CrossRef]
9. El-Ansary, M.; Saadi, G.; Abd El-Hamid, S.M. Mesenchymal stem cells are a rescue approach for recovery of deteriorating kidney function. *Nephrology* **2012**, *17*, 650–657. [CrossRef]
10. Gu, F.; Wang, D.; Zhang, H.; Feng, X.; Gilkeson, G.S.; Shi, S.; Sun, L. Allogeneic mesenchymal stem cell transplantation for lupus nephritis patients refractory to conventional therapy. *Clin. Rheumatol.* **2014**, *33*, 1611–1619. [CrossRef]
11. Wang, D.; Li, J.; Zhang, Y.; Zhang, M.; Chen, J.; Li, X.; Hu, X.; Jiang, S.; Shi, S.; Sun, L. Umbilical cord mesenchymal stem cell transplantation in active and refractory systemic lupus erythematosus: A multicenter clinical study. *Arthritis Res. Ther.* **2014**, *16*, R79. [CrossRef] [PubMed]
12. Meyer-Schwesinger, C.; Lange, C.; Bröcker, V.; Agustian, P.A.; Lehmann, U.; Raabe, A.; Brinkmeyer, M.; Kobayashi, E.; Schiffer, M.; Büsche, G.; et al. Bone marrow-derived progenitor cells do not contribute to podocyte turnover in the puromycin aminoglycoside and renal ablation models in rats. *Am. J. Pathol.* **2011**, *178*, 494–499. [CrossRef] [PubMed]
13. Budisavljevic, M.N.; Hodge, L.; Barber, K.; Fulmer, J.R.; Durazo-Arvizu, R.A.; Self, S.E.; Kuhlmann, M.; Raymond, J.R.; Greene, E.L. Oxidative stress in the pathogenesis of experimental mesangial proliferative glomerulonephritis. *Am. J. Physiol. Renal. Physiol.* **2003**, *285*, F1138–F1148. [CrossRef] [PubMed]
14. Fang, Y.; Tian, X.; Bai, S.; Fan, J.; Hou, W.; Tong, H.; Li, D. Autologous transplantation of adipose-derived mesenchymal stem cells ameliorates streptozotocin-induced diabetic nephropathy in rats by inhibiting oxidative stress, pro-inflammatory cytokines and the p38 MAPK signaling pathway. *Int. J. Mol. Med.* **2012**, *30*, 85–92. [PubMed]
15. Zeng, W.; Xiao, J.; Zheng, G.; Xing, F.; Tipoe, G.L.; Wang, X.; He, C.; Chen, Z.; Liu, Y. Antioxidant treatment enhances human mesenchymal stem cell anti-stress ability and therapeutic efficacy in an acute liver failure model. *Sci. Rep.* **2015**, *5*, 11100. [CrossRef]
16. Petrangeli, E.; Coroniti, G.; Brini, A.T.; De Girolamo, L.; Stanco, D.; Niada, S.; Silecchia, G.; Morgante, E.; Lubrano, C.; Russo, M.A.; et al. Hypoxia promotes the inflammatory response and stemness features in visceral fat stem cells from obese subjects. *J. Cell Physiol.* **2016**, *231*, 668–679. [CrossRef]

17. Liu, H.; Xue, W.; Ge, G.; Luo, X.; Li, Y.; Xiang, H.; Ding, X.; Tian, P.; Tian, X. Hypoxic preconditioning advances CXCR4 and CXCR7 expression by activating HIF-1alpha in MSCs. *Biochem. Biophys. Res. Commun.* **2010**, *401*, 509–515. [CrossRef]

18. Huang, T.F.; Yew, T.L.; Chiang, E.R.; Ma, H.L.; Hsu, C.Y.; Hsu, S.H.; Hsu, Y.T.; Hung, S.C. Mesenchymal stem cells from a hypoxic culture improve and engraft Achilles tendon repair. *Am. J. Sport. Med.* **2013**, *41*, 1117–1125. [CrossRef]

19. Yew, T.L.; Chang, M.C.; Hsu, Y.T.; He, F.Y.; Weng, W.H.; Tsai, C.C.; Chiu, F.Y.; Hung, S.C. Efficient expansion of mesenchymal stem cells from mouse bone marrow under hypoxic conditions. *J. Tissue Eng. Regen. Med.* **2013**, *7*, 984–993. [CrossRef]

20. Chen, Y.M.; Chien, C.T.; Hu-Tsai, M.I.; Wu, K.D.; Tsai, C.C.; Wu, M.S.; Tsai, T.J. Pentoxifylline attenuates experimental mesangial proliferative glomerulonephritis. *Kidney Int.* **1999**, *56*, 932–943. [CrossRef]

21. Saito, T.; Sumithran, E.; Glasgow, E.F.; Atkins, R.C. The enhancement of aminonucleoside nephrosis by the co-administration of protamine. *Kidney Int.* **1987**, *32*, 691–699. [CrossRef] [PubMed]

22. Gavrieli, Y.; Sherman, Y.; Ben-Sasson, S.A. Identification of programmed cell death in situ via specific labeling of nuclear DNA fragmentation. *J. Cell Biol.* **1992**, *119*, 493–501. [PubMed]

23. Hu, X.; Yu, S.P.; Fraser, J.L.; Lu, Z.; Ogle, M.E.; Wang, J.A.; Wei, L. Transplantation of hypoxia-preconditioned mesenchymal stem cells improves infarcted heart function via enhanced survival of implanted cells and angiogenesis. *J. Thorac. Cardiovasc. Surg.* **2008**, *135*, 799–808. [PubMed]

24. Yu, X.; Lu, C.; Liu, H.; Rao, S.; Cai, J.; Liu, S.; Kriegel, A.J.; Greene, A.S.; Liang, M.; Ding, X. Hypoxic preconditioning with cobalt of bone marrow mesenchymal stem cells improves cell migration and enhances therapy for treatment of ischemic acute kidney injury. *PLoS ONE* **2013**, *8*, e62703. [CrossRef] [PubMed]

25. Li, B.; Morioka, T.; Uchiyama, M.; Oite, T. Bone marrow cell infusion ameliorates progressive glomerulosclerosis in an experimental rat model. *Kidney Int.* **2006**, *69*, 323–330. [CrossRef] [PubMed]

26. Rampino, T.; Gregorini, M.; Bedino, G.; Piotti, G.; Gabanti, E.; Ibatici, A.; Sessarego, N.; Piacenza, C.; Balenzano, C.T.; Esposito, P.; et al. Mesenchymal stromal cells improve renal injury in anti-Thy 1 nephritis by modulating inflammatory cytokines and scatter factors. *Clin. Sci.* **2011**, *120*, 25–36. [CrossRef] [PubMed]

27. Sakr, S.; Rashed, L.; Zarouk, W.; El-Shamy, R. Effect of mesenchymal stem cells on anti-Thy1,1 induced kidney injury in albino rats. *Asian Pac. J. Trop. Biomed.* **2013**, *3*, 174–181. [CrossRef]

28. Tsuda, H.; Yamahara, K.; Ishikane, S.; Otani, K.; Nakamura, A.; Sawai, K.; Ichimaru, N.; Sada, M.; Taguchi, A.; Hosoda, H.; et al. Allogenic fetal membrane-derived mesenchymal stem cells contribute to renal repair in experimental glomerulonephritis. *Am. J. Physiol. Renal. Physiol.* **2010**, *299*, F1004–F1013. [CrossRef]

29. Uchimura, H.; Marumo, T.; Takase, O.; Kawachi, H.; Shimizu, F.; Hayashi, M.; Saruta, T.; Hishikawa, K.; Fujita, T. Intrarenal injection of bone marrow-derived angiogenic cells reduces endothelial injury and mesangial cell activation in experimental glomerulonephritis. *J. Am. Soc. Nephrol.* **2005**, *16*, 997–1004. [CrossRef]

30. Abe-Yoshio, Y.; Abe, K.; Miyazaki, M.; Furusu, A.; Nishino, T.; Harada, T.; Koji, T.; Kohno, S. Involvement of bone marrow-derived endothelial progenitor cells in glomerular capillary repair in habu snake venom-induced glomerulonephritis. *Virchows Archiv* **2008**, *453*, 97–106. [CrossRef]

31. Li, D.; Wang, N.; Zhang, L.; Hanyu, Z.; Xueyuan, B.; Fu, B.; Shaoyuan, C.; Zhang, W.; Xuefeng, S.; Li, R.; et al. Mesenchymal stem cells protect podocytes from apoptosis induced by high glucose via secretion of epithelial growth factor. *Stem Cell Res. Ther.* **2013**, *4*, 103. [CrossRef] [PubMed]

32. Zoja, C.; Garcia, P.B.; Rota, C.; Conti, S.; Gagliardini, E.; Corna, D.; Zanchi, C.; Bigini, P.; Benigni, A.; Remuzzi, G.; et al. Mesenchymal stem cell therapy promotes renal repair by limiting glomerular podocyte and progenitor cell dysfunction in adriamycin-induced nephropathy. *Am. J. Physiol. Renal. Physiol.* **2012**, *303*, F1370–F1381. [CrossRef] [PubMed]

33. Ezquer, M.E.; Ezquer, F.E.; Arango-Rodríguez, M.L.; Conget, P.A. MSC transplantation: A promising therapeutic strategy to manage the onset and progression of diabetic nephropathy. *Biol. Res.* **2012**, *45*, 289–296. [CrossRef] [PubMed]

34. Salmon, A.B.; Perez, V.I.; Bokov, A.; Jernigan, A.; Kim, G.; Zhao, H.; Levine, R.L.; Richardson, A. Lack of methionine sulfoxide reductase A in mice increases sensitivity to oxidative stress but does not diminish life span. *FASEB J.* **2009**, *23*, 3601–3608. [CrossRef] [PubMed]

35. Valle-Prieto, A.; Conget, P.A. Human mesenchymal stem cells efficiently manage oxidative stress. *Stem Cells Dev.* **2010**, *19*, 1885–1893. [CrossRef] [PubMed]

36. Li, Y.; Li, W.; Liu, C.; Yan, M.; Raman, I.; Du, Y.; Fang, X.; Zhou, X.J.; Mohan, C.; Li, Q.Z. Delivering Oxidation Resistance-1 (OXR1) to Mouse Kidney by Genetic Modified Mesenchymal Stem Cells Exhibited Enhanced Protection against Nephrotoxic Serum Induced Renal Injury and Lupus Nephritis. *J. Stem Cell Res. Ther.* **2014**, *4*. [CrossRef]

37. Miyazaki, Y.; Shimizu, A.; Pastan, I.; Taguchi, K.; Naganuma, E.; Suzuki, T.; Hosoya, T.; Yokoo, T.; Saito, A.; Miyata, T.; et al. Keap1 inhibition attenuates glomerulosclerosis. *Nephrol. Dial. Transpl.* **2014**, *29*, 783–791. [CrossRef]

38. Pergola, P.E.; Raskin, P.; Toto, R.D.; Meyer, C.J.; Huff, J.W.; Grossman, E.B.; Krauth, M.; Ruiz, S.; Audhya, P.; Christ-Schmidt, H.; et al. Bardoxolone methyl and kidney function in CKD with type 2 diabetes. *N. Engl. J. Med.* **2011**, *365*, 327–336. [CrossRef]

39. de Zeeuw, D.; Akizawa, T.; Audhya, P.; Bakris, G.L.; Chin, M.; Christ-Schmidt, H.; Goldsberry, A.; Houser, M.; Krauth, M.; Lambers Heerspink, H.J.; et al. Bardoxolone methyl in type 2 diabetes and stage 4 chronic kidney disease. *N. Engl. J. Med.* **2013**, *369*, 2492–2503. [CrossRef]

40. Chen, M.; Hou, Y.; Lin, D. Polydatin protects bone marrow stem cells against oxidative injury: Involvement of Nrf 2/ARE Pathways. *Stem Cells Int.* **2016**, *2016*, 9394150. [CrossRef]

41. Rosova, I.; Dao, M.; Capoccia, B.; Link, D.; Nolta, J.A. Hypoxic preconditioning results in increased motility and improved therapeutic potential of human mesenchymal stem cells. *Stem Cells* **2008**, *26*, 2173–2182. [CrossRef] [PubMed]

42. Annabi, B.; Lee, Y.T.; Turcotte, S.; Naud, E.; Desrosiers, R.R.; Champagne, M.; Eliopoulos, N.; Galipeau, J.; Beliveau, R. Hypoxia promotes murine bone-marrow-derived stromal cell migration and tube formation. *Stem Cells* **2003**, *21*, 337–347. [CrossRef] [PubMed]

Article

Impact of Intravenous Iron on Oxidative Stress and Mitochondrial Function in Experimental Chronic Kidney Disease

Faisal Nuhu [1], Anne-Marie Seymour [1] and Sunil Bhandari [2,*]

[1] School of Life Sciences (Biomedical), University of Hull, Kingston upon Hull HU67RX, UK;
FISAFUN@YAHOO.CO.UK (F.N.); ANDI.SEYMOUR.19@GMAIL.COM (A.-M.S.)

[2] Hull York Medical School & Department of Renal Medicine, Hull University Teaching Hospitals Trust,
Anlaby Road, Kingston upon Hull HU32JZ, UK

* Correspondence: Sunil.bhandari@hey.nhs.uk; Tel.: +44-1482674308

Received: 10 September 2019; Accepted: 16 October 2019; Published: 21 October 2019

Abstract: Background: Mitochondrial dysfunction is observed in chronic kidney disease (CKD). Iron deficiency anaemia (IDA), a common complication in CKD, is associated with poor clinical outcomes affecting mitochondrial function and exacerbating oxidative stress. Intravenous (iv) iron, that is used to treat anaemia, may lead to acute systemic oxidative stress. This study evaluated the impact of iv iron on mitochondrial function and oxidative stress. Methods: Uraemia was induced surgically in male Sprague-Dawley rats and studies were carried out 12 weeks later in two groups sham operated and uraemic (5/6 nephrectomy) rats not exposed to i.v. iron versus sham operated and uraemic rats with iv iron. Results: Induction of uraemia resulted in reduced iron availability (serum iron: 31.1 ± 1.8 versus 46.4 ± 1.4 μM), low total iron binding capacity (26.4 ± 0.7 versus 29.5 ± 0.8 μM), anaemia (haematocrit: 42.5 ± 3.0 versus $55.0 \pm 3.0\%$), cardiac hypertrophy, reduced systemic glutathione peroxidase activity (1.12 ± 0.11 versus 1.48 ± 0.12 U/mL), tissue oxidative stress (oxidised glutathione: 0.50 ± 0.03 versus 0.36 ± 0.04 nmol/mg of tissue), renal mitochondrial dysfunction (proton/electron leak: 61.8 ± 8.0 versus 22.7 ± 5.77) and complex I respiration (134.6 ± 31.4 versus 267.6 ± 26.4 pmol/min/μg). Iron therapy had no effect on renal function and cardiac hypertrophy but improved anaemia and systemic glutathione peroxidase (GPx) activity. There was increased renal iron content and complex II and complex IV dysfunction. Conclusion: Iron therapy improved iron deficiency anaemia in CKD without significant impact on renal function or oxidant status.

Keywords: anaemia; chronic kidney disease; iron; mitochondrial dysfunction; oxidative stress

---

1. Introduction

Iron-deficiency anaemia (IDA) is a major health problem worldwide. It is commonly associated with the progression of chronic kidney disease (CKD), affecting both quality of life and mortality [1–4]. Iron deficiency can exacerbate mitochondrial dysfunction and enhance oxidative stress in this patient population [5]. Mitochondrial proteins involved in oxidative phosphorylation (OXPHOS) pathway (respiratory complexes I-III) are iron complexes. Other mitochondrial enzymes, including aconitase of the Krebs cycle, require iron-sulphur (Fe-S) clusters (ISC) for their function [6,7]. Thus, derailment of mitochondrial iron homeostasis can result in human diseases associated with mitochondrial dysfunction such as Friedreich's ataxia [8]. Iron deficiency distorts the tightly regulated biosynthesis of haem and ISC which are needed for mitochondrial function and aggravate mitochondrial oxidative stress [9]. Mitochondria are also increasingly recognised as major contributors to reactive oxygen species (ROS) production [10]. In dysfunctional mitochondria, the proton or potentially electron leak at complexes I and III causes excessive wasting of molecular oxygen into superoxide radical ($O_2\bullet^-$). This can lead to the generation of more radicals (hydoxy (OH^-) and peroxynitrite ($ONOO^-$) radicals) [10]. Therefore, parenteral iron therapy employed in clinical practice as an integral component of managing anaemia of CKD may enhance mitochondrial function, and reduce overall oxidative stress (pro-oxidant versus anti-oxidant activity) without compromising renal function.

The mechanisms of progression of CKD are complex and multi-factorial and not completely elucidated. However, evidence implicating mitochondrial dysfunction in the initiation and progression of kidney disease comes from mitochondrial cytopathies [11]. Mitochondrial cytopathies (inherited or sporadic mtDNA mutations in mitochondrial genes) in kidneys lead to glomerular diseases, tubular defects and cystic kidney disease. Focal segmental glomerular sclerosis (FSGS), an example of glomerular disease emanating from mtDNA mutations, is a frequent cause of end stage kidney disease [12,13]. Other evidence of mitochondrial dysfunction in renal disease has come from in vivo and in vitro studies [14,15]. Mitochondrial dysfunction with reduced complex I, II and IV expression potentiated podocytes injury, impaired nephrin synthesis and increased ROS production [14]. Patients with iron deficiency anaemia from causes such as gastro-intestinal loss or menstruation do not appear to develop overt renal dysfunction. This suggests compensatory upregulation of mitochondrial function even in uraemic scenarios [16]. Although there is evidence of iron deficiency in CKD, tissue iron levels may vary between organs and may be preserved in the kidney minimising any detrimental renal effect.

Studies to date have provided evidence that the 5/6 nephrectomy used in this study is a suitable animal model of CKD showing enhanced vulnerability to oxidative stress and mitochondrial dysfunction [17]. However, limited information is available on the iron status of the model and response to therapy with intravenous (iv) iron. Most studies on the impact of iv iron are limited to acute systemic oxidative effects, disregarding their longer-term impact and benefits. Despite the central role of mitochondria (within the kidney) in the possible initiation and progression of CKD [18–20] and the integral role of iron in key mitochondrial proteins (aconitase, complex I, II or III), the impact of parenteral iv iron therapy as employed in clinical practice on mitochondrial function, oxidative stress and CKD progression has not been sufficiently characterised.

The aim of this study was to determine the longer-term impact of iv iron administration on these parameters in an experimental animal model of CKD. The Ferumoxytol therapy (one form of available parenteral iron) protocol used in this study mimics that of clinical practice using an equivalent weight adjusted bolus injection at a dose of 510 mg in adults (i.e., 8–10 mg/Kg body weight) [21]. Ferumoxytol is a third-generation iron complex whose slow dissociation from the carbohydrate complex leads to the release of less "labile" iron, thus allowing a rapid bolus infusion of high doses clinically with favourable outcomes [22,23].

Initially, the aim was to ensure that the phenotype of the uraemic model exhibited IDA and further that iv iron therapy would ameliorate this deficiency. It was hypothesised that compromised renal mitochondrial function in this model would increase susceptibility to oxidative stress. Parenteral iron therapy could improve mitochondrial function of the remnant kidney, lessening the deleterious effect of oxidative stress. Therefore, iron status (systemic and tissue) and iron deficiency (ID) anaemia in the 5/6 nephrectomy model of CKD were studied and the impact of iv iron investigated. Hence, renal mitochondrial function in uraemia and renal and systemic oxidative stress before and following iron treatment were studied in detail.

2. Materials and Methods

2.1. Induction of Experimental Uraemic Model

All procedure and animals in this study were in accordance with the UK Animals (Scientific Procedure) Act 1986 and were approved by the University of Hull Ethical Review Process (No. PPL 70/7966). Experimental uraemia was induced in male Sprague-Dawley rats (obtained from Charles River Laboratories, Kent, UK) via a one-stage subtotal nephrectomy, as described previously [17].

Briefly, animals (250 g) were anaesthetised with 3% isofluorane in 3 L/min O_2 and subsequently maintained on 2.5% isofluorane in 1 L/min oxygen. Depth of anaesthesia was confirmed using the pedal withdrawal reflex. Rimadyl was administered (4 mg/Kg body weight) pre-operatively via s/c injection for post-operative pain relief. A midline abdominal incision was made and the left kidney was exposed and decapsulated. Following clamping of the renal vasculature, approximately half of the kidney was excised comprised principally of cortical tissue. Haemorrhaging was controlled using Surgicel® (Johnson & Johnson, Maidenhead, Berkshire, UK) before the remnant kidney was replaced. The right kidney was then exposed and decapsulated. Renal vasculature was ligated using a non-absorbable suture (Mersilk® Johnson & Johnson, Maidenhead, Berkshire, UK) prior to excision of the kidney. Sterile isotonic saline (0.9% w/v) was administered into the abdominal cavity prior to closure to compensate for intraoperative fluid losses. The abdominal muscular layer was closed using an absorbable suture (Ethicon 3-0 Vicryl braided, Johnson & Johnson, Maidenhead, Berkshire, UK.) The dermal layer was closed with non-absorbable sutures (Ethicon 3-0 blue monofilament, Johnson & Johnson, Maidenhead, Berkshire, UK.) Sham animals were subjected to a sham procedure comprised of exposure and decapsulation of both kidneys.

Iron therapy was initiated 6 weeks post-surgery by a single intravenous (iv) injection of ferumoxytol (supplied by Takaeda UK Ltd., Holborn, London, UK) at a dose of 10 mg/Kg body weight. All animals were maintained in individual cages for a total of 12 weeks post-surgery (six weeks after the iv iron) and pair fed (sham and uraemic) with a standard chow diet. Water was available ad libitum.

2.2. Model Characterisation

Urine samples collected over 24 h was filtered through Millex syringe-driven Filter unit (Merck KGaA, Darmstadt, Germany) and serum samples collected at week 12 were analysed using the RX Monza analyser (Randox, Antrim, UK) for creatinine, urea and total protein according to manufacturer's protocol. Renal function was assessed by glomerular filtration rate (GFR) or creatinine clearance calculated using equation 1. Cardiac hypertrophy was evaluated by wet heart weight to tibia length ratio (HW/TL). Haematocrit was measured on an ABL77 Radiometer (Battery Universe Inc., USA) to confirm anaemia and packed cell volume (PCV) was subsequently measured to assess the impact of iv iron on anaemia. Briefly, heparinised blood samples were centrifuged and the ratio of packed red cell volume to whole blood volume calculated to give PCV. Iron status was determined from serum and urine biochemistry. Markers of iron status including serum iron, transferrin and total iron binding capacity were measured on the RX Monza analyser using Randox kits (Randox Laboratory Ltd., Crumlin, UK) as were urine samples.

Serum ferritin was analysed using the Enzyme linked immunosorbent assay ELISA ferritin commercial Kit (Abcam, Cambridge UK). Hepatic, renal and cardiac tissue contents of non-bound and total iron were measured. Briefly, 200 mg of tissue or faecal excrete was extracted with 1 mL 7.35 mM sodium acetate trihydrate buffer (4.65 pH) for 10 min and centrifuged at 12,000× *g*, 4 °C in a microfuge (Scientific Laboratory Supplies, UK) for 10 min and the supernatant filtered through Millex syringe-driven Filter unit (Merck KGaA, Germany), the resultant filtrate and urine filtrate were analysed for non-bound iron on the RX Monza.

Hepatic, renal and cardiac iron contents were evaluated by total elemental iron analysis on Perkin Elmer Optima 5300DV emission ICP-OES instrument (PerkinElmer, Inc, Waltham, MA, USA). Briefly, Tissue or serum samples were extracted with concentrated HNO_3 (Romil SpA trace metals, Cambridge UK) and digested in Teflon microwave vessels (MARS Xpress, CEM Ltd., Buckingham

UK). The samples were allowed to cool, diluted with ultra-pure water and analysed on the Perkin Elmer Optima 5300 DV emission ICP instrument.

$$\text{Creatinine Clearance (mL/min/Kg body weight)} = \frac{\left[\frac{[\text{Creatinine}_{\text{urine}}]}{[\text{Creatinine}_{\text{serum}}]} \times \frac{\text{Volume}_{\text{urine}}(\text{mL})}{\text{Time (h)} \times 60} \right]}{\text{Body Weight (kg)}}$$

2.3. Mitochondrial Function

Mitochondrial function was studied using the Seahorse XFp analyser (Agilent Technologies, Santa Clara, CA USA). The left kidney was excised, minced and mitochondria were isolated as previously described [17] in mitochondrial isolation buffer (containing 70 mM sucrose, 210 mM mannitol, 5 mM HEPES (4-(2-hydroxyethyl)-1-piperazineethanesulphonic acid), 1 mM EGTA (ethylene glycol-bis (betaaminoethylether)-N,N,N'N'-tetraacetic acid) and 0.5% (w/v) fatty acid-free BSA(bovine serum albumin), pH 7.2). The protein content was determined using the Bio-Rad protein assay. Mitochondrial coupling or electron flow experiments were carried out at 37 °C according to Roger et al. [24] and results were analysed on the Wave 2.3.0 software (Agilent Technologies, Santa Clara, CA USA).

2.4. Oxidative Stress

The impact of oxidative stress in this experimental model of CKD was evaluated by measuring lipid peroxidation through the levels of thiobarbuturic acid reactive substances (TBARS) according to modified method of Seljeskog et al. [25] and glutathione (both reduced and oxidised) using high performance liquid chromatography (HPLC) [26].

The kidney is a major source of glutathione peroxidase (GPx), an anti-oxidant; hence, its expression and activity is affected in CKD [4]. The activity of GPx was measured using the commercially available Ransel kit (Randox laboratories, Crumlin, UK) as per Paglia and Valentine [27]. The decrease in absorbance following the concomitant oxidation of NADPH (nicotinamide adenine dinucleotide phosphate hydrogen to NADP$^+$ (nicotinamide adenine dinucleotide phosphate) was measured at 340 nm.

2.5. Transmission Electron Microscopy

The remnant kidney of uraemic animals was treated for ultrastructural analysis using a modified method of Rezzani et al. [28]. Briefly, renal tissue was fixed in 4% paraformaldehyde (pH 7.4) overnight at 4 °C and immersed in 2% osmium tetroxide at 4 °C for 1 hr. Tissue was dehydrated by immersion in graded ethanol and propylene oxide and embedded in Araldite-Epon resin. Representative blocks were taken subsequently with diamond knife and stained with uranyl acetate and lead citrate and observed using JEOL 2010 (JEOL, Inc, Peabody, MA, USA) high resolution transmission electron microscope at 80 kV to evaluate mitochondrial injury.

2.6. Statistical Analysis

The difference between two groups (uraemic and sham) was calculated using unpaired Student's t test. Comparisons between treated and untreated groups were made using analysis of variance (ANOVA) on SPSS software. Data are presented as a mean ± standard error of the mean (SEM) or the standard deviations (SD). A p value less than 0.05 was considered statistically significant.

3. Results

3.1. Renal Function

Uraemic animals demonstrated reduced renal clearance (estimated by glomerular filtration rate (GFR)) as evidenced by increased serum creatinine and urea concentrations (Table 1). Increased urinary and decreased serum protein (indicators of proteinuria) supported the renal insufficiency observed in this model. The remnant kidney underwent significant remodelling indicated by an increase of 37% and 48% kidney mass in untreated and iron treated uraemic groups, respectively (Figure 1).

Table 1. Markers of renal function in sham and uraemic animals with and without iv iron. Data are presented as mean ± SEM. GFR (glomerular filtration rate) * $p < 0.05$; sham versus uraemic; ‡$p < 0.05$; uraemic untreated versus treated.

Characterisation of Uraemic model in CKD at week 12				
	Untreated (*n* = 22)		Iron Treated (*n* = 12)	
	Sham	Uraemic	Sham	Uraemic
Weight gain over 12 weeks (g)	301.5 ± 11.5	301.0 ± 13.7	297.4 ± 14.6	303.3 ± 12.8
Serum				
Creatinine (μM)	38.43 ± 1.73	86.32 ± 4.09 *	50.32 ± 1.65	76.11 ± 2.86 *‡
Urea (mM)	10.81 ± 0.94	20.83 ± 1.60 *	8.70 ± 0.31	20.68 ± 1.79 *
Total protein (g/dL)	5.60 ± 0.14	5.13 ± 0.14 *	6.67 ± 0.22	6.67 ± 0.08 ‡
24 h Urinary	(*n* = 9)	(*n* = 9)	(*n* = 5)	(*n* = 5)
Total Protein (g/L)	1.44 ± 0.17	2.89 ± 0.31 *	1.39 ± 0.11	2.97 ± 0.30 *
Creatinine (mM)	17.02 ± 1.27	11.61 ± 1.08 *	18.41 ± 3.74	9.21 ± 1.01 *‡
Total volume (mL)	14.33 ± 1.75	23.75 ± 2.68 *	16.40 ± 2.16	21.6 ± 2.86 *
GFR (ml/min/Kg body weight)	7.86 ± 0.84	3.96 ± 1.03 *	7.53 ± 0.97	3.22 ± 0.76 *

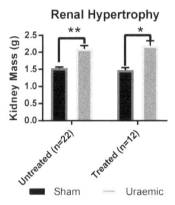

Figure 1. Renal hypertrophy in uraemic and sham animals (*n* = 22) and in animals exposed to intravenous (iv) iron therapy at six weeks was assessed by measuring left kidney mass. Data are presented as mean ± SEM, (* $p < 0.05$ and ** $p < 0.01$).

Uraemic animals exposed to iv iron therapy had a significantly lower serum creatinine ($p < 0.05$) and increased serum protein than those without iron. There was no change in the degree of proteinuria or renal dysfunction as a result of iron therapy in the uraemic group (Table 1).

3.2. Left Ventricular (LV) Hypertrophy

Induction of uraemia resulted in significant cardiac hypertrophy evidenced by an increased heart weight to tibia length ratio (HW/TL) (Figure 2). This is in agreement with previous observations [17]. Administration of iron did not impact on the extent of LV hypertrophy.

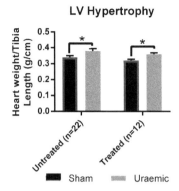

Figure 2. Cardiac hypertrophy 12 weeks post-surgical induction of uraemia was evaluated by measurement of heart weight to tibia length ratio in uraemia and sham animals with and without iv iron. Data are presented as mean ± SEM (* $p < 0.05$).

3.3. Anaemia and Iron Status

The iron profile and packed cell volume in this model is given in Table 2. Uraemia was associated with anaemia characterised by a reduced haematocrit (Figure 3A) and a decreased serum iron. There was also increased faecal iron loss which may reflect reduced absorption or possible gastrointestinal bleeding and also increased urinary loss (Figure 3C). Serum transferrin was reduced alongside enhanced urinary loss (Figure 4) and lowered total iron binding capacity (TIBC). Liver iron stores and cardiac total iron concentrations were unchanged.

Table 2. Markers of iron status in sham and uraemic animals with and without iron therapy. Data are presented as mean ± SEM. * $p < 0.05$; sham versus uraemic. ‡$p < 0.05$; uraemic untreated versus treated. TIBC = total iron bonding capacity.

Anaemia Characterisation at week 12				
	Untreated (*n* = 22)		Iron Treated (*n* = 12)	
	Sham	Uraemic	Sham	Uraemic
Serum				
TIBC (µM)	29.46 ± 0.83	26.43 ± 0.72 *	33.55 ± 1.16	29.09 ± 0.79 *‡
Ferritin $_{(n\,=\,8)}$ (µM)	0.12 ± 0.03	0.13 ± 0.03	0.12 ± 0.01	0.11 ± 0.03
Iron $_{(n\,=\,11)}$ (µM)	46.38 ± 1.44	31.11 ± 1.80 *	32.82 ± 0.97	28.89 ± 1.65
Packed cell volume	0.58 ± 0.02	0.50 ± 0.01 *	0.57 ± 0.01	0.54 ± 0.03
Tissue Iron (*n* = 7) (micromole/g of tissue)				
Liver stores	2.91 ± 0.22	3.26 ± 0.18	3.57 ± 0.27	4.72 ± 0.20
Liver (non-bound)	0.34 ± 0.03	0.38 ± 0.02	0.34 ± 0.02	0.31 ± 0.00*‡
Kidney	2.00 ± 0.27	1.90 ± 0.10	1.90 ± 0.08	2.77 ± 0.40
Heart ($\times 10^{-3}$) (total)	1.57 ± 0.07	1.85 ± 0.18	1.40 ± 0.07	1.55 ± 0.07
Heart ($\times 10^{-3}$) (non-bound)	0.30 ± 0.02	0.33 ± 0.02	0.26 ± 0.03	0.26 ± 0.02 ‡

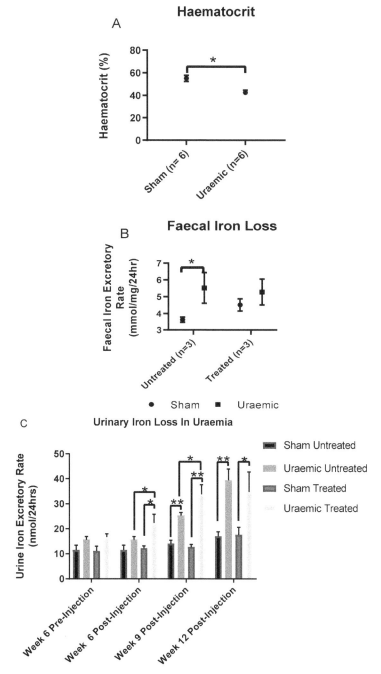

Figure 3. Iron analysis. (**A**) Haematocrit was measured to confirm anaemia; (**B**) Faecal Iron loss as a measure of iron malabsorption; (**C**) Urinary iron excretion was evaluated to study the cause of iron deficiency. Data are presented as mean ± SEM (* $p < 0.05$, ** $p < 0.01$).

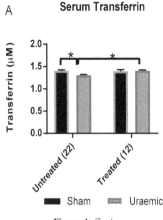

Serum Transferrin

Figure 4. *Cont.*

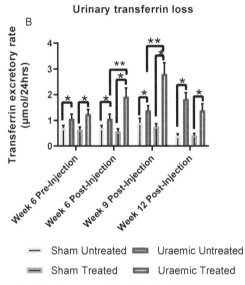

Figure 4. Transferrin analysis (**A**): Serum transferrin level and (**B**): Urinary transferrin loss at various stages of uraemia. Data are presented as mean ± SEM (* $p < 0.05$, ** $p < 0.01$).

3.4. Impact of Iron Therapy

Intravenous iron therapy had a modest impact on iron deficiency anaemia in uraemic animals. There was restoration of serum transferrin and TIBC to a level similar to that observed in the sham group with an 8% increased PCV in the uraemic group without any significant change in the sham animals (Table 2). Increased faecal iron content was observed in the iron treated sham group (Figure 3B). Urinary transferrin and iron excretion in uraemic and sham operated groups were unchanged by week 12 in treated animals, in contrast to measurements 3 weeks after the iron bolus (Figure 4). Total iron measured by the elemental iron analysis in the uraemic remnant kidney was 46% higher in the treated group relative to the baseline data; this did not reach statistical significance. In cardiac tissue, there was a non-significant 22% reduction. Liver iron was increased significantly by 33% in the iron treated uraemic group relative to the iron treated sham group. This reflected a 45% increase relative to the untreated uraemic group (Table 2).

3.5. Systemic and Renal Oxidative Stress

This experimental model of CKD was associated with a 24% reduction of systemic GPx antioxidant activity (Figure 5) without evidence of systemic lipid peroxidation (Figure 6). This may reflect a possibly generalised reduction in protein synthesis or a marker of oxidative stress. There was an increased concentration of oxidised glutathione (GSSG) (Figure 7A) in the remnant kidney without any change in the reduced form (GSH) (Figure 7B). Treatment with iv iron was associated with reduced TBARS ($p < 0.01$) and upregulation of systemic GPx activity by 35% and 32% in sham and uraemic groups, respectively, relative to untreated but lower levels when comparing sham versus uraemic exposed to iv iron (Figures 5 and 6).

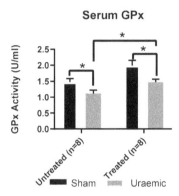

Figure 5. Serum glutathione peroxidase activity. Systemic anti-oxidant capacity was investigated through the measurement of glutathione peroxidase activity in the serum of uraemic and sham animals. Results are presented as mean ± SEM (* $p < 0.05$).

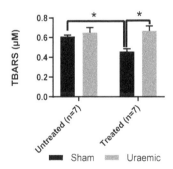

Figure 6. Serum TBARS. TBARS (thiobarbuturic acid reactive substances) were measured to access lipid peroxidation in uraemic and sham animals. Results are presented as mean ± SEM. (* $p < 0.01$).

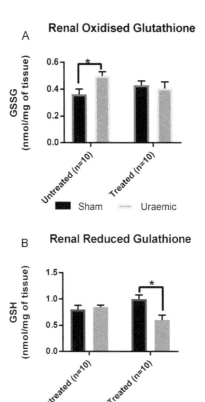

Figure 7. Endogenous antioxidant glutathione level in kidney tissue. (**A**) Renal oxidised glutathione in sham ($n = 10$) and uraemic animals ($n = 10$) with and without i.v. iron therapy; (**B**) renal reduced glutathione in sham ($n = 10$) and uraemic animals ($n = 10$) with and without i.v. iron therapy. Results are presented as mean ± SEM. (* $p < 0.05$).

3.6. Renal Mitochondrial Function

Uraemic animals demonstrated that in renal tissue mitochondria, there was a significant increase in inefficiency (enhanced proton leak and complex I dysfunction) (Figure 8a). Iron therapy produced a mixed and complex result with no change in the protein leak but an increased maximal respiration and respiratory reserve capacity suggesting improved mitochondrial oxidative capacity. However, there was a reduction of complex II and complex IV driven respiration (Figure 8b), which would suggest a degree of mitochondrial dysfunction.

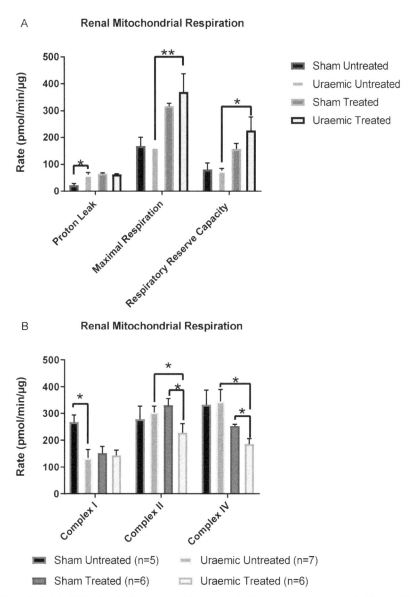

Figure 8. Isolated Mitochondrial measures of function including Respiratory rates and mitochondrial respiration in the presence of: (**A**) 0.5 μg mitochondrial protein, 10 mM succinate and 2 μM rotenone; (**B**) 0.6g mitochondrial protein, 10 mM pyruvate, 2 mM malate and 4 μM FCCP (carbonyl cyanide 4-(trifluoromethoxy) phenylhydrazone) with or without 10 mM malonate. In Fig 8B the electron transport chains complexes I, II and IV were measured. Results are presented as mean ± SEM. (* $p < 0.05$; ** $p < 0.01$). Proton leak = (minimum rate measured after Oligomycin injection) − (non-mitochondrial respiration rate or minimum rate measured after injection of Antimycin A); Maximal respiration = (maximal rate measured after FCCP injection) − (non-mitochondrial respiration rate); Respiratory reserve capacity = (maximal respiration − basal respiration).

4. Discussion

4.1. Induction of Uraemia and Impact of Iron Therapy

A significant deterioration of renal function was observed 12 weeks post-surgical induction of uraemia as indicated by the 124.6% and 92.7% increments in serum creatinine and urea, respectively. This is consistent with previous findings [29]. Progressive renal damage causes increased retention of creatinine and urea [30] resulting in decreased urinary levels as observed in Table 1. Impairment of kidney function as a result of persistent and progressive renal damage increases glomerular permeability and decreases tubular protein and fluid reabsorption. This in turn explains the 100% and 94% increments in urinary protein and volume, respectively. Weight gain 12 weeks post-surgery was similar between sham and uraemic groups, showing that malnutrition or loss of muscle mass reported in patients with CKD [31] was less likely to be a confounding factor. The elevated protein loss in urine correlated with a reduction in serum total protein.

The remnant left kidney of uraemic animals underwent compensatory hypertrophy indicated by increased kidney weight without affecting renal function (measured by GFR, Table 1). This change in the remnant kidney could be an adaptive response in an attempt to "normalise" or improve renal function, albeit with limited success. Previous work from this group has demonstrated progressive compensatory hypertrophy of the remnant kidney at week 6 (18.8%; $p < 0.05$), with diminishing function [32].

Parenteral iron treatment did not affect renal function, but increased serum total protein and transferrin concentrations. There are several potential safety issues concerning iv iron therapy including increased oxidative stress, infection and proteinuria as biomarkers [33–35]. Nephrotoxicity of iv iron therapy is dependent on the iron formulation as reported by Agarwal et al. [36]. These authors reported that unlike ferric gluconate, iron sucrose produced a 78% increased proteinuric response that was unaltered following repeated doses of iv iron. This was consistent with other reports of worsening proteinuria in response to iron sucrose therapy but not ferric gluconate [37]. The lack of significant change in urinary proteins levels by 6 weeks post therapy indicated that ferumoxytol did not elicit a chronic proteinuria effect in uraemic animals in this study. This is not unsurprising given that there are known physiochemical differences between iron preparations; hence, this confounder cannot be excluded [38].

4.2. Anaemia in Uraemia and the Effect of Iron

Anaemia significantly increases the risk of morbidity and mortality in CKD [39]. Iron deficiency anaemia in CKD is associated with diminished cytochrome c oxidase activity, decreased mitochondrial oxidative capacity and reduced total anti-oxidant capacity resulting in enhanced mitochondrial oxidative stress [40]. Therefore, anaemia correction by erythropoietin and/or iron replenishing therapy is an integral component in the management of anaemia of CKD. The observation of reduced haematocrit as an indicator of anaemia is consistent with previous findings, which was improved following erythropoietin treatment [29]. Previous data indicated an inverse correlation between serum creatinine and haematocrit, suggesting the degree of anaemia is related to the severity of renal dysfunction [32]. Iron replenishment therapy via iv administration of iron complexes such as the third generation preparations (ferric carboxymaltose, iron isomaltoside and ferumoxytol) and the older formulations (low molecular weight iron dextran, iron sucrose and ferric gluconate) has proven to be effective in correcting iron deficiency anaemia in CKD [41,42].

Experimental uraemia resulted in a biomarker profile comparable to the clinical scenario of anaemia of inflammatory/chronic disease characterised by decreased serum iron with reduced serum TIBC [43]. This, together with maintenance of ferritin levels and liver iron content in sham and uraemic groups, indicates the inability to access stored iron in uraemia, similar to the classical setting of a pro-inflammatory state [44]. In absolute iron deficiency, reduction of serum iron would indicate a more readily available transferrin for iron binding (giving rise to increased TIBC). The reduction of TIBC found here can partly be explained by the decreased circulating transferrin (perhaps partly related to the reduction in protein concentrations). This observation was in agreement with the report of Alfrey and Hammond [45] where serum iron and transferrin decreased rapidly following the induction of nephrotoxic syndrome. The investigators also observed increased urinary iron and transferrin loss similar to this study's observations. Urinary transferrin loss at week 12 of uraemia was 241% greater in uraemic animals compared to sham. Urinary iron loss increased by 66%. The present study has shown an inverse relationship between serum and faecal iron. No sign of blood in the faecal excreta of uraemic animals is indicative of little or no intestinal bleeding. Hence, the increase in faecal iron excretion is suggestive of malabsorption of iron or impaired absorption in the gut. The evidence also highlights increased urinary iron loss in relation to the severity of renal dysfunction. These two factors may be critical in determining the mechanism of iron deficiency anaemia in this model of CKD.

Studies have shown the elevation of inflammatory markers and concomitant upregulated expression of hepcidin [46,47] can lead to functional iron deficiency (ID) anaemia in CKD [48,49]. Given the central role of hepcidin in iron metabolism, assessment of serum, urinary and hepatic hepcidin levels and inflammatory markers such as interleukins (IL-1 and IL-6) could provide insight into the aetiology of iron deficiency. Nonetheless, uraemia may mediate hepcidin over-secretion resulting in enhanced destruction of ferroportin [50] and accumulation of dietary absorbed iron in the enterocytes. Subsequent loss of the iron via enterocyte shedding could explain the 52.7% increment in faecal iron in uraemic animals and the ensuing ID. However, hepcidin over-secretion may also prevent the release of iron from hepatocyte stores, causing an increase in hepatic iron, a phenomenon not observed in the present study. ID impairs red blood cells (RBCs) production, which could explain the presence of anaemia in this study. Persistent anaemia leads to significant compensatory left ventricular hypertrophy (as observed in this model of CKD in Figure 2), which eventually results in congestive heart failure in later stages of uraemia [51].

Iron therapy in the present study resulted in a significantly increased PCV (8%) in the uraemic group. Two prospective randomised studies found that a greater increase in haemoglobin above baseline was observed in CKD patients on ferumoxytol therapy than those on oral iron [52,53]. Parenteral ferumoxutol therapy in a randomised study was effective in raising the mean haemoglobin level and tolerable in patients in whom oral iron was ineffective [53]. Iron treatment restored serum transferrin levels in uraemic animals without changing urinary transferrin loss, suggesting increased synthesis. Serum iron remained low in the iron treated group with significant reduction in the sham group which could in part be due to the enhanced urinary loss. Iron therapy results in a rapid increase in circulating iron levels, which might trigger a homeostatic response [54]. This includes increased expression of transferrin and the transferrin receptor, which mediates cellular iron uptake. It is expressed at low levels in hepatocytes and is down-regulated in response to iron. Liver overload occurs when transferrin is completely saturated and hepatocytes internalise non-transferrin-bound iron present in the bloodstream explaining the observation of increased liver iron. Consequently, over time, total iron binding capacity increases as serum iron falls, as observed here.

Despite maintenance in total cardiac iron content, iron therapy led to a trend in reduced non-bound iron in cardiac and hepatic tissues that accounts for the cytotoxicity of iv iron. Intravenous iron therapy was associated with increased accumulation of iron in the liver. This is similar to the clinical evidence where iv iron therapy in haemodialysis patients was associated with iron accumulation in the spleen and liver but not the heart [55]. The accumulated iron in the spleen and liver serves as reserves that maintained erythropoiesis and could explain the amelioration of anaemia in the present study 6 weeks after bolus iv iron injection. The urinary iron loss alongside the transferrin loss observed in uraemic animals was exacerbated following therapy. There were no mortalities or observable side effects associated with ferumoxytol therapy, though adverse effects such as dizziness, pruritus, headache, fatigue and nausea have been reported in clinical studies [56]. These could not be reliably assessed in this rat model of CKD.

4.3. Oxidative Stress

This model of CKD was accompanied by a reduction of serum GPx activity suggesting depression in systemic antioxidant capacity. This did not translate into systemic oxidative stress, and thus, may be an indication of an early stage of the disease process or a degree of adaptation of the oxidative system to uraemia. The observation of reduced GPx was in line with the reports of Romeu et al. [57]. Serum TBARS in uraemic group were comparable to sham, indicating no systemic oxidative damage at this stage of CKD. This does not exclude an initial acute effect as a result of uraemia but may also suggest compensation or adaptation during the first weeks. This is in contrast to reports of increased systemic TBARS and GSSG in patients with CKD [58]. Patients with CKD were characterised by increased markers of systemic oxidative stress [59], such as increased level of serum lipid peroxidation markers [58], GSSG [57] and protein carbonyls [60]. Blood is rich in both enzymatic and non-enzymatic antioxidant components to detoxify reactive oxygen species (ROS). However, in the event of increased cellular oxidative activity, excess ROS can spill into the circulation initiating a cycle of ROS induced ROS generation; ROS mediated loss of anti-oxidant capacity and culminate in overt systemic oxidative stress [61]. Therefore, the depression in systemic GPx activity here could be an early event that increases the vulnerably to systemic oxidative stress later in CKD if there is no adequate compensation. Increased kidney GSSG levels were found in uraemic animals in this study. GSH is a reductant that reduces free radicals in oxidation reactions leading to the generation of GSSG. Hence, increased GSSG levels may be indicative of enhanced pro-oxidant activity.

The improved iron deficiency anaemia by iv ferumoxytol in the present study enhanced GPx activity considering the increased evidence of systemic lipid peroxidation, indicating potential long-term benefit of iv iron to CKD patients with ID anaemia. There are conflicting reports regarding the impact of iv iron on oxidative stress in CKD patients [5], as it is associated with some increase or no effect on systemic oxidative stress [62,63]. These conflicting reports could be attributed to differences in iron formulation and the dosage used [64,65]; severity of the disease and whether or not patient is on dialysis [66]. Following iv administration of 100 mg iron sucrose to stage 3 or 4 CKD patients, Agarwal et al. [66] found increased lipid peroxidation within 15 to 30 min that completely resolved within 24 h. Unequivocally, iv iron precipitates acute oxidative toxicity as demonstrated by the recent report of Kuo et al. [67]. In their in vitro studies, the investigators reported transient increases in ROS generation between 1–3 h and enhanced NADPH oxidase activity within 30–60 min following 160 µg/mL iron sucrose supplementation, which normalised after 4 h. Administration of the antioxidant, N-acetylcysteine, together with iron therapy attenuated ROS production and its associated endothelial dysfunction [67]. Hence, antioxidant therapy use concomitantly with iv iron clinically may alleviate acute iron oxidative toxicity and facilitate the appreciation of the many chronic benefits highlighted in this study.

4.4. Mitochondrial Dysfunction

The remnant kidney of uraemic animals demonstrated mitochondrial dysfunction as illustrated by increased proton/electron leak. Proton/electron leaks whether due to specific uncoupling proteins or non-specific transfer of protons/electrons into the matrix results in loss of membrane potential [68,69]. The conversion of ADP to ATP by mitochondrial complex V is dependent on membrane potential, the loss of which severely compromises bioenergetics and could partly explain the exacerbation of kidney dysfunction in this study. The kidney is a metabolic organ requiring high energy (ATP) to drive its function including active reabsorption of solutes [70]. Tubular cells are rich in mitochondria, and consequently, any injury would compromise renal function and precipitate CKD [71]. The uraemic kidney in this study demonstrated several structural and biogenetic abnormalities. Transmission electron microscopic study of the remnant kidney (uraemic) revealed existence of swollen mitochondria with loss of cristae and matrix density (Figure 9). Mitochondrial matrix swelling and loss of cristae membranes were evident after renal ischaemia in rats, affecting ATP regeneration after reperfusion [72].

A: Uraemic Kidney

B: Sham Kidney

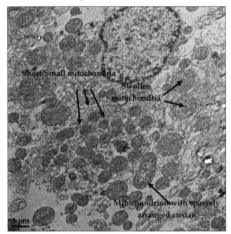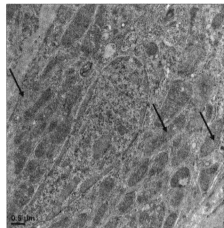

Figure 9. Transmission electron microscopic representation of uraemic mitochondria (**A**) with evidence of mitochondrial fragmentation (fission) as indicated by the presence of smaller mitochondrial spheres; swollen mitochondria with sparsely arranged cristae relative to sham mitochondria (**B**). Arrows indicate mitochondria.

Our observation of mitochondria with rounded morphology in the uraemic kidney is similar to the report of Lan et al. [73]. In a similar study, the remnant kidney following 5/6 nephrectomy showed fragmented and dysmorphic mitochondria with evidence of swelling and disrupted cristae architectures [20]. The authors reported diminished mitochondrial function and reduced antioxidant capacity alongside oxidative stress similar to the observation presented here. Under normal conditions, antioxidant enzymes (such as glutathione peroxidase, peroxyredoxin, glutaredoxin 2, thioredoxin and catalase) protect the mitochondria from ROS attack, and hence prevent membrane damage and peroxidation [74]. However, in conditions of diminished antioxidant activity as observed in this model of CKD, damage to mitochondrial inner membrane can occur, leading to the inexorable decline in mitochondrial function and worsen kidney function and its associated complications.

The mechanisms underlying loss of cristae in the present model are unclear but ongoing work is focused on changes in mitochondrial membrane cardiolipin (CL) content and remodelling as possible factors. Indeed, there is increased vulnerability of CL to peroxidation owing to its close proximity to site of ROS production and in part due to its relative high content of unsaturated fatty acyl chains [75,76]. This could explain the increased evidence of mitochondrial fission as shown by the presence of fragmented mitochondria (Figure 9a) in the uraemic kidney. Mitochondrial fission involved the division of the mitochondrion into two daughter organelles, and when in excess, results in mitochondrial fragmentation. Mitochondrial fragmentation is increasingly evident in many kidney diseases [77,78].

Uraemic animals showed mitochondrial complex I respiratory dysfunction in the remnant kidney, which was not improved by iron therapy. In addition, iron therapy was associated with reduced complex II and complex IV driven respiration that could be related to the increased accumulation of iron observed in the remnant kidney of uraemic animals. Indeed, dysfunctional mitochondria can potentiate excessive generation of ROS. As reported by Zhu et al. [79], mitochondrial dysfunction underlined by decreased expression of complexes I, II and IV was associated with increased generation of ROS and oxygen consumption which is not coupled to ATP production. However, despite these cellular changes iv iron appeared to increase maximal respiration and respiratory reserve capacity suggestion a degree of mitochondrial adaptation or upregulation of numbers or function at this stage of CKD. This requires further work to elicit the complex changes occurring within the kidney.

5. Conclusions

The findings presented here have confirmed the phenotype of iron deficiency anaemia in experimental uraemia. It has also been demonstrated that there is both mitochondrial functional adaptation and cellular dysfunction and evidence of changes in renal and systemic oxidative stress. These findings suggest that mitochondrial activity is increased in the remnant kidney tissue to compensate for reduced renal mass. This is supported by the modest decrease in renal function despite the removal of a large majority of renal tissue. The data also suggest that kidney injury may impact on mitochondrial biogenesis, ultra-structure organisation and function. Further work assessing mitochondrial mass will help clarify this further. Correction of iron deficiency anaemia with a bolus of ferumoxytol in uraemic animals was associated with a partial restoration of systemic antioxidant GPx activity and importantly no deterioration in renal function or increase in proteinuria. The data suggest that timely administration of iv iron may help to alleviate the complications of iron deficiency relating to oxidative stress in CKD patients. This study further highlights the need for therapies targeting mitochondria specifically as a part of routine CKD management, in addition to the iron and antioxidant therapies. It is not known if similar observations occur with other iron preparations which may have subtle different physiochemical properties.

Author Contributions: F.N., S.B. and A.-M.S. conception and design of research, F.N. perform experiments, F.N performed sample preparations, F.N. prepared figures, drafted manuscript, F.N., S.B. and A.-M.S. edited and revised manuscript and approved final version of manuscript.

Funding: This research was funded by a grant from the Takeda and the East Riding cardiac Trust.

Acknowledgments: We thank Kath Bulmer, Laura Goodlass, Andrew Gordon and Danielle Webster for their technical support and dedication. Special thanks go to John Greenman and Roger Sturmey for their invaluable contribution to this study.

Conflicts of Interest: All authors have received research grants from the East Riding Cardiac Trust, UK and Tadeka, UK, and funding was also received from the Local Hull Teaching Hospitals NHS Trust Renal Research Charitable Fund to fund the project and the salary of Faisal Nuhu. The funders had no role in the design of the study; in the collection, analyses or interpretation of data; in the writing of the manuscript, or in the decision to publish the results.

References

1. Mehdi, U.; Toto, R.D. Anemia, Diabetes, and Chronic Kidney Disease. *Diabetes Care* **2009**, *32*, 1320–1326. [CrossRef] [PubMed]
2. Kovesdy, C.; Trivedi, B.; Kalantar-Zadeh, K.; Anderson, J. Association of anemia with outcomes in men with moderate and severe chronic kidney disease. *Kidney Int.* **2006**, *69*, 560–564. [CrossRef] [PubMed]
3. Regidor, D.L.; Kopple, J.D.; Kovesdy, C.P.; Kilpatrick, R.D.; McAllister, C.J.; Aronovitz, J.; Greenland, S.; Kalantar-Zadeh, K. Associations between Changes in Hemoglobin and Administered Erythropoiesis-Stimulating Agent and Survival in Hemodialysis Patients. *J. Am. Soc. Nephrol.* **2006**, *17*, 1181–1191. [CrossRef] [PubMed]
4. Bhandari, S. Beyond efficacy and safety-the need for convenient and cost-effective iron therapy in health care. *NDT Plus* **2011**, *4*, i14–i19. [CrossRef]
5. Nuhu, F.; Bhandari, S. Oxidative Stress and Cardiovascular Complications in Chronic Kidney Disease, the Impact of Anaemia. *Pharmaceuticals* **2018**, *11*, 103. [CrossRef]
6. Horowitz, M.P.; Greenamyre, J.T. Mitochondrial Iron Metabolism and Its Role in Neurodegeneration. *J. Alzheimer's Dis.* **2010**, *20*, S551–S568. [CrossRef]
7. Urrutia, P.J.; Mena, N.P.; Núñez, M.T. The interplay between iron accumulation, mitochondrial dysfunction, and inflammation during the execution step of neurodegenerative disorders. *Front. Pharmacol.* **2014**, *5*, 38. [CrossRef]
8. Abeti, R.; Parkinson, M.H.; Hargreaves, I.P.; Angelova, P.R.; Sandi, C.; Pook, M.A.; Giunti, P.; Abramov, A.Y. Mitochondrial energy imbalance and lipid peroxidation cause cell death in Friedreich's ataxia'. *Cell Death Dis.* **2016**, *7*, e2237. [CrossRef]
9. Vaubel, R.A.; Isaya, G. Iron-Sulfur Cluster Synthesis, Iron Homeostasis and Oxidative Stress in Friedreich Ataxia. *Mol Cell Neurosci* **2013**, *55*, 50–61. [CrossRef]

10. Wong, H.-S.; Dighe, P.A.; Mezera, V.; Monternier, P.-A.; Brand, M.D. Production of superoxide and hydrogen peroxide from specific mitochondrial sites under different bioenergetics conditions. *J. Biol. Chem.* **2017**, *292*, 16804–16809. [CrossRef]

11. Hall, A.; Unwin, R.; Hanna, M.; Duchen, M.; Duchen, M. Renal function and mitochondrial cytopathy (MC): More questions than answers? *QJM: Int. J. Med.* **2008**, *101*, 755–766. [CrossRef] [PubMed]

12. Kiffel, J.; Rahimzada, Y.; Trachtman, H. Focal segmental glomerulosclerosis and chronic kidney disease in pediatric patients. *Adv. Chronic. Kidney Dis.* **2011**, *18*, 332–338. [CrossRef] [PubMed]

13. Liu, J.; Xie, J.; Zhang, X.; Tong, J.; Hao, X.; Ren, H.; Wang, W.; Chen, N. Serum C3 and Renal Outcome in Patients with Primary Focal Segmental Glomerulosclerosis. *Sci. Rep.* **2017**, *7*, 4095. [CrossRef] [PubMed]

14. Zhu, C.; Huang, S.; Yuan, Y.; Ding, G.; Chen, R.; Liu, B.; Yang, T.; Zhang, A. Mitochondrial dysfunction mediates aldosterone-induced podocyte damage: A therapeutic target of PPARγ. *Am. J. Pathol.* **2011**, *178*, 2020–2031. [CrossRef] [PubMed]

15. Granata, S.; Gassa, A.D.; Tomei, P.; Lupo, A.; Zaza, G. Mitochondria: A new therapeutic target in chronic kidney disease. *Nutr. Metab.* **2015**, *12*, 49. [CrossRef] [PubMed]

16. Cummings, B.S.; Parker, J.C.; Lash, L.H. Role of cytochrome P450 and glutathione S-transferase alpha in metabolism and cytotixicty of trichlorethylene in rat kidney. *Biochem. Pharmacol.* **2000**, *59*, 531–543. [CrossRef]

17. Taylor, D.; Bhandari, S.; Seymour, A.-M.L. Mitochondrial dysfunction in uremic cardiomyopathy. *Am. J. Physiol. Physiol.* **2015**, *308*, F579–F587. [CrossRef]

18. Szeto, H.H. Pharmacologic Approaches to Improve Mitochondrial Function in AKI and CKD. *J. Am. Soc. Nephrol.* **2017**, *28*, 2856–2865. [CrossRef]

19. Bigelman, E.; Cohen, L.; Aharon-Hananel, G.; Levy, R.; Rozenbaum, Z.; Saada, A.; Keren, G.; Entin-Meer, M. Pathological presentation of cardiac mitochondria in a rat model for chronic kidney disease. *PLoS ONE* **2018**, *13*, e0198196. [CrossRef]

20. Chen, J.-F.; Liu, H.; Ni, H.-F.; Lv, L.-L.; Zhang, M.-H.; Zhang, A.-H.; Tang, R.-N.; Chen, P.-S.; Liu, B.-C. Improved Mitochondrial Function Underlies the Protective Effect of Pirfenidone against Tubulointerstitial Fibrosis in 5/6 Nephrectomized Rats. *PLoS ONE* **2013**, *8*, 8–83593. [CrossRef]

21. Hetzel, D.; Strauss, W.; Bernard, K.; Li, Z.; Urboniene, A.; Allen, L.F. A Phase III, randomized, open-label trial of ferumoxytol compared with iron sucrose for the treatment of iron deficiency anemia in patients with a history of unsatisfactory oral iron therapy. *Am. J. Hematol.* **2014**, *89*, 646–650. [CrossRef] [PubMed]

22. MacDougall, I.C.; Strauss, W.E.; McLaughlin, J.; Li, Z.; Dellanna, F.; Hertel, J. A randomized comparison of ferumoxytol and iron sucrose for treating iron deficiency anemia in patients with CKD. *Clin. J. Am. Soc. Nephrol.* **2014**, *9*, 705–712. [CrossRef] [PubMed]

23. Schiller, B.; Bhat, P.; Sharma, A. Safety and Effectiveness of Ferumoxytol in Hemodialysis Patients at 3 Dialysis Chains in the United States Over a 12-Month Period. *Clin. Ther.* **2014**, *36*, 70–83. [CrossRef] [PubMed]

24. Rogers, G.W.; Brand, M.D.; Petrosyan, S.; Ashok, D.; Elorza, A.A.; Ferrick, D.A.; Murphy, A.N. High Throughput Microplate Respiratory Measurements Using Minimal Quantities Of Isolated Mitochondria. *PLoS ONE* **2011**, *6*, e21746. [CrossRef]

25. Seljeskog, E.; Hervig, T.; Mansoor, M.A. A novel HPLC method for the measurement of thiobarbituric acid reactive substances (TBARS). A comparison with a commercially available kit. *Clin. Biochem.* **2006**, *39*, 947–954. [CrossRef]

26. Kand'Ár, R.; Žáková, P.; Lotková, H.; Kučera, O.; Červinková, Z.; Královcová, P. Determination of reduced and oxidized glutathione in biological samples using liquid chromatography with fluorimetric detection. *J. Pharm. Biomed. Anal.* **2007**, *43*, 1382–1387. [CrossRef]

27. Paglia, D.E.; Valentine, W.N. Studies on the quantitative and qualitative characterization of erythrocyte glutathione peroxidase. *J. Lab. Clin. Med.* **1967**, *70*, 158–169.

28. Stacchiotti, A.; Favero, G.; Giugno, L.; Lavazza, A.; Reiter, R.J.; Rodella, L.F.; Rezzani, R. Mitochondrial and Metabolic Dysfunction in Renal Convoluted Tubules of Obese Mice: Protective Role of Melatonin. *PLoS ONE* **2014**, *9*, e111141. [CrossRef]

29. Smith, K.; Semple, D.; Aksentijević, D.; Bhandari, S.; Seymour, A.M. Functional and metabolic adaptation in uraemic cardiomyopathy. *Front. Biosci.* **2010**, *E2*, 1492–1501. [CrossRef]

30. Smith, K.; Semple, D.; Bhandari, S.; Seymour, A.M. The cellular basis of uraemic cardiomyopathy—A role of erythropoietin? *Eur. J. Heart Fail.* **2009**, *11*, 732–738. [CrossRef]

31. Wang, X.H.; Mitch, W.E. Mechanisms of muscle wasting in chronic kidney disease. *Nat. Rev. Nephrol.* **2014**, *10*, 504–516. [CrossRef] [PubMed]

32. Reddy, V.; Bhandari, S.; Seymour, A.M. Myocardial function, energy provision, and carnitine deficiency in experimental uremia. *J. Am. Soc. Nephrol.* **2007**, *18*, 84–92. [CrossRef] [PubMed]

33. Auerbach, M.; Macdougall, I.C. Safety of intravenous iron formulations: Facts and folklore. *Blood Transfus* **2014**, *12*, 296–300. [PubMed]

34. Agarwal, R.; Leehey, D.J.; Olsen, S.M.; Dahl, N.V. Proteinuria Induced by Parenteral Iron in Chronic Kidney Disease—A Comparative Randomized Controlled Trial. *Clin. J. Am. Soc. Nephrol.* **2011**, *6*, 114–121. [CrossRef] [PubMed]

35. Del Vecchio, L.; Longhi, S.; Locatelli, F. Safety concerns about intravenous iron therapy in patients with chronic kidney disease. *Clin. Kid* **2016**, *9*, 260–267. [CrossRef] [PubMed]

36. Agarwal, R.; Rizkala, A.; Kaskas, M.; Minasian, R.; Trout, J. Iron sucrose causes greater proteinuria than ferric gluconate in non-dialysis chronic kidney disease. *Kidney Int.* **2007**, *72*, 638–642. [CrossRef]

37. Besarab, A.; Levin, A. Defining a renal anemia management period. *Am. J. Kidney Dis.* **2000**, *36*, S13–S23. [CrossRef]

38. Bhandari, S.; Pereira, D.I.A.; Chappell, H.F.; Drakesmith, H. Intravenous Irons: From Basic Science to Clinical Practice. *Pharmaceuticals* **2018**, *11*, 82. [CrossRef]

39. Besarab, A.; Coyne, D.W. Iron supplementation to treat anemia in patients with chronic kidney disease. *Nat. Rev. Nephrol.* **2010**, *6*, 699–710. [CrossRef]

40. Mace, T.A.R.; Syed, A.; Bhandari, S. Iron (III) isomaltoside 1000. *Expert Rev. Hematol.* **2013**, *6*, 239–246. [CrossRef]

41. Bhandari, S.; Kalra, P.A.; Kothari, J.; Ambühl, P.M.; Christensen, J.H.; Essaian, A.M.; Thomsen, L.L.; MacDougall, I.C.; Coyne, D.W. A randomized, open-label trial of iron isomaltoside 1000 (Monofer®) compared with iron sucrose (Venofer®) as maintenance therapy in haemodialysis patients. *Nephrol. Dial. Transplant.* **2015**, *30*, 1577–1589. [CrossRef] [PubMed]

42. Kalra, P.A.; Bhandari, S.; Agarwal, D.; Wirtz, G.; Klauser-Braun, R.; Thomsen, L.L.; Coyne, D.W. A randomized trial of iron isomaltoside 1000 versus oral iron in non-dialysis-dependent chronic kidney disease patients with anaemia. *Nephrol. Dial. Transplant.* **2016**, *31*, 646–655. [CrossRef] [PubMed]

43. Ottenjann, M.; Weingart, C.; Arndt, G.; Kohn, B. Characterization of the Anemia of Inflammatory Disease in Cats with Abscesses, Pyothorax, or Fat Necrosis. *J. Veter- Intern. Med.* **2006**, *20*, 1143–1150. [CrossRef]

44. Wessling-Resnick, M. Iron homeostasis and the inflammatory response. *Annu. Rev. Nutr.* **2010**, *30*, 105–122. [CrossRef]

45. Alfrey, A.C.; Hammond, W.S. Renal iron handling in the nephrotic syndrome. *Kidney Int.* **1990**, *37*, 1409–1413. [CrossRef] [PubMed]

46. Nemeth, E.; Rivera, S.; Gabayan, V.; Keller, C.; Taudorf, S.; Pedersen, B.K.; Ganz, T. IL-6 mediates hypoferremia of inflammation by inducing the synthesis of the iron regulatory hormone hepcidin. *J. Clin. Investig.* **2004**, *113*, 1271–1276. [CrossRef]

47. Wrighting, D.M.; Andrews, N.C. Interleukin-6 induces hepcidin expression through STAT3. *Blood* **2006**, *108*, 3204–3209. [CrossRef]

48. Pietrangelo, A.; Dierssen, U.; Valli, L.; Garuti, C.; Rump, A.; Corradini, E.; Ernst, M.; Klein, C.; Trautwein, C. STAT3 Is Required for IL-6-gp130–Dependent Activation of Hepcidin In Vivo. *Gastroenterology* **2007**, *132*, 294–300. [CrossRef]

49. Falzacappa, M.V.; Vujic, S.M.; Kessler, R.; Stolte, J.; Hentze, M.W.; Muckenthaler, M.U. STAT3 mediates hepatic hepcidin expression and its inflammatory stimulation. *Blood* **2007**, *109*, 353–358. [CrossRef]

50. Naigamwalla, D.Z.; Webb, J.A.; Giger, U. Iron deficiency anemia. *Can. Vet. J.* **2012**, *53*, 250–256.

51. Silverberg, D.S.; Wexler, D.; Blum, M.; Wollman, Y.; Sheps, D.; Iaina, A.; Schwartz, D.; Keren, G. The Interaction between Heart Failure, Renal Failure and Anemia—The Cardio-Renal Anemia Syndrome. *Blood Purif.* **2004**, *22*, 277–284. [CrossRef] [PubMed]

52. Schwenk, M.H. Ferumoxytol: A New Intravenous Iron Preparation for the Treatment of Iron Deficiency Anemia in Patients with Chronic Kidney Disease. *Pharmacother. J. Hum. Pharmacol. Drug Ther.* **2010**, *30*, 70–79. [CrossRef] [PubMed]

53. Vadhan-Raj, S.; Strauss, W.; Ford, D.; Bernard, K.; Boccia, R.; Li, J. Allen LFEfficacy and safety of IV ferumoxytol for adults with iron deficiency anemia previously unresponsive to or unable to tolerate oral iron. *Am. J. Hematol.* **2014**, *89*, 7–12. [CrossRef] [PubMed]

54. Ganz, T.; Nemeth, E. Hepcidin and iron homeostasis. *Biochim. Biophys. Acta* **2012**, *1823*, 1434–1443. [CrossRef]

55. Ghoti, H.; Rachmilewitz, E.A.; Simon-Lopez, R.; Gaber, R.; Katzir, Z.; Konen, E.; Kushnir, T.; Girelli, D.; Campostrini, N.; Fibach, E.; et al. Evidence for tissue iron overload in long-term hemodialysis patients and the impact of withdrawing parenteral iron. *Eur. J. Haematol.* **2012**, *89*, 87–93. [CrossRef]

56. Singh, A.; Patel, T.; Hertel, J.; Bernardo, M.; Kausz, A.; Brenner, L. Safety of Ferumoxytol in Patients with Anaemia and CKD. *Am. J. Kidney Dis.* **2008**, *52*, 907–915. [CrossRef]

57. Romeu, M.; Nogues, R.; Marcas, L.; Sánchez-Martos, V.; Mulero, M.; Martinez-Vea, A.; Mallol, J.; Giralt, M. Evaluation of oxidative stress biomarkers in patients with chronic renal failure: A case control study. *BMC Res. Notes* **2010**, *3*, 20. [CrossRef]

58. Caimi, G.; Carollo, C.; Hopps, E.; Montana, M.; Presti, R.L. Protein oxidation in chronic kidney disease. *Clin. Hemorheol. Microcirc.* **2013**, *54*, 409–413.

59. Floccari, F.; Aloisi, C.; Crasci, E.; Sofi, T.; Campo, S.; Tripodo, D.; Criseo, M.; Frisina, N.; Buemi, M. Oxidative stress in uremia. *Med. Res. Rev.* **2005**, *25*, 473–486. [CrossRef]

60. Witko-Sarsat, V.; Friedlander, M.; Khoa, T.N.; Capeillère-Blandin, C.; Nguyen, A.T.; Canteloup, S.; Dayer, J.M.; Jungers, P.; Drüeke, T.; Descamps-Latscha, B. Advanced oxidation protein products as novel mediators of inflammation and monocyte activation in chronic renal failure. *J. Immunol.* **1998**, *161*, 2524–2532.

61. Kao, M.P.C.; Ang, D.S.C.; Pall, A.; Struthers, A.D. Oxidative stress in renal dysfunction: Mechanisms, clinical sequelae and therapeutic options. *J. Hum. Hypertens* **2010**, *24*, 1–8. [CrossRef] [PubMed]

62. Ganguli, A.; Kohli, H.S.; Khullar, M.; Gupta, K.L.; Jha, V.; Sakhuja, V. Lipid Peroxidation Products Formation with Various Intravenous Iron Preparations in Chronic Kidney Disease. *Ren. Fail.* **2009**, *31*, 106–110. [CrossRef] [PubMed]

63. Sağlam, F.; Cavdar, C.; Uysal, S.; Cavdar, Z.; Camsari, T. Effect of Intravenous Iron Sucrose on Oxidative Stress in Peritoneal Dialysis Patients. *Ren. Fail.* **2007**, *29*, 849–854. [CrossRef] [PubMed]

64. Zager, R.A.; Johnson, A.C.; Hanson, S.Y.; Wasse, H. Parenteral iron formulations. A comparative toxicologic analysis and mechanisms of cell injury. *Am. J. Kidney Dis.* **2002**, *40*, 90–103. [CrossRef] [PubMed]

65. Bailie, G.R.; Schuler, C.; Leggett, R.E.; Li, H.-D.; Patadia, H.; Levin, R. Oxidative effect of several intravenous iron complexes in the rat. *BioMetals* **2013**, *26*, 473–478. [CrossRef]

66. Agarwal, R.; Vasavada, N.; Sachs, N.G.; Chase, S. Oxidative stress and renal injury with intravenous iron in patients with chronic kidney disease. *Kidney Int.* **2004**, *65*, 2279–2289. [CrossRef]

67. Kuo, K.-L.; Hung, S.-C.; Lee, T.-S.; Tarng, D.-C. Iron Sucrose Accelerates Early Atherogenesis by Increasing Superoxide Production and Upregulating Adhesion Molecules in CKD. *J. Am. Soc. Nephrol.* **2014**, *25*, 2596–2606. [CrossRef]

68. Boudina, S.; Sena, S.; Theobald, H.; Sheng, X.; Wright, J.J.; Hu, X.X.; Aziz, S.; Johnson, J.I.; Bugger, H.; Zaha, V.G.; et al. Mitochondrial Energetics in the Heart in Obesity-Related Diabetes: Direct Evidence for Increased Uncoupled Respiration and Activation of Uncoupling Proteins. *Diabetes* **2007**, *56*, 2457–2466. [CrossRef]

69. Fink, B.D.; Herlein, J.A.; Almind, K.; Cinti, S.; Kahn, C.R.; Sivitz, W.I. Mitochondrial proton leak in obesity-resistant and obesity-prone mice. *Am. J. Physiol. Integr. Comp. Physiol.* **2007**, *293*, R1773–R1780. [CrossRef]

70. Bhargava, P.; Schnellmann, R.G. Mitochondrial energetics in the kidney. *Nat. Rev. Nephrol.* **2017**, *13*, 629–646. [CrossRef]

71. Che, R.; Yuan, Y.; Huang, S.; Zhang, A. Mitochondrial dysfunction in the pathophysiology of renal diseases. *Am. J. Physiol. Physiol.* **2014**, *306*, F367–F378. [CrossRef]

72. Liu, S.; Soong, Y.; Seshan, S.V.; Szeto, H.H. Novel cardiolipin therapeutic protects endothelial mitochondria during renal ischemia and mitigates microvascular rarefaction, inflammation, and fibrosis. *Am. J. Physiol. Physiol.* **2014**, *306*, F970–F980. [CrossRef] [PubMed]

73. Lan, R.; Geng, H.; Singha, P.K.; Saikumar, P.; Böttinger, E.P.; Weinberg, J.M.; Venkatachalam, M.A. Mitochondrial Pathology and Glycolytic Shift during Proximal Tubule Atrophy after Ischemic AKI. *J. Am. Soc. Nephrol.* **2016**, *27*, 3356–3367. [CrossRef] [PubMed]

74. Ren, X.; Zou, L.; Zhang, X.; Branco, V.; Wang, J.; Carvalho, C.; Holmgren, A.; Lu, J. Redox Signaling Mediated by Thioredoxin and Glutathione Systems in the Central Nervous System. *Antioxid. Redox Signal.* **2017**, *27*, 989–1010. [CrossRef] [PubMed]

75. Pope, S.; Land, J.M.; Heales, S.J. Oxidative stress and mitochondrial dysfunction in neurodegeneration: Cardiolipin a critical target? *Biochim. Biophys. Acta* **2008**, *1777*, 794–799. [CrossRef] [PubMed]

76. Petrosillo, G.; Moro, N.; Ruggiero, F.M.; Paradies, G. Melatonin inhibits cardiolipin peroxidation in mitochondria and prevents the mitochondrial permeability transition and cytochrome c release. *Free Radic. Boil. Med.* **2009**, *47*, 969–974. [CrossRef] [PubMed]

77. Brooks, C.; Wei, Q.; Cho, S.G.; Dong, Z.I. Regulation of mitochondrial dynamics in acute kidney injury in cell culture and rodent models. *J. Clin. Investig.* **2009**, *119*, 1275–1285. [CrossRef]

78. Zhan, M.; Usman, I.M.; Sun, L.; Kanwar, Y.S. Disruption of renal tubular mitochondrial quality control by Myo-inositol oxygenase in diabetic kidney disease. *J. Am. Soc. Nephrol.* **2015**, *26*, 1304–1321. [CrossRef]

79. Bayir, H.; Fadeel, B.; Palladino, M.J.; Witasp, E.; Kurnikov, I.V.; Tyurina, Y.Y.; Tyurin, V.A.; Amoscato, A.A.; Jiang, J.; Kochanek, P.M.; et al. Apoptotic interactions of cytochrome c: Redox flirting with anionic phospholipids within and outside of mitochondria. *Biochim. Biophys. Acta* **2006**, *1757*, 648–659. [CrossRef]

Review

Oleuropein, a Bioactive Compound from *Olea europaea* L., as a Potential Preventive and Therapeutic Agent in Non-Communicable Diseases

Chiara Nediani [1,*], Jessica Ruzzolini [1], Annalisa Romani [2] and Lido Calorini [1,3]

[1]   Department of Experimental and Clinical Biomedical Sciences "Mario Serio", University of Florence, viale Morgagni 50, 50134 Florence, Italy; jessica.ruzzolini@unifi.it (J.R.); lido.calorini@unifi.it (L.C.)

[2]   PHYTOLAB (Pharmaceutical, Cosmetic, Food Supplement, Technology and Analysis)-DiSIA, University of Florence, Via U. Schiff, 6, 50019 Sesto Fiorentino, Florence, Italy; annalisa.romani@unifi.it

[3]   Istituto Toscano Tumori and Center of Excellence for Research, Transfer and High Education (DENOTHE), University of Florence, Piazza di San Marco 4, 50121 Florence, Italy

*   Correspondence: chiara.nediani@unifi.it; Tel.: +39-055-275-1203

Received: 3 October 2019; Accepted: 19 November 2019; Published: 22 November 2019

Abstract: Growing scientific literature data suggest that the intake of natural bioactive compounds plays a critical role in preventing or reducing the occurrence of human chronic non-communicable diseases (NCDs). Oleuropein, the main phenolic component of *Olea europaea* L., has attracted scientific attention for its several health beneficial properties such as antioxidant, anti-inflammatory, cardio- and neuro-protective, and anti-cancer. This article is a narrative review focused on the current literature concerning the effect of oleuropein in NCDs, such as neuro- and cardiovascular diseases, diabetes mellitus, chronic kidney diseases, and cancer, by its putative antioxidant and anti-inflammatory activity, but also for its other peculiar actions such as an autophagy inducer and amyloid fibril growth inhibitor and, finally, for its anti-cancer effect. Despite the increasing number of published studies, looking at the beneficial effects of oleuropein, there is limited clinical evidence focused on the benefits of this polyphenol as a nutraceutical product in humans, and many problems are still to be resolved about its bioavailability, bioaccessibility, and dosage. Thus, future clinical randomized trials are needed to establish the relation between the beneficial effects and the mechanisms of action occurring in the human body in response to the intake of oleuropein.

Keywords: *Olea europaea* L.; oleuropein; extra-virgin olive oil; health effects; non-communicable diseases; oxidative stress; inflammation; autophagy; amyloid

1. Introduction

The great progress of medical research has highly contributed to decreased mortality due to severe pathologies. But, on the other hand, a longer life expectancy has been associated with a greater incidence of illness and disability.

Non-communicable diseases (NCDs) are a group of long-lasting and slowly progressive chronic disorders [1]. The World Health Organization (WHO) recently reported that NCDs are the leading causes of death and disability for the general population, regardless of age, region, or gender [2]. NCDs have been deeply studied and some common key features have been identified; these include the intracellular presence of oxidative stress due to abnormal production of reactive oxidative species (ROS), inadequate antioxidant defense, and dysregulation of the autophagy pathway, responsible for the maintenance of cellular proteostasis [3]. Also inflammation is implicated in NCDs [4], since its level in an organism is closely related to cellular redox and an autophagic state [5,6].

Moreover, the health care costs associated with NCDs highlight the importance of finding new therapies for these pathological conditions, and it has been shown that healthy and equilibrated dietary patterns are useful in the prevention of NCDs [7].

The consumption of extra virgin olive oil (EVOO) is common in the Mediterranean Diet, which is largely known to have several health benefits and to increase longevity, as reported by the United Nations Educational Scientific and Cultural Organization (UNESCO) in 2010 [8,9]. As recently reported in the III International Conference on Virgin Olive Oil and Health Consensus Report, EVOO intake is also associated with reduced risk of most ageing-related diseases including cardiovascular and neurodegenerative diseases (CVD and NDD), and some types of cancer [10]. Initially, the beneficial properties of EVOO were attributed to functional components such as monounsaturated and polyunsaturated fatty acids (MUFAs and PUFAs), like oleic acid (55 to 83% of total fatty acid (FA)), the essential FA, linoleic acid (3 to 21% of total FA), and linolenic acid (0 to 1.5% of total FA). However, recent epidemiological and experimental studies also show that minor bioactive compounds, including phenolic alcohols, such as hydroxytyrosol (HT, 3,4-dihydroxyphenylethanol, 3,4-DHPEA) and tyrosol (*p*-hydroxyphenylethanol, *p*-HPEA), secoiridoid derivatives, phenolic acids, lignans, and flavonoids contribute to the beneficial effects of EVOO [11–13]. A high biophenol content confers a high stability to EVOOs, preventing EVOO autoxidation and contributing to a long shelf-life.

Oleuropein (Ole) is the major phenolic compound in the olive tree, *Olea europaea* L., and is particularly abundant in unprocessed olive fruit and leaves, with concentrations up to 140 mg g^{-1} on a dry matter basis in young olives [14], and 60–90 mg g^{-1} of dry matter in the leaves [15]. In *Olea europaea*, Ole, demethyloleuropein, ligstroside, and oleoside 11-methyl ester are abundant secoiridoids [16] whereas verbascoside [17] is the main hydroxycinnamic derivative of olives [18]

Ole belongs to the secoiridoids, which are abundant in *Oleaceas, Gentianales Cornales*, as well as many other plants. Iridoids and secoiridoids are compounds that are usually glycosidically bound, and are produced from the secondary metabolism of terpenes, as precursors of various indole alkaloids. The secoiridoids in *Oleaceae* are usually derived from the oleoside type of glucosides (oleosides), which are characterized by an exocyclic 8,9-olefinic functionality, a combination of elenolic acid and a glucosidic residue [16]. Ole is an ester of elenolic acid and HT, and has a oleosidic skeleton that is common to the secoiridoid glucosides of *Oleaceae* (Figure 1)

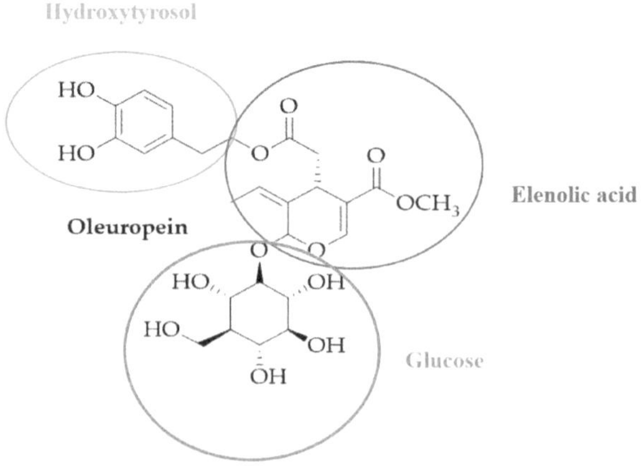

Figure 1. Chemical structure of oleuropein.

Ole present in green olives, during the oil mechanical extraction process, is hydrolysed by the activity of endogenous β-glucosidases to form oleuropein aglycone (OleA), responsible for the bitter and pungent taste of EVOO. OleA together with other derivative secoiridoid species, such as the dialdehydic derivative of decarboxymethyl elenolic acid bound to either HT (3,4-dihydroxyphenylethanol-elenolic acid dialdehyde, 3,4-DHPEA-EDA, oleacein), or to tyrosol (*p*-hydroxyphenylethanol-elenolic acid dialdehyde, *p*-HPEA-EDA, oleocanthal), and ligstroside aglycone (*p*-HPEAEA), represents the minor polar compounds that determine the antioxidant capacity of EVOO. In recent years, oleocanthal and oleacein have attracted interest from the scientific community [19] due to their inflammatory effects. The first study was due to its similar structure to ibuprofen [20], the second for its ability to stimulate the expression of CD163, an anti-inflammatory gene [21]. The secoiridoid most extensively studied is OleA, whose content is dependent on the oil production process, as previously reported [22].

The relevance of bioactive components in EVOO has been strengthened by the European Food Safety Authority (EFSA), that in 2011, released a health claim [23,24] on the efficacy of oil phenols (5 mg/day per 20 g of EVOO, HT and OleA) in protecting low-densitiy lipoprotein (LDL) from oxidation, the initial event of atherosclerotic plaque formation. This is of interest because it is unique as a health claim that associates a specific dosage of a natural bioactive component of food with cardiovascular risk (LDL cholesterol oxidation) reduction [25].

Leaves of olive tree are a hystorical Mediterranean herbal drug, used as a traditional remedy for health promotion and a therapy for chronic conditions. The differences in Ole content depend on the cultivar, production area, and leaf tissue conditions (fresh, frozen, dried, or lyophilized). Commercial *Olea* leaf extracts, standardized in Ole content, were used to obtain food supplements with specific biological and biomedical properties [26].

Various methods have been developed for the qualitative and quantitative analysis of the occurrence of phenolic and secoiridoid compounds, from the simplest techniques, such as TLC [27], to the more sophisticated ones, such as reversed phase HPLC [22,28,29], GC-MS, FAMS, or TMS [30]. In the fruits, phenyl acids, flavonoids, and secoiridoids have been reported, the phenolic compounds representing 1–3% (*w/v*) [31]. In the leaves, 19% (*w/w*) is Ole and 1.8% (*w/w*) is flavonoids, of which 0.8% is luteolin 7-glucoside [15].

Recently, both oleuropein isoforms, glycosidic form and aglycones, have attracted scientific attention by virtue of their health benefits, such as antioxidant, anti-inflammatory, cardio- and neuro-protective, and anti-cancer effects. These pharmacological activities are mainly due to their putative radical scavenging features, due to the ortho-diphenolic group. Mechanistic studies indicate that these compounds are also able to act at different sites, interfering with protein function and gene expression, or modifying cellular pathways relevant to the NCDs pathological processes [25,32], suggesting that the actions of oleuropein in various disorders may result from shared molecular mechanisms. As reported above, dysregulated autophagy is a common feature of NCDs. This dysregulation seems to be due to increased oxidative stress, so, although these mechanisms are generally viewed as cell autonomous, recent evidence suggests an occurrence of an interplay between autophagy and oxidative stress that influences the inflammatory state of tissues, linked with NCD development [3] (Figure 2). The aim of this review is to collect and discuss the data available in the literature concerning the effect of oleuropein isoforms, Ole and OleA, in NCDs by their putative antioxidant and anti-inflammatory activities, but also through their other peculiar actions as autophagy inducers and amyloid fibril growth inhibitors. The last part of this review is dedicated to the anti-cancer effect of oleuropein and its ability to sensitize and potentiate the action of current therapies.

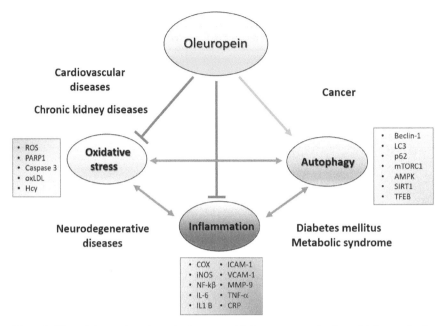

Figure 2. Effect of oleuropein on interplay between oxidative stress, autophaghy and inflammation in non-communicable diseases. AMPK, 5′ adenosine monophosphate-activated protein kinase; Beclin-1 autophagy-specific marker; COX, Cyclooxygenase; CRP, C Reactive Protein; Hcy, homocysteine; ICAM-1, Intercellular Adhesion Molecule 1; IL-1β, interleukin-1β; IL-6, interleukin-6; iNOS, inducible form of nitric oxide synthase; LC3 autophagy-specific marker; MMP-9, metalloproteinases-9; mTOR, mammalian target of rapamycin; NF-kB, Nuclear Factor Kappa-Light-Chain-Enhancer of Activated B Cells; oxLDL, oxidized low-density lipoprotein; p62 autophagy-specific marker; PARP1, Poly (ADP-ribose) polymerase; ROS, Reactive Oxygen Species; SIRT-1, NAD-dependent deacetylase sirtuin-1; TFEB, Transcription factor EB; TNF-α, tumour necrosis factor-α; VCAM-1, Vascular Cell Adhesion Molecule 1.

2. Oleuropein As an Antioxidant

The strong antioxidant properties of oleuropein is well known, and is shared with other phenols present in olive leaves and olive oil. In its chemical structure oleuropein contains an ortho-diphenolic group able to scavenge ROS through hydrogen donation, and to stabilize oxygen radicals with an intramolecular hydrogen bond. In particular, a o-diOH substitution confers a high antioxidant property, whereas single hydroxyl substitutions, e.g., tyrosol, provide none [33]. Ole in vitro can inhibit, in a dose-dependent manner, copper sulphate-induced oxidation of LDLs, assessed through a decrease in thiobarbituric acid-reacting substances and lipid peroxide by-product content [34,35]. In vivo, rabbits fed with an Ole-rich diet showed a higher serum antioxidant levels able to counteract LDL oxidation, and a reduction of total, free, and esterified cholesterol levels compared to animals receiving a standard diet [36]. Moreover, in humans, Visioli et al. [37] proved that Ole supplementation in healthy volunteers decreased, in a dose-dependent manner, the urinary excretion of 8-iso-PGF2α, suggesting a lower lipid peroxidation. A scavenging effect of Ole, similar to ascorbic acid and α-tocopherol, was shown in vitro against hypochlorous acid, a potent oxidant species produced in vivo by neutrophil myeloperoxidase at the site of inflammation [33], as well as against nitric oxide, as reported by De la Puerta et al. [38]. The first experimental evidence of the direct antioxidant cardioprotective effect of Ole against the post-ischemic oxidative burst after coronary occlusion, was reported by Manna et al. [39]. Using isolated rat hearts pretreated with Ole, subjected to global ischemia and then reperfused, they observed a decrease of creatine kinase and a reduced glutathione release in the perfusate, as well as a decrease of oxidized glutathione and in the lipid peroxidation level. Ole was also able to exert, in an indirect way, its antioxidant action by stimulating the expression of intracellular antioxidant enzymes *via* the activaction of Nuclear factor erythroid 2-related factor 2 (NrF2) transcription [40], as well as by increasing the level of non enzymatic antioxidants such as glutathione, α-tocoferol, β-carotene, and ascorbic acid [41–43].

3. Oleuropein As an Anti-Inflammatory and CVD Protective Agent

Inflammation is a crucial and defensive response induced by tissue damage or infection, and represents the "common soil" of multi-factorial diseases, playing a crucial role in promoting many disabling illnesses, such as atherosclerosis, diabetes mellitus, metabolic syndrome, cancer, chronic kidney diseases, and neurodegenerative diseases [44]. It can be divided into two types, acute and chronic. Chronic inflammation is correlated with the production of ROS that may cause oxidative damage and the depletion of antioxidants [45]. Macrophages, one of the main factors in the inflammatory response, produce ROS, but also pro-inflammatory cytokines and chemokines, including IL-1, IL-6, TNF-a, and IFN-γ. IL-6 seems to be the central mediator of the inflammatory response and an index of increased frailty [46–49]. Therefore, besides the release of several inflammatory cytokines or mediators, damaged tissues also release monocyte chemoattractant proteins (MCP-1), cyclooxygenase (COX), inducible form of nitric oxide synthase (iNOS), metalloproteinases (MMP), and adhesion molecules. In addition, nuclear factor Kappa β (NF-kβ) occupies a key upstream position in a complex signal transduction pathway, controlling the production of countless pro-inflammatory mediators [50].

In 2006, the PREDIMED trial first showed the anti-inflammatory effect of the Mediterranean Diet (MD) supplemented with EVOO for three months (compared with a low fat diet), through a remarkable decrease of serum C-Reactive Protein (CRP), IL-6, endothelial and monocytary adhesion molecules (ICAM-1 and VCAM-1), and chemokines, in a group of 722 partecipants [51]. Many other sub-studies of the PREDIMED trial have confirmed the anti-inflammatory properties of MD with EVOO by studying the changes in biomarkers associated with atherogenesis, such as peripheral blood mononuclear cell expression of cell surface inflammatory mediators (adhesion molecule and pro-inflammatory ligand CD40 expression on T lymphocytes and monocytes) or other molecules associated with systemic inflammation, such as those that induce the expression of adhesion molecules and activating NF- kB (TNFR60), or playing a role in T cell proliferation (TNFR80) [52–54]. Di Daniele et al. [55] demonstrated that the Italian MD in nephropatic patients could be a useful tool in the treatment of cardiovascular comorbidity related to renal dysfunction, causing a significant decrease in serum homocysteine (Hcy), dependant on a methylenetetrahydrofolate reductase genotype. In fact, Hcy, during the autoxidation process, induces impairment of the endothelium by producing ROS, with consequent involvement in atherosclerosis [56,57]. All these studies support that adherence to the MD with EVOO can modify inflammation, regardless of shared genetic and environmental factors.

In this context, many scientists have focused their attention on the possibility of using individual EVOO polyphenolic compounds like oleuropein, as a promising alternative anti-inflammatory agent, due to its capability to inhibit the synthesis of pro-inflammatory cytokines [58,59] and lipoxygenase activity [4], or to modulate inflammatory parameters [60].

Starting from in vitro results, Miles et al. [61] observed that Ole was the most powerful inhibitor of the production of IL-1β, compared with other phenols from EVOO, from human whole blood cells stimulated by lipopolysaccharide (LPS). Ryu S. et al. [62] verified that Ole was able to modulate the phenotype of LPS-activated murine macrophages, RAW 264.7, through the downregulation of key markers in inflammation pathways such as iNOS, COX-2, NFKB, and JNK, and of the two pro-inflammatory interleukins, IL-6 and IL-1β. The same authors also showed the efficacy of Ole in the reduction of LPS-induced NO in a zebrafish embryo model.

OleA is able to modulate the tumor microenvironment, at least in part, through its anti-inflammatory properties, as reported by Margheri et al. [63]. Using "senescence-associated-secretory-phenotype" (SASP) fibroblasts, that show features of cancer-associated fibroblasts, they found that treatment with OleA decreased both the levels of SASP pro-angiogenic factors in the fibroblasts, and the release of the same in cell media, particularly IL-8. Interestingly, when endothelial progenitor cells and resident mature microvascular endothelial cells were exposed to these latter cell media, vasculogenesis and angiogenesis was inhibited by a decrease of MMPs and by the urokinase-type plasminogen activator, suggesting a mechanistic interpretation of the anti-angiogenic activities for cancer prevention by OleA.

The anti-inflammatory effect of Ole is better appreciated by studies using in vivo animal models. Giner et al. [64] demonstrated that Ole was able to ameliorate the symptoms of dextran sulfate sodium(DSS)-induced colitis in mice through the reduction of COX-2, iNOS, and MMP-9, and the suppression of p38 MAPK phosphorylation, which may be due to the up-regulation of annexin A1 [33]. Impellizzeri et al. [59] found that OleA could attenuate TNF-α and IL-1β production in a mouse model of carrageenan-induced pleurisy. The same pathways of TNF-α and IL-1β were also affected by Ole in a rat model of post-traumatic stress disorder [65], and in rats with spinal cord trauma [66]. Ole also showed its beneficial effect in an ovariectomy/inflammation experimental model of bone loss in rats, modulating parameters of inflammation, such us fibrinogen and spleen weight [67].

Recently, a study by Larussa T. et al. [68] demonstrated that the administration of OleA on colonic biopsies taken from ulcerative colitis patients led to a decrease of COX-2 and IL-17 levels, considerably reducing the inflammation of the colonic tissue. This evidence encourages the use of oleuropein as an inflammation-modulator.

Lipid-Regulating, Anti-Hypertensive and Antidiabetic Effects of Oleuropein

CVD is a group of disorders affecting heart and/or blood vessels. CVD, including coronary heart disease (CHD), cerebrovascular disease, and peripheral arterial disease, are characterized by fatty deposits in the inner walls of the blood vessels supplying the heart and brain, that may cause an arrest of blood flow to these organs. The cardiovascular protective effect of oleuropein is supported by many in vivo animal studies and human clinical trials that showed, in addition to its antioxidant and anti-inflammatory properties, its lipid-lowering activity, anti-hypertensive, and hypoglycemic action [69–71].

Lockyer et al. [72] conducted a randomized, controlled trial on pre-hypertensive volunteers, who after an intake of Ole-enriched olive leaf extract for six weeks (136 mg Ole; 6 mg HT), showed significantly lower blood pressure (BP), plasma total cholesterol, LDL cholesterol, and triglycerids relative to the control, with a 5.76% reduction in coronary heart disease risk. Another trial on patients with stage-1 hypertension, showed that a daily dose of 2×500 mg of olive leaf extract (with 16–24% Ole) for four weeks, lowered systolic and diastolic BP with an effect comparable to that exerted by an effective dose (12.5–25 mg twice daily) of Captopril (the standard therapy for stage-1 hypertension), and reduced total plasma LDL and triglyceride levels. The authors concluded that the dual effect of olive leaf extract in lowering BP, probably due to angiotensin converting enzyme inhibition and calcium channel blocking activities, and improving lipid profiles, is advantageous for reducing the risk for CVD [73].

Insulin resistance is a systemic disorder, in which there is a reduced action of insulin despite an "hyperinsulinaemia" condition, that affects many organs, in particular the liver and adipose tissue, and leads to development of two NCDs, type 2 diabetes mellitus (T2DM) and metabolic syndrome, well known cardiovascular risk factors. Recent research has described the beneficial properties of OleA and Ole-enriched olive leaf extracts against T2DM, and other metabolic syndrome associated conditions. In particular, OleA prevents amylin aggregation into amyloid fibrils, whose pancreatic presence is considered one of the causes of the sufferance and functional impairment of insulin-secreting cells in T2DM (see 5: Oleuropein as anti–amiloid mean) [74] Therefore, many studies conducted in animal and cell models have reported that Ole has the property of decreasing blood glucose and cholesterol levels, and improving oral glucose tolerance and insulin sensitivity [41,75,76]. These findings were confirmed by human clinical trial results showing that treatment with Ole improved glucose homeostasis, reduced glycated hemoglobin and fasting insulin levels, suggesting a significant anti-diabetic effect [77–79]. Interestingly, in the context of these latter metabolic disorders, both characterized by insulin-resistance, de BocK et al. [78] showed a recovery of insulin sensitivity and pancreatic β-cell secretion capacity, in a group of overweight middle-aged men that received capsules of oleuropein-leaf extracts for 12 weeks, corroborating previous findings on the hypoglycemic effect of oleuropein [41,71,80].

Another disease highly associated with insulin resistance and the metabolic syndrome is non-alcoholic fatty liver disease (NAFLD), that affects about 25% of the world population, and the following non-alcoholic steatohepatitis (NASH). Research on cell and animal models have reported that oleuropein may counteract these conditions through different actions, including (i) an anti-lipidemic activity [81], (ii) protection and prevention of liver damage [82–84], and (iii) by interfering with signaling pathways involved in lipogenesis and in the onset of fatty liver disease [69]. Unfortunately, today these findings are not adequately supported by human studies, and remains unproven.

Therefore, in addition to the reported properties above, the ability of oleuropein to inhibit endothelial activation, monocyte cell adhesion and platelet aggregation within the concentration range expected after the nutritional intake from MD, suggest that oleuropein may also be considered an anti-atherogenic agent, reflecting its CVD protective activity [85–89]

4. Oleuropein As an Autophagy Inducer

Autophagy is a process by which the cells removes damaged organelles, malformed proteins or amyloid aggregate accumulation through lysosomal degradation. This is a process highly conserved and is required to maintain cellular homeostasis. It starts with the formation of a phagophore (that coincides with membrane isolation) that grows and terminates in auto-phagosome completion, which follows its fusion with lysosomes to form auto-phagolysosomes. Beclin-1 and LC3 are typical markers of autophagy activation, involved in the first steps of phagophore formation, while p62 participates in cargo recognition by lysosomes [90]. The target of rapamycin complex 1 (mTORC1) and the AMP-activated protein kinase (AMPK) are the stress sensors that control autophagy. However, while mTORC1 is an autophagy inhibitor activated by serum, nutrients, growth factors, etc., AMPK is instead an autophagy inducer, activated by low energy conditions and polyphenols.

Dysregulated autophagy is a common feature in NCDs implicated in NDD, metabolic syndrome, diabetes, CVDs, gastrointestinal diseases, and cancer [3]. As a master regulator of protein, lipid and carbohydrate metabolism, altered autophagy may concomitantly promote metabolic disorders and diseases associated with ageing, unhealthy diets, and inflammation. Indeed, knockout of the Atg7 gene in mice, an essential gene for autophagy, shows in vivo typical Parkinson' disease (PD) features like Lewy bodies (LBs) formation, including endogenous synuclein and neuronal loss, as well as hepatomegaly with mutant hepatocytes showing accumulation of ubiquitin-positive aggregates [91,92]. A high fat-diet and genetically obese mice showed a decrease in autophagy flux, linked to elevated inflammatory gene expression [93–95]. Interestingly, autophagy seems to have a role in hypothalamic agouti-related peptide neurons in the regulation of food intake and energy balance, suggesting that the ability to regulate hypothalamic autophagy for modulating energy homeostasis may have implications in the development of new therapeutic options for obesity, and metabolic syndrome conditions [96]. Autophagic flux is also inhibited in pancreatic β-cells exposed to fatty acids, thus suppressing insulin secretion, a crucial factor for promoting T2DM to type-I diabetes conversion [97]. In the context of CDV, several studies show that autophagy might have beneficial or detrimental roles depending on the stage and type of the considered cardiovascular disease [4]. A beneficial function of autophagy has been observed in ischemia-reperfusion, cardiac hypertrophy, and atrial fibrillation. However, the majority of cardiac disorders suggests that autophagy may be a common cellular pathway that can be targeted for therapeutic gain, and the growing number of cardioprotective therapies affecting autophagic activity confirms this evidence [3,98,99]. Autophagy is also pivotal for intestinal homeostasis, appropriate intestinal immune responses, and anti-microbial protection, as well as neuronal and microglial functions [100]. In cancer cells, autophagy may exert either a tumor-promoting or tumor-suppressing effect [3]. Thus, it is still debated whether autophagy induction or inhibition may represent the most promising approach for future cancer treatments. Interestingly, cancer cells may also use autophagy as a resistance mechanism against chemotherapy [101]. In conclusion, autophagy is a key factor in the pathogenesis and regulation of various kinds of diseases, serving as a potential and effective target for their intervention. Therefore, the use of substances, such as polyphenols, that modulate autophagy and minimize the collateral effect, may be a valid therapeutic approach [102].

Some of the studies that contribute to demonstrating the healthful actions of oleuropein against pathologies involving autophagy dysfunction, acting as an autophagy enhancer through several mechanisms, and its potential use as a nutraceutical agent in several NCDs are summarized below

4.1. Oleuropein and NDDs

In our previous study performed in neuroblastoma cell lines, we found that OleA induced autophagy by activation of the Ca^{2+}/Calmodulin Protein Kinase Kinase β (CaMKKβ)/AMPK/mTOR signalling axis. We proposed that OleA might induce autophagy through a Ca^{2+} increase in the cytoplasma from the endoplasmic reticulum that, in turn, activated Ca^{2+}/CaMKKβ, and subsequently AMPK signaling. This complex facilitates mTORC1 inhibition and ULK1 activation to generate autophagic vacuole induction. We demonstrated that SH-SY5Y cells treated with 50 μM OleA showed an increased level of Beclin-1, critical for inducing autophagy, correlated with a biphasic elevation of the phosphorylation of residue Thr172 of AMPK [103]. The effects of OleA as an autophagy inducer have also been investigated in animal transgenic models. Grossi et al. [104], using a wildtype and TgCRND8 transgenic mouse model for human Aβ pathology, demonstrated that a diet supplemented with OleA restored the defective autophagic flux through an improvement of the fusion of lysosomes to autophagic vesicles, resulting in a remarkable cortex plaque reduction, and a recovery of the mice cognitive performance. They suggested that autophagy might be activated by inhibition of the mTOR pathway, reflected by the phosphorylation decrease of its target p70S6 protein kinase, shown in cell culture. These data indicate that autophagy may be considered as a strategic anti-amyloid mechanism, and suggest that OleA and/or its derivatives may exert their neuroprotective function in the brain, crossing the blood-brain barrier, acting as autophagy–related anti-amyolid agents, enhancing the clearance of Aβ plaque deposition. The cognitive recovery showed in these Alzheimer's disease (AlzD) animal models supports the hypothesis that a diet supplementated with these polyphenols may have beneficial effects in slowing cognitive decline in patients with clinical signs of this disease.

Activation of NAD-dependent deacetylase sirtuin-1 (SIRT-1) is another mechanism through which OleA may modulate autophagy. SIRT1, a class III HDAC involved in the pathogenesis of several NCDs, deacetylates histones and non-histone proteins, such as transcription factors like p53, NF-κB, and FOXO, by transferring the acetyl group to NAD+. SIRT-1 influences autophagy directly (but also oxidative stress and apoptosis), via deacetylation of key components of this pathway. It showed a functional crosstalk with Poly (ADP-ribose) polymerase-1 (PARP-1) through NAD^+ cofactor availability, and so any changes in levels of intracellular NAD^+ and/or PARP-1 activity may influence SIRT-1 activity [105]. Luccarini et al. [106] showed that PARP-1 activation matched with a significant accumulation of PAR polymers in the cortex of TgCRND8 mice at the early (3.5 month) and intermediate (six month) stages of Aβ deposition. The same TgCRND8 mice fed with a supplementation of OleA showed a rescue of both PARP-1 activation, the accumulation of its product, and increased SIRT-1 expression. Moreover, OleA was able to reduce the rise of the apoptotic mediators phospho-NF-κB and phospho-p53.

4.2. Oleuropein and Cardioprotection

Miceli et al. [107] studied the effect of OleA as an autophagy enhancer in a cardiomyocyte model, characterized by autophagy dysfunction induced by oxidative stress due to a monoamine oxidase-A (MAO-A) overexpression. MAO-A is an isoform of FAD-dependent enzymes, that catalyzes oxidative deamination of catecholamines and serotonin in the heart, producing the corresponding aldehyde, H_2O_2, and ammonia. Previous studies have reported that MAO-A expression and activity increased in chronic cardiac diseases [108–111]. They found that OleA conferred cardioprotection, not simply by its antioxidant action, but through restoration of defective autophagic flux autophagy, reflected by auto-phagolysosome formation, measured by p62 and cathepsin-B levels increase, and the transcriptional factor EB (TFEB) activation and translocation to the nucleus. Translocation of TFEB to the nucleus modulated the transcription of autophagy genes prevented by MAO-A activation, reducing its transcriptional activity. They demonstrated that transcriptional regulation of autophagy by OleA was correlated with a significant cell death decrease, and to mitochondrial functionality recovery. These improvements disappeared after TFEB silencing, leading to the hypothesis that TFEB activaction was crucial for the protective effects of OleA against MAO-A-induced autophagy dysfunction. In addition, TFEB translocation and autophagy recovery induced by OleA did not affect ROS status in cardiomyocytes, further highlighting its peculiarity as an autophagy inducer.

4.3. Oleuropein and NAFLD

Using C57BL/6J mice fed a high-fat diet (HFD) for eight weeks, an animal model that well mimics human metabolic syndrome, with mice developing steatosis, metabolic and cardiovascular diseases, Porcu et al. [112] found an improvement in liver steatosis in mice fed the HFD with Ole that correlated with an increase of autophagy via the AMPK/ULK1 pathway, compared with animals fed with standard diet.

4.4. Oleuropein and Cancer

Recently HY et al. [113] found that inhibition of autophagy in a Triple-Negative Breast Cancer cell line promoted migration and invasion, as demonstrated by exposition with Hepatocyte Growth Factor (HGT), or 3-methyladenine, an inhibitor of autophagy. On the contrary, the co-treatment with HT or Ole significantly suppressed HGF or 3-MA induced cell migration and invasion, by reversing LC3 II/I and Beclin-1 downregulation, and p62 upregulation.

Increased autophagy seems to be a defensive mechanism against treatment with doxorubicin (DXR). Papachristodoulou et al. [114] demonstrated in prostate cancer cells, that Ole is capable of lowering the cytotoxic dose of DXR significantly, without losing its anti-proliferative effect, via an induction of autophagy (see: Section 7. Chemiotherapy potentiation by Oleuropein).

These findings contribute to demonstrate the healthful actions of oleuropein against pathologies involving autophagy dysfunction, acting as an autophagy enhancer throught different mechanisms, and suggest its potential use as a nutraceutical agent in several NCDs.

5. Oleuropein as Anti–Amyloid Tool

Many neurodegenerative pathologies, among which the most common are AlzD and PD, together with T2DM, are amyloid diseases (AD), and belong to the NCD group. In general, AD are diseases that are potentially fatal, defined by the occurrence of deposition of insoluble fibrillar polymeric material, grown from misfolded proteins (amyloid) in several organs. The core of these amyloids is made of unbranched polymeric fibrils of characteristic protein or peptides, typical for each disease, such as Aβ peptides for AlzD, α-synuclein for PD, amylin (hIAPP) for T2DM, and transthyretin (TTR) for familial amyloid cardiomyopathy [115–117]. Amyloidogenic proteins are characterized by β-sheet conformation, and share a common pathway of fibril formation. This latter is a complex process that involves the formation of an intermediate (soluble) oligomer form, following insoluble protofibril growth. Recently some authors have demonstrated that the cytotoxicity of different amyloidogenic proteins is due to soluble, intermediate oligomeric species, rather than to insoluble fibrillary amyloids [118]. Their cytotoxicity involves the disruption of calcium homeostasis, destabilization of membranes, ROS production, and apoptosis induction, all factors that determine cell suffering and death [119]. Interestingly, neurodegenerative diseases may extend outside the central nervous system (CNS), and can also involve the gastrointestinal tract (GI). Indeed, the same protein aggregates are present both in the enteric nervous system (ENS) and the CNS, leading to the hypothesis that the disease may start in the ENS and then spread retrogradely toward the CNS, or vice versa, and suggests that it may spread through a prion-like diffusion of misfolded protein accumulation, due to an imbalance between their production and clearance by autophagy systems [120].

So, the research of compounds interfering with aggregation of amyloid proteins is recognized as a valuable approach to build new therapeutic molecules. This is true expecially for AlzD, the most common form of dementia-related neurodegenerative disease among the elder people (aged 60 years and over), marked by a progressive decline in cognitive function and memory. Aggregates of Aβ peptides and neurofibrillary tangles of hyperphosphorylated tau proteins occurring in hypothalamic and cortical neurons are typical signs of this disease. PD is the second most common neurodegenerative disease, and is characterized by degeneration of dopaminergic neurons in the substantia nigra pars compacta due to deposition of intracellular inclusions known as LBs, the major component of which is α-synuclein. Although the clinical pathologies of these diseases have been described a long time ago, today there are drugs available only effective in reducing the symptoms of these diseases. The deposition of senile plaques and LBs in neuronal cells induces chronic stress, including oxidative stress and activation of microglial cells for the release of several pro-inflammatory cytokines, chemokines, and ROS, that are the major cause of these disorders [121].

OleA has been found to decrease toxic oligomers formation in vitro experiments of Aβ peptide and α-synuclein amyloid aggregation, as well as to promote fibril and plaque disaggregation [122–124]. These actions reflect its beneficial effects against amyloid toxicity to cultured cells [122] and in transgenic model organisms [125,126]. Using a simplified model of AlzD expressing human Aβ peptide, Diomede et al. [125] found that the larvae of a transgenic strain CL2006 of *Caenorhabditis elegans* fed with OleA, showed in the cytoplasm of muscle cells of the body wall, a reduction of Aβ plaque deposits, a lower content of toxic Aβ oligomers, a marked decrease of paralysis, and an increase of life expectancy compared with untreated animals.

hIAPP is a peptide hormone co-secreted with insulin by pancreatic β-cells, and fibrillar deposits of hIAPP amyloid aggregates in islets of Langerhans are a well known of T2DM. hIAPP aggregation together with oxidative stress (via NADPH-oxidase) leads to hIAPP toxicity, and plays a pivotal role in T2DM pathogenesis [127,128]. Rigacci et al. [74] showed that OleA occurrence, during the aggregation process, drove the formation of structurally different aggregates by hindering their binding with the membrane cells, resulting in a decrease of membrane damage, and protection of rat insulinoma cells against aggregate cytotoxicity, the main aspect responsible for cell sufferance. Similar results were obtained by Leri et al. [129] that extend the above finding to the OleA/TTR system, the latter is involved in a subset of familial or sporadic amyloid diseases including senile systemic amyloidosis (SSA), familial amyloid polyneuropathy and cardiomyopathy (FAP/FAC), for which no effective therapy has yet been found. This polyphenol was able to interfere with TTR fibril assembly and to promote mature fibril disruption. In this study, OleA protection against amyloid TTR toxicity, tested on in vitro HL-1 cells, resulted from stabilizing an oligomer-like intermediate that interacts with the plasma membrane without altering its integrity. In addition, OleA was also found to be able to disassemble pre-formed TTR mature fibrils into the same non-toxic oligomer-like intermediates [129].

Another interesting aspect of the anti-cytotoxic action of OleA, in the contest of amyloydosis, was reported by Leri et al. [130]. Using another amyloidogenic protein, a variant of human β2-microglobulin (β$_2$m) [131–133] a 99 residue-long human protein belonging to the major histocompatibility complex class I (MHC I) associated with a familial form of systemic amyloidosis, they showed that it exhibited an enhanced amyloidogenic tendency to aggregate in vitro with respect to the wild-type protein. In this study, they found that OleA modified not only the conformational and biophysical properties of the amyloid fibrils, favoring the appearance of non-toxic aggregates, but also modified the cell bilayer surface properties, decreasing aggregate interaction with the plasma membrane of exposed cells, and enhancing cell resistance against the toxic effects of the aggregates.

All these data suggest a possible use of OleA as a novel and promising pharmacological tool, acting directly on amyloid formation *via* the protein self-assembly pathway, for prevention and therapy of systemic amyloidosis.

6. Oleuropein As an Anticancer Agent

Current protocols for cancer treatment are dependent on the condition of the tumor at time of diagnosis. If diagnosed early, the tumor mass may be removed by surgery, but if it has spread to lymph nodes, surgery will be more intensive, and chemotherapy and immunotherapy will likely be added to the treatment. Up-to-now, chemotherapy and immunotherapy represent a promising route for a more effective, life-saving cure for most human cancers. Despite advancements in these therapies, many patients with metastatic lesions still face a significant mortality risk. Furthermore, chemotherapy and immunotherapy may result in patient resistance, and generate host side effects. Therefore, new strategies that target cancer cells and also reduce resistance and patient side effects, may help the development of new treatments. Thus, the combination of conventional treatment with biological agents (so-called complementary therapy) may enhance the efficacy of treatment, and reduce drug resistance. In addition, complementary therapy may provide a reduction in side effects and improve the overall quality of life of patients during therapy.

Oleuropein may contribute to therapy in several ways, including its inhibitory role in some crucial cancer cell activities, and these are summarized in the Figure 3.

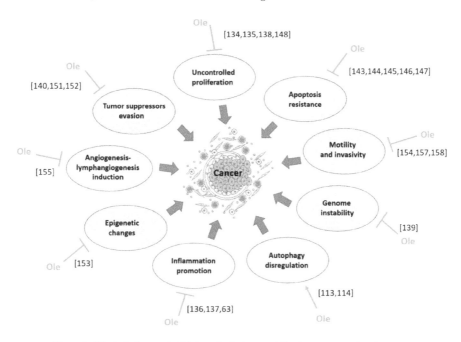

Figure 3. Effect of oleuropein (Ole) on the factors contributing to cancer development.

6.1. Pro-Apoptotic and Anti-Proliferative Effects of Oleuropein

Bouallagui et al. [134], investigating Ole-enriched extract and its derivative HT, found a consistent inhibition of the proliferation of luminal breast cancer cells (MCF-7 cells), which were arrested in G0/G1 phase. The probable mechanism of growth-arrest was Cyclin D1 inhibition by these polyphenols. Han et al. [135] also reported in the same cancer cells, a blocking of the transition from G1 to S phase, caused by HT and OleA. Elamin et al. [136] was able to extend the use of Ole to the less responsive basal-like breast cancer cells (MDA-MB-231 cells), and demonstrated its ability to abrogate NF-kB expression, a well-known transcription factor involved in the control of many genes driving cancer development and progression, e.g., inflammation, immune reaction, proliferation, and apoptosis. This last finding was also confirmed by Liu et al. [137].

Further exposing BPH-1 normal prostate cells, androgen-sensitive LNCaP, and androgen-insensitive DU145 prostate cancer cells to Ole, promoted an anti-oxidant action in normal cells, whereas in cancer cells, it induced pro-oxidant and anti-proliferative effects, suggesting a quite cancer-specific effect [138].

It is also known that an Ole-enriched diet prevents azoxymethane-induced pre-neoplastic lesions of the colon, reducing dysplasia and DNA damage [139].

Cardeno et al. [140] showed that Ole and HT significantly inhibits HIF-1a and promotes the expression of p53 in HT-29 human colon adenocarcinoma cells, as a critical change to limit proliferation, and induce apoptosis.

Additional evidence suggests that one of the best inhibitors of human colon carcinoma cells is the HT oleate form, suggesting that long chain fatty acids, such oleate, may facilitate Ole activity [141].

Ole from Corregiola leaf extracts expresses a very high level of anti-proliferative activity on pancreatic cancer cells (MiaPaCa-2 cells), opening up a possibile treatment for one of the most aggressive human cancers.

Samara et al. [142] studied 51 analogs of Ole on several human cancer cells, and found that analog 24, non-toxic for normal cells, expresses the highest level of inhibitory activity in vitro (human colon cancer cells HCT-116, human cervical carcinoma cells HeLa, MCF-7 cells) as well as in vivo (B16-F10 mouse melanoma cells). Of a particular importance was the finding that Ole analog 24 expresses a promotion of natural immune responses, from Natural Killer cells and Limphokine-activated Killer cells.

Several authors showed Ole promoted apoptosis in cancer cells, like HeLa cells [143], HepG2 human hepatoma cells [144], SH-SY5Y human neuroblastoma cells [145], and HCT116 cells [146]. Taken together, the above researches provide significant insights into the contribution of Ole in treating cancer cells, disclosing several targets of its pro-apoptotic activity, such as activation of the JNK pathway, suppression of PI3K/AKT signaling, and activation of caspase-9 and 3 gene expression.

Additionally, pro-apoptotic activity of Ole has been seen against HL60 human promyelocytic leukemia cells [147].

6.2. Multiple Checkprotein of Transcription of Oleuropein

Further indications of the multiple targets of Ole activity on cancer cell machinery has emerged from the following contributions. Sirianni et al. [148] demonstrated that HT and Ole inhibit estrogen-dependent proliferation in MCF-7 cells, affecting extracellular-regulated kinases 1/2 (ERK 1/2) of the mitogen activating protein kinase family.

More-recently, Momtaz et al. [149] has shown the influence of Ole on melanoma. Melanoma is certainly one of the most aggressive skin cancers, due to its progression to drug resistance and its organ dissemination. Among the signalling pathways able to control melanoma development, janus kinase signal transducers and activators of transcription (JAKs/STATs) are the most critical, and polyphenols are able to target the most active, STAT3.

Furthermore, Ole was found to affect T-type Ca^{2+} channels altering the dynamics of intracellular Ca^{2+} in mesothelioma cancer cells. T-type calcium channels are low voltage channels, which open up when the membrane is depolarized, and calcium enters into various cells with different responses. On the other hand, mesothelioma is a cancer with a very poor prognosis, with an urgent need for new targeted therapies [150].

In MCF-7 cells, Ole exhibits an additional ability that extends its anti-cancer effects to the modulation of tumor suppressor genes, such as onco-miRNAs (miRNA-21 and miR-155) [151]. Researches by Tezcan G. et al. [152] serve to underline that Ole may modulate expression of miRNAs, miR-137, -145, and -153, in glioblastoma multiforme (GBM) cancer stem cells.

Bayat et al. [153], recently proved that Ole modulates epigenetic inhibiting histone deacetylases (HDAC2 and HDAC3). The use of HDAC inhibitors in cancer treatment represents a new approach to therapy, like reactivation of tumor suppressor genes. Although, this treatment causes side effects in the treated patients, Ole might have a role in some complementary therapies using HDAC inhibitors.

6.3. Other Biological Activities of Oleuropein

Ole was reported to express a potent inhibitory activity on tumor xenografts, disrupting actin filaments, thus abrogating proliferation, motility, and invasiveness [154]. The several cancer cell lines used in the experiments is an additional parameter of importance in this latter study (GMB cells, renal adenocarcinoma cells, breast cancer cells, melanoma cells, and colorectal adenocarcinoma cells).

Starting from the epidemiological observation that obesity is associated with an increased risk of developing many cancers, and metastatic dissemination represents the leading cause of mortality of cancer patients, a study by Song et al. [155] suggests that Ole inhibits tumor growth and lymph node metastasis in mouse melanoma cells, abrogating angiogenesis and lymphangiogenesis through the reduction of the peroxisome proliferator-activated receptor γ and the infiltration of M2 macrophages, both responsible for the secretion of angiogenesis and lymphangiogenesis inducers, VEGFA and D, respectively.

Evidence for the role of Ole in promoting the differentiation of K562 multipotent leukemia cells toward a monocyte lineage, was reported by Samet et al. [156]. Further anti-cancer/pro-apoptotic activity of Ole on leukemic cells, like HL60 human promyelocytic leukemia cells, was reported by Anter et al. [147].

The anticancer effect of Ole on glioma cells was characterized by a decrease of matrix MMP-2 and -9 activity, leading to a significant reduction in their ability to invade extracellular tissues [157]. In accord with this last observation, Ole was found to promote a reduction in the metastatic ability of breast cancer cells that was ascribed to a MMP-2 and -9 decrease, strengthened by a promotion of tissue inhibitors of MMP (TIMP) 1,3,4 [158]. It is known that a balance of MMP and TIMP regulates cancer cell invasion and dissemination.

7. Chemiotherapy Potentiation by Oleuropein

Due to the several anticancer properties of oleuropein, including anti-proliferative and pro-apoptosis activity, it was investigated whether it might represent an effective agent for complementary cancer therapy. In addition, it is well known that most anticancer drugs induce side-effects and toxicity in tumor-bearing patients, which oleuropein might be able to overwhelm.

A study reported by Papachristodoulou et al. [114] shows that co-treatment with doxorubicin and Ole affected cell proliferation of PC3 prostate cancer cells in an additive manner, even using a very low dose of doxorubicin. These authors also showed that the co-treatment did not modify cell cycle distribution and apoptosis of these cells in a significant way, but was able to induce a significant promotion of autophagy. Tumor cells are characterized by high energy use, even during starvation, when autophagy may sustain mitochondrial functions. Thus, the autophagy-dependence of cancer cells discloses a new therapeutic target for Ole, as reported above. Moreover, Ole has been shown to protect against the cardiotoxicity of doxorubicin [159]; this is an additional ability that further promotes the use of oleuropein in cancer co-treatments.

GBM is considered one of the most malignant human cancers, and therapy is up-to-now only palliative. GBM expresses a capillary network which contributes to tumor expansion and invasion, for which a targeted therapy using a monoclonal anti-VEGA antibody, bevacizumab, might be effective. However, this treatment often promotes an enhanced aggressive phenotype in resistant GBM cells. Tezcan et al. [160] were able to demonstrate that Ole synergistically increases bevacizumab's anti-angiogenesis and anti-migration effects. Ole has the ability to promote the effects of bevacizumab, preventing VEGFA, MMP-2 and -9 activities. A large body of clinical and experimental evidence indicates a key role of PI3K/Akt/mTOR hyper-activation in GBM biology, which in turn, sustains cell metabolism by promoting protein synthesis and suppressing autophagy, the major protein degradation pathway [161]. In our previous study, we showed that in BRAF melanoma cells, Ole affected cell proliferation by downregulation of the pAKT/pS6 pathway [162]. Further studies and validation are required, but it is likely that Ole, through its mTOR inhibition and autophagy induction, may help in the development of new therapeutic strategies against GBM.

A further histotype of cancer with no effective treatment is hepatocellular carcinoma (HCC), which forms metastases and develops drug resistance very early. Thus, an effective and low-toxicity therapy is required. Sherif et al. [163] has demonstrated that Ole greatly potentiates the reduction of MMP-7 gene expression in HepG2 cells induced by cisplatin. This ability was found to be instrumental to reduce the cancer promoting ability of nerve growth factor (NGF) on HepG2 cells. Indeed, mature NGF is secreted from its precursor form, pro-NGF, through MMP-7 proteolytic cleavage, and exerts a pro-survival effect on HCC cells. The co-stimulation of Ole with cisplatin also enhances caspase-3 gene expression in these cells, potentiating their apoptotic rate.

Thereafter, our laboratory [162] demonstrated that Ole enhances chemotherapy of BRAF melanoma cells, by downregulating the pAKT/pS6 pathway. Of a particular significance, the finding that Ole was able to promote the death effect of Everolimus, a mTOR inhibitor, in Vemurafenib-resistant BRAF melanoma cells, points to a possibility for its use in treating resistant melanoma cells. OleA also contributed to the cytotoxic effect of dacarbazine against BRAF melanoma cells. As in resistant melanoma cells, exposure to OleA was found to reverse trastuzumab resistance in HER2-overexpressing breast cancer cells [164].

In addition to chemotherapy, Ole has been proved to enhance the radiation sensitivity of nasopharyngeal carcinoma cells repressing mRNA-519d [165].

On the whole, oleuropein has attracted the attention of several researchers, due to its ability to discriminate between cancer and normal cells, inhibit proliferation, and promote apoptosis in several tumors, including those tumors which are considered the most aggressive, such as mesothelioma, GBM and melanoma. Finally, a real potentiating effect of oleuropein on standard chemotherapy has been demonstrated.

8. Bioavailability of Oleuropein

The beneficial effects of olive leaves or different preparations (e.g., infusions, extracts) have been known since ancient times, and have been used as traditional herbal remedies for the treatment of many diseases (such as diabetes mellitus, artherial hypertension, and bronchial asthma), or to alleviate their symptoms. Olive leaves can be a good source for the development of new potentially functional foods that may contribute, through basic nutrition, to optimal health conditions reducing the risk of NCDs. Therefore, special attention is paid to the recovery, recycling, and upgrading of food waste and by-products [166–169]. Ole is the major constituent of the secoiridoid family in olive leaves. HT is the primary metabolite of Ole/OleA, and shares some of the above described biological properties, but possesses a greater antioxidant capacity. Although this feature increases the importance of HT, obtaining it in a synthetic form is expensive, so methods using Ole as a source of HT production, have been developed [170–172].

The possibility that these biophenols may exert their biological effects depends on the probability of reaching key molecular targets in human tissues at a sufficient dose, which is dependant to their metabolism and bioavailability. However, the data on the metabolism of oleuropein from EVOO or olive leaves in humans are poor, and often the results on the level and the form found in plasma, and/or excreted in urine, are conflicting [173–175]. This discrepancy may be explained by the fact that oleuropein bioavailability is influenced by several factors, such as the route of administration, genotype, age, sex, interaction with food, and by the different extraction processes and analytical methods used [176]. A recent human trial showed that oral Ole ingestion is resistant to the acidic conditions of the stomach, and it is rapidly absorbed (55–60%) in the intestinal tract, reaching a maximum plasma concentration (23–30 min, depending on the preparation, liquid vs. capsule) earlier than conjugated metabolites of HT, glucuronidated and sulfated (at 64–93 min), that made up 96–99% of the Ole phenolic metabolites detected in plasma and urine after intake [177]. These data suggest a potential complete metabolization of Ole to HT, and other degradation products. The efficacy in vivo of these compounds regarding their absorption and metabolism kinetics once ingested, should be checked. In fact, the major criticism of the in vitro studies using these molecules is that the doses used are at greater concentrations (μmol/L–mmol/L) compared to the metabolite concentrations measured in plasma, which are only at the nmol/L concentration [178]. Therefore, delivery systems have been developed based on the esterification/lipophilisation and encapsulation of phenolic compounds, or using the creation of liposomes and/or nanoparticles of bioactive compounds, to increase their bioavailability and bioaccessibility [179–182].

Recently, much attention has been given to the gut microbiota, considered as a metabolic "organ" which impacts host nutrition, and may influence the bioavailability and bioaccessibility of olive phenolic compounds *via* biotransformation into other active substances, which have interesting beneficial health properties in bowel diseases [166,183]. Mosele et al. [184], in an in vitro model experiment, observed that Ole was rapidly deglycosylated during 6 h of incubation with human fecal microbiota, becoming OleA; the latter was degradated into elenolic acid and HT by microbial esterase activity, until it disappeared after 48 h. On the contrary, HT constantly increased during the same fermentation period. This finding was confirmed by the same authors in an in vivo study, that showed that after intake of phenol-rich olive oil for three weeks, the concentration of free HT was significantly increased in the faeces of all the participants in the study. Other reserches have shown that the conversion of Ole into HT was performed by lactic acid bacteria, in particular by *Lactobacillus plantarum* [185], and recently some authors developed oral granules for the co-delivery of *L. plantarum* and a standardized olive leaf extract (Phenolea®Active F, PhenoFarm s.r.L, Rome, Italy), in order to foster Ole metabolism and provide high levels of HT [171].

9. Conclusions

The evidence presented in this review demonstrates the several biological activities of oleuropein including antioxidant, anti-inflammatory and anticancer properties. Several epidemiological studies have reported a strict association between a diet rich in this polyphenol and the prevention of several NCDs, that are among the main causes of morbidity and mortality in the world. In conclusion, several in vitro and in vivo studies have demonstrated the ability of oleuropein (and its derivatives) to counteract oxidative stress and inflammation, to modulate the autophagy pathway, as well as to interfere in the amyloid aggregation process, suggesting its use, not only in the prevention, but also as a complementary therapy of some diseases. Despite the low bioavailabilty of oleuropein, some clinical trials reported several beneficial effects after administration of this compound, confirming the results obtained in vitro and in vivo studies. The effective daily dose of oleuropein to be administered in humans to achieve a theraputic effect is not known, but clinical and experimental evidence suggest that regular intake of this compound can be effective in the long term, representing a continuous low-intensity stimulus to the cellular defence against NCDs [186].

Author Contributions: Conceptualization, C.N.; writing—original draft preparation, C.N., J.R., L.C. and A.R. writing—review and editing, C.N. and J.R.; supervision, C.N.; funding acquisition, C.N. and L.C. All authors proofread the manuscript.

Funding: This study was financially supported by grants from Istituto Toscano Tumori and Ente Cassa di Risparmio di Firenze.

Acknowledgments: The authors thanks Annalisa Noce and Giulia Morrone for their critical revision, and Marcella Tarducci for the revision of the English language.

Conflicts of Interest: The authors declare no conflict of interest.

References

1. World Health Organization. *Global Action Plan for the Prevention and Control of Noncommunicable Diseases: 2013–2020*; WHO: Geneva, Switzerland, 2013; ISBN 978-92-4-150623-6.

2. Reddy, K.S. Global Burden of Disease Study 2015 provides GPS for global health 2030. *Lancet* **2016**, *388*, 1448–1449. [CrossRef]

3. Peña-Oyarzun, D.; Bravo-Sagua, R.; Diaz-Vega, A.; Aleman, L.; Chiong, M.; Garcia, L.; Bambs, C.; Troncoso, R.; Cifuentes, M.; Morselli, E.; et al. Autophagy and oxidative stress in non-communicable diseases: A matter of the inflammatory state? *Free Radic. Biol. Med.* **2018**, *124*, 61–78. [CrossRef] [PubMed]

4. Lavandero, S.; Chiong, M.; Rothermel, B.A.; Hill, J.A. Autophagy in cardiovascular biology. *J. Clin. Investig.* **2015**, *125*, 55–64. [CrossRef] [PubMed]

5. El Assar, M.; Angulo, J.; Rodríguez-Mañas, L. Oxidative stress and vascular inflammation in aging. *Free Radic. Biol. Med.* **2013**, *65*, 380–401. [CrossRef] [PubMed]

6. Levine, B.; Mizushima, N.; Virgin, H.W. Autophagy in immunity and inflammation. *Nature* **2011**, *469*, 323–335. [CrossRef]

7. Grosso, G.; Bella, F.; Godos, J.; Sciacca, S.; Del Rio, D.; Ray, S.; Galvano, F.; Giovannucci, E.L. Possible role of diet in cancer: Systematic review and multiple meta-analyses of dietary patterns, lifestyle factors, and cancer risk. *Nutr. Rev.* **2017**, *75*, 405–419. [CrossRef]

8. Grosso, G.; Godos, J.; Lamuela-Raventos, R.; Ray, S.; Micek, A.; Pajak, A.; Sciacca, S.; D'Orazio, N.; Del Rio, D.; Galvano, F. A comprehensive meta-analysis on dietary flavonoid and lignan intake and cancer risk: Level of evidence and limitations. *Mol. Nutr. Food Res.* **2017**, *61*, 1600930. [CrossRef]

9. Grosso, G.; Micek, A.; Godos, J.; Pajak, A.; Sciacca, S.; Galvano, F.; Giovannucci, E.L. Dietary Flavonoid and Lignan Intake and Mortality in Prospective Cohort Studies: Systematic Review and Dose-Response Meta-Analysis. *Am. J. Epidemiol.* **2017**, *185*, 1304–1316. [CrossRef]

10. Gaforio, J.J.; Visioli, F.; Alarcón-de-la-Lastra, C.; Castañer, O.; Delgado-Rodríguez, M.; Fitó, M.; Hernández, A.F.; Huertas, J.R.; Martínez-González, M.A.; Menendez, J.A.; et al. Virgin Olive Oil and Health: Summary of the III International Conference on Virgin Olive Oil and Health Consensus Report, JAEN (Spain) 2018. *Nutrients* **2019**, *11*, 2039. [CrossRef]

11. Servili, M.; Sordini, B.; Esposto, S.; Urbani, S.; Veneziani, G.; Di Maio, I.; Selvaggini, R.; Taticchi, A. Biological Activities of Phenolic Compounds of Extra Virgin Olive Oil. *Antioxidants* **2013**, *3*, 1–23. [CrossRef]

12. Waterman, E.; Lockwood, B. Active components and clinical applications of olive oil. *Altern. Med. Rev.* **2007**, *12*, 331–342. [PubMed]

13. Casaburi, I.; Puoci, F.; Chimento, A.; Sirianni, R.; Ruggiero, C.; Avena, P.; Pezzi, V. Potential of olive oil phenols as chemopreventive and therapeutic agents against cancer: A review of in vitro studies. *Mol. Nutr. Food Res.* **2013**, *57*, 71–83. [CrossRef] [PubMed]

14. Amiot, M.J.; Fleuriet, A.; Macheix, J.J. Importance and evolution of phenolic compounds in olive during growth and maturation. *J. Agric. Food Chem.* **1986**, *34*, 823–826. [CrossRef]

15. Le Tutour, B.; Guedon, D. Antioxidative activities of *Olea europaea* leaves and related phenolic compounds. *Phytochemistry* **1992**, *31*, 1173–1178. [CrossRef]

16. Soler-Rivas, C.; Espín, J.C.; Wichers, H.J. Oleuropein and related compounds. *J. Sci. Food Agric.* **2000**, *80*, 1013–1023. [CrossRef]

17. Ryan, D.; Robards, K.; Prenzler, P.; Jardine, D.; Herlt, T.; Antolovich, M. Liquid chromatography with electrospray ionisation mass spectrometric detection of phenolic compounds from *Olea europaea*. *J. Chromatogr. A* **1999**, *855*, 529–537. [CrossRef]

18. Servili, M.; Esposto, S.; Fabiani, R.; Urbani, S.; Taticchi, A.; Mariucci, F.; Selvaggini, R.; Montedoro, G.F. Phenolic compounds in olive oil: Antioxidant, health and organoleptic activities according to their chemical structure. *Inflammopharmacology* **2009**, *17*, 76–84. [CrossRef]

19. Lozano-Castellón, J.; López-Yerena, A.; Rinaldi de Alvarenga, J.F.; Romero del Castillo-Alba, J.; Vallverdú-Queralt, A.; Escribano-Ferrer, E.; Lamuela-Raventós, R.M. Health-promoting properties of oleocanthal and oleacein: Two secoiridoids from extra-virgin olive oil. *Crit. Rev. Food Sci. Nutr.* **2019**, 1–17. [CrossRef]

20. Beauchamp, G.K.; Keast, R.S.J.; Morel, D.; Lin, J.; Pika, J.; Han, Q.; Lee, C.-H.; Smith, A.B.; Breslin, P.A.S. Ibuprofen-like activity in extra-virgin olive oil. *Nature* **2005**, *437*, 45–46. [CrossRef]

21. Filipek, A.; Czerwińska, M.E.; Kiss, A.K.; Wrzosek, M.; Naruszewicz, M. Oleacein enhances anti-inflammatory activity of human macrophages by increasing CD163 receptor expression. *Phytomedicine* **2015**, *22*, 1255–1261. [CrossRef]
22. Kanakis, P.; Termentzi, A.; Michel, T.; Gikas, E.; Halabalaki, M.; Skaltsounis, A.-L. From Olive Drupes to Olive Oil. An HPLC-Orbitrap-based Qualitative and Quantitative Exploration of Olive Key Metabolites. *Planta Med.* **2013**, *79*, 1576–1587. [CrossRef] [PubMed]
23. EFSA Panel on Dietetic Products; Nutrition and Allergies (NDA). Scientific Opinion on the substantiation of health claims related to polyphenols in olive and protection of LDL particles from oxidative damage (ID 1333, 1638, 1639, 1696, 2865), maintenance of normal blood HDL cholesterol concentrations (ID 1639), mainte: Polyphenols in olive related health claims. *EFSA J.* **2011**, *9*, 2033.
24. The European Commission. Establishing a list of permitted health claims made on foods, other than those referring to the reduction of disease risk and to children's development and health—Commission Regulation (EU) No 432/2012. *Eur-Lex* **2012**, *55*, 1–40.
25. Piroddi, M.; Albini, A.; Fabiani, R.; Giovannelli, L.; Luceri, C.; Natella, F.; Rosignoli, P.; Rossi, T.; Taticchi, A.; Servili, M.; et al. Nutrigenomics of extra-virgin olive oil: A review: Nutrigenomics of extra-virgin olive oil. *BioFactors* **2017**, *43*, 17–41. [CrossRef] [PubMed]
26. Romani, A.; Mulas, S.; Heimler, D. Polyphenols and secoiridoids in raw material (*Olea europaea* L. leaves) and commercial food supplements. *Eur. Food Res. Technol.* **2017**, *243*, 429–435. [CrossRef]
27. Capasso, R.; Evidente, A.; Scognamiglio, F. A simple thin layer chromatographic method to detect the main polyphenols occurring in olive oil vegetation waters. *Phytochem. Anal.* **1992**, *3*, 270–275. [CrossRef]
28. Ficarra, P.; Ficarra, R.; de Pasquale, A.; Monforte, M.T.; Calabrò, M.L. HPLC analysis of oleuropein and some flavonoids in leaf and bud of *Olea europaea* L. *Farmaco* **1991**, *46*, 803–815. [PubMed]
29. De Laurentis, N.; Crescenzo, G.; Lai, O.R.; Milillo, M.A. Investigation on the extraction and concentration of oleuropein and flavonoids in *Olea europaea* L. based products. *Pharm. Pharmacol. Lett.* **1997**, *7*, 27–30.
30. Baracco, A.; Bertin, G.; Gnocco, E.; Legorat, M.; Sedocco, S.; Catinella, S.; Favretto, D.; Traldi, P. A comparison of the combination of fast-atom bombardment with tandem mass spectrometry and of gas chromatography with mass spectrometry in the analysis of a mixture of kaempferol, kaempferide, luteolin and oleouropein. *Rapid Commun. Mass Spectrom.* **1995**, *9*, 427–436. [CrossRef]
31. Brenes, M.; Garcia, P.; Duran, M.C.; Garrido, A. Concentration of Phenolic Compounds Change in Storage Brines of Ripe Olives. *J. Food Sci.* **1993**, *58*, 347–350. [CrossRef]
32. Menendez, J.A.; Joven, J.; Aragonès, G.; Barrajón-Catalán, E.; Beltrán-Debón, R.; Borrás-Linares, I.; Camps, J.; Corominas-Faja, B.; Cufí, S.; Fernández-Arroyo, S.; et al. Xenohormetic and anti-aging activity of secoiridoid polyphenols present in extra virgin olive oil: A new family of gerosuppressant agents. *Cell Cycle* **2013**, *12*, 555–578. [CrossRef]
33. Visioli, F.; Bellomo, G.; Galli, C. Free Radical-Scavenging Properties of Olive Oil Polyphenols. *Biochem. Biophys. Res. Commun.* **1998**, *247*, 60–64. [CrossRef] [PubMed]
34. Visioli, F.; Bellomo, G.; Montedoro, G.; Galli, C. Low density lipoprotein oxidation is inhibited in vitro by olive oil constituents. *Atherosclerosis* **1995**, *117*, 25–32. [CrossRef]
35. Visioli, F.; Galli, C. Oleuropein protects low density lipoprotein from oxidation. *Life Sci.* **1994**, *55*, 1965–1971. [CrossRef]
36. Coni, E.; Di Benedetto, R.; Di Pasquale, M.; Masella, R.; Modesti, D.; Mattei, R.; Carlini, E.A. Protective effect of oleuropein, an olive oil biophenol, on low density lipoprotein oxidizability in rabbits. *Lipids* **2000**, *35*, 45–54. [CrossRef] [PubMed]
37. Visioli, F.; Caruso, D.; Galli, C.; Viappiani, S.; Galli, G.; Sala, A. Olive Oils Rich in Natural Catecholic Phenols Decrease Isoprostane Excretion in Humans. *Biochem. Biophys. Res. Commun.* **2000**, *278*, 797–799. [CrossRef]
38. de la Puerta, R.; Dominguez, M.E.M.; Ruiz-Gutierrez, V.; Flavill, J.A.; Hoult, J.R.S. Effects of virgin olive oil phenolics on scavenging of reactive nitrogen species and upon nitrergic neurotransmission. *Life Sci.* **2001**, *69*, 1213–1222. [CrossRef]
39. Manna, C.; Migliardi, V.; Golino, P.; Scognamiglio, A.; Galletti, P.; Chiariello, M.; Zappia, V. Oleuropein prevents oxidative myocardial injury induced by ischemia and reperfusion. *J. Nutr. Biochem.* **2004**, *15*, 461–466. [CrossRef]

40. Parzonko, A.; Czerwińska, M.E.; Kiss, A.K.; Naruszewicz, M. Oleuropein and oleacein may restore biological functions of endothelial progenitor cells impaired by angiotensin II via activation of Nrf2/heme oxygenase-1 pathway. *Phytomedicine* **2013**, *20*, 1088–1094. [CrossRef]

41. Al-Azzawie, H.F.; Alhamdani, M.-S.S. Hypoglycemic and antioxidant effect of oleuropein in alloxan-diabetic rabbits. *Life Sci.* **2006**, *78*, 1371–1377. [CrossRef]

42. Jemai, H.; El Feki, A.; Sayadi, S. Antidiabetic and Antioxidant Effects of Hydroxytyrosol and Oleuropein from Olive Leaves in Alloxan-Diabetic Rats. *J. Agric. Food Chem.* **2009**, *57*, 8798–8804. [CrossRef]

43. Kotyzová, D.; Hodková, A.; Eybl, V. The effect of olive oil phenolics—Hydroxytyrosol and oleuropein on antioxidant defence status in acute arsenic exposed rats. *Toxicol. Lett.* **2011**, *205*, S222. [CrossRef]

44. Dessì, M.; Noce, A.; Agnoli, A.; De Angelis, S.; Fuiano, L.; Tozzo, C.; Taccone-Gallucci, M.; Fuiano, G.; Federici, G. The usefulness of the prognostic inflammatory and nutritional index (PINI) in a haemodialysis population. *Nutr. Metab. Cardiovasc. Dis.* **2009**, *19*, 811–815. [CrossRef] [PubMed]

45. Jacob, K.D.; Noren Hooten, N.; Trzeciak, A.R.; Evans, M.K. Markers of oxidant stress that are clinically relevant in aging and age-related disease. *Mech. Ageing Dev.* **2013**, *134*, 139–157. [CrossRef] [PubMed]

46. Bandeen-Roche, K.; Walston, J.D.; Huang, Y.; Semba, R.D.; Ferrucci, L. Measuring Systemic Inflammatory Regulation in Older Adults: Evidence and Utility. *Rejuvenation Res.* **2009**, *12*, 403–410. [CrossRef] [PubMed]

47. Barzilay, J.I. Insulin Resistance and Inflammation as Precursors of Frailty: The Cardiovascular Health Study. *Arch. Intern. Med.* **2007**, *167*, 635. [CrossRef]

48. Collerton, J.; Martin-Ruiz, C.; Davies, K.; Hilkens, C.M.; Isaacs, J.; Kolenda, C.; Parker, C.; Dunn, M.; Catt, M.; Jagger, C.; et al. Frailty and the role of inflammation, immunosenescence and cellular ageing in the very old: Cross-sectional findings from the Newcastle 85+ Study. *Mech. Ageing Dev.* **2012**, *133*, 456–466. [CrossRef]

49. Fried, L.P.; Xue, Q.-L.; Cappola, A.R.; Ferrucci, L.; Chaves, P.; Varadhan, R.; Guralnik, J.M.; Leng, S.X.; Semba, R.D.; Walston, J.D.; et al. Nonlinear Multisystem Physiological Dysregulation Associated With Frailty in Older Women: Implications for Etiology and Treatment. *J. Gerontol. Ser. A Biol. Sci. Med Sci.* **2009**, *64*, 1049–1057. [CrossRef]

50. Hassen, I.; Casabianca, H.; Hosni, K. Biological activities of the natural antioxidant oleuropein: Exceeding the expectation—A mini-review. *J. Funct. Foods* **2015**, *18*, 926–940. [CrossRef]

51. Estruch, R. Effects of a Mediterranean-Style Diet on Cardiovascular Risk Factors: A Randomized Trial. *Ann. Intern. Med.* **2006**, *145*, 1–11. [CrossRef]

52. Estruch, R. Anti-inflammatory effects of the Mediterranean diet: The experience of the PREDIMED study. *Proc. Nutr. Soc.* **2010**, *69*, 333–340. [CrossRef]

53. Mena, M.-P.; Sacanella, E.; Vazquez-Agell, M.; Morales, M.; Fitó, M.; Escoda, R.; Serrano-Martínez, M.; Salas-Salvadó, J.; Benages, N.; Casas, R.; et al. Inhibition of circulating immune cell activation: A molecular antiinflammatory effect of the Mediterranean diet. *Am. J. Clin. Nutr.* **2009**, *89*, 248–256. [CrossRef] [PubMed]

54. Urpi-Sarda, M.; Casas, R.; Chiva-Blanch, G.; Romero-Mamani, E.S.; Valderas-Martínez, P.; Salas-Salvadó, J.; Covas, M.I.; Toledo, E.; Andres-Lacueva, C.; Llorach, R.; et al. The Mediterranean Diet Pattern and Its Main Components Are Associated with Lower Plasma Concentrations of Tumor Necrosis Factor Receptor 60 in Patients at High Risk for Cardiovascular Disease. *J. Nutr.* **2012**, *142*, 1019–1025. [CrossRef] [PubMed]

55. Di Daniele, N.; Di Renzo, L.; Noce, A.; Iacopino, L.; Ferraro, P.M.; Rizzo, M.; Sarlo, F.; Domino, E.; De Lorenzo, A. Effects of Italian Mediterranean organic diet vs. low-protein diet in nephropathic patients according to MTHFR genotypes. *J. Nephrol.* **2014**, *27*, 529–536. [CrossRef] [PubMed]

56. Zhang, X.; Li, H.; Jin, H.; Ebin, Z.; Brodsky, S.; Goligorsky, M.S. Effects of homocysteine on endothelial nitric oxide production. *Am. J. Physiol. -Ren. Physiol.* **2000**, *279*, F671–F678. [CrossRef] [PubMed]

57. Pastore, A.; Noce, A.; Di Giovamberardino, G.; De Stefano, A.; Callà, C.; Zenobi, R.; Dessì, M.; Di Daniele, N. Homocysteine, cysteine, folate and vitamin B12 status in type 2 diabetic patients with chronic kidney disease. *J. Nephrol.* **2015**, *28*, 571–576. [CrossRef]

58. Giamarellos-Bourboulis, E.J.; Geladopoulos, T.; Chrisofos, M.; Koutoukas, P.; Vassiliadis, J.; Alexandrou, I.; Tsaganos, T.; Sabracos, L.; Karagianni, V.; Pelekanou, E.; et al. Oleuropein: A novel immunomodulator conferring prolonged survival in experimental sepsis by pseudomonas aeruginosa. *Shock* **2006**, *26*, 410–416. [CrossRef]

59. Impellizzeri, D.; Esposito, E.; Mazzon, E.; Paterniti, I.; Di Paola, R.; Bramanti, P.; Morittu, V.M.; Procopio, A.; Britti, D.; Cuzzocrea, S. The effects of oleuropein aglycone, an olive oil compound, in a mouse model of carrageenan-induced pleurisy. *Clin. Nutr.* **2011**, *30*, 533–540. [CrossRef]

60. de la Puerta, R.; Gutierrez, V.R.; Hoult, J.R.S. Inhibition of leukocyte 5-lipoxygenase by phenolics from virgin olive oil. *Biochem. Pharmacol.* **1999**, *57*, 445–449. [CrossRef]

61. Miles, E.A.; Zoubouli, P.; Calder, P.C. Differential anti-inflammatory effects of phenolic compounds from extra virgin olive oil identified in human whole blood cultures. *Nutrition* **2005**, *21*, 389–394. [CrossRef]

62. Ryu, S.-J.; Choi, H.-S.; Yoon, K.-Y.; Lee, O.-H.; Kim, K.-J.; Lee, B.-Y. Oleuropein Suppresses LPS-Induced Inflammatory Responses in RAW 264.7 Cell and Zebrafish. *J. Agric. Food Chem.* **2015**, *63*, 2098–2105. [CrossRef]

63. Margheri, F.; Menicacci, B.; Laurenzana, A.; Del Rosso, M.; Fibbi, G.; Cipolleschi, M.G.; Ruzzolini, J.; Nediani, C.; Mocali, A.; Giovannelli, L. Oleuropein aglycone attenuates the pro-angiogenic phenotype of senescent fibroblasts: A functional study in endothelial cells. *J. Funct. Foods* **2019**, *53*, 219–226. [CrossRef]

64. Giner, E.; Recio, M.-C.; Ríos, J.-L.; Giner, R.-M. Oleuropein Protects against Dextran Sodium Sulfate-Induced Chronic Colitis in Mice. *J. Nat. Prod.* **2013**, *76*, 1113–1120. [CrossRef]

65. Lee, B.; Shim, I.; Lee, H.; Hahm, D.-H. Effect of oleuropein on cognitive deficits and changes in hippocampal brain-derived neurotrophic factor and cytokine expression in a rat model of post-traumatic stress disorder. *J. Nat. Med.* **2018**, *72*, 44–56. [CrossRef]

66. Khalatbary, A.; Zarrinjoei, G. Anti-Inflammatory Effect of Oleuropein in Experimental Rat Spinal Cord Trauma. *Iran. Red Crescent Med. J.* **2012**, *14*, 229–234.

67. Puel, C.; Mathey, J.; Agalias, A.; Kati-coulibaly, S.; Mardon, J.; Obled, C.; Davicco, M.-J.; Lebecque, P.; Horcajada, M.-N.; Skaltsounis, A.L.; et al. Dose–response study of effect of oleuropein, an olive oil polyphenol, in an ovariectomy/inflammation experimental model of bone loss in the rat. *Clin. Nutr.* **2006**, *25*, 859–868. [CrossRef]

68. Larussa, T.; Oliverio, M.; Suraci, E.; Greco, M.; Placida, R.; Gervasi, S.; Marasco, R.; Imeneo, M.; Paolino, D.; Tucci, L.; et al. Oleuropein Decreases Cyclooxygenase-2 and Interleukin-17 Expression and Attenuates Inflammatory Damage in Colonic Samples from Ulcerative Colitis Patients. *Nutrients* **2017**, *9*, 391. [CrossRef]

69. Park, S.; Choi, Y.; Um, S.-J.; Yoon, S.K.; Park, T. Oleuropein attenuates hepatic steatosis induced by high-fat diet in mice. *J. Hepatol.* **2011**, *54*, 984–993. [CrossRef]

70. Poudyal, H.; Campbell, F.; Brown, L. Olive Leaf Extract Attenuates Cardiac, Hepatic, and Metabolic Changes in High Carbohydrate–, High Fat–Fed Rats. *J. Nutr.* **2010**, *140*, 946–953. [CrossRef]

71. Murotomi, K.; Umeno, A.; Yasunaga, M.; Shichiri, M.; Ishida, N.; Koike, T.; Matsuo, T.; Abe, H.; Yoshida, Y.; Nakajima, Y. Oleuropein-Rich Diet Attenuates Hyperglycemia and Impaired Glucose Tolerance in Type 2 Diabetes Model Mouse. *J. Agric. Food Chem.* **2015**, *63*, 6715–6722. [CrossRef]

72. Lockyer, S.; Rowland, I.; Spencer, J.P.E.; Yaqoob, P.; Stonehouse, W. Impact of phenolic-rich olive leaf extract on blood pressure, plasma lipids and inflammatory markers: A randomised controlled trial. *Eur. J. Nutr.* **2017**, *56*, 1421–1432. [CrossRef]

73. Susalit, E.; Agus, N.; Effendi, I.; Tjandrawinata, R.R.; Nofiarny, D.; Perrinjaquet-Moccetti, T.; Verbruggen, M. Olive (*Olea europaea*) leaf extract effective in patients with stage-1 hypertension: Comparison with Captopril. *Phytomedicine* **2011**, *18*, 251–258. [CrossRef]

74. Rigacci, S.; Guidotti, V.; Bucciantini, M.; Parri, M.; Nediani, C.; Cerbai, E.; Stefani, M.; Berti, A. Oleuropein aglycon prevents cytotoxic amyloid aggregation of human amylin. *J. Nutr. Biochem.* **2010**, *21*, 726–735. [CrossRef] [PubMed]

75. Eidi, A.; Eidi, M.; Darzi, R. Antidiabetic effect of *Olea europaea* L. in normal and diabetic rats. *Phytother. Res.* **2009**, *23*, 347–350. [CrossRef] [PubMed]

76. Hadrich, F.; Garcia, M.; Maalej, A.; Moldes, M.; Isoda, H.; Feve, B.; Sayadi, S. Oleuropein activated AMPK and induced insulin sensitivity in C2C12 muscle cells. *Life Sci.* **2016**, *151*, 167–173. [CrossRef]

77. Carnevale, R.; Silvestri, R.; Loffredo, L.; Novo, M.; Cammisotto, V.; Castellani, V.; Bartimoccia, S.; Nocella, C.; Violi, F. Oleuropein, a component of extra virgin olive oil, lowers postprandial glycaemia in healthy subjects: Oleuropein lowers postprandial glycaemia in healthy subjects. *Br. J. Clin. Pharmacol.* **2018**, *84*, 1566–1574. [CrossRef] [PubMed]

78. de Bock, M.; Derraik, J.G.B.; Brennan, C.M.; Biggs, J.B.; Morgan, P.E.; Hodgkinson, S.C.; Hofman, P.L.; Cutfield, W.S. Olive (*Olea europaea* L.) Leaf Polyphenols Improve Insulin Sensitivity in Middle-Aged Overweight Men: A Randomized, Placebo-Controlled, Crossover Trial. *PLoS ONE* **2013**, *8*, e57622. [CrossRef]

79. Wainstein, J.; Ganz, T.; Boaz, M.; Bar Dayan, Y.; Dolev, E.; Kerem, Z.; Madar, Z. Olive Leaf Extract as a Hypoglycemic Agent in Both Human Diabetic Subjects and in Rats. *J. Med. Food* **2012**, *15*, 605–610. [CrossRef]

80. Alkhateeb, H.; Al-Duais, M.; Qnais, E. Beneficial effects of oleuropein on glucose uptake and on parameters relevant to the normal homeostatic mechanisms of glucose regulation in rat skeletal muscle. *Phytother. Res.* **2018**, *32*, 651–656. [CrossRef]

81. Andreadou, I.; Iliodromitis, E.K.; Mikros, E.; Constantinou, M.; Agalias, A.; Magiatis, P.; Skaltsounis, A.L.; Kamber, E.; Tsantili-Kakoulidou, A.; Kremastinos, D.T. The olive constituent oleuropein exhibits anti-ischemic, antioxidative, and hypolipidemic effects in anesthetized rabbits. *J. Nutr.* **2006**, *136*, 2213–2219. [CrossRef]

82. Hur, W.; Kim, S.W.; Lee, Y.K.; Choi, J.E.; Hong, S.W.; Song, M.J.; Bae, S.H.; Park, T.; Um, S.-J.; Yoon, S.K. Oleuropein reduces free fatty acid-induced lipogenesis via lowered extracellular signal-regulated kinase activation in hepatocytes. *Nutr. Res.* **2012**, *32*, 778–786. [CrossRef]

83. Domitrović, R.; Jakovac, H.; Marchesi, V.V.; Šain, I.; Romić, Ž.; Rahelić, D. Preventive and therapeutic effects of oleuropein against carbon tetrachloride-induced liver damage in mice. *Pharmacol. Res.* **2012**, *65*, 451–464. [CrossRef] [PubMed]

84. Kim, S.W.; Hur, W.; Li, T.Z.; Lee, Y.K.; Choi, J.E.; Hong, S.W.; Lyoo, K.-S.; You, C.R.; Jung, E.S.; Jung, C.K.; et al. Oleuropein prevents the progression of steatohepatitis to hepatic fibrosis induced by a high-fat diet in mice. *Exp. Mol. Med.* **2014**, *46*, e92. [CrossRef] [PubMed]

85. Lou-Bonafonte, J.M.; Arnal, C.; Navarro, M.A.; Osada, J. Efficacy of bioactive compounds from extra virgin olive oil to modulate atherosclerosis development. *Mol. Nutr. Food Res.* **2012**, *56*, 1043–1057. [CrossRef]

86. Carluccio, M.A.; Siculella, L.; Ancora, M.A.; Massaro, M.; Scoditti, E.; Storelli, C.; Visioli, F.; Distante, A.; De Caterina, R. Olive Oil and Red Wine Antioxidant Polyphenols Inhibit Endothelial Activation: Antiatherogenic Properties of Mediterranean Diet Phytochemicals. *Arterioscler. Thromb. Vasc. Biol.* **2003**, *23*, 622–629. [CrossRef] [PubMed]

87. Dell'Agli, M.; Fagnani, R.; Mitro, N.; Scurati, S.; Masciadri, M.; Mussoni, L.; Galli, G.V.; Bosisio, E.; Crestani, M.; De Fabiani, E.; et al. Minor Components of Olive Oil Modulate Proatherogenic Adhesion Molecules Involved in Endothelial Activation. *J. Agric. Food Chem.* **2006**, *54*, 3259–3264. [CrossRef]

88. Lockyer, S.; Corona, G.; Yaqoob, P.; Spencer, J.P.E.; Rowland, I. Secoiridoids delivered as olive leaf extract induce acute improvements in human vascular function and reduction of an inflammatory cytokine: A randomised, double-blind, placebo-controlled, cross-over trial. *Br. J. Nutr.* **2015**, *114*, 75–83. [CrossRef]

89. Dell'Agli, M.; Maschi, O.; Galli, G.V.; Fagnani, R.; Dal Cero, E.; Caruso, D.; Bosisio, E. Inhibition of platelet aggregation by olive oil phenols via cAMP-phosphodiesterase. *Br. J. Nutr.* **2008**, *99*, 945–951. [CrossRef]

90. Stefani, M.; Rigacci, S. Beneficial properties of natural phenols: Highlight on protection against pathological conditions associated with amyloid aggregation: Phenols Protection Against Amyloid Diseases. *BioFactors* **2014**, *40*, 482–493. [CrossRef]

91. Sato, S.; Hattori, N. Dopaminergic Neuron-Specific Autophagy-Deficient Mice. In *Mitophagy*; Hattori, N., Saiki, S., Eds.; Springer: New York, NY, USA, 2018; Volume 1759, pp. 173–175. ISBN 978-1-4939-7749-9.

92. Komatsu, M.; Waguri, S.; Ueno, T.; Iwata, J.; Murata, S.; Tanida, I.; Ezaki, J.; Mizushima, N.; Ohsumi, Y.; Uchiyama, Y.; et al. Impairment of starvation-induced and constitutive autophagy in *Atg7* -deficient mice. *J. Cell Biol.* **2005**, *169*, 425–434. [CrossRef]

93. Yoshizaki, T.; Kusunoki, C.; Kondo, M.; Yasuda, M.; Kume, S.; Morino, K.; Sekine, O.; Ugi, S.; Uzu, T.; Nishio, Y.; et al. Autophagy regulates inflammation in adipocytes. *Biochem. Biophys. Res. Commun.* **2012**, *417*, 352–357. [CrossRef]

94. Yang, L.; Li, P.; Fu, S.; Calay, E.S.; Hotamisligil, G.S. Defective Hepatic Autophagy in Obesity Promotes ER Stress and Causes Insulin Resistance. *Cell Metab.* **2010**, *11*, 467–478. [CrossRef] [PubMed]

95. Park, H.-W.; Park, H.; Semple, I.A.; Jang, I.; Ro, S.-H.; Kim, M.; Cazares, V.A.; Stuenkel, E.L.; Kim, J.-J.; Kim, J.S.; et al. Pharmacological correction of obesity-induced autophagy arrest using calcium channel blockers. *Nat. Commun.* **2014**, *5*, 4834. [CrossRef] [PubMed]

96. Kaushik, S.; Rodriguez-Navarro, J.A.; Arias, E.; Kiffin, R.; Sahu, S.; Schwartz, G.J.; Cuervo, A.M.; Singh, R. Autophagy in Hypothalamic AgRP Neurons Regulates Food Intake and Energy Balance. *Cell Metab.* **2011**, *14*, 173–183. [CrossRef] [PubMed]

97. Mir, S.U.R.; George, N.M.; Zahoor, L.; Harms, R.; Guinn, Z.; Sarvetnick, N.E. Inhibition of Autophagic Turnover in β-Cells by Fatty Acids and Glucose Leads to Apoptotic Cell Death. *J. Biol. Chem.* **2015**, *290*, 6071–6085. [CrossRef] [PubMed]

98. Nemchenko, A.; Chiong, M.; Turer, A.; Lavandero, S.; Hill, J.A. Autophagy as a therapeutic target in cardiovascular disease. *J. Mol. Cell. Cardiol.* **2011**, *51*, 584–593. [CrossRef] [PubMed]

99. Rifki, O.F.; Hill, J.A. Cardiac Autophagy: Good With the Bad. *J. Cardiovasc. Pharmacol.* **2012**, *60*, 248–252. [CrossRef]

100. Ke, P.; Shao, B.-Z.; Xu, Z.-Q.; Chen, X.-W.; Liu, C. Intestinal Autophagy and Its Pharmacological Control in Inflammatory Bowel Disease. *Front. Immunol.* **2017**, *7*, 695. [CrossRef]

101. Fang, L.; Li, B.; Guan, J.; Xu, H.; Shen, G.; Gao, Q.; Qin, Z. Transcription factor EB is involved in autophagy-mediated chemoresistance to doxorubicin in human cancer cells. *Acta Pharm. Sin.* **2017**, *38*, 1305–1316. [CrossRef]

102. de Pablos, R.M.; Espinosa-Oliva, A.M.; Hornedo-Ortega, R.; Cano, M.; Arguelles, S. Hydroxytyrosol protects from aging process via AMPK and autophagy; a review of its effects on cancer, metabolic syndrome, osteoporosis, immune-mediated and neurodegenerative diseases. *Pharmacol. Res.* **2019**, *143*, 58–72. [CrossRef]

103. Rigacci, S.; Miceli, C.; Nediani, C.; Berti, A.; Cascella, R.; Pantano, D.; Nardiello, P.; Luccarini, I.; Casamenti, F.; Stefani, M. Oleuropein aglycone induces autophagy via the AMPK/mTOR signalling pathway: A mechanistic insight. *Oncotarget* **2015**, *6*, 35344–35357. [CrossRef]

104. Grossi, C.; Rigacci, S.; Ambrosini, S.; Ed Dami, T.; Luccarini, I.; Traini, C.; Failli, P.; Berti, A.; Casamenti, F.; Stefani, M. The polyphenol oleuropein aglycone protects TgCRND8 mice against Aß plaque pathology. *PLoS ONE* **2013**, *8*, e71702. [CrossRef] [PubMed]

105. Chung, S.; Yao, H.; Caito, S.; Hwang, J.; Arunachalam, G.; Rahman, I. Regulation of SIRT1 in cellular functions: Role of polyphenols. *Arch. Biochem. Biophys.* **2010**, *501*, 79–90. [CrossRef] [PubMed]

106. Luccarini, I.; Pantano, D.; Nardiello, P.; Cavone, L.; Lapucci, A.; Miceli, C.; Nediani, C.; Berti, A.; Stefani, M.; Casamenti, F. The Polyphenol Oleuropein Aglycone Modulates the PARP1-SIRT1 Interplay: An In Vitro and In Vivo Study. *J. Alzheimers Dis.* **2016**, *54*, 737–750. [CrossRef] [PubMed]

107. Miceli, C.; Santin, Y.; Manzella, N.; Coppini, R.; Berti, A.; Stefani, M.; Parini, A.; Mialet-Perez, J.; Nediani, C. Oleuropein Aglycone Protects against MAO-A-Induced Autophagy Impairment and Cardiomyocyte Death through Activation of TFEB. *Oxidative Med. Cell. Longev.* **2018**, *2018*, 8067592. [CrossRef] [PubMed]

108. Manni, M.E.; Rigacci, S.; Borchi, E.; Bargelli, V.; Miceli, C.; Giordano, C.; Raimondi, L.; Nediani, C. Monoamine Oxidase Is Overactivated in Left and Right Ventricles from Ischemic Hearts: An Intriguing Therapeutic Target. *Oxidative Med. Cell. Longev.* **2016**, *2016*, 4375418. [CrossRef] [PubMed]

109. Nediani, C.; Raimondi, L.; Borchi, E.; Cerbai, E. Nitric Oxide/Reactive Oxygen Species Generation and Nitroso/Redox Imbalance in Heart Failure: From Molecular Mechanisms to Therapeutic Implications. *Antioxid. Redox Signal.* **2011**, *14*, 289–331. [CrossRef]

110. Santin, Y.; Sicard, P.; Vigneron, F.; Guilbeau-Frugier, C.; Dutaur, M.; Lairez, O.; Couderc, B.; Manni, D.; Korolchuk, V.I.; Lezoualc'h, F.; et al. Oxidative Stress by Monoamine Oxidase-A Impairs Transcription Factor EB Activation and Autophagosome Clearance, Leading to Cardiomyocyte Necrosis and Heart Failure. *Antioxid. Redox Signal.* **2016**, *25*, 10–27. [CrossRef]

111. Anderson, E.J.; Efird, J.T.; Davies, S.W.; O'Neal, W.T.; Darden, T.M.; Thayne, K.A.; Katunga, L.A.; Kindell, L.C.; Ferguson, T.B.; Anderson, C.A.; et al. Monoamine Oxidase is a Major Determinant of Redox Balance in Human Atrial Myocardium and is Associated With Postoperative Atrial Fibrillation. *J. Am. Heart Assoc.* **2014**, *3*, e000713. [CrossRef]

112. Porcu, C.; Sideri, S.; Martini, M.; Cocomazzi, A.; Galli, A.; Tarantino, G.; Balsano, C. Oleuropein Induces AMPK-Dependent Autophagy in NAFLD Mice, Regardless of the Gender. *Int. J. Mol. Sci.* **2018**, *19*, 3948. [CrossRef]

113. Lu, H.-Y.; Zhu, J.-S.; Zhang, Z.; Shen, W.-J.; Jiang, S.; Long, Y.-F.; Wu, B.; Ding, T.; Huan, F.; Wang, S.-L. Hydroxytyrosol and Oleuropein Inhibit Migration and Invasion of MDA-MB-231 Triple-Negative Breast Cancer Cell via Induction of Autophagy. *Anticancer Agents Med. Chem.* **2019**. [CrossRef]

114. Papachristodoulou, A.; Tsoukala, M.; Benaki, D.; Kostidis, S.; Gioti, K.; Aligiannis, N.; Pratsinis, H.; Kletsas, D.; Skaltsounis, A.-L.; Mikros, E.; et al. Oleuropein is a Powerful Sensitizer of Doxorubicin-mediated Killing of Prostate Cancer Cells and Exerts Its Action via Induction of Autophagy. *J. Cancer Res. Treat.* **2018**, *4*, 61–68. [CrossRef]

115. Stefani, M.; Dobson, C.M. Protein aggregation and aggregate toxicity: New insights into protein folding, misfolding diseases and biological evolution. *J. Mol. Med.* **2003**, *81*, 678–699. [CrossRef] [PubMed]

116. Chiti, F.; Dobson, C.M. Protein Misfolding, Amyloid Formation, and Human Disease: A Summary of Progress Over the Last Decade. *Annu. Rev. Biochem.* **2017**, *86*, 27–68. [CrossRef] [PubMed]

117. Rigacci, S.; Stefani, M. Nutraceutical Properties of Olive Oil Polyphenols. An Itinerary from Cultured Cells through Animal Models to Humans. *Int. J. Mol. Sci.* **2016**, *17*, 843. [CrossRef]

118. Ngoungoure, V.L.N.; Schluesener, J.; Moundipa, P.F.; Schluesener, H. Natural polyphenols binding to amyloid: A broad class of compounds to treat different human amyloid diseases. *Mol. Nutr. Food Res.* **2015**, *59*, 8–20. [CrossRef]

119. Malchiodi-Albedi, F.; Paradisi, S.; Matteucci, A.; Frank, C.; Diociaiuti, M. Amyloid Oligomer Neurotoxicity, Calcium Dysregulation, and Lipid Rafts. *Int. J. Alzheimers Dis.* **2011**, *2011*, 906964. [CrossRef]

120. Natale, G.; Pasquali, L.; Paparelli, A.; Fornai, F. Parallel manifestations of neuropathologies in the enteric and central nervous systems: Neurodegeneration and the gut. *Neurogastroenterol. Motil.* **2011**, *23*, 1056–1065. [CrossRef]

121. Dinda, B.; Dinda, M.; Kulsi, G.; Chakraborty, A.; Dinda, S. Therapeutic potentials of plant iridoids in Alzheimer's and Parkinson's diseases: A review. *Eur. J. Med. Chem.* **2019**, *169*, 185–199. [CrossRef]

122. Rigacci, S.; Guidotti, V.; Bucciantini, M.; Nichino, D.; Relini, A.; Berti, A.; Stefani, M. Aβ(1-42) aggregates into non-toxic amyloid assemblies in the presence of the natural polyphenol oleuropein aglycon. *Curr. Alzheimer Res.* **2011**, *8*, 841–852. [CrossRef]

123. Palazzi, L.; Bruzzone, E.; Bisello, G.; Leri, M.; Stefani, M.; Bucciantini, M.; Polverino de Laureto, P. Oleuropein aglycone stabilizes the monomeric α-synuclein and favours the growth of non-toxic aggregates. *Sci. Rep.* **2018**, *8*. [CrossRef]

124. Mohammad-Beigi, H.; Aliakbari, F.; Sahin, C.; Lomax, C.; Tawfike, A.; Schafer, N.P.; Amiri-Nowdijeh, A.; Eskandari, H.; Møller, I.M.; Hosseini-Mazinani, M.; et al. Oleuropein derivatives from olive fruit extracts reduce α-synuclein fibrillation and oligomer toxicity. *J. Biol. Chem.* **2019**, *294*, 4215–4232. [CrossRef] [PubMed]

125. Diomede, L.; Rigacci, S.; Romeo, M.; Stefani, M.; Salmona, M. Oleuropein aglycone protects transgenic C. elegans strains expressing Aβ42 by reducing plaque load and motor deficit. *PLoS ONE* **2013**, *8*, e58893. [CrossRef] [PubMed]

126. Luccarini, I.; Ed Dami, T.; Grossi, C.; Rigacci, S.; Stefani, M.; Casamenti, F. Oleuropein aglycone counteracts Aβ42 toxicity in the rat brain. *Neurosci. Lett.* **2014**, *558*, 67–72. [CrossRef] [PubMed]

127. Borchi, E.; Bargelli, V.; Guidotti, V.; Berti, A.; Stefani, M.; Nediani, C.; Rigacci, S. Mild exposure of RIN-5F β-cells to human islet amyloid polypeptide aggregates upregulates antioxidant enzymes via NADPH oxidase-RAGE: An hormetic stimulus. *Redox Biol.* **2014**, *2*, 114–122. [CrossRef]

128. Khemtémourian, L.; Antoinette Killian, J.; Höppener, J.W.M.; Engel, M.F.M. Recent Insights in Islet Amyloid Polypeptide-Induced Membrane Disruption and Its Role in β-Cell Death in Type 2 Diabetes Mellitus. *Exp. Diabetes Res.* **2008**, *2008*, 421287. [CrossRef]

129. Leri, M.; Nosi, D.; Natalello, A.; Porcari, R.; Ramazzotti, M.; Chiti, F.; Bellotti, V.; Doglia, S.M.; Stefani, M.; Bucciantini, M. The polyphenol Oleuropein aglycone hinders the growth of toxic transthyretin amyloid assemblies. *J. Nutr. Biochem.* **2016**, *30*, 153–166. [CrossRef]

130. Leri, M.; Oropesa-Nuñez, R.; Canale, C.; Raimondi, S.; Giorgetti, S.; Bruzzone, E.; Bellotti, V.; Stefani, M.; Bucciantini, M. Oleuropein aglycone: A polyphenol with different targets against amyloid toxicity. *Biochim. Biophys. Acta BBA Gen. Subj.* **2018**, *1862*, 1432–1442. [CrossRef]

131. Valleix, S.; Gillmore, J.D.; Bridoux, F.; Mangione, P.P.; Dogan, A.; Nedelec, B.; Boimard, M.; Touchard, G.; Goujon, J.-M.; Lacombe, C.; et al. Hereditary Systemic Amyloidosis Due to Asp76Asn Variant β₂-Microglobulin. *N. Engl. J. Med.* **2012**, *366*, 2276–2283. [CrossRef]

132. Leri, M.; Bemporad, F.; Oropesa-Nuñez, R.; Canale, C.; Calamai, M.; Nosi, D.; Ramazzotti, M.; Giorgetti, S.; Pavone, F.S.; Bellotti, V.; et al. Molecular insights into cell toxicity of a novel familial amyloidogenic variant of β2-microglobulin. *J. Cell. Mol. Med.* **2016**, *20*, 1443–1456. [CrossRef]

133. Mangione, P.P.; Esposito, G.; Relini, A.; Raimondi, S.; Porcari, R.; Giorgetti, S.; Corazza, A.; Fogolari, F.; Penco, A.; Goto, Y.; et al. Structure, Folding Dynamics, and Amyloidogenesis of D76N β₂-Microglobulin: ROLES OF SHEAR FLOW, HYDROPHOBIC SURFACES, AND α-CRYSTALLIN. *J. Biol. Chem.* **2013**, *288*, 30917–30930. [CrossRef]

134. Bouallagui, Z.; Han, J.; Isoda, H.; Sayadi, S. Hydroxytyrosol rich extract from olive leaves modulates cell cycle progression in MCF-7 human breast cancer cells. *Food Chem. Toxicol.* **2011**, *49*, 179–184. [CrossRef] [PubMed]

135. Han, J.; Talorete, T.P.N.; Yamada, P.; Isoda, H. Anti-proliferative and apoptotic effects of oleuropein and hydroxytyrosol on human breast cancer MCF-7 cells. *Cytotechnology* **2009**, *59*, 45–53. [CrossRef] [PubMed]

136. Elamin, M.H.; Daghestani, M.H.; Omer, S.A.; Elobeid, M.A.; Virk, P.; Al-Olayan, E.M.; Hassan, Z.K.; Mohammed, O.B.; Aboussekhra, A. Olive oil oleuropein has anti-breast cancer properties with higher efficiency on ER-negative cells. *Food Chem. Toxicol.* **2013**, *53*, 310–316. [CrossRef] [PubMed]

137. Liu, L.; Ahn, K.S.; Shanmugam, M.K.; Wang, H.; Shen, H.; Arfuso, F.; Chinnathambi, A.; Alharbi, S.A.; Chang, Y.; Sethi, G.; et al. Oleuropein induces apoptosis via abrogating NF-κB activation cascade in estrogen receptor–negative breast cancer cells. *J. Cell. Biochem.* **2019**, *120*, 4504–4513. [CrossRef] [PubMed]

138. Vanella, L. Antiproliferative effect of oleuropein in prostate cell lines. *Int. J. Oncol.* **2012**, *41*, 31–38. [CrossRef] [PubMed]

139. Sepporta, M.V.; Fuccelli, R.; Rosignoli, P.; Ricci, G.; Servili, M.; Fabiani, R. Oleuropein Prevents Azoxymethane-Induced Colon Crypt Dysplasia and Leukocytes DNA Damage in A/J Mice. *J. Med. Food* **2016**, *19*, 983–989. [CrossRef]

140. Cárdeno, A.; Sánchez-Hidalgo, M.; Rosillo, M.A.; de la Lastra, C.A. Oleuropein, a Secoiridoid Derived from Olive Tree, Inhibits the Proliferation of Human Colorectal Cancer Cell Through Downregulation of HIF-1α. *Nutr. Cancer* **2013**, *65*, 147–156. [CrossRef]

141. Bernini, R.; Carastro, I.; Palmini, G.; Tanini, A.; Zonefrati, R.; Pinelli, P.; Brandi, M.L.; Romani, A. Lipophilization of Hydroxytyrosol-Enriched Fractions from *Olea europaea* L. Byproducts and Evaluation of the in Vitro Effects on a Model of Colorectal Cancer Cells. *J. Agric. Food Chem.* **2017**, *65*, 6506–6512. [CrossRef]

142. Samara, P.; Christoforidou, N.; Lemus, C.; Argyropoulou, A.; Ioannou, K.; Vougogiannopoulou, K.; Aligiannis, N.; Paronis, E.; Gaboriaud-Kolar, N.; Tsitsilonis, O.; et al. New semi-synthetic analogs of oleuropein show improved anticancer activity in vitro and in vivo. *Eur. J. Med. Chem.* **2017**, *137*, 11–29. [CrossRef]

143. Yao, J.; Wu, J.; Yang, X.; Yang, J.; Zhang, Y.; Du, L. Oleuropein induced apoptosis in HeLa cells via a mitochondrial apoptotic cascade associated with activation of the c-Jun NH2-terminal kinase. *J. Pharmacol. Sci.* **2014**, *125*, 300–311. [CrossRef]

144. Yan, C.-M.; Chai, E.-Q.; Cai, H.-Y.; Miao, G.-Y.; Ma, W. Oleuropein induces apoptosis via activation of caspases and suppression of phosphatidylinositol 3-kinase/protein kinase B pathway in HepG2 human hepatoma cell line. *Mol. Med. Rep.* **2015**, *11*, 4617–4624. [CrossRef] [PubMed]

145. Seçme, M.; Eroğlu, C.; Dodurga, Y.; Bağcı, G. Investigation of anticancer mechanism of oleuropein via cell cycle and apoptotic pathways in SH-SY5Y neuroblastoma cells. *Gene* **2016**, *585*, 93–99. [CrossRef] [PubMed]

146. Zeriouh, W.; Nani, A.; Belarbi, M.; Dumont, A.; de Rosny, C.; Aboura, I.; Ghanemi, F.Z.; Murtaza, B.; Patoli, D.; Thomas, C.; et al. Correction: Phenolic extract from oleaster (*Olea europaea* var. Sylvestris) leaves reduces colon cancer growth and induces caspase-dependent apoptosis in colon cancer cells via the mitochondrial apoptotic pathway. *PLoS ONE* **2017**, *12*, e0176574. [CrossRef] [PubMed]

147. Anter, J.; Fernández-Bedmar, Z.; Villatoro-Pulido, M.; Demyda-Peyras, S.; Moreno-Millán, M.; Alonso-Moraga, Á.; Muñoz-Serrano, A.; Luque de Castro, M.D. A pilot study on the DNA-protective, cytotoxic, and apoptosis-inducing properties of olive-leaf extracts. *Mutat. Res. Genet. Toxicol. Environ. Mutagenesis* **2011**, *723*, 165–170. [CrossRef]

148. Sirianni, R.; Chimento, A.; De Luca, A.; Casaburi, I.; Rizza, P.; Onofrio, A.; Iacopetta, D.; Puoci, F.; Andò, S.; Maggiolini, M.; et al. Oleuropein and hydroxytyrosol inhibit MCF-7 breast cancer cell proliferation interfering with ERK1/2 activation. *Mol. Nutr. Food Res.* **2010**, *54*, 833–840. [CrossRef]

149. Momtaz, S.; Niaz, K.; Maqbool, F.; Abdollahi, M.; Rastrelli, L.; Nabavi, S.M. STAT3 targeting by polyphenols: Novel therapeutic strategy for melanoma: STAT3 targeting by polyphenols. *BioFactors* **2017**, *43*, 347–370. [CrossRef]

150. Marchetti, C.; Clericuzio, M.; Borghesi, B.; Cornara, L.; Ribulla, S.; Gosetti, F.; Marengo, E.; Burlando, B. Oleuropein-Enriched Olive Leaf Extract Affects Calcium Dynamics and Impairs Viability of Malignant Mesothelioma Cells. *Evid. -Based Complementary Altern. Med.* **2015**, *2015*, 908493. [CrossRef]

151. Abtin, M.; Alivand, M.R.; Khaniani, M.S.; Bastami, M.; Zaeifizadeh, M.; Derakhshan, S.M. Simultaneous downregulation of miR-21 and miR-155 through oleuropein for breast cancer prevention and therapy. *J. Cell. Biochem.* **2018**, *119*, 7151–7165. [CrossRef]

152. Tezcan, G.; Tunca, B.; Bekar, A.; Budak, F.; Sahin, S.; Cecener, G.; Egeli, U.; Taskapılıoglu, M.O.; Kocaeli, H.; Tolunay, S.; et al. *Olea europaea* leaf extract improves the treatment response of GBM stem cells by modulating miRNA expression. *Am. J. Cancer Res.* **2014**, *4*, 572–590.

153. Bayat, S.; Shekari Khaniani, M.; Choupani, J.; Alivand, M.R.; Mansoori Derakhshan, S. HDACis (class I), cancer stem cell, and phytochemicals: Cancer therapy and prevention implications. *Biomed. Pharmacother.* **2018**, *97*, 1445–1453. [CrossRef]

154. Hamdi, H.K.; Castellon, R. Oleuropein, a non-toxic olive iridoid, is an anti-tumor agent and cytoskeleton disruptor. *Biochem. Biophys. Res. Commun.* **2005**, *334*, 769–778. [CrossRef] [PubMed]

155. Song, H.; Lim, D.Y.; Jung, J.I.; Cho, H.J.; Park, S.Y.; Kwon, G.T.; Kang, Y.-H.; Lee, K.W.; Choi, M.-S.; Park, J.H.Y. Dietary oleuropein inhibits tumor angiogenesis and lymphangiogenesis in the B16F10 melanoma allograft model: A mechanism for the suppression of high-fat diet-induced solid tumor growth and lymph node metastasis. *Oncotarget* **2017**, *8*, 32027–32042. [CrossRef] [PubMed]

156. Samet, I.; Han, J.; Jlaiel, L.; Sayadi, S.; Isoda, H. Olive (*Olea europaea*) Leaf Extract Induces Apoptosis and Monocyte/Macrophage Differentiation in Human Chronic Myelogenous Leukemia K562 Cells: Insight into the Underlying Mechanism. *Oxidative Med. Cell. Longev.* **2014**, *2014*, 1–16. [CrossRef] [PubMed]

157. Liu, M.; Wang, J.; Huang, B.; Chen, A.; Li, X. Oleuropein inhibits the proliferation and invasion of glioma cells via suppression of the AKT signaling pathway. *Oncol. Rep.* **2016**, *36*, 2009–2016. [CrossRef] [PubMed]

158. Hassan, Z.K.; Elamin, M.H.; Daghestani, M.H.; Omer, S.A.; Al-Olayan, E.M.; Elobeid, M.A.; Virk, P.; Mohammed, O.B. Oleuropein induces anti-metastatic effects in breast cancer. *Asian Pac. J. Cancer Prev.* **2012**, *13*, 4555–4559. [CrossRef] [PubMed]

159. Andreadou, I.; Mikros, E.; Ioannidis, K.; Sigala, F.; Naka, K.; Kostidis, S.; Farmakis, D.; Tenta, R.; Kavantzas, N.; Bibli, S.-I.; et al. Oleuropein prevents doxorubicin-induced cardiomyopathy interfering with signaling molecules and cardiomyocyte metabolism. *J. Mol. Cell. Cardiol.* **2014**, *69*, 4–16. [CrossRef] [PubMed]

160. Tezcan, G.; Taskapilioglu, M.O.; Tunca, B.; Bekar, A.; Demirci, H.; Kocaeli, H.; Aksoy, S.A.; Egeli, U.; Cecener, G.; Tolunay, S. *Olea europaea* leaf extract and bevacizumab synergistically exhibit beneficial efficacy upon human glioblastoma cancer stem cells through reducing angiogenesis and invasion in vitro. *Biomed. Pharmacother.* **2017**, *90*, 713–723. [CrossRef]

161. Ryskalin, L.; Gaglione, A.; Limanaqi, F.; Biagioni, F.; Familiari, P.; Frati, A.; Esposito, V.; Fornai, F. The Autophagy Status of Cancer Stem Cells in Gliobastoma Multiforme: From Cancer Promotion to Therapeutic Strategies. *IJMS* **2019**, *20*, 3824. [CrossRef]

162. Ruzzolini, J.; Peppicelli, S.; Andreucci, E.; Bianchini, F.; Scardigli, A.; Romani, A.; la Marca, G.; Nediani, C.; Calorini, L. Oleuropein, the Main Polyphenol of *Olea europaea* Leaf Extract, Has an Anti-Cancer Effect on Human BRAF Melanoma Cells and Potentiates the Cytotoxicity of Current Chemotherapies. *Nutrients* **2018**, *10*, 1950. [CrossRef]

163. Sherif, I.O.; Al-Gayyar, M.M.H. Oleuropein potentiates anti-tumor activity of cisplatin against HepG2 through affecting proNGF/NGF balance. *Life Sci.* **2018**, *198*, 87–93. [CrossRef]

164. Menendez, J.A.; Vazquez-Martin, A.; Colomer, R.; Brunet, J.; Carrasco-Pancorbo, A.; Garcia-Villalba, R.; Fernandez-Gutierrez, A.; Segura-Carretero, A. Olive oil's bitter principle reverses acquired autoresistance to trastuzumab (Herceptin™) in HER2-overexpressing breast cancer cells. *BMC Cancer* **2007**, *7*, 80. [CrossRef] [PubMed]

165. Xu, T.; Xiao, D. Oleuropein enhances radiation sensitivity of nasopharyngeal carcinoma by downregulating PDRG1 through HIF1α-repressed microRNA-519d. *J. Exp. Clin. Cancer Res.* **2017**, *36*, 3. [CrossRef] [PubMed]

166. Žugčić, T.; Abdelkebir, R.; Alcantara, C.; Collado, M.C.; García-Pérez, J.V.; Meléndez-Martínez, A.J.; Režek Jambrak, A.; Lorenzo, J.M.; Barba, F.J. From extraction of valuable compounds to health promoting benefits of olive leaves through bioaccessibility, bioavailability and impact on gut microbiota. *Trends Food Sci. Technol.* **2019**, *83*, 63–77. [CrossRef]

167. Roselló-Soto, E.; Koubaa, M.; Moubarik, A.; Lopes, R.P.; Saraiva, J.A.; Boussetta, N.; Grimi, N.; Barba, F.J. Emerging opportunities for the effective valorization of wastes and by-products generated during olive oil production process: Non-conventional methods for the recovery of high-added value compounds. *Trends Food Sci. Technol.* **2015**, *45*, 296–310. [CrossRef]

168. Granato, D.; Nunes, D.S.; Barba, F.J. An integrated strategy between food chemistry, biology, nutrition, pharmacology, and statistics in the development of functional foods: A proposal. *Trends Food Sci. Technol.* **2017**, *62*, 13–22. [CrossRef]

169. Romani, A.; Ieri, F.; Urciuoli, S.; Noce, A.; Marrone, G.; Nediani, C.; Bernini, R. Health Effects of Phenolic Compounds Found in Extra-Virgin Olive Oil, By-Products, and Leaf of *Olea europaea* L. *Nutrients* **2019**, *11*, 1776. [CrossRef]

170. Savournin, C.; Baghdikian, B.; Elias, R.; Dargouth-Kesraoui, F.; Boukef, K.; Balansard, G. Rapid high-performance liquid chromatography analysis for the quantitative determination of oleuropein in *Olea europaea* leaves. *J. Agric. Food Chem.* **2001**, *49*, 618–621. [CrossRef]

171. Aponte, M.; Ungaro, F.; d'Angelo, I.; De Caro, C.; Russo, R.; Blaiotta, G.; Dal Piaz, F.; Calignano, A.; Miro, A. Improving in vivo conversion of oleuropein into hydroxytyrosol by oral granules containing probiotic Lactobacillus plantarum 299v and an *Olea europaea* standardized extract. *Int. J. Pharm.* **2018**, *543*, 73–82. [CrossRef]

172. Erbay, Z.; Icier, F. The Importance and Potential Uses of Olive Leaves. *Food Rev. Int.* **2010**, *26*, 319–334. [CrossRef]

173. Visioli, F.; Galli, C.; Bornet, F.; Mattei, A.; Patelli, R.; Galli, G.; Caruso, D. Olive oil phenolics are dose-dependently absorbed in humans. *FEBS Lett.* **2000**, *468*, 159–160. [CrossRef]

174. Miró-Casas, E.; Farré Albaladejo, M.; Covas, M.I.; Rodriguez, J.O.; Menoyo Colomer, E.; Lamuela Raventós, R.M.; de la Torre, R. Capillary gas chromatography-mass spectrometry quantitative determination of hydroxytyrosol and tyrosol in human urine after olive oil intake. *Anal. Biochem.* **2001**, *294*, 63–72. [CrossRef]

175. Vissers, M.N.; Zock, P.L.; Roodenburg, A.J.C.; Leenen, R.; Katan, M.B. Olive Oil Phenols Are Absorbed in Humans. *J. Nutr.* **2002**, *132*, 409–417. [CrossRef]

176. Lemonakis, N.; Mougios, V.; Halabalaki, M.; Skaltsounis, A.-L.; Gikas, E. A novel bioanalytical method based on UHPLC-HRMS/MS for the quantification of oleuropein in human serum. Application to a pharmacokinetic study: Quantification of oleuropein in human serum. *Biomed. Chromatogr.* **2016**, *30*, 2016–2023. [CrossRef]

177. de Bock, M.; Thorstensen, E.B.; Derraik, J.G.B.; Henderson, H.V.; Hofman, P.L.; Cutfield, W.S. Human absorption and metabolism of oleuropein and hydroxytyrosol ingested as olive (*Olea europaea* L.) leaf extract. *Mol. Nutr. Food Res.* **2013**, *57*, 2079–2085. [CrossRef]

178. Visioli, F.; De La Lastra, C.A.; Andres-Lacueva, C.; Aviram, M.; Calhau, C.; Cassano, A.; D'Archivio, M.; Faria, A.; Favé, G.; Fogliano, V.; et al. Polyphenols and human health: A prospectus. *Crit. Rev. Food Sci. Nutr.* **2011**, *51*, 524–546. [CrossRef]

179. Hu, J.; Zou, X.; He, Y.; Chen, F.; Deng, Z. Esterification of Quercetin Increases Its Transport Across Human Caco-2 Cells: Synthesize quercetin ester to improve bioavailability ... . *J. Food Sci.* **2016**, *81*, H1825–H1832. [CrossRef]

180. Pagnussatt, F.A.; de Lima, V.R.; Dora, C.L.; Costa, J.A.V.; Putaux, J.-L.; Badiale-Furlong, E. Assessment of the encapsulation effect of phenolic compounds from Spirulina sp. LEB-18 on their antifusarium activities. *Food Chem.* **2016**, *211*, 616–623. [CrossRef]

181. Gibis, M.; Ruedt, C.; Weiss, J. In vitro release of grape-seed polyphenols encapsulated from uncoated and chitosan-coated liposomes. *Food Res. Int.* **2016**, *88*, 105–113. [CrossRef]

182. Gleeson, J.P.; Ryan, S.M.; Brayden, D.J. Oral delivery strategies for nutraceuticals: Delivery vehicles and absorption enhancers. *Trends Food Sci. Technol.* **2016**, *53*, 90–101. [CrossRef]

183. Noce, A.; Marrone, G.; Di Daniele, F.; Ottaviani, E.; Wilson Jones, G.; Bernini, R.; Romani, A.; Rovella, V. Impact of Gut Microbiota Composition on Onset and Progression of Chronic Non-Communicable Diseases. *Nutrients* **2019**, *11*, 1073. [CrossRef]

184. Mosele, J.I.; Martín-Peláez, S.; Macià, A.; Farràs, M.; Valls, R.-M.; Catalán, Ú.; Motilva, M.-J. Faecal microbial metabolism of olive oil phenolic compounds: In vitro and in vivo approaches. *Mol. Nutr. Food Res.* **2014**, *58*, 1809–1819. [CrossRef] [PubMed]
185. Santos, M.M.; Piccirillo, C.; Castro, P.M.L.; Kalogerakis, N.; Pintado, M.E. Bioconversion of oleuropein to hydroxytyrosol by lactic acid bacteria. *World J. Microbiol. Biotechnol.* **2012**, *28*, 2435–2440. [CrossRef] [PubMed]
186. Liguri, G.; Stefani, M. Recent advances in basic and clinical research on the prevention and treatment of the metabolic syndrome and related disorders by the use of olive polyphenols. *J. Gerontol. Geriatr.* **2017**, 48–58.

Review

Effects and Mechanisms of Tea for the Prevention and Management of Diabetes Mellitus and Diabetic Complications: An Updated Review

Jin-Ming Meng [1], Shi-Yu Cao [1], Xin-Lin Wei [2], Ren-You Gan [2,*], Yuan-Feng Wang [3], Shu-Xian Cai [4], Xiao-Yu Xu [1], Pang-Zhen Zhang [5] and Hua-Bin Li [1,*]

1   Guangdong Provincial Key Laboratory of Food, Nutrition and Health, Department of Nutrition, School of Public Health, Sun Yat-sen University, Guangzhou 510080, China; mengjm@mail2.sysu.edu.cn (J.-M.M.); caoshy3@mail2.sysu.edu.cn (S.-Y.C.); xuxy53@mail2.sysu.edu.cn (X.-Y.X.)

2   Department of Food Science & Technology, School of Agriculture and Biology, Shanghai Jiao Tong University, Shanghai 200240, China; weixinlin@sjtu.edu.cn

3   College of Life Sciences, Shanghai Normal University, 100 Guilin Road, Shanghai 200234, China; yfwang@shnu.edu.cn

4   Key Laboratory of Ministry of Education for Tea Science, Hunan Agricultural University, Changsha 410128, China; caishuxian@hunau.edu.cn

5   School of Agriculture and Food, The University of Melbourne, Parkville, Victoria 3010, Australia; pangzhen.zhang@unimelb.edu.au

*   Correspondence: renyougan@sjtu.edu.cn (R.-Y.G.); lihuabin@mail.sysu.edu.cn (H.-B.L.); Tel.: +86-21-3420-8517 (R.-Y.G.); +86-20-8733-2391 (H.-B.L.)

Received: 14 May 2019; Accepted: 6 June 2019; Published: 10 June 2019

Abstract: Diabetes mellitus has become a serious and growing public health concern. It has high morbidity and mortality because of its complications, such as diabetic nephropathy, diabetic cardiovascular complication, diabetic neuropathy, diabetic retinopathy, and diabetic hepatopathy. Epidemiological studies revealed that the consumption of tea was inversely associated with the risk of diabetes mellitus and its complications. Experimental studies demonstrated that tea had protective effects against diabetes mellitus and its complications via several possible mechanisms, including enhancing insulin action, ameliorating insulin resistance, activating insulin signaling pathway, protecting islet β-cells, scavenging free radicals, and decreasing inflammation. Moreover, clinical trials also confirmed that tea intervention is effective in patients with diabetes mellitus and its complications. Therefore, in order to highlight the importance of tea in the prevention and management of diabetes mellitus and its complications, this article summarizes and discusses the effects of tea against diabetes mellitus and its complications based on the findings from epidemiological, experimental, and clinical studies, with the special attention paid to the mechanisms of action.

Keywords: tea; polyphenol; epigallocatechin-3-gallate; diabetes mellitus; complication; mechanisms

1. Introduction

Diabetes mellitus, one of the most common metabolic disorders in the world, is featured by hyperglycemia caused by either decreased insulin secretion or insulin resistance [1]. The incidence of diabetes mellitus in adults has been increasing in the last decades [2,3]. Diabetes mellitus has been the fifth leading cause of death in the world, and the International Diabetes Mellitus Federation predicted that 592 million people worldwide will suffer from diabetes mellitus by the year 2035 [4]. Numerous studies have demonstrated that diabetes mellitus, especially type 2 diabetes mellitus (T2DM), could induce diverse complications, such as diabetic nephropathy, diabetic cardiovascular complications, neuropathy, eye, and liver complications, which have been the major causes of its morbidity and mortality [4,5]. Therefore, it is necessary and urgent to find effective strategies for the prevention and management of diabetes mellitus and its complications [6].

As a popular drink worldwide, tea has many bioactivities and healthy benefits, such as antioxidant, anticancer, hepatoprotective, cardioprotective, anti-obesity, improving intestinal flora, and antidiabetic effects [7–14]. Due to the different characteristics and fermentation degrees caused by various manufacturing processes, tea can be classified into six main categories, including unfermented green tea, slightly fermented white tea, partly fermented yellow tea, semi-fermented oolong tea, fully fermented black tea, and post-fermented dark tea [15,16]. Moreover, tea contains many bioactive components, especially polyphenols, such as catechins (Figure 1), flavonols, theaflavins, and thearubigins, which have the potential to decrease the risk of diabetes mellitus and its complications [17].

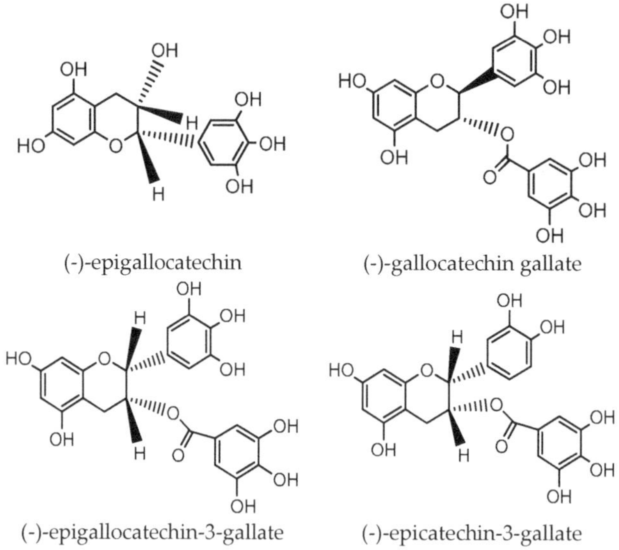

(-)-epigallocatechin   (-)-gallocatechin gallate

(-)-epigallocatechin-3-gallate   (-)-epicatechin-3-gallate

Figure 1. Chemical structures of main catechins in tea.

The effects of tea against diabetes mellitus and its complications have been widely studied. Epidemiological research found that the consumption of tea was negatively associated with the risk of diabetes mellitus and its complications [18,19]. Further, recent in vitro, in vivo, and clinical trials further supported the effects of tea on the prevention and treatment of diabetes mellitus and its complications [20,21]. In addition, tea is a potential hypoglycemic substance with low cost, good patient compliance, and fewer side effects compared with many synthetic hypoglycemic drugs [22]. In order to provide an updated understanding of tea targeting diabetes mellitus and its complications, we searched related literature of epidemiological, experimental, and clinical studies based on PubMed and Web of Science databases and reviewed and discussed the protective effects of tea against diabetes mellitus and its complications, highlighting the related molecular mechanisms.

2. Epidemiological Investigations

Concerning the wide consumption of tea, a number of epidemiological studies have evaluated the effects of tea on diabetes mellitus and its complications.

Several cohort studies have estimated the effects of tea on diabetes mellitus. A cohort study pointed out that the consumption of tea showed protective effects against T2DM (RR = 0.55, 95% CI (0.55, 1.08)) for Vietnamese adults [23]. Another prospective cohort study revealed a negative relationship between the risk of diabetes mellitus and the consumption of tea (HR = 0.77, 95% CI (0.59, 1.00)) for subjects aged less than 60 years old in the United States [24]. It was also reported that tea intake was negatively associated with diabetes mellitus (HR = 0.66, 95% CI (0.61, 1.22) in British subjects [25]. In addition, a prospective cohort study demonstrated an inverse association between green tea intake and the risk of diabetes mellitus (*p*-trend = 0.02) only for women in the Japanese population [26]. Furthermore, the Singapore Chinese health prospective study found that more than one cup of black tea per day could reduce the risk of diabetes mellitus by 14% (RR = 0.86, 95% CI (0.74, 1.00)) [27]. A retrospective cohort study found that green tea was inversely associated with T2DM (OR = 0.67, 95% CI (0.47, 0.94)), while black tea and oolong tea showed no significant effects for Japanese adults [28]. For black tea, the reasons of inconsistent results may be related to the differences of dose and frequency of consumption as well as research subjects [27,28].

Some case-control studies also have evaluated the effects of tea on diabetes mellitus. For instances, a case-control study found that tea could reduce the risk of T2DM (OR = 0.66, 95% CI (0.49, 0.89)) for Vietnamese adults [29]. Another case-control study revealed that long-term drinking of green tea had preventive effects on diabetic retinopathy (OR = 0.49, 95% CI (0.26–0.90)), and people who regularly drink green tea had a 50% lower risk of developing diabetic retinopathy than those who don't drink green tea in China [30]. A population-based case-control study in Shantou, China found that long-term consumption of oolong tea could reduce the risk of hypercholesterolemia and triglycerides (OR = 0.10, 95% CI (0.06–0.16)) in southern China [31]. Additionally, one descriptive study revealed that long-term tea intake had negative relation with T2DM in Cyprus [32].

Moreover, several meta-analyses also supported the protective effects of tea consumption against diabetes mellitus. These meta-analyses included cohort studies conducted in different countries, such as America, China, Japan, and South Korea, and involved subjects of different races, genders, and ages. It was found that tea could increase the fasting blood insulin level (1.30 U/L, 95% CI (0.36–2.24)) [6], and tea consumption ≥ four cups per day could reduce the risk of T2DM (RR = 0.8, 95% CI (0.7, 0.93)) [18]. Further, another meta-analysis revealed that three to four cups of tea per day had an approximately 20% lower risk of diabetes mellitus than no tea per day (RR = 0.82, 95% CI (0.73, 0.94)) [33]. In addition, a meta-analysis including sixteen cohorts revealed a significant linear and inverse association between tea consumption and the risk of T2DM (*p* = 0.02) [34], and it was also found that more than three cups of tea per day is beneficial for the prevention of T2DM (RR = 0.84, 95% CI (0.73, 0.97) [35].

However, there are also some inconsistent results in epidemiological investigations. For instance, a prospective cohort study reported that the consumption of tea was not associated with T2DM [19]. In addition, compared with those not consuming oolong tea, multivariable adjusted hazard ratios (HR) for developing diabetes mellitus were 1.64 (95% CI (1.11–2.40)) for those drinking two or more cups of oolong per day [36]. The reasons of negative findings may be due to different sensitivities of different ethnic groups to tea, differences of tea composition in different regions, and bad control of drinking time and dose. Further, green tea was found no effects on T2DM in two meta-analysis [37,38], which may be related to the quality of the included studies, the level of evidence, and the size of the sample.

In summary, many epidemiological evidences have supported the efficiency of tea consumption against diabetes mellitus and its complications (Table 1), although inconsistent findings also exist. In addition, studies are still lacking concerning about the association between tea and diabetic complications, which should be further investigated in the future.

Table 1. The relationship of tea consumption and diabetes mellitus by epidemiological studies.

Diseases	Tea Type	Study Type	Participants	Dose	Results	Ref.
Diabetes mellitus	Tea	Prospective cohort study	Individuals (N = 7006) aged 32–88 without diabetes mellitus	N/A	The consumption of tea showed and decreased risk of diabetes mellitus for nonelderly adults who had previously lost weight.	[34]
Diabetes mellitus	Green tea	Cohort study	Elderly Japanese men and women (N = 11,717)	N/A	Women with a higher intake of green tea had a lower risk of diabetes mellitus.	[26]
Diabetes mellitus	Black Tea	placebo-controlled study	Total participants (N = 24) aged 20–60	N/A	Drinking black tea could decrease postprandial blood sugar.	[39]
T2DM	Tea	Population-based cohort study	Danish non-diabetic women with singleton pregnancies (N = 71,239)	8 cups per day	The consumption of tea showed protective effects against T2DM (RR = 0.55, 95% CI (0.55, 1.08).	[23]
T2DM	Tea	Prospective Cohort study.	African American women (N = 46,906)	N/A	The consumption of tea wasn't associated with T2DM.	[19]
T2DM	Tea	Prospective cohort study.	British men (N = 4055) and women (N = 1768)	N/A	Tea intake was beneficial for DM (HR = 0.66, 95% CI (0.61, 1.22)), $p < 0.05$.	[25]
T2DM	Tea	Case-Control study	Newly diagnosed diabetic cases (N = 599) Hospital-based controls (N = 599)	2 cups per day	Habitual drinking tea could reduce the risk of T2DM (OR = 0.66, 95% CI (0.49–0.89)).	[29]
T2DM	Tea	Case-Cohort Study	Total participants (N = 16,835)	≥1 cups per day	The consumption of tea has negative relation with T2DM 1 cup/day (HR = 0.84, 95% CI (0.71, 1.00) ≥2 cups/day (HR = 0.93, 95% CI (0.81, 1.05))	[40]
T2DM	Tea	Meta-analysis	Total participants (N = 545,517); Cases with T2DM (N = 37,445)	N/A	The consumption of tea has negative relation with T2DM ($p = 0.02$).	[34]
T2DM	Tea	Meta-analysis	N/A	N/A	Drinking tea daily (≥3 cups/day) is associated with a lower risk of T2DM (RR = 0.84, 95% CI (0.73, 0.97)	[35]
T2DM	Tea	Meta-analysis	Total participants (N = 324,141); Cases with T2DM (N = 11,400)	N/A	Tea consumption a ≥4 cups per day may lower the risk of T2DM.	[18]
T2DM	Tea	Meta-analysis	Total participants (N = 457,922)	N/A	The consumption of tea was associated with reduced risk of diabetes mellitus.	[33]
T2DM	Tea	Descriptive study	Total participants (N = 940)	N/A	Long-term tea intake had effects on the prevention and treatment of diabetes mellitus.	[32]
T2DM	Green tea	Meta-analysis	N/A	N/A	The consumption of tea wasn't associated with T2DM.	[38]
T2DM	Green tea	Meta-analysis	N/A	N/A	Tea or tea extract could maintain stable fasting insulin level in patients with T2DM.	[6]
T2DM	Green tea	Meta-analysis	Total participants (N = 510)	N/A	Green tea had no effect on insulin sensitivity and blood glucose control.	[37]
T2DM	Black tea	Cohort study.	Total participants (N = 36,908)	≥1 cups per day	Black tea had association with T2DM (RR = 0.86, 95% CI (0.74, 1.00)).	[27]
T2DM	Oolong tea	Prospective cohort study.	Japanese male workers (N = 4975)	≥1 cups per day	Long-term consumption of oolong tea may be a predictive factor for new onset diabetes mellitus. 1 cup/day (HR = 1.00, 95% CI (0.67–1.49). ≥2cups/day (HR = 1.64, 95% CI (1.11–2.40))	[56]
Diabetic nephropathy	Green tea	Cohort study	Diabetic patients (N = 42)	N/A	Green tea extract could reduce proteinuria in diabetic patients.	[41]
Diabetic Retinopathy	Green tea	Case-Control Study	Cases with diabetic retinopathy (N = 100) and diabetic patients without retinopathy (N = 100)	N/A	Long-term drinking green tea had preventive effects on diabetic retinopathy (OR = 0.49, 95% CI (0.26–0.90)).	[30]

Abbreviations: T2DM, type 2 diabetes mellitus; N/A, not available.

3. Experimental Studies

The effects of tea on diabetes mellitus and its complications have been widely studied by in vitro and in vivo experimental studies, and the relative mechanisms of action have also been widely explored.

3.1. Diabetes Mellitus

3.1.1. Type 1 Diabetes Mellitus (T1DM)

T1DM is characterized by progressively destroyed pancreatic β-cells and reducing or no insulin secretion [17], accounting for 5–10% diabetes mellitus [42]. Increasing studies have found the effects of tea against T1DM [43–45].

The main effective catechin of green tea is epigallocatechin gallate (EGCG) [46]. EGCG could protect the functions of pancreatic β-cells by inhibiting inflammatory factors and reducing reactive oxygen species (ROS) in vitro [47]. Further, EGCG could down-regulate the production of inducible nitric oxide synthase (iNOS) to protect pancreatic islet β-cells [48]. In addition, green tea was also found to reduce blood sugar level by promoting pancreatic β-cells to produce more insulin in diabetic mice [49]. Furthermore, dark tea containing gallic acid, a water-soluble ingredient, could promote skeletal muscle glucose transport in the absence of insulin by stimulating protein kinase B (Akt) phosphorylation [50].

3.1.2. Type 2 Diabetes Mellitus (T2DM)

T2DM is defined as insulin resistance in the target tissue and a relative lack of insulin secreted by islet β-cells [51], accounting for 90–95% diabetes mellitus [42]. Increasing studies showed that tea was effective in preventing and managing T2DM [6]. Next, the molecular mechanisms of tea against T2DM are discussed according to the types of tea.

A type II arabinogalactan, 7WA, isolated from green tea, could increase glucose-stimulated insulin secretion through cyclic adenosine monophosphate-Akt (cAMP-Akt) pathway [44]. Additionally, green tea polyphenols, primarily EGCG, could activate the 5′-adenylic acid-activated protein kinase (AMPK) pathway to improve the closure of insulin stress signal pathway caused by phosphorylation of insulin receptor substrate-1 (IRS-1), finally ameliorating the insulin resistant status of human hepG2 hepatoma cells [52]. In addition, it was reported that supplement of green tea polyphenols could improve insulin sensitivity by upregulating the insulin signaling protein levels in insulin-resistant rats [53]. Moreover, green tea catechins, especially EGCG, could improve insulin resistance by scavenging ROS, which was able to block the transduction of insulin signal and prevent IRS-1 from binding to insulin receptor by decreasing tumor necrosis factor (TNF)-α-induced c-jun NH2-terminal kinase (JNK) phosphorylation [48,54]. Furthermore, EGCG played an insulin-like role in down-regulating the gene and protein expression of hepatocyte nuclear factor (HNF4), a key transcription factor controlling gluconeogenesis enzymes, such as phosphoenolpyruvate carboxykinase and glucose-6-phosphatase [55]. Moreover, green tea catechins could promote adipocyte differentiation and increase insulin sensitivity by directly activating peroxisome proliferator-activated receptor γ (PPARγ) [56]. EGCG-enriched green tea extract could also prevent T2DM by stimulating the production of soluble receptors for advanced glycation of end products (sRAGE) through a disintegrin and metallopoteases10 (ADAM10)-induced ectodomain shedding of extracellular RAGE [57].

Black tea regularly had antioxidant and anti-inflammatory effects [58] which could exert effects against T2DM. Black tea, abundant in theaflavins (accounting for 68.4% tea polyphenols), played a hypoglycemic role by inhibiting the action of ROS, such as singlet oxygen, superoxide, and hydroxyl radicals [20]. Further, black tea could reduce the risk of T2DM by inhibiting obesity through the phosphorylation of key metabolic regulator AMPK and promoting the browning of white adipose tissue [59].

Studies found that white tea had higher levels of tea polyphenols and better antioxidant activity than black tea [60]. White tea could exhibit antidiabetic activity by reducing insulin resistance, hyperlipidemia, and oxidative stress [61]. Additionally, white tea lowered blood sugar level by increasing insulin sensitivity and the synthesis of liver glycogen in T2DM rats [62]. Moreover, it was revealed that the combination of white tea and moringa oleifera had a good hypoglycemic effect [63].

It was found that the water extract of pu-erh tea contained less polyphenols but more caffeine, which could improve insulin sensitivity [5,64]. An in vitro study found that qingzhuan tea (a type of dark tea) had an inhibitory effect on α-glucosidase, which was attributed to EGCG and gallocatechin gallate (GCG) [65]. Pu-erh tea polysaccharides was also reported to regulate postprandial blood sugar by inhibiting α-glucosidase but have no effect on α-amylase activity, with older pu-erh tea exhibiting a higher inhibitory effect [66]. Moreover, it was found that ripened pu-erh tea had a better effect than raw pu-erh tea on the control of postprandial blood glucose in T2DM mice [67]. Additionally, pu-erh tea polysaccharides promoted adipocyte differentiation and glucose uptake by mimicking the properties of PPARγ and glucose transporter type 4 (GLUT4), ameliorating insulin resistance and lowering blood sugar [68]. Furthermore, Fu brick tea attenuated insulin resistance by down-regulating signal regulatory protein-α (SIRP-α) expression and activating insulin signaling in a Akt/GLUT4/FoxO1 and the target of rapamycin (mTOR)/S6K1 pathways in the skeletal muscle of male Sprague–Dawley rats [69].

Yellow tea could ameliorate glucose intolerance and insulin resistance without dose dependence [70]. Further, the roasted yellow tea could improve insulin sensitivity and reduce fasting blood sugar due to the strong affinity of GCG to target protein-glycosidase, and the strong inhibition effect of GCG on α-glucosidase activity [71].

In general, different types of tea exhibit antidiabetic effects in vitro and in vivo. Tea catechins, theaflavins, polysaccharides, and caffeine should be mainly responsible for the antidiabetic effects of tea. Notably, these bioactive compounds in tea can regulate signal pathways and key molecules involved in the regulation of insulin, blood sugar, and energy metabolism.

3.2. Diabetic Complications

3.2.1. Diabetic Nephropathy

Diabetic nephropathy is one of the major microvascular complications of diabetes mellitus [72]. Its obvious pathological changes were persistent proteinuria, changes in creatinine clearance, mesangial matrix dilatation, thickening of glomerular basement membrane, and glomerular sclerosis [73]. Numerous studies demonstrated that tea could ameliorate the pathological process of diabetic nephropathy through the antioxidant and anti-inflammatory properties [74,75]. The effects and related molecular mechanisms of tea against diabetic kidney injury are discussed below.

Green tea extract could provide a beneficial effect against long-term diabetic nephropathy via suppressing hyperglycaemia, preventing glycogen accumulation in the proximal tubules, and improving serum and urine parameters (e.g., glucose, glycosylated proteins and creatinine, and blood urea nitrogen) [70]. Green tea could defend renal tubular by reducing the urinary activity of renal tubular epithelial-cell enzymes [76]. Furthermore, green tea catechins could protect kidney function by reducing the permeability of glomerular filtration membrane through inhibiting thrombosis with lowered microsomal phospholipase A2 and regulating arachidonic acid cascade system [42]. An in vivo study also found that green tea could improve glomerular filtration and reduce the rate of creatinine increase and renal hypertrophy [77]. Further, in diabetic spontaneously hypertensive rats (SHRs), green tea prevented podocyte apoptosis and albuminuria by rising p-low-density lipoprotein receptor-related protein 6 (p-LRP6) expression and blocking glycogen synthase kinase 3 interaction with p53 (GSK3-p53) [78]. Another study also found green tea polyphenols could attenuate the urinary protein excretion and characteristic morphological changes of diabetic nephropathy by decreasing blood glucose levels [79]. Additionally, (+)–catechins might ameliorate renal dysfunction in diabetic mice by inhibiting advanced glycation end product (AGE) formation and cutting off inflammatory pathways via trapping metabolite methylglyoxal [80]. Also, green tea catechins could reduce the oxidative damage and inflammatory reaction in the kidney by regulating the activity of 5′-lipoxygenase and inhibiting the generation of superoxide radicals, oxidative proteins, lipids, and leukotriene B-4 in the kidneys of diabetic rats [81]. Moreover, green tea flavonoids could reduce ROS via three pathways, including the activation of PPARγ in the eukaryotic elongation factor-2 kinase (EEF2K) pathway by enhancing 5′AMPK, the induction of nuclear factor-erythrocyte-associated factor 2 (Nrf2), by activating the Kelch-like ECH-associated protein 1-antioxidant-responsive element (Keap1-ARE) signaling, and the regulation of Mn superoxide dismutase production via Forkhead box O3 (FOXO3) -Akt pathway by increasing sirtuin-1 [82]. In addition, green tea catechins, especially EGCG and epicatechin gallate (ECG), could improve the thickening of the basement membrane by relieving the damage of matrix metalloproteinase (MMP), which could degrade extracellular matrix and fibrosis, finally alleviating diabetic nephropathy [83–85].

Besides green tea, other types of tea also show protective effects against diabetic nephropathy. Pu-erh tea could ameliorate diabetic nephropathy by decreasing RAGE expression and glomerular IgG deposit through inhibiting AGE accumulation [73]. Cuiyu tea (a dark tea) polypeptides were reported to stimulate the PKCζ/JNK/nuclear factor-κB (NF-κB)/THF-α/iNOS, advanced glycation end products (AGEs)/RAGE/TGF-1 pathway, up-regulate the expression of podocin in glomeruli, and decrease the release of proinflammatory cytokines, thereby ameliorating diabetic nephropathy [86]. Further, oolong tea polysaccharides could reduce renal tissue inflammation and improve the glomerular vascular permeability of glutathione peroxidase (GSH-PX) by enhancing the activity of superoxide dismutase and GSH-PX [87]. In general, tea exhibits good effects against diabetic nephropathy in vitro and in vivo.

3.2.2. Diabetic Cardiovascular Diseases

Cardiovascular complications, containing cardiomyopathy, atherosclerosis, coronary ischemia, and vascular disease, are associated with the high morbidity and mortality of diabetes mellitus [77,88], among which cardiomyopathy is responsible for 80% [17]. It was reported that tea could improve cardiovascular complications by decreasing hyperglycemia, adjusting lipid metabolism, activating signaling pathways, down-regulating the inflammatory factors, and so on.

Tea polyphenols could improve myocardial glycolipid energy metabolism and interfere with adiponectin mRNA and protein expression through AMPK activation, which was involved in insulin signaling [89]. Also, tea polyphenols could stimulate the activity of AMPK via the Ca^{2+}/Ca-MKK/AMPK-mediated signaling pathway [90]. Additionally, tea polyphenols could regulate autophagy via mTOR and Akt signaling pathways, which was beneficial for the prevention and treatment of diabetic cardiomyopathy [91–93].

An in vivo study found that green tea could inhibit cardiac dyslipidemia, lipid peroxidation, and protein glycosylation through improving the activities of Ca^{2+}-ATP and Na^+/K^+-ATP enzymes to regulate the content of Ca^{2+} and Na^+ [94]. Furthermore, EGCG could improve metabolic and cardiovascular pathophysiology by stimulating the production of nitric oxide (NO) from endothelium via phosphatidylinositol 3-hydroxykinase (PI3k)-dependent pathways [95]. Additionally, EGCG could inhibit inflammatory factors such as NF-κB and activator-1, which played an important role in vascular inflammation caused by insulin resistance [96,97]. In addition, it was found that green tea extract could reduce the progression of atherosclerosis by reversing endothelial dysfunction [98]. Also, MMP-9 played an important role in atherosclerosis, and green tea catechins could inhibit the mRNA expression and the activity of MMPs [83,99]. Further, green tea catechins increased plasma total antioxidant activity and prevented diabetic cardiovascular autonomic dysfunction by blocking changes in arterial pressure variability [77]. Moreover, the green tea extract inhibited the accumulation of aortic collagen, reduced the solubility of collagen, and decreased AGEs and collagen cross-linking, finally preventing diabetic cardiomyopathy in streptozotocin diabetic rats [98,100]. It was also reported that green tea flavonoids could alleviate the contraction of aortic strips, and green tea extract could protect against free radical and glucose-mediated protein damage [101].

Both black tea theaflavins and green tea catechins significantly attenuated high glucose-induced block of insulin signaling, reduced lipid accumulation, inhibited fatty acid synthesis, and stimulated fatty acid oxidation by activating the LKB1-AMPK pathway [54,102,103]. Furthermore, insulin deficiency and insulin resistance could induce exaggerated vasoconstriction [104], and black tea polyphenols could improve vasoconstriction through PI3K-Akt pathway and endothelial nitric oxide synthase (eNOS) phosphorylation [105,106].

White tea catechins could reduce the absorption of cholesterol in the intestines and increase the excretion of cholesterol and total fat in the feces [107]. Further, white tea could control the Krebs cycle by decreasing pyruvate through regulating lactic acid and the lactate dehydrogenase levels in the heart at the prediabetic state, thereby preventing diabetic cardiovascular disease [108–110]. In addition, white tea could regulate cardiac metabolic disorders by up-regulating the expression of cardiac GLUT1 and GLUT3 mRNA [87]. Quercetin, an important flavonoid found in write tea, could prevent diabetic vascular complications in both insulin deficiency and resistance by inhibiting inflammatory pathways, especially the NF-κB signaling [104].

Yellow tea "Junshan Yinzhen" could improve insulin resistance and the disorders of glucose and lipid metabolism in diabetic rats, which may be related to the high content of polyphenols, polysaccharides, and alkaloids in yellow tea [111]. Besides, yellow tea could control glucose effectively by maintaining normal expression of thioredoxin interacting protein, which played an important role in the synthesis and release of glucose in the liver [112].

Oolong tea contained less catechins than green tea, but more catechins than black tea [113]. Pu-erh tea extract could inhibit inflammation of visceral adipose tissue by down-regulating the inflammatory factors and inducing the expression of G-protein coupled receptor (Gpr120) [114].

Therefore, tea and its bioactive components, can be good protectors for cardiovascular complications of diabetes.

3.2.3. Diabetic Neuropathy

Neurodegeneration is characterized by increased free radical production and oxidative stress [115]. It has been proved that tea had neuroprotective effects due to its anti-inflammatory and antioxidant properties [116]. An in vivo study found that green tea could prevent autonomic nervous dysfunction by blocking the change of arterial pressure variability [77]. Furthermore, green tea extract could restore the analgesic effect of morphine on diabetic neuropathic pain by inhibiting the production of NO [117]. Further, EGCG could reduce the formation of neural tube defects in embryo caused by maternal diabetes mellitus in mice through blocking the expression and activity of DNA methyltransferase, and inhibiting DNA hypermethylation, and restoring the expression of neural tube closure essential gene [118]. However, the protective effects of tea other than green tea on diabetic neuropathy have been much less investigated, and it could be interesting to investigate whether other types of tea can be also effective to protect against diabetic neuropathy.

3.2.4. Diabetic Retinopathy

Diabetic retinopathy is a common microvascular complication of diabetes mellitus [119]. Hyperglycemia, oxidative stress, and advanced glycation end products are all risk factors of diabetic retinopathy [120]. Tea has shown protective effects on diabetic retinopathy. In diabetic rats, EGCG could protect the retina by decreasing the level of anion and preventing the formation of acellular capillaries and pericyte ghosts [121]. Also, green tea could protect the nerves of diabetic retinas and regulate the subretinal environment by reducing the production of ROS by increasing glutamate transporter expression, reestablishing intercellular connections, and restoring glutamine/glutamate circulation [122]. In addition, green tea at very low dose could improve antioxidant defense, reduce inflammatory markers, and prevent retinal basement membrane thickening [123]. Further, black tea could delay the development of diabetic cataracts by lowering blood sugar, thereby inhibiting pathological biochemical indicators [124]. Oolong tea extract could increase plasma retinol levels in diabetic rats [125]. Overall, tea acts as a potent neuroprotector in diabetic retinas.

3.2.5. Diabetic Hepatopathy

Diabetic hepatopathy is potentially less common [126] but tends to be more prevalent among children [127]. Several studies suggested that tea and tea polyphenols could play important roles in diabetic liver injury through their antioxidant and anti-inflammatory activities [128,129].

In apparently healthy individuals, green tea extract could reduce oxidative stress and reduce the risk of diabetic liver diseases by lowering the malondialdehyde level and increasing the glutathione level [126]. In addition, green tea could ameliorate liver inflammation and damage caused by diabetes mellitus by lowering angiotensin II receptors [130]. Further, black tea extract protected the liver by increasing cellular antioxidant capacity and reducing membrane lipid peroxidation, inhibiting oxidative stress in diabetic and obese rats caused by alloxan and high cholesterol diets [17]. A dietary supplement of yellow tea and write tea regulated glucose and lipid metabolism by reducing the expression of fatty acid synthase, a membrane surface molecule leading to cell apoptosis, and sterol response element-binding protein 1 in db/db mice [15].

Notably, the molecular mechanisms of EGCG on diabetes mellitus and its complications are summarized in Figure 2.

3.2.6. Other Complications

Tea is also beneficial for other diabetic complications, such as osteoporosis, periodontal disease, and reproductive dysfunction. For example, green tea could treat periodontal disease by decreasing the expression of pro-inflammatory cytokine TNF-α and the osteoclastogenic mediator receptor activator of the NF-κB ligand (RANKL) and up-regulating the expression of anti-inflammatory cytokine interleukin-10, osteogenesis-related factor runt-related transcription factor 2 (RUNX-2), and anti-osteoclastogenic factor osteoprotegerin (OPG) [131]. Moreover, epigallocatechin (EGC) had a positive effect on bone metabolism by promoting osteoblast activity and inhibiting osteoclast differentiation [132].

3.3. Adjuvant Therapy

Currently, acarbose, rosiglitazone, and metformin are the main antidiabetic drugs used in clinics [66,133]. Several studies reported that tea had synergistic effects with antidiabetic drugs on diabetes and its complications, making tea a promising adjuvant for diabetes treatment. It was shown that pu-erh tea could enhance the effect of rosiglitazone on antidiabetic nephropathy by preventing the diabetes-induced accumulation of AGEs and re-establishing a normal RAGE level in vivo [69]. Black tea and acarbose also showed a mixed-type effect on the modulation of postprandial hyperglycemia by inhibiting the α-glucosidase activity in the small intestine [134]. Low concentrations of green tea polyphenols or EGCG had a synergistic effect with acarbose on α-amylase and α-glucosidase in vitro [135].

To sum up, a great number of studies indicated that tea and its bioactive components could be used for the prevention and treatment of diabetes mellitus and its complications (Table 2). The main mechanisms of action included protecting pancreatic β-cells, ameliorating insulin resistance, anti-inflammatory, and antioxidant potentials (Figure 3). Furthermore, tea showed a synergistic effect with certain antidiabetic drugs on diabetes and its complications.

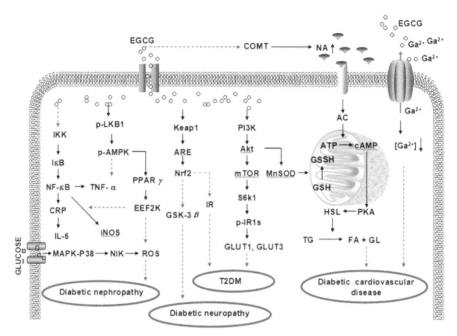

Figure 2. The molecular mechanisms of EGCG against diabetes mellitus and its complications. EGCG has shown effects against T2DM by improving IR, against diabetic cardiovascular disease by decreasing TG and [Ga^{2+}], against diabetic nephropathy by decreasing ROS and against diabetic neuropathy by increasing Nrf2. The arrow means the direction of actions, and the black full lines indicate upregulation and red dotted lines refer to downregulation or inhibition. CRP, C-reactive protein; MAPK p38-NIK, NF-κB inducing kinase; LKB1, kelch-like ECH-associated protein-1; EEF2K, eukaryotic elongation factor-2 kinase; ARE, antioxidant-responsive element; GSK-3β, glycogen synthase kinase-3β; IR, insulin resistance; MnSOD, Mn superoxide dismutase; NA, noradrenalin; s6k1, ribosomal protein S6 kinase 1; AC, adenylate cyclase; HSL, hormone-sensitive lipase; TG, triglyceride; FA, fatty acid; GL, glycerinum; GSH, glutathione; GSSH, oxidized glutathione; mTOR, the target of rapamycin; EGCG, epigallocatechin gallate; IKK, IκB kinase; NF-κB, nuclear factor-κB; iNOS, inducible nitric oxide synthase; TNF-α, tumor necrosis factor-α; Nrf2, nuclear factor-erythrocyte-associated factor 2; PI3K, phosphatidylinositol 3-hydroxykinase; Akt, protein kinase B; AMPK, adenylic acid-activated protein kinase; T2DM, type 2 diabetes mellitus; GLUT, glucose transporter type; PKA, protein kinase A; ATP, adenosine triphosphate; cAMP, cyclic Adenosine monophosphate; COMT, catechol-O-methyltransferase, an enzyme responsible for the degradation of noradrenalin.

Table 2. The effects of tea on diabetes mellitus and its complications by in vitro and in vivo studies.

Tea Types	Constituents	Diseases Types	Study Types	Models	Dose	Effects	Mechanisms	Ref.
Green tea	EGCG	Diabetic cardiovascular disease	In vivo	Alloxan-induced diabetic rabbits	50 mg/kg/day	Improved late endothelial progenitor cells(L-EPCs); Promoted reendothelialization.	Activated Akt/eNOS pathway	[ ]
	EGCG	Diabetic cardiomyopathy	In vivo	Wistar rats	50 mg/kg/day	Enhanced cardiac function; Increased ADSC repair capability;	↑ Insulin-like growth factor 1 ↑ H9c2 cell cycle	[ ]
	EGCG	diabetic neuropathy	In vivo	Male Wistar rats	0.1% (w/v)	Improved cerebral function.	↓ Neuronal degeneration ↓ Apoptotic cell death	[ ]
	Polyphenols	Diabetic Retinopathy	In vivo	Wistar-Kyoto rats	5.7 g/kg/day	Protected the retina against glutamate toxicity.	↓ ROS	[ ]
	Polyphenols	Diabetic cardiovascular disease	In vivo	Male Wistar rats	0.8, 1.6, and 3.2 g/L	Reduced fat deposit; Ameliorated hypoadiponectinemia in HF-fed rats; Relieved high glucose-induced adiponectin decrease.	↓ Extracellular signal regulated kinase 1/2 phosphorylation ↑ PPARγ ↓ Adiponectin decrease	[ ]
	Polyphenols	Diabetic cardiovascular disease	In vitro	Cardiac muscle of rats	200 mg/kg	Ameliorated the effects of high-fructose diet on insulin signaling, lipid metabolism and inflammation.	↑ P13k, Akt1 ↑ Glut1, Glut4, glycogen synthase 1 ↑ Anti-inflammatory protein ↓ GSK-3β, TNF, IL-1B and IL-6	[ ]
	Polyphenols	Diabetic cardiovascular disease	In vivo	STZ-induced rats	300 mg/kg/day	Protected rat heart.	↓ $[Ca^{2+}]$ and $[Na^{+}]$ ↑ Activities of Ca^{2+}-ATPase and Na^{+}/K^{+}-ATPase	[ ]
		Diabetic cardiovascular disease	In vivo	STZ-induced rats	300 mg/kg/day	Reduced the risk of diabetic cardiovascular disease.	↓ Cholesterol, triglyceride ↓ Free fatty acid and LDL-C ↑ HDL-C	[ ]
		Diabetic cardiomyopathy	In vivo	Diabetic rats	300 mg/kg/day	Treated diabetic cardiomyopathy.	↓ AGEs ↓ Collagen cross-linking	[ ]
		diabetic retinopathy	In vivo	Rats	200 mg/kg/day	Prevented and treated diabetic retinopathy.	↓ SOD and catalase enzyme	[ ]
		Diabetic hepatopathy	In vivo	Male Wistar rats	1.5% (w/v)	Prevented diabetic tissue injury.	↑ GSH-Px, SOD, catalase	[ ]
		Diabetic hepatopathy	In vivo	Male Wistar rats	1.5% (w/v)	Protected tissue.	↑ GSH-Px, SOD, catalase ↓ MDA, alkaline phosphatase	[ ]
		Diabetic nephropathy and hepatopathy	In vivo	Male Sprague–Dawley rats	0.1% (w/v)	Protected renal and hepatic tissues from injury.	↑ Total antioxidant levels ↓ Malonyldialdehyde (MDA) ↓ Angiotensin II AT1 receptor	[ ]
		Diabetes mellitus-induced periodontitis	In vivo	STZ-induced rats	N/A	Treated diabetes mellitus-induced periodontitis.	↓ TNF-α and RANKL ↑ RUNX-2, OPG ↑ Interleukin-10 (IL-10)	[ ]
		diabetic spinal cord	In vivo	STZ-induced rats	N/A	Improved diabetic spinal cord.	↑ GFAP	[ ]

Table 2. *Cont.*

Tea Types	Constituents	Diseases Types	Study Types	Models	Dose	Effects	Mechanisms	Ref.
Black tea		T1DM	In vivo	Female CD-1 mice	0.01% (w/v)	Promoted insulin secretion and regenerated damaged pancreas and protected pancreatic β- cells.	↓ Nitrosative stressRUNX-2, OPG↓ ROS	[20]
		Diabetes mellitus	In vivo	STZ-induced rats	0.5 mL/day	Regenerated damaged pancreas and protected pancreatic β-cells.	↓ Nitrosative stress	[143]
		T2DM	In vivo	STZ-induced rats	0.01 mL/g/day	Ameliorated diabetes mellitus associated oxidative stress.	↑GSH	[144]
		Diabetic complication	In vivo	Diabetic animals	50 mg/mL	Attenuated oxidative stress mediated tissue damage.	↓ DNA fragmentation ↓ Activation of caspase-3 ↑ Oxidative stress related parameters	[108]
		Diabetic tissue injury	In vivo	Adult male Wistar albino rat	50 and 100 mg/kg/day	Protected the liver	↑Cellular antioxidant capacity ↓ Membrane lipid peroxidation ↓ Oxidative stress	[17]
	EGC, GC, GCG	bone metabolism	In vitro	Cultured rat osteoblast-like osteosarcoma cell line UMR-106	N/A	Improved bone metabolism	↑Osteoblast activity ↓ Osteoclast differentiation	[132]
White tea		T2DM	In vivo	Male Sprague–Dawley rats	0.5% (w/v)	Lowered blood sugar levels.	↑Insulin sensitivity ↑The synthesis of liver glycogen	[62]
		Diabetic cardiovascular diseases	In vivo	Male Wistar rats	0.01 mg/mL	Prevented cardiovascular diseases.	↑Insulin sensitivity ↑Cardiac acetate and alanine contents and protein oxidation	[88]
		Diabetes mellitus	In vitro	human hepatocellular carcinoma (HepG2) cell	25 mg/mL	Improved glucose and lipid metabolism.	↓ Glucose uptake and transport	[145]
		Diabetic reproductive dysfunction	In vivo	STZ-induced prediabetic rat model	10 mg/mL	Improved epididymal sperm motility and restored sperm viability.	↑ GLUT3 protein ↑ Lactate dehydrogenase ↑ Lactate content.	[146]

Table 2. *Cont.*

Tea Types	Constituents	Diseases Types	Study Types	Models	Dose	Effects	Mechanisms	Ref.
Dark tea	EGCG, ECG	Diabetes mellitus	In vitro	N/A	50 mg/mL	Treated diabetes mellitus.	↓ α-glucosidase	[65]
	TP;TPS	Diabetes mellitus	In vivo	Diabetic rats	50 mg/kg	Reduced postprandial blood sugar.	↓ α-glucosidase	[47]
	Polysaccharides	T2DM	In vivo	Male ICR mice	40 mg/kg	Lowered the blood glucose levels and reversed oxidative stress.	↑ SOD activity ↑ Malondialdehyde contents ↑ GSH-Px	[48]
		T2DM	In vivo	Male ICR mice	1 and 5 mg/kg	Improved insulin resistance.	↓ α-glucosidase Maintain α-amylase	[66]
		T2DM	In vitro In vivo	HepG2 cells db/db mice	100, 200, and 400 mg/kg/day	Improved insulin resistance and maintained glucose homeostasis.	↑ Glucose uptake ↓ Intestinal sucrase, maltase, and porcine pancreatic amylase activity	[1]
		T2DM	In vivo	Male Sprague–Dawley rats	400 mg/kg/day	Alleviated insulin resistance and chronic kidney disease.	↓ SIRP-α ↑ PI3K/Akt ↑ Nrf2 expression in kidney ↓ GSK-3β phosphorylation Activated Akt/GLUT4, FoxO1 and mTOR/S6k1 pathways	[69]
		diabetic nephropathy	In vivo	db/db mice and db/m mice	1 g/kg/day	Attenuated the increases in urinary albumin, serum creatinine, and mesangial matrix.	↓ AGEs ↓ Receptor for AGE expression in glomeruli ↓ Carbonyl compounds	[72]
Oolong tea	Polysaccharide	diabetic tissue and kidney	In vivo	STZ-induced diabetic diabetic mice	50, 100, and 200 mg/kg	Prevented diabetic tissue and kidney diseases.	↑ SOD and GSH-PX activity ↓ MDA	[87]
	Polysaccharide	Diabetic immune disease	In vivo	STZ-induced diabetic mice	100, 300, and 600 mg/kg in mice 50, 100, and 200 mg/kg in rats	Improved immunomodulatory function.	↑ The activity of NK cells Intensify DTH ↑ Phagocytotic function of peritoneal macrophage	[49]
Yellow tea	EGCGCG	Diabetes mellitus	In vitro	N/A	1% (w/v)	CGC reduced postprandial blood sugar more effectively.	↓ α-glucosidase	[71]
		Diabetic complications	In vivo	db/db mice	N/A	Lowered the serum total and low-density lipoprotein cholesterol and triglyceride levels. Increased glucose tolerance.	↓ The lipid synthesis ↓ SRET fatorl, SREP 1 ↓ Acetyl-CoA carboxylase α, ↓ Fatty acid synthase	[16]

Table 2. *Cont.*

Tea Types	Constituents	Diseases Types	Study Types	Models	Dose	Effects	Mechanisms	Ref.
Tea	EGCG	T1DM	In vitro	RINm5F cells	20–40 μM	Protected pro-inflammatory cytokine and induced injuries in insulin-producing cells.	↓iNOS and NO	[47]
	EGCG	T1DM	in vivo	C57BL/KsJ mice	100 mg/kg/day	Protected pancreatic islets.	↓iNOS	[56]
	EGCG	T2DM	In vivo	Diabetic patients	300, 600, and 900 mg/day	Decreased pathogenesis of proinflammation and improved diabetes mellitus.	↓ Free radicals; ↓ S100A12-RAGE axis by stimulating sRAGE	[57]
	Catechins	T2DM	In vivo In vitro	Male obese KK-ay and C57BL/6J mice; 3T3-L1 adipocytes	20 mg/kg/day	Decreased glucose levels and increased glucose tolerance in animals.	↓ ROS; ↓ JNK phosphorylation; ↑ GLUT-4 translocation	[58]
	EGCG	T2DM	In vitro	Human HepG2 cells	N/A	Attenuated insulin signaling blockade.	↓ Phosphorylation of IRS-1; ↑ 5'AMPK	[62]
	EGCG	T2DM	In vivo	Sprague–Dawley rats	1–100 μM	Improved endothelial dysfunction and insulin resistance and protected against myocardial I/R injury.	↑ NO via PI3k pathway; ↑ Plasma adiponectin	[65]
		diabetic nephropathy	In vivo	Diabetic SHR rats	5.7 g/kg/day	Reduced podocyte apoptosis, foot process effacement and albuminuria.	↓ CSK3-p53; ↑ LRP6	[78]
		diabetic nephropathy	In vivo	STZ-induced diabetic rats	5% (w/v)	Improved diabetic nephropathy.	↓ MMP-9, TIMP-1; ↑ MMP-2, TIMP-2	[83]
		diabetic nephropathy	In vivo	Male Sprague–Dawley rats	0.25% and 0.5% (w/w)	Reduced renal oxidative damage and inflammatory reactions.	↑ Activity of 5'-lipoxygenase; ↓ leukotriene B-4	[81]
	Catechins	diabetic nephropathy	In vivo	Sprague–Dawley rats	0.25% and 0.5% (w/w)	Improved kidney function.	↓ Thromboxane A(2) synthesis; ↑ Prostacyclin synthesis	[151,152]

Abbreviations: iNOS, inducible nitric oxide synthase; RANKL, receptor activator of nuclear factor kappa-B ligand; OPG, osteoprotegerin; RUNX-2, runt-related transcription factor 2; GFAP, glial fibrillary acidic protein; SREP, sterol regulatory element-binding transcription factor 1; SREP, synthase and sterol response element-binding protein; TIMP, tissue inhibitor of metalloproteinases; STZ, streptozotocin; SHR, spontaneous hypertension rat; ICR, Institute of Cancer Research; Akt, protein kinase B; eNOS, endothelial nitric oxide synthase; PPARγ, peroxisome proliferator-activated receptorγ; PI3K, phosphatidylinositol 3-hydroxykinase; GLUT, glucose transporter type; GSK-3β, glycogen synthase kinase-3β; TNF, tumor necrosis factor; AGEs, advanced glycation end products; SOD, superoxide dismutase; GSH-Px, glutathione peroxidase; SIRP, signal regulatory protein; Nrf2, nuclear factor-erythrocyte-associated factor 2; mTOR, the target of rapamycin; S6k1, ribosomal protein S6 kinase 1; JNK, jun NH2-terminal kinase; w/v, weight/volume; w/w, weight/weight.

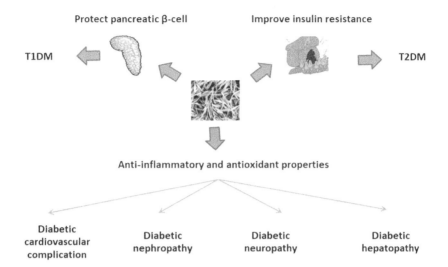

Figure 3. The association between tea and diabetes and its complications. Tea has effects on type 1 diabetes mellitus (T1DM) and type 2 diabetes mellitus (T2DM) by protecting pancreatic β-cells and ameliorating insulin resistance. Besides, due to the anti-inflammatory and antioxidant properties of tea, diabetic complications, including diabetic cardiovascular complication, diabetic nephropathy, diabetic neuropathy, and diabetic hepatic tissue injury, could be prevented and treated by tea and its bioactive components.

4. Clinical Trials

Several clinical trials have assessed the role of tea in treating diabetes mellitus and diabetic complications.

A double-blind, randomized, controlled clinical trial (RCT) found that green tea could improve bone mineral levels in patients from Brazil with diabetes mellitus [153]. Another RCT observed that green tea extract significantly reduced bone resorption markers and altered bone conversion in T2DM patients [154]. Furthermore, a phase I clinical trial involving 63 patients with T2DM found that drinking 4 cups of green tea per day for two months significantly reduced body weight and systolic blood pressure [155]. Another RCT conducted in Taiwan observed that green tea extract significantly improved insulin resistance and increased glucagon-like peptide 1 [156]. It was proven that green tea could reduce risk factors of diabetes mellitus such as average arterial pressure, waist-to-hip ratio, and glutamic-pyruvic transaminase, but had little effect on fasting blood sugar and hemoglobin A1c (HbA1c), which may be related to the short time span of the study, for subjects in Mauritius [21]. Another RCT conducted in British showed that green tea extract could reduce proteinuria in diabetic patients [41]. Further, it was reported that postprandial blood sugar could be decreased in people drinking black tea [39]. A clinical trial conducted in Kuwait also revealed that drinking black tea for one year could significantly reduce HbA1c level and pro-inflammatory CD3[+] CD4[+] IL-17[+] cells, and eliminate serum total cholesterol, thereby preventing diabetes mellitus and its complications [22]. Moreover, another trial demonstrated that black tea could protect against diabetes mellitus and diabetic cardiovascular disease through its anti-inflammatory and antioxidant properties [58]. Oolong tea was proven to be an effective adjunctive oral hypoglycemic substance for T2DM in a clinical trial in diabetic patients from Taiwan taking normal hypoglycemic drugs [157].

In brief, clinical trials involving different countries and different people showed that tea could prevent and manage diabetes mellitus and its complications, mainly by improving insulin resistance and decreasing postprandial blood sugar (Table 3).

Table 3. The effects of tea on diabetes mellitus and its complications based on clinical trials.

Tea Types	Diseases Types	Study Types	Participants	Dose and Duration	Results	Ref.
Green tea	Diabetes mellitus	RCT	Patients with T2DM (N = 63)	0, 2, 4 cups per day	↓ Body weight, body mass index, waist circumference and systolic blood pressure.	[155]
Green tea	Diabetes mellitus and diabetic nephropathy	RCT	Patients with diabetes mellitus (N = 60)	2 capsules containing 1120 mg polyphenols per day for 20 weeks.	No significant effect on diabetes mellitus and diabetic nephropathy.	[158]
Green tea	T2DM and diabetic cardiomyopathy	RCT	Subjects with T2DM and lipid abnormalities (N = 92)	500 mg per day	↓ Triglyceride ↑ High density lipoprotein cholesterol ↑ Glucagon-like peptide 1 in the therapeutic arm	[156]
Green tea	Diabetic osteoporosis	RCT	Patients with diabetes mellitus (N = 35)	1120 mg polyphenols per day	↑ Bone mineral content ↓ PTH	[153]
Green tea	Bone turnover induced by diabetes mellitus	RCT	Patients with T2DM (N = 72)	500 mg per day	↓ Fasting serum osteocalcin ↓ FBG ↓ HbA1C	[154]
Black tea	T2DM and diabetic cardiovascular	N/A	Patients with T2DM (N = 46)	150, 300, 450, and 600 mL black tea during the weeks 1, 2, 3 and 4.	↓ Serum malondialdehyde ↓ Serum C-reactive protein ↑ Glutathione	[58]
Oolong tea	T2DM	N/A	Patients with T2DM	1500 mL per day	↓ Concentrations of plasma glucose and fructosamine	[73]
Green and black tea	T2DM	RCT	White persons (N = 49)	0, 375, or 750 mg per day for 3 months	No significant effect on T2DM.	[159]

N/A, not available; RCT, randomized, controlled clinical trial; FBG, Fasting blood glucose; T2DM, type 2 diabetes mellitus; PTH, parathyroid hormone; HbA1C, hemoglobin A1c.

5. Conclusions

Diabetes mellitus and its complications have become an important public health problem. Epidemiological studies found that drinking tea could reduce the risk of diabetes mellitus and diabetic complications, and among these studies, green tea, black tea, and oolong tea were in the majority, while epidemiological studies on white tea, dark tea, and yellow tea were less common. In addition, experimental studies have shown that tea could protect against diabetes mellitus and diabetic complications by improving insulin resistance, activating the insulin signaling pathway, playing an insulin-like role, improving oxidative stress, and alleviating inflammatory response. Further, tea has synergistic effects with certain antidiabetic drugs. Moreover, clinical trials have shown that tea played a positive role in the prevention and treatment of diabetes mellitus and its complications. Additionally, different types of tea have different main bioactive ingredients, which may be applicable to different diabetic complications. Therefore, tea could be used as a beverage, or be developed into functional foods or nutraceuticals, for the prevention and management of diabetes mellitus and its complications, such as diabetic nephropathy, diabetic cardiovascular disease, and diabetic retinopathy. In the future, more bioactive components in tea for the prevention and management of diabetes mellitus and its complications should be separated and identified, especially for the dark tea. The molecular mechanisms of tea and its bioactive components should be further studied. In addition, because of the differences of doses and effects of tea between experimental and clinical studies, it is still difficult to conclude whether the effective doses from animal studies might have beneficial effects on human. Therefore, more clinical trials should be carried out to verify the protective effects of tea on diabetes mellitus and its complications. In addition, special attention should be paid to the safety of tea and tea products.

Author Contributions: Conceptualization, J.-M.M., R.-Y.G. and H.-B.L.; writing—original draft preparation, J.-M.M., S.-Y.C. and X.-Y.X.; writing—review and editing, X.-L.W., Y.-F.W., S.-X.C., P.-Z.Z., R.-Y.G., and H.-B.L.; supervision, R.-Y.G. and H.-B.L.; funding acquisition, R.-Y.G. and H.-B.L.

Funding: This study was supported by the National Key R&D Program of China (No. 2018YFC1604400), Shanghai Basic and Key Program (No. 18JC1410800), the Agri-X Interdisciplinary Fund of Shanghai Jiao Tong University (No. Agri-X2017004), and the Key Project of Guangdong Provincial Science and Technology Program (No. 2014B020205002).

Conflicts of Interest: The authors declare no conflict of interest.

References

1. Assoc, A.D. Diagnosis and classification of diabetes mellitus. *Diabetes Care* **2014**, *37*, S81–S90.
2. Whiting, D.R.; Guariguata, L.; Weil, C.; Shaw, J. IDF diabetes atlas: Global estimates of the prevalence of diabetes for 2011 and 2030. *Diabetes Res. Clin. Pract.* **2011**, *94*, 311–321. [CrossRef] [PubMed]
3. Shaw, J.E.; Sicree, R.A.; Zimmet, P.Z. Global estimates of the prevalence of diabetes for 2010 and 2030. *Diabetes Res. Clin. Pract.* **2010**, *87*, 4–14. [CrossRef] [PubMed]
4. Guariguata, L.; Whiting, D.R.; Hambleton, I.; Beagley, J.; Linnenkamp, U.; Shaw, J.E. Global estimates of diabetes prevalence for 2013 and projections for 2035. *Diabetes Res. Clin. Pract.* **2014**, *103*, 137–149. [CrossRef] [PubMed]
5. Du, W.H.; Peng, S.M.; Liu, Z.H.; Shi, L.; Tan, L.F.; Zou, X.Q. Hypoglycemic effect of the water extract of Pu-erh tea. *J. Agric. Food Chem.* **2012**, *60*, 10126–10132. [CrossRef]
6. Li, Y.; Wang, C.; Huai, Q.; Guo, F.; Liu, L.; Feng, R.; Sun, C. Effects of tea or tea extract on metabolic profiles in patients with type 2 diabetes mellitus: A meta-analysis of ten randomized controlled trials. *Diabetes Res. Clin. Pract.* **2016**, *32*, 2–10. [CrossRef] [PubMed]
7. Gan, R.Y.; Li, H.B.; Sui, Z.Q.; Corke, H. Absorption, metabolism, anti-cancer effect and molecular targets of epigallocatechin gallate (EGCG): An updated review. *Crit. Rev. Food Sci. Nutr.* **2018**, *58*, 924–941. [CrossRef]
8. Li, F.; Li, S.; Li, H.-B.; Deng, G.-F.; Ling, W.-H.; Xu, X.-R. Antiproliferative activities of tea and herbal infusions. *Food Funct.* **2013**, *4*, 530–538. [CrossRef]
9. Li, S.; Gan, L.-Q.; Li, S.-K.; Zheng, J.-C.; Xu, D.-P.; Li, H.-B. Effects of herbal infusions, tea and carbonated beverages on alcohol dehydrogenase and aldehyde dehydrogenase activity. *Food Funct.* **2014**, *5*, 42–49. [CrossRef]
10. Li, Y.; Li, S.; Lin, S.-J.; Zhang, J.-J.; Zhao, C.-N.; Li, H.-B. Microwave-assisted extraction of natural antioxidants from the exotic gordonia axillaris fruit: Optimization and identification of phenolic compounds. *Molecules* **2017**, *22*, 1481. [CrossRef]
11. Meng, X.; Li, S.; Li, Y.; Gan, R.Y.; Li, H.B. Gut microbiota's relationship with liver disease and role in hepatoprotection by dietary natural products and probiotics. *Nutrients* **2018**, *10*, 1457. [CrossRef] [PubMed]
12. Meng, X.; Li, Y.; Li, S.; Gan, R.-Y.; Li, H.-B. Natural products for prevention and treatment of chemical-induced liver injuries. *Compr. Rev. Food Sci. Food Saf.* **2018**, *17*, 472–495. [CrossRef]
13. Tao, J.; Li, S.; Gan, R.-Y.; Zhao, C.-N.; Meng, X.; Li, H.-B. Targeting gut microbiota with dietary components on cancer: Effects and potential mechanisms of action. *Crit. Rev. Food Sci. Nutr.* **2019**, 1–13. [CrossRef] [PubMed]
14. Xu, X.-Y.; Zhao, C.-N.; Cao, S.-Y.; Tang, G.-Y.; Gan, R.-Y.; Li, H.-B. Effects and mechanisms of tea for the prevention and management of cancers: An updated review. *Crit. Rev. Food Sci. Nutr.* **2019**, 1–13. [CrossRef] [PubMed]
15. Teng, Y.; Li, D.X.; Guruvaiah, P.; Xu, N.; Xie, Z.W. Dietary supplement of large yellow tea ameliorates metabolic syndrome and attenuates hepatic steatosis in db/db Mice. *Nutrients* **2018**, *10*, 75. [CrossRef] [PubMed]
16. Ning, J.M.; Li, D.X.; Luo, X.J.; Ding, D.; Song, Y.S.; Zhang, Z.Z.; Wan, X.C. Stepwise identification of six tea (camellia sinensis (L.)) categories based on catechins, caffeine, and theanine contents combined with fisher discriminant analysis. *Food Anal. Meth.* **2016**, *9*, 3242–3250. [CrossRef]
17. Ramadan, G.; El-Beih, N.M.; El-Ghffar, E.A.A. Modulatory effects of black v. green tea aqueous extract on hyperglycaemia, hyperlipidaemia and liver dysfunction in diabetic and obese rat models. *Br. J. Nutr.* **2009**, *102*, 1611–1619. [CrossRef]
18. Jing, Y.L.; Han, G.J.; Hu, Y.; Bi, Y.; Li, L.R.; Zhu, D.L. Tea consumption and risk of type 2 diabetes: A meta-analysis of cohort studies. *J. Gen. Intern. Med.* **2009**, *24*, 557–562. [CrossRef]
19. Boggs, D.A.; Rosenberg, L.; Ruiz-Narvaez, E.A.; Palmer, J.R. Coffee, tea, and alcohol intake in relation to risk of type 2 diabetes in African American women. *Am. J. Clin. Nutr.* **2010**, *92*, 960–966. [CrossRef]
20. Tang, W.P.; Li, S.M.; Liu, Y.; Huang, M.T.; Ho, C.T. Anti-diabetic activity of chemically profiled green tea and black tea extracts in a type 2 diabetes mice model via different mechanisms. *J. Funct. Foods* **2013**, *5*, 1784–1793. [CrossRef]

21. Toolsee, N.A.; Aruoma, O.I.; Gunness, T.K.; Kowlessur, S.; Dambala, V.; Murad, F.; Googoolye, K.; Daus, D.; Indelicato, J.; Rondeau, P.; et al. Effectiveness of green tea in a randomized human cohort: Relevance to diabetes and its complications. *BioMed Res. Int.* **2013**, *2013*, 412379. [CrossRef] [PubMed]

22. Mahmoud, F.; Haines, D.; Al-Ozairi, E.; Dashti, A. Effect of black tea consumption on intracellular cytokines, regulatory T cells and metabolic biomarkers in type 2 diabetes patients. *Phytother. Res.* **2016**, *30*, 454–462. [CrossRef] [PubMed]

23. Hinkle, S.N.; Laughon, S.K.; Catov, J.M.; Olsen, J.; Bech, B.H. First trimester coffee and tea intake and risk of gestational diabetes mellitus: A study within a national birth cohort. *BJOG Int. J. Obstet. Gynaecol.* **2015**, *122*, 420–428. [CrossRef] [PubMed]

24. Greenberg, J.A.; Axen, K.V.; Schnoll, R.; Boozer, C.N. Coffee, tea and diabetes: The role of weight loss and caffeine. *Int. J. Obes.* **2005**, *29*, 1121–1129. [CrossRef] [PubMed]

25. Hamer, M.; Witte, D.R.; Mosdol, A.; Marmot, M.G.; Brunner, E.J. Prospective study of coffee and tea consumption in relation to risk of type 2 diabetes mellitus among men and women: The whitehall II study. *Br. J. Nutr.* **2008**, *100*, 1046–1053. [CrossRef] [PubMed]

26. Hirata, A.; Ohnaka, K.; Tashiro, N.; Wang, Z.; Kohno, M.; Kiyohara, C.; Kono, S.; Takayanagi, R. Effect modification of green tea on the association between rice intake and the risk of diabetes mellitus: A prospective study in Japanese men and women. *Asia Pac. J. Clin. Nutr.* **2017**, *26*, 545–555. [PubMed]

27. Odegaard, A.O.; Pereira, M.A.; Koh, W.P.; Arakawa, K.; Lee, H.P.; Yu, M.C. Coffee, tea, and incident type 2 diabetes: The Singapore chinese health study. *Am. J. Clin. Nutr.* **2008**, *88*, 979–985. [CrossRef]

28. Iso, H.; Date, C.; Wakai, K.; Fukui, M.; Tamakoshi, A.; Grp, J.S. The relationship between green tea and total caffeine intake and risk for self-reported type 2 diabetes among Japanese adults. *Ann. Intern. Med.* **2006**, *144*, 554–562. [CrossRef]

29. Nguyen, C.T.; Lee, A.H.; Pham, N.M.; Do, V.V.; Ngu, N.D.; Tran, B.Q.; Binns, C. Habitual tea drinking associated with a lower risk of type 2 diabetes in Vietnamese adults. *Asia Pac. J. Clin. Nutr.* **2018**, *27*, 701–706.

30. Ma, Q.H.; Chen, D.D.; Sun, H.P.; Yan, N.; Xu, Y.; Pan, C.W. Regular Chinese green tea consumption is protective for diabetic retinopathy: A clinic-based case-control study. *J. Diabetes Res.* **2015**, *2015*, 231570. [CrossRef]

31. Yi, D.Q.; Tan, X.R.; Zhao, Z.G.; Cai, Y.M.; Li, Y.M.; Lin, X.Y.; Lu, S.L.; Chen, Y.S.; Zhang, Q.Y. Reduced risk of dyslipidaemia with oolong tea consumption: A population-based study in southern China. *Br. J. Nutr.* **2014**, *111*, 1421–1429. [CrossRef] [PubMed]

32. Panagiotakos, D.B.; Lionis, C.; Zeimbekis, A.; Gelastopoulou, K.; Papairakleous, N.; Das, U.N.; Polychronopoulos, E. Long-term tea intake is associated with reduced prevalence of (type 2) diabetes mellitus among elderly people from mediterranean islands: MEDIS epidemiological study. *Yonsei Med. J.* **2009**, *50*, 31–38. [CrossRef] [PubMed]

33. Huxley, R.; Lee, C.M.Y.; Barzi, F.; Timmermeister, L.; Czernichow, S.; Perkovic, V.; Grobbee, D.E.; Batty, D.; Woodward, M. Coffee, Decaffeinated coffee, and tea consumption in relation to incident type 2 diabetes mellitus: A systematic review with meta-analysis. *Arch. Intern. Med.* **2009**, *169*, 2053–2063. [CrossRef] [PubMed]

34. Yang, W.S.; Wang, W.Y.; Fan, W.Y.; Deng, Q.; Wang, X. Tea consumption and risk of type 2 diabetes: A dose-response meta-analysis of cohort studies. *Br. J. Nutr.* **2014**, *111*, 1329–1339. [CrossRef] [PubMed]

35. Yang, J.; Mao, Q.X.; Xu, H.X.; Ma, X.; Zeng, C.Y. Tea consumption and risk of type 2 diabetes mellitus: A systematic review and meta-analysis update. *BMJ Open* **2014**, *4*, e005632. [CrossRef] [PubMed]

36. Hayashino, Y.; Fukuhara, S.; Okamura, T.; Tanaka, T.; Ueshima, H.; Grp, H.-O.R. High oolong tea consumption predicts future risk of diabetes among Japanese male workers: A prospective cohort study. *Diabetic Med.* **2011**, *28*, 805–810. [CrossRef] [PubMed]

37. Wang, X.; Tian, J.; Jiang, J.; Li, L.; Ying, X.; Tian, H.; Nie, M. Effects of green tea or green tea extract on insulin sensitivity and glycaemic control in populations at risk of type 2 diabetes mellitus: A systematic review and meta-analysis of randomised controlled trials. *J. Hum. Nutr. Diet.* **2014**, *27*, 501–512. [CrossRef] [PubMed]

38. Yu, J.Y.; Song, P.G.; Perry, R.; Penfold, C.; Cooper, A.R. The effectiveness of green tea or green tea extract on insulin resistance and glycemic control in type 2 diabetes mellitus: A meta-analysis. *Diabetes Metab. J.* **2017**, *41*, 251–262. [CrossRef] [PubMed]

39. Butacnum, A.; Chongsuwat, R.; Bumrungpert, A. Black tea consumption improves postprandial glycemic control in normal and pre-diabetic subjects: A randomized, double-blind, placebo-controlled crossover study. *Asia Pac. J. Clin. Nutr.* **2017**, *26*, 59–64.

40. Van Woudenbergh, G.J.; Kuijsten, A.; Drogan, D.; Van Der, A.D.L.; Romaguera, D.; Ardanaz, E.; Amiano, P.; Barricarte, A.; Beulens, J.W.J.; Boeing, H.; et al. Tea consumption and incidence of type 2 diabetes in europe: The EPIC-interact case-cohort study. *PLoS ONE* **2012**, *7*, e36910.

41. Borges, C.M.; Papadimitriou, A.; Duarte, D.A.; Lopes de Faria, J.M.; Lopes de Faria, J.B. The use of green tea polyphenols for treating residual albuminuria in diabetic nephropathy: A double-blind randomised clinical trial. *Sci. Rep.* **2016**, *6*, 28282. [CrossRef] [PubMed]

42. Nunes, A.R.; Alves, M.G.; Moreira, P.I.; Oliveira, P.F.; Silva, B.M. Can tea consumption be a safe and effective therapy against diabetes mellitus-induced neurodegeneration? *Curr. Neuropharmacol.* **2014**, *12*, 475–489. [CrossRef] [PubMed]

43. Islam, M.S.; Choi, H. Green tea, anti-diabetic or diabetogenic: A dose response study. *Biofactors* **2007**, *29*, 45–53. [CrossRef] [PubMed]

44. Wang, H.J.; Shi, S.S.; Bao, B.; Li, X.J.; Wang, S.C. Structure characterization of an arabinogalactan from green tea and its anti-diabetic effect. *Carbohydr. Polym.* **2015**, *124*, 98–108. [CrossRef] [PubMed]

45. Chemler, J.A.; Lock, L.T.; Koffas, M.A.; Tzanakakis, E.S. Standardized biosynthesis of flavan-3-ols with effects on pancreatic β-cell insulin secretion. *Appl. Microbiol. Biotechnol.* **2007**, *77*, 797–807. [CrossRef] [PubMed]

46. Pastoriza, S.; Mesias, M.; Cabrera, C.; Rufian-Henares, J.A. Healthy properties of green and white teas: An update. *Food Funct.* **2017**, *8*, 2650–2662. [CrossRef] [PubMed]

47. Zhang, Z.; Ding, Y.; Dai, X.; Wang, J.; Li, Y. Epigallocatechin-3-gallate protects pro-inflammatory cytokine induced injuries in insulin-producing cells through the mitochondrial pathway. *Eur. J. Pharmacol.* **2011**, *670*, 311–316. [CrossRef]

48. Yan, J.Q.; Zhao, Y.; Suo, S.; Liu, Y.; Zhao, B.L. Green tea catechins ameliorate adipose insulin resistance by improving oxidative stress. *Free Radic. Biol. Med.* **2012**, *52*, 1648–1657. [CrossRef]

49. Ortsater, H.; Grankvist, N.; Wolfram, S.; Kuehn, N.; Sjoholm, A. Diet supplementation with green tea extract epigallocatechin gallate prevents progression to glucose intolerance in db/db mice. *Nutr. Metab.* **2012**, *9*, 11. [CrossRef]

50. Ma, X.; Tsuda, S.; Yang, X.; Gu, N.; Tanabe, H.; Oshima, R.; Matsushita, T.; Egawa, T.; Dong, A.J.; Zhu, B.W.; et al. Pu-erh tea hot-water extract activates Akt and induces insulin-independent glucose transport in rat skeletal muscle. *J. Med. Food* **2013**, *16*, 259–262. [CrossRef]

51. Hameed, I.; Masoodi, S.R.; Mir, S.A.; Nabi, M.; Ghazanfar, K.; Ganai, B.A. Type 2 diabetes mellitus: From a metabolic disorder to an inflammatory condition. *World J. Diabetes* **2015**, *6*, 598–612. [CrossRef] [PubMed]

52. Lin, C.L.; Lin, J.K. Epigallocatechin gallate (EGCG) attenuates high glucose-induced insulin signaling blockade in human hepG2 hepatoma cells. *Mol. Nutr. Food Res.* **2008**, *52*, 930–939. [CrossRef] [PubMed]

53. Qin, B.L.; Polansky, M.M.; Harry, D.; Anderson, R.A. Green tea polyphenols improve cardiac muscle mRNA and protein levels of signal pathways related to insulin and lipid metabolism and inflammation in insulin-resistant rats. *Mol. Nutr. Food Res.* **2010**, *54*, S14–S23. [CrossRef] [PubMed]

54. Nishikawa, T.; Kukidome, D.; Sonoda, K.; Fujisawa, K.; Matsuhisa, T.; Motoshima, H.; Matsumura, T.; Araki, E. Impact of mitochondrial ROS production in the pathogenesis of insulin resistance. *Diabetes Res. Clin. Pract.* **2007**, *77*, S161–S164. [CrossRef] [PubMed]

55. Yasui, K.; Tanabe, H.; Okada, N.; Fukutomi, R.; Ishigami, Y.; Isemura, M. Effects of catechin-rich green tea on gene expression of gluconeogenic enzymes in rat hepatoma H4IIE cells. *Biomed. Res.* **2010**, *31*, 183–189. [CrossRef] [PubMed]

56. Shin, D.W.; Kim, S.N.; Lee, S.M.; Lee, W.; Song, M.J.; Park, S.M.; Lee, T.R.; Baik, J.-H.; Kim, H.K.; Hong, J.-H.; et al. (−)-Catechin promotes adipocyte differentiation in human bone marrow mesenchymal stem cells through PPARγ transactivation. *Biochem. Pharmacol.* **2009**, *77*, 125–133. [CrossRef] [PubMed]

57. Huang, S.M.; Chang, Y.H.; Chao, Y.C.; Lin, J.A.; Wu, C.H.; Lai, C.Y.; Chan, K.C.; Tseng, S.T.; Yen, G.C. EGCG-rich green tea extract stimulates sRAGE secretion to inhibit S100A12-RAGE axis through ADAM10-mediated ectodomain shedding of extracellular RAGE in type 2 diabetes. *Mol. Nutr. Food Res.* **2013**, *57*, 2264–2268. [CrossRef]

58. Neyestani, T.R.; Shariatzade, N.; Kalayi, A.; Gharavi, A.; Khalaji, N.; Dadkhah, M.; Zowghi, T.; Haidari, H.; Shab-Bidar, S. Regular daily intake of black tea improves oxidative stress biomarkers and decreases serum C-reactive protein levels in type 2 diabetic patients. *Ann. Nutr. Metab.* **2010**, *57*, 40–49. [CrossRef]

59. Yamashita, Y.; Wang, L.Q.; Wang, L.H.; Tanaka, Y.; Zhang, T.S.; Ashida, H. Oolong, black and pu-erh tea suppresses adiposity in mice via activation of AMP-activated protein kinase. *Food Funct.* **2014**, *5*, 2420–2429. [CrossRef]

60. Hilal, Y.; Engelhardt, U. Correction/Erratum characterisation of white tea-comparison to green and black tea. *J. Verbrauch. Lebensm.* **2009**, *4*, 218–220.

61. Sanlier, N.; Atik, İ.; Atik, A. A minireview of effects of white tea consumption on diseases. *Trends Food Sci. Technol.* **2018**, *82*, 82–88. [CrossRef]

62. Islam, M.S. Effects of the aqueous extract of white tea (*Camellia sinensis*) in a streptozotocin-induced diabetes model of rats. *Phytomedicine* **2011**, *19*, 25–31. [CrossRef] [PubMed]

63. Xu, N.; Chu, J.; Wang, M.; Chen, L.; Zhang, L.; Xie, Z.W.; Zhang, J.S.; Ho, C.T.; Li, D.X.; Wan, X.C. Large yellow tea attenuates macrophage-related chronic inflammation and metabolic syndrome in high-fat diet treated mice. *J. Agric. Food Chem.* **2018**, *66*, 3823–3832. [CrossRef] [PubMed]

64. Yamauchi, R.; Kobayashi, M.; Matsuda, Y.; Ojika, M.; Shigeoka, S.; Yamamoto, Y.; Tou, Y.; Inoue, T.; Katagiri, T.; Murai, A.; et al. Coffee and caffeine ameliorate hyperglycemia, fatty liver, and inflammatory adipocytokine expression in spontaneously diabetic KK-A^y Mice. *J. Agric. Food Chem.* **2010**, *58*, 5597–5603. [CrossRef] [PubMed]

65. Liu, S.Y.; Yu, Z.; Zhu, H.K.; Zhang, W.; Chen, Y.Q. In vitro α-glucosidase inhibitory activity of isolated fractions from water extract of qingzhuan dark tea. *BMC Complement. Altern. Med.* **2016**, *16*, 378. [CrossRef] [PubMed]

66. Deng, Y.-T.; Lin-Shiau, S.-Y.; Shyur, L.-F.; Lin, J.-K. Pu-erh tea polysaccharides decrease blood sugar by inhibition of α-glucosidase activity in vitro and in mice. *Food Funct.* **2015**, *6*, 1539–1546. [CrossRef] [PubMed]

67. Ding, Q.Z.; Zheng, W.; Zhang, B.W.; Chen, X.J.; Zhang, J.; Pang, X.; Zhang, Y.; Jia, D.X.; Pei, S.R.; Dong, Y.S.; et al. Comparison of hypoglycemic effects of ripened pu-erh tea and raw pu-erh tea in streptozotocin-induced diabetic rats. *RSC Adv.* **2019**, *9*, 2967–2977. [CrossRef]

68. Lin, H.-C.; Lee, C.-T.; Yen, Y.-Y.; Chu, C.-L.; Hsieh, Y.-P.; Yang, C.-S.; Lan, S.-J. Systematic review and meta-analysis of anti-hyperglycaemic effects of pu-erh tea. *Int. J. Food Sci. Technol.* **2019**, *54*, 516–525. [CrossRef]

69. Du, H.; Wang, Q.; Yang, X. Fu Brick Tea alleviates chronic kidney disease of rats with high fat diet consumption through attenuating insulin resistance in skeletal muscle. *J. Agric. Food Chem.* **2019**, *67*, 2839–2847. [CrossRef]

70. Renno, W.M.; Abdeen, S.; Alkhalaf, M.; Asfar, S. Effect of green tea on kidney tubules of diabetic rats. *Br. J. Nutr.* **2008**, *100*, 652–659. [CrossRef]

71. Zhou, J.; Zhang, L.; Meng, Q.L.; Wang, Y.J.; Long, P.P.; Ho, C.T.; Cui, C.J.; Cao, L.T.; Li, D.X.; Wan, X.C. Roasting improves the hypoglycemic effects of a large-leaf yellow tea infusion by enhancing the levels of epimerized catechins that inhibit α-glucosidase. *Food Funct.* **2018**, *9*, 5162–5168. [CrossRef] [PubMed]

72. Navarro-Gonzalez, J.F.; Mora-Fernandez, C.; Muros de Fuentes, M.; Garcia-Perez, J. Inflammatory molecules and pathways in the pathogenesis of diabetic nephropathy. *Nat. Rev. Nephrol.* **2011**, *7*, 327–340. [CrossRef] [PubMed]

73. Yan, S.J.; Wang, L.; Li, Z.; Zhu, D.N.; Guo, S.C.; Xin, W.F.; Yang, Y.F.; Cong, X.; Ma, T.; Shen, P.P.; et al. Inhibition of advanced glycation end product formation by pu-erh tea ameliorates progression of experimental diabetic nephropathy. *J. Agric. Food Chem.* **2012**, *60*, 4102–4110. [CrossRef] [PubMed]

74. Hase, M.; Babazono, T.; Karibe, S.; Kinae, N.; Iwamoto, Y. Renoprotective effects of tea catechin in streptozotocin-induced diabetic rats. *Int. Urol. Nephrol.* **2006**, *38*, 693–699. [CrossRef] [PubMed]

75. Yaribeygi, H.; Atkin, S.L.; Sahebkar, A. Interleukin-18 and diabetic nephropathy: A review. *J. Cell. Physiol.* **2019**, *234*, 5674–5682. [CrossRef] [PubMed]

76. Jeong, B.C.; Kim, B.S.; Kim, J.I.; Kim, H.H. Effects of green tea on urinary stone formation: An in vivo and in vitro study. *J. Endourol.* **2006**, *20*, 356–361. [CrossRef]

77. Fiorino, P.; Evangelista, F.S.; Santos, F.; Magri, F.M.M.; Delorenzi, J.C.M.O.B.; Ginoza, M.; Farah, V. The effects of green tea consumption on cardiometabolic alterations induced by experimental diabetes. *Exp. Diabetes Res.* **2012**, *2012*, 309231. [CrossRef]

78. Peixoto, E.B.; Papadimitriou, A.; Teixeira, D.A.T.; Montemurro, C.; Duarte, D.A.; Silva, K.C.; Joazeiro, P.P.; de Faria, J.M.L.; de Faria, J.B.L. Reduced LRP6 expression and increase in the interaction of GSK3β with p53 contribute to podocyte apoptosis in diabetes mellitus and are prevented by green tea. *J. Nutr. Biochem.* **2015**, *26*, 416–430. [CrossRef]

79. Yokozawa, T.; Nakagawa, T.; Oya, T.; Okubo, T.; Juneja, L.R. Green tea polyphenols and dietary fibre protect against kidney damage in rats with diabetic nephropathy. *J. Pharm. Pharmacol.* **2005**, *57*, 773–780. [CrossRef]

80. Zhu, D.N.; Wang, L.; Zhou, Q.L.; Yan, S.J.; Li, Z.; Sheng, J.; Zhang, W.S. (+)-Catechin ameliorates diabetic nephropathy by trapping methylglyoxal in type 2 diabetic mice. *Mol. Nutr. Food. Res.* **2014**, *58*, 2249–2260. [CrossRef]

81. Choi, J.H.; Chai, Y.M.; Joo, G.J.; Rhee, I.K.; Lee, I.S.; Kim, K.R.; Choi, M.S.; Rhee, S.J. Effects of green tea catechin on polymorphonuclear leukocyte 5′-lipoxygenase activity, leukotriene B-4 synthesis, and renal damage in diabetic rats. *Ann. Nutr. Metab.* **2004**, *48*, 151–155. [CrossRef] [PubMed]

82. Mohabbulla Mohib, M.; Fazla Rabby, S.M.; Paran, T.Z.; Mehedee Hasan, M.; Ahmed, I.; Hasan, N.; Abu Taher Sagor, M.; Mohiuddin, S.; Hsu, T.-C. Protective role of green tea on diabetic nephropathy—A review. *Cogent Biol.* **2016**, *2*, 1248166. [CrossRef]

83. Petroski, M.D.; Deshaies, R. Effects of green tea on matrix metalloproteinases in streptozotocin-induced diabetic rats. *J. Clin. Biochem. Nutr.* **2005**, *37*, 77–85.

84. Nagase, H.; Visse, R.; Murphy, G. Structure and function of matrix metalloproteinases and TIMPs. *Cardiovasc. Res.* **2006**, *69*, 562–573. [CrossRef] [PubMed]

85. Sarkar, J.; Nandy, S.K.; Chowdhury, A.; Chakraborti, T.; Chakraborti, S. Inhibition of MMP-9 by green tea catechins and prediction of their interaction by molecular docking analysis. *Biomed. Pharmacother.* **2016**, *84*, 340–347. [CrossRef] [PubMed]

86. Deng, X.M.; Sun, L.L.; Lai, X.F.; Xiang, L.M.; Li, Q.H.; Zhang, W.J.; Zhang, L.Z.; Sun, S.L. Tea polypeptide ameliorates diabetic nephropathy through RAGE and NF-κB signaling pathway in type 2 diabetes mice. *J. Agric. Food Chem.* **2018**, *66*, 11957–11967. [CrossRef] [PubMed]

87. Ni, D.; Chen, Y.; Song, C.; Xie, B.; Zhou, S. Effect of oolong tea polysaccharide on hepatic-nephritic antioxidation and histommorphology in the diabetic rats. *J. Tea Sci.* **2003**, *23*, 11–15.

88. Alves, M.G.; Martins, A.D.; Teixeira, N.F.; Rato, L.; Oliveira, P.F.; Silva, B.M. White tea consumption improves cardiac glycolytic and oxidative profile of prediabetic rats. *J. Funct. Foods* **2015**, *14*, 102–110. [CrossRef]

89. Lin, C.; Zhang, M.; Zhang, Y.; Yang, K.; Hu, J.; Si, R.; Zhang, G.; Gao, B.; Li, X.; Xu, C.; et al. Helix B surface peptide attenuates diabetic cardiomyopathy via AMPK-dependent autophagy. *Biochem. Biophys. Res. Commun.* **2017**, *482*, 665–671. [CrossRef]

90. Zhou, H.; Chen, Y.; Huang, S.W.; Hu, P.F.; Tang, L.J. Regulation of autophagy by tea polyphenols in diabetic cardiomyopathy. *J. Zhejiang Univ.-Sci. B* **2018**, *19*, 333–341. [CrossRef]

91. Fahie, K.; Zachara, N.E. Molecular functions of glycoconjugates in autophagy. *J. Mol. Biol.* **2016**, *428*, 3305–3324. [CrossRef] [PubMed]

92. Trivedi, P.C.; Bartlett, J.J.; Perez, L.J.; Brunt, K.R.; Legare, J.F.; Hassan, A.; Kienesberger, P.C.; Pulinilkunnil, T. Glucolipotoxicity diminishes cardiomyocyte TFEB and inhibits lysosomal autophagy during obesity and diabetes. *Biochim. Biophys. Acta Mol. Cell Biol. Lipids* **2016**, *1861*, 1893–1910. [CrossRef] [PubMed]

93. Velazquez, A.P.; Graef, M. Autophagy regulation depends on ER homeostasis controlled by lipid droplets. *Autophagy* **2016**, *12*, 1409–1410. [CrossRef] [PubMed]

94. Babu, P.V.A.; Sabitha, K.E.; Shyamaladevi, C.S. Green tea impedes dyslipidemia, lipid peroxidation, protein glycation and ameliorates Ca^{2+}-ATPase and Na^+/K^+-ATPase activity in the heart of streptozotocin-diabetic rats. *Chem.-Biol. Interact.* **2006**, *162*, 157–164. [CrossRef] [PubMed]

95. Potenza, M.A.; Marasciulo, F.L.; Tarquinio, M.; Tiravanti, E.; Colantuono, G.; Federici, A.; Kim, J.A.; Quon, M.J.; Montagnani, M. EGCG, a green tea polyphenol, improves endothelial function and insulin sensitivity, reduces blood pressure, and protects against myocardial I/R injury in SHR. *Am. J. Physiol.-Endocrinol. Metab.* **2007**, *292*, E1378–E1387. [CrossRef]

96. Mahmoud, M.F.; Hassan, N.A.; El Bassossy, H.M.; Fahmy, A. Quercetin protects against diabetes-induced exaggerated vasoconstriction in rats: Effect on low grade inflammation. *PLoS ONE* **2013**, *8*, e63784. [CrossRef] [PubMed]

97. Braicu, C.; Ladomery, M.R.; Chedea, V.S.; Irimie, A.; Berindan-Neagoe, I. The relationship between the structure and biological actions of green tea catechins. *Food Chem.* **2013**, *141*, 3282–3289. [CrossRef]

98. Babu, P.V.A.; Sabitha, K.E.; Shyamaladevi, C.S. Therapeutic effect of green tea extract on advanced glycation and cross-linking of collagen in the aorta of streptozotocin diabetic rats. *Clin. Exp. Pharmacol. Physiol.* **2006**, *33*, 351–357. [CrossRef]

99. Minatti, J.; Wazlawik, E.; Hort, M.A.; Zaleski, F.L.; Ribeiro-do-Valle, R.M.; Maraschin, M.; da Silva, E.L. Green tea extract reverses endothelial dysfunction and reduces atherosclerosis progression in homozygous knockout low-density lipoprotein receptor mice. *Nutr. Res.* **2012**, *32*, 684–693. [CrossRef]

100. Babu, P.V.A.; Sabitha, K.E.; Srinivasan, P.; Shyamaladevi, C.S. Green tea attenuates diabetes induced Maillard-type fluorescence and collagen cross-linking in the heart of streptozotocin diabetic rats. *Pharmacol. Res.* **2007**, *55*, 433–440. [CrossRef]

101. Tijburg, L.M.B.; Mattern, T.; Folts, J.D.; Weisgerber, U.M.; Katan, M.B. Tea flavonoids and cardiovascular diseases: A review. *Crit. Rev. Food Sci. Nutr.* **1997**, *37*, 771–785. [CrossRef] [PubMed]

102. Murase, T.; Misawa, K.; Haramizu, S.; Hase, T. Catechin-induced activation of the LKB1/AMP-activated protein kinase pathway. *Biochem. Pharmacol.* **2009**, *78*, 78–84. [CrossRef]

103. Zhao, P.; Kuai, J.K.; Gao, J.J.; Sun, L.; Wang, Y.; Yao, L.N. Delta opioid receptor agonist attenuates lipopolysaccharide-induced myocardial injury by regulating autophagy. *Biochem. Biophys. Res. Commun.* **2017**, *492*, 140–146. [CrossRef] [PubMed]

104. Yaribeygi, H.; Atkin, S.L.; Pirro, M.; Sahebkar, A. A review of the anti-inflammatory properties of antidiabetic agents providing protective effects against vascular complications in diabetes. *J. Cell. Physiol.* **2019**, *234*, 8286–8294. [CrossRef] [PubMed]

105. Anter, E.; Chen, K.; Shapira, O.M.; Karas, R.H.; Keaney, J.F. P38 Mitogen-activated protein kinase activates eNOS in endothelial cells by an estrogen receptor α-dependent pathway in response to black tea polyphenols. *Circ. Res.* **2005**, *96*, 1072–1078. [CrossRef] [PubMed]

106. Anter, E.; Thomas, S.R.; Schulz, E.; Shapira, O.M.; Vita, J.A.; Keaney, J.F. Activation of endothelial nitric-oxide synthase by the p38 MAPK in response to black tea polyphenols. *J. Biol. Chem.* **2004**, *279*, 46637–46643. [CrossRef] [PubMed]

107. Rahma, A.; Martini, R.; Kusharto, C.M.; Damayanthi, E.; Rohdiana, D. White tea camellia sinensis and moringa oleifera as antihyperglycemic agent on streptozotocin-induced diabetic sprague dawley rats. *Jurnal Gizi dan Pangan* **2017**, *12*, 179–186. [CrossRef]

108. Bhattacharya, S.; Gachhui, R.; Sil, P.C. Effect of Kombucha, a fermented black tea in attenuating oxidative stress mediated tissue damage in alloxan induced diabetic rats. *Food Chem. Toxicol.* **2013**, *60*, 328–340. [CrossRef]

109. Rodrigues, B.; Cam, M.C.; McNeill, J.H. Metabolic disturbances in diabetic cardiomyopathy. *Mol. Cell. Biochem.* **1998**, *180*, 53–57. [CrossRef]

110. How, O.J.; Aasum, E.; Severson, D.L.; Chan, W.Y.A.; Essop, M.F.; Larsen, T.S. Increased myocardial oxygen consumption reduces cardiac efficiency in diabetic mice. *Diabetes* **2006**, *55*, 466–473. [CrossRef]

111. Xu, J.Y.; Wang, M.; Zhao, J.P.; Wang, Y.H.; Tang, Q.; Khan, I.A. Yellow tea (*Camellia sinensis* L.), a promising Chinese tea: Processing, chemical constituents and health benefits. *Food Res. Int.* **2018**, *107*, 567–577. [CrossRef] [PubMed]

112. Han, M.M.; Zhao, G.S.; Wang, Y.J.; Wang, D.X.; Sun, F.; Ning, J.M.; Wan, X.C.; Zhang, J.S. Safety and anti-hyperglycemic efficacy of various tea types in mice. *Sci. Rep.* **2016**, *6*, 31703. [CrossRef] [PubMed]

113. Zhu, Q.Y.; Hackman, R.M.; Ensunsa, J.L.; Holt, R.R.; Keen, C.L. Antioxidative activities of oolong tea. *J. Agric. Food Chem.* **2002**, *50*, 6929–6934. [CrossRef] [PubMed]

114. Cai, X.B.; Hayashi, S.; Fang, C.Y.; Hao, S.M.; Wang, X.J.; Nishiguchi, S.; Tsutsui, H.; Sheng, J. Pu-erh tea extract-mediated protection against hepatosteatosis and insulin resistance in mice with diet-induced obesity is associated with the induction of de novo lipogenesis in visceral adipose tissue. *J. Gastroenterol.* **2017**, *52*, 1240–1251. [CrossRef] [PubMed]

115. Shammas, M.A.; Neri, P.; Koley, H.; Batchu, R.B.; Bertheau, R.C.; Munshi, V.; Prabhala, R.; Fulciniti, M.; Tai, Y.; Treon, S.P.; et al. Specific killing of multiple myeloma cells by (-)-epigaflocatechin-3-gallate extracted from green tea: Biologic activity and therapeutic implications. *Blood* **2006**, *108*, 2804–2810. [CrossRef] [PubMed]

116. Lee, H.; Bae, J.H.; Lee, S.R. Protective effect of green tea polyphenol EGCG against neuronal damage and brain edema after unilateral cerebral ischemia in gerbils. *J. Neurosci. Res.* **2004**, *77*, 892–900. [CrossRef] [PubMed]

117. Singal, A.; Anjaneyulu, M.; Chopra, K. Modulatory role of green tea extract on antinociceptive effect of morphine in diabetic mice. *J. Med. Food* **2005**, *8*, 386–391. [CrossRef] [PubMed]

118. Zhong, J.X.; Xu, C.; Reece, E.A.; Yang, P.X. The green tea polyphenol EGCG alleviates maternal diabetes-induced neural tube defects by inhibiting DNA hypermethylation. *Am. J. Obstet. Gynecol.* **2016**, *215*, 368. [CrossRef] [PubMed]

119. Barber, A.J. A new view of diabetic retinopathy: A neurodegenerative disease of the eye. *Prog. Neuro-Psychopharmacol. Biol. Psychiatry* **2003**, *27*, 283–290. [CrossRef]

120. Rahimi-Madiseh, M.; Malekpour-Tehrani, A.; Bahmani, M.; Rafieian-Kopaei, M. The research and development on the antioxidants in prevention of diabetic complications. *Asian Pac. J. Trop. Med.* **2016**, *9*, 825–831. [CrossRef]

121. Mustata, G.T.; Rosca, M.; Biemel, K.M.; Reihl, O.; Smith, M.A.; Viswanathan, A.; Strauch, C.; Du, Y.; Tang, J.; Kern, T.S.; et al. Paradoxical effects of green tea (Camellia Sinensis) and antioxidant vitamins in diabetic rats: Improved retinopathy and renal mitochondrial defects but deterioration of collagen matrix glycoxidation and cross-linking. *Diabetes* **2005**, *54*, 517–526. [CrossRef] [PubMed]

122. Silva, K.C.; Rosales, M.A.B.; Hamassaki, D.E.; Saito, K.C.; Faria, A.M.; Ribeiro, P.A.O.; de Faria, J.B.L.; de Faria, J.M.L. Green tea is neuroprotective in diabetic retinopathy. *Investig. Ophthalmol. Vis. Sci.* **2013**, *54*, 1325–1336. [CrossRef] [PubMed]

123. Kumar, B.; Gupta, S.K.; Nag, T.C.; Srivastava, S.; Saxena, R. Green tea prevents hyperglycemia-induced retinal oxidative stress and inflammation in streptozotocin-induced diabetic rats. *Ophthalmic Res.* **2012**, *47*, 103–108. [CrossRef] [PubMed]

124. Vinson, J.A.; Zhang, J. Black and green teas equally inhibit diabetic cataracts in a streptozotocin-induced rat model of diabetes. *J. Agric. Food Chem.* **2005**, *53*, 3710–3713. [CrossRef]

125. Sook, S.J.; Quan, Z.-J. Effect of oolong tea extracts on plasma glucose level and antioxidant system in diabetic rats. *J. Community Nutr.* **2006**, *8*, 208–214.

126. Al-Hussaini, A.A.; Sulaiman, N.M.; AlZahrani, M.D.; Alenizi, A.S.; Khan, M. Prevalence of hepatopathy in type 1 diabetic children. *BMC Pediatr.* **2012**, *12*, 160. [CrossRef] [PubMed]

127. Akbar, A.A.; Daryoush, M.; Ali, R.; Mehrdad, N. Green tea attenuates hepatic tissue injury in STZ-streptozotocin-induced diabetic rats. *J. Anim. Vet. Adv.* **2012**, *11*, 2081–2090. [CrossRef]

128. Xiao, J.; Lu, R.; Shen, X.; Wu, M. Green tea extracts protected against carbon tetrachloride-induced chronic liver damage and cirrhosis. *Chin. J. Prev. Med.* **2002**, *36*, 243–246.

129. Li, Y.-M.; Zhang, X.-G.; Zhou, H.-L.; Chen, S.-H.; Zhang, Y.; Yu, C.-H. Effects of tea polyphenols on hepatic fibrosis in rats with alcoholic liver disease. *Hepatobil. Pancreat. Dis. Int.* **2004**, *3*, 577–579.

130. Thomson, M.; Al-Qattan, K.; Mansour, M.H.; Ali, A. Green tea attenuates oxidative stress and downregulates the expression of angiotensin II AT_1 receptor in renal and hepatic tissues of streptozotocin-induced diabetic rats. *Evid.-Based Complement. Altern. Med.* **2012**, *2012*, 409047. [CrossRef]

131. Gennaro, G.; Claudino, M.; Cestari, T.M.; Ceolin, D.; Germino, P.; Garlet, G.P.; de Assis, G.F. Green tea modulates cytokine expression in the periodontium and attenuates alveolar bone resorption in type 1 diabetic rats. *PLoS ONE* **2015**, *10*, e0134784. [CrossRef] [PubMed]

132. Ko, C.H.; Lau, K.M.; Choy, W.Y.; Leung, P.C. Effects of tea catechins, epigallocatechin, gallocatechin, and gallocatechin gallate, on bone metabolism. *J. Agric. Food Chem.* **2009**, *57*, 7293–7297. [CrossRef] [PubMed]

133. Li, J.; Shen, X.P. Effect of rosiglitazone on inflammatory cytokines and oxidative stress after intensive insulin therapy in patients with newly diagnosed type 2 diabetes. *Diabetol. Metab. Syndr.* **2019**, *11*, 35. [CrossRef] [PubMed]

134. Satoh, T.; Igarashi, M.; Yamada, S.; Takahashi, N.; Watanabe, K. Inhibitory effect of black tea and its combination with acarbose on small intestinal α-glucosidase activity. *J. Ethnopharmacol.* **2015**, *161*, 147–155. [CrossRef] [PubMed]

135. Gao, J.J.; Xu, P.; Wang, Y.F.; Wang, Y.Q.; Hochstetter, D. Combined Effects of Green Tea Extracts, Green Tea Polyphenols or Epigallocatechin Gallate with Acarbose on Inhibition against α-Amylase and alpha-Glucosidase in Vitro. *Molecules* **2013**, *18*, 11614–11623. [CrossRef]

136. Huang, H.; Jin, C.Y.; Bi, X.K.; Zhao, Y.B.; Xu, S.J.; Wang, M.H.; Yu, L.; Sun, Y.X.; Hu, D. Green tea polyphenol epigallocatechin-3-gallate promotes reendothelialization in carotid artery of diabetic rabbits by reactivating Akt/eNOS pathway. *Front. Pharmacol.* **2018**, *9*. [CrossRef] [PubMed]

137. Chen, T.S.; Liou, S.Y.; Kuo, C.H.; Pan, L.F.; Yeh, Y.L.; Liou, J.; Padma, V.V.; Yao, C.H.; Kuo, W.W.; Huang, C.Y. Green tea epigallocatechin gallate enhances cardiac function restoration through survival signaling expression in diabetes mellitus rats with autologous adipose tissue-derived stem cells. *J. Appl. Physiol.* **2017**, *123*, 1081–1091. [CrossRef]

138. Itoh, T.; Imano, M.; Nishida, S.; Tsubaki, M.; Hashimoto, S.; Ito, A.; Satou, T. (-)-Epigallocatechin-3-gallate protects against neuronal cell death and improves cerebral eunction after traumatic brain injury in rats. *Neuromol. Med.* **2011**, *13*, 300–309. [CrossRef]

139. Tian, C.; Ye, X.L.; Zhang, R.; Long, J.; Ren, W.Y.; Ding, S.B.; Liao, D.; Jin, X.; Wu, H.M.; Xu, S.Q.; et al. Green tea polyphenols reduced fat deposits in high fat-fed rats via erk1/2-PPAR gamma-adiponectin pathway. *PLoS ONE* **2013**, *8*, e53796. [CrossRef]

140. Babu, P.V.A.; Sabitha, K.E.; Shyamaladevi, C.S. Green tea extract impedes dyslipidaemia and development of cardiac dysfunction in streptozotocin-diabetic rats. *Clin. Exp. Pharmacol. Physiol.* **2006**, *33*, 1184–1189. [CrossRef]

141. Abolfathi, A.A.; Mohajeri, D.; Rezaie, A.; Nazeri, M. Protective effects of green tea extract against hepatic tissue injury in streptozotocin-induced diabetic rats. *Evid.-Based Complement. Altern. Med.* **2012**, *2012*, 740671. [CrossRef] [PubMed]

142. Renno, W.M.; Alkhalaf, M.; Afsari, Z.; Abd-El-Basset, E.; Mousa, A. Consumption of green tea alters glial fibriliary acidic protein immunoreactivity in the spinal cord astrocytes of STZ-diabetic rats. *Nutr. Neurosci.* **2008**, *11*, 32–40. [CrossRef] [PubMed]

143. Manikandan, R.; Sundaram, R.; Thiagarajan, R.; Sivakumar, M.R.; Meiyalagan, V.; Arumugam, M. Effect of black tea on histological and immunohistochemical changes in pancreatic tissues of normal and streptozotocin-induced diabetic mice (Mus musculus). *Microsc. Res. Tech.* **2009**, *72*, 723–726. [CrossRef] [PubMed]

144. Kumar, D.; Rizvi, S.I. Black tea extract improves anti-oxidant profile in experimental diabetic rats. *Arch. Physiol. Biochem.* **2015**, *121*, 109–115. [CrossRef] [PubMed]

145. Tenore, G.C.; Stiuso, P.; Campiglia, P.; Novellino, E. In vitro hypoglycaemic and hypolipidemic potential of white tea polyphenols. *Food Chem.* **2013**, *141*, 2379–2384. [CrossRef] [PubMed]

146. Dias, T.R.; Alves, M.G.; Rato, L.; Casal, S.; Silva, B.M.; Oliveira, P.F. White tea intake prevents prediabetes-induced metabolic dysfunctions in testis and epididymis preserving sperm quality. *J. Nutr. Biochem.* **2016**, *37*, 83–93. [CrossRef] [PubMed]

147. Huang, Q.F.; Chen, S.H.; Chen, H.; Wang, Y.F.; Wang, Y.Q.; Hochstetter, D.; Xu, P. Studies on the bioactivity of aqueous extract of pu-erh tea and its fractions: In vitro antioxidant activity and alpha-glycosidase inhibitory property, and their effect on postprandial hyperglycemia in diabetic mice. *Food Chem. Toxicol.* **2013**, *53*, 75–83. [CrossRef]

148. Xu, P.; Chen, H.; Wang, Y.Q.; Hochstetter, D.; Zhou, T.; Wang, Y.F. Oral administration of pu-erh tea polysaccharides lowers blood glucose levels and enhances antioxidant status in alloxan-induced diabetic mice. *J. Food Sci.* **2012**, *77*, H246–H252. [CrossRef]

149. Yuqiong, C.; Zhi, Y.U.; Yun, Z.; Dejiang, N.I.; Bijun, X.I.E.; Jirong, Z. Influence of oolong tea polysaccharides on immunomodulatory function of diabetic mice and rats. *Acta Nutr. Sin.* **2006**, *28*, 156–159.

150. Song, E.K.; Hur, H.; Han, M.K. Epigallocatechin gallate prevents autoimmune diabetes induced by multiple low doses of streptozotocin in mice. *Arch. Pharm. Res.* **2003**, *26*, 559–563. [CrossRef]

151. Rhee, S.J.; Kim, M.J.; Kwag, O.G. Effects of green tea catechin on prostaglandin synthesis of renal glomerular and renal dysfunction in streptozotocin-induced diabetic rats. *Asia Pac. J. Clin. Nutr.* **2002**, *11*, 232–236. [CrossRef] [PubMed]

152. Rhee, S.J.; Choi, J.H.; Park, M.R. Green tea catechin improves microsomal phospholipase A$_2$ activity and the arachidonic acid cascade system in the kidney of diabetic rats. *Asia Pac. J. Clin. Nutr.* **2002**, *11*, 226–231. [CrossRef] [PubMed]

153. Nogueira de Amorim, L.M.N.; Vaz, S.R.; Cesario, G.; Coelho, A.S.G.; Botelho, P.B. Effect of green tea extract on bone mass and body composition in individuals with diabetes. *J. Funct. Foods* **2018**, *40*, 589–594. [CrossRef]

154. Mirzaei, K.; Hossein-Nezhad, A.; Karimi, M.; Hosseinzadeh-Attar, M.J.; Jafari, N.; Najmafshar, A.; Larijani, B. Effect of green tea extract on bone turnover markers in type 2 diabetic patients; a double-blind, placebo-controlled clinical trial study. *DARU J. Pharm. Sci.* **2009**, *17*, 38–44.

155. Mousavi, A.; Vafa, M.; Neyestani, T.; Khamseh, M.; Hoseini, F. The effects of green tea consumption on metabolic and anthropometric indices in patients with Type 2 diabetes. *J. Res. Med. Sci.* **2013**, *18*, 1080–1086. [PubMed]

156. Liu, C.Y.; Huang, C.J.; Huang, L.H.; Chen, I.J.; Chiu, J.P.; Hsu, C.H. Effects of green tea extract on insulin resistance and glucagon-like peptide 1 in patients with type 2 diabetes and lipid abnormalities: A randomized, double-blinded, and placebo-controlled trial. *PLoS ONE* **2014**, *9*, e91163. [CrossRef] [PubMed]

157. Hosoda, K.; Wang, M.F.; Liao, M.L.; Chuang, C.K.; Iha, M.; Clevidence, B.; Yamamoto, S. Antihyperglycentic effect of oolong tea in type 2 diabetes. *Diabetes Care* **2003**, *26*, 1714–1718. [CrossRef] [PubMed]

158. Vaz, S.R.; de Amorim, L.M.N.; de Nascimento, P.V.F.; Veloso, V.S.P.; Nogueira, M.S.; Castro, I.A.; Mota, J.F.; Botelho, P.B. Effects of green tea extract on oxidative stress and renal function in diabetic individuals: A randomized, double-blinded, controlled trial. *J. Funct. Foods* **2018**, *46*, 195–201. [CrossRef]

159. MacKenzie, T.; Leary, L.; Brooks, W.B. The effect of an extract of green and black tea on glucose control in adults with type 2 diabetes mellitus: Double-blind randomized study. *Metabolism* **2007**, *56*, 1340–1344. [CrossRef]

Article

Lespedeza bicolor Extract Ameliorated Renal Inflammation by Regulation of NLRP3 Inflammasome-Associated Hyperinflammation in Type 2 Diabetic Mice

Ji Eun Park [1], Heaji Lee [1], Sun Yeou Kim [2] and Yunsook Lim [1,*]

[1] Department of Food and Nutrition, Kyung Hee Univerity, 26 Kyung Hee-Daero, Dongdamun-Gu, Seoul 02447, Korea; gh1003@khu.ac.kr (J.E.P.); ji3743@khu.ac.kr (H.L.)

[2] Gachon Institute of Pharmaceutical Science, Gachon University, #191, Hambakmoero, Yeonsu-gu, Incheon 21936, Korea; sunnykim@gachon.ac.kr

* Correspondence: ylim@khu.ac.kr; Tel.: +82-2-961-0262; Fax: +82-2-961-0260

Received: 18 December 2019; Accepted: 5 February 2020; Published: 10 February 2020

Abstract: Type 2 diabetes mellitus (T2DM) is a chronic metabolic disorder characterized by hyperglycemia. The chronic hyperglycemic condition causes hyperinflammation via activation of nucleotide-binding oligomerization domain-like pyrin domain containing receptor 3 (NLRP3) inflammasome and abnormally leads to morphological and functional changes in kidney. A previous study showed a protective effect of *Lespedeza bicolor* extract (LBE) on endothelial dysfunction induced by methylglyoxal glucotoxicity. We aimed to investigate whether LBE ameliorated renal damage through regulation of NLRP3 inflammasome-dependent hyper-inflammation in T2DM mice. After T2DM induction by a high fat diet and low dose of streptozotocin (30 mg/kg), the mice were administered with different dosages of LBE (100 or 250 mg/kg/day) by gavage for 12 weeks. LBE supplementation ameliorated kidney dysfunction demonstrated by urine albumin-creatinine at a low dose and plasma creatinine, blood urea nitrogen (BUN), and glomerular hypertrophy at a high dose. Furthermore, a high dose of LBE supplementation significantly attenuated renal hyper-inflammation associated with NLRP3 inflammasome and oxidative stress related to nuclear factor erythroid 2-related factor 2 (Nrf-2) in T2DM mice. Meanwhile, a low dose of LBE supplementation up-regulated energy metabolism demonstrated by phosphorylation of adenosine monophosphate kinase (AMPK) and Sirtuin (SIRT)-1 in T2DM mice. In conclusion, the current study suggested that LBE, in particular, at a high dose could be used as a beneficial therapeutic for hyperglycemia-induced renal damage in T2DM.

Keywords: *Lespedeza bicolor*; type 2 diabetes; renal inflammation; NLRP3 inflammasome; energy metabolism; oxidative stress

---

1. Introduction

Diabetes is a critical metabolic syndrome associated with aberrant glucose metabolism, and cause chronic damage and dysfunction of various organs, such as blood vessels, heart, nerves, eyes, liver, and kidneys. In particular, hyperglycemia-induced renal inflammation can develop chronic lesions with histological and functional defects in kidney [1,2].

Hyperglycemia results in overproduction of reactive oxygen species (ROS), which cause oxidative stress in various organs in cases of diabetes [3,4]. Oxidative stress due to uncontrolled blood glucose leads to activation of the nucleotide-binding oligomerization domain-like pyrin domain containing receptor 3 (NLRP3) [5]. Recent studies have shown that activation of NLRP3 inflammasome in renal cells promotes renal inflammation and contributes to chronic kidney damage [6,7]. NLRP3 inflammasome acts as the molecular sensor that responds to dangers such as pathogen-associated molecular patterns (PAMPs) and danger-associated molecular patterns (DAMPs) [6]. In sensing those dangers, NLRP3 can recruit the apoptosis-associated speck-like proteins including caspase recruitment domain (ASC) and pro-caspase-1 [6]. Activated NLRP3 inflammasome allows the activation of interleukin (IL)-1β by cleaved caspase-1, and is involved in inflammatory response [6].

Pro-inflammatory cytokines include tumor necrosis factor-α (TNF-α), which is activated by free radicals involved in proinflammatory signals by binding to TNF-α receptors on tubular cell surfaces [8]. These responses trigger activation of nuclear factor kappa B (NF-κB) by particularly encouraging the phosphorylated IκB (p-IκB), which allows nuclear translocation of NF-κB [9]. NF-κB activation induces inflammatory cytokines including IL-6 and IL-1β, and maximizes inflammatory response [10]. Chemokines including monocyte chemoattractant protein-1 (MCP-1) are also involved in inflammatory response by recruiting active components of inflammatory cells and adhesion molecules including intercellular adhesion molecule 1 (ICAM-1) [11]. The inflammatory mediators are involved in the attachment of leukocytes, which can release proteolytic enzymes leading to renal damage [11,12]. The various changes promote the loss of function, viability, and harmful mutations. Eventually, excessive oxidative stress and chronic inflammation accelerate radical-mediated damage, resulting in cell degradation and renal damage [13,14]. Hence, suppressing the activation of NLRP3 inflammasome and subsequent hyper-inflammatory response would be a therapeutic target strategy for ameliorating renal damage [15–18].

The adenosine monophosphatekinase (AMPK)/Sirtuin 1 (SIRT1)/ peroxisome proliferator-activated receptor gamma coactivator α (PGC-1α) signaling pathway is also related to renal damage [19]. SIRT1 is known to protect pathogenesis of diabetic nephropathy (DN) along with regulation of mitochondrial biogenesis [19]. In diabetes, p65 acetylation accelerates the transcription activity of the NF-κB complex [10]. However, SIRT1 interacts with the p65 subunit of the NF-κB complex, deacetylates p65, and consequently suppresses NF-κB activation [20]. Previous studies have focused on the fact that SIRT1 suppresses NLRP3 inflammasome activation [20,21]. Moreover, SIRT1 was found to ameliorate podocyte loss and albuminuria by suppressing the expression of claudin-1 in podocytes [20]. SIRT1 also prevented hyperglycema-induced mesangial expansion by intensifying the AMPK-mammalian target of rapamycin (mTOR) signaling pathway [22]. In addition, PGC-1α, a downstream molecule of AMPK/SIRT1 signaling pathway, suppressed ROS overexpression and renal hyper-inflammation [23]. Hence, activation of the AMPK/SIRT1/PGC-1α pathway could be a possible mechanism associated with the therapeutic approach for hyperglycemia-induced renal damage.

Lespedeza bicolor (LB), named by American botanist Asa Gray, is a species of warm-season perennial deciduous shrub, which belongs to the genus *Lespedeza* (Leguminosae), and widely grows in the United States, Asia, and Australia [24]. LB has been used traditionally for the treatment of inflammation of the urinary tract, nephritis, and diabetes [25,26]. Recently, some studies have reported that natural compounds have therapeutic effects on various organ damages [27]. LB also contains many compounds such as genistein, quercetin, daidzein, catechin, rutin, luteolin, and naringin [28]. These natural phytochemicals in *Lespedeza bicolor* extract (LBE) have been determined for their antioxidant and anti-inflammatory activities, as well as their blood glucose lowering effect in hyperglycemia [27,28]. In particular, various polyphenols such as genistein, quercetin, and naringin have an antioxidant function—electron donating and ROS scavenging activity. Our previous study showed that LBE attenuated advanced glycation end product (AGE) formation and breakage in addition to endothelial dysfunction, which was triggered by methylglyoxal-induced glucotoxicity in vitro [29,30]. Furthermore, LB attenuated methylglyoxal (MGO)-induced diabetic renal damage in vitro and in vivo [31]. However, effects of LBE on NLRP3 inflammasome-associated hyperinflammation and AMPK/SIRT1/PGC-1α signaling under hyperglycemic condition have not yet been revealed. Therefore, we investigated whether LBE has ameliorating effects on renal damage by suppressing NLRP3 inflammasome-related hyperinflammation and activating AMPK/SIRT1/PGC-1α signaling in type 2 diabetes mellitus (T2DM) mice.

2. Materials and Methods

2.1. Extraction of Lespedeza bicolor

Aerial parts of LB were obtained from Jayeonchunsa Co. (Damyang, Korea). LBE was extracted with 70% ethanol at room temperature overnight. Then, the extract was filtered, evaporated, and dry frozen. The obtained hydroalcoholic extract of LBE was kept at −20 °C until it was used. The extract was dissolved in distilled water at 25 mg/mL (LL) and 62.5 mg/mL (HL) independently.

2.2. Animals and Study Design

Male 4-week-old C57BL/6 mice (n = 50) were purchased from Raon Bio (Gyeonggi-do, South Korea) and were housed in 2–3 per cage in a 12 h light/12 h dark cycle under controlled temperature (22 ± 1 °C) and humidity (50 ± 5%). After 1 week for acclimation, mice were randomly grouped into 2 groups: a normal control group (NC; n = 10) which was fed a rodent diet (10% kcal fat, Research Diets, New Brunswick, NJ, USA), and a diabetic group (DM; n = 30) which was fed with a high-fat-containing rodent diet (40% kcal fat, Research Diets, New Brunswick, NJ, USA). Food and distilled water were supplied ad libitium.

After 4 weeks of diet treatment, diabetic groups were injected twice with streptozotocin (30 mg/kg body weight, Sigma Aldrich, St. Louis, MO, USA) into peritoneum by a 1 week interval in citrate buffer (pH 4.5) to induce T2DM. Simultaneously, the NC mice were injected with only citric acid buffer. Fasting blood glucose (FBG) levels were measured every week from the tail vein using OneTouch Select blood glucometer (LifeScan Inc., Milpitas, CA, USA) until 5 weeks from the last injection. Mice measured at FBG > 140.4 mg/dL (7.8 mmol/L) at least twice were considered as being in a diabetic state. Diabetes was induced in 30 out of 40 mice. The induction protocol of diabetes was in reference to a previous study by Zhang et al. [32].

Mice considered in a diabetic state were divided into three groups, and all groups (n = 10 per group) were differently treated as follows: (A) the NC group, 10% kcal control diet-fed non-diabetic mice group, was supplemented with distilled water; (B) the diabetic control (DMC) group, 40% kcal high fat diet (HFD)-fed diabetic mice group, was supplemented with distilled water; (C) the LL group, HFD-fed diabetic mice group, was supplemented with a low dosage of LBE (100mg/kg vody weight (BW)); and (D) the HL group, HFD-fed diabetic mice group, was supplemented with a high dosage of LBE (250mg/kg BW). Distilled water or LBE freshly dissolved in distilled water was administrated by oral gavage every day for 12 weeks, and 10 h fasting blood glucose level from tail vein was monitored once a week during all supplementation.

At the end of the supplementation period, mice were anesthetized by inhalation with diethyl ether (Duksan, Seoul, Korea). The blood samples were collected by cardiac puncture in heparin-coated tubes (Sigma Aldrich, St. Louis, MO, USA), and were centrifuged at 850× g at 4 °C for 15 min to obtain plasma. The kidney was removed from each mouse, weighed, and washed by saline. The kidney tissues were frozen in liquid nitrogen, and were stored at −80 °C before the experiment. Other portions of the kidney were fixed with 10% formaldehyde for paraffin embedding. All experiment protocol was approved by the Institutional Animal Care and Use Committee of Kyung Hee University (KHUASP(SE)-19-076 on 06/14/2019).

2.3. Hemoglobin A1c (HbA1c)

HbA1c levels were measured according to commercial reagent methods (Crystal Chem., Downers, Grove, Elk Grove Village, IL, USA).

2.4. Renal Function Test

Renal function was examined by measurement of urinary albumin/creatinine ratio (ACR), plasma creatinine, and blood urea nitrogen (BUN). To measure the degree of urinary albumin excretion, spot urine samples were collected by bladder massage at the initial (0–4 week), mid (4–8 week), and late (8–12 week) stages of the experiment. Urinary albumin excretion was determined according to bromocresol green (BCG) albumin quantification method using a commercial albumin assay kit (Bioassay, Hayward, CA, USA). Quantitative urinary creatinine and plasma creatinine levels were measured by Jaffe method [33]. Levels of BUN were examined using a commercial BUN assay kit (Asan pharmaceutical, Seoul, South Korea) according to the manufacturer's instructions.

2.5. Histological Analysis

Kidney was isolated, fixed in 10% formaldehyde solution, dehydrated, and then embedded in paraffin. Sections of renal tissues were cut into 5 μm thickness and stained with hematoxylin and eosin (H&E) through removal of paraffin in xylene and rehydration in alcohol, as per concentration of the series. The stained tissues on slide glass were mounted with histological mounting medium (Histomount, Atlanta, GA, USA) after drying. All images were taken using an optical microscope (Nikon ECLIPSE Ci, Nikon Instrument, Tokyo, Japan).

2.6. Protein Extraction and Western Blot Analysis

The kidneys were homogenized in the hypotonic lysis buffer (1.5 mM $MgCl_2$, 10 mM 4-(2-hydroxyethyl)-1-piperazineethanesulfonic acid (HEPES), 10 mM KCl, 0.05% nonidet P-40 (NP40), 0.5 mM dithiothreitol (DTT), and distilled water) with protease and phosphotease inhibitor (Thermo Fisher, Waltham, MA, USA), shacked on ice for 1 h, and centrifuged at 1945× g at 4 °C for 10 min. The supernatants were centrifuged again at 9078× g at 4 °C for 30 min and final supernatants were used as a cytosol extract for Western blot analysis. The remaining pellets were re-homogenized in hypertonic lysis buffer (1.5 mM $MgCl_2$, 5 mM HEPES, 0.5 mM DTT, 0.2 mM EDTA, 26% glycerol, and distilled water) with 4.6 M NaCl on ice. After shaking on ice for 1 h, the homogenates were centrifuged at 9078× g at 4 °C for 20 min. Then, supernatants were used as nuclear extract for Western blot analysis. Total protein amount of the extract was quantified by bovine serum albumin (BCA) protein assay (ThermoFisher Scientific, Grand Island, NY, USA).

Protein samples were separated with SDS-PAGE and transferred onto poly-vinylidine fluoride (PVDF) membranes (Millipore, Marlborough, MA, USA). After blocking in 3% bovine serum albumin (BSA) in phosphate-buffed saline–0.1% Tween 20 (PBS-T), the membranes were incubated at 4 °C with primary antibodies. Then, the membranes were washed with PBS-T and incubated with respective horseradish peroxide (HRP)-conjugated secondary antibodies for 1 h, and then washed with PBS-T again. The chemiluminescent signals were developed using ECL solution (Bio-rad, Hercules, CA, USA). Images of the developed bands were recorded and quantified with the Syngene G box (Syngene, Cambridge, UK).

2.7. Statistical Analysis

Data were expressed as mean ± standard error of the mean (S.E.M.). Statistical significance of differences existed within the experiment. Experimental groups were examined by one-way analysis of variance (ANOVA) using SPSS (version 23.0 for Windows, SPSS Inc., Chicago, IL, USA). Post-hoc analysis was used to identify the differences among the experimental groups at $p < 0.05$ and the corresponding ethical approval code.

3. Results

3.1. Effect of LBE Supplementation on Body Weight, Food Intake, Fasting Blood Glucose (FBG), and Glycated Hemoglobin (HbA1c) in T2DM Mice

The body weight of the DMC group was significantly increased compared to those of the NC group (Table 1). Simultaneously, there was no effect on body weight change among the DM groups. FBG of the DMC group showed significant elevation compared to that of the NC group, but the LL group showed lower FBG compared to the DMC group (Table 1). Levels of HbA1c in the DMC group were significantly higher than those in the NC group. However, the LL and the HL groups showed lower levels of HbA1c compared to the DMC group.

Table 1. Effect of *Lespedeza bicolor* extract (LBE) supplementation on body weight, food intake, kidney weight, fasting blood glucose level (FBG), and hemoglobin A1c (HbA1c) in T2DM mice.

Group	NC	DMC	LL	HL
Body Weight (g)				
Before treatment	26.76 ± 0.75	$30.94 \pm 0.86^*$	31.07 ± 1.01	32.52 ± 1.68
After treatment	30.73 ± 0.61	$40.27 \pm 2.36^*$	40.27 ± 2.36	40.34 ± 2.59
Gain	3.98 ± 0.33	$8.89 \pm 0.70^*$	8.09 ± 1.34	7.82 ± 1.72
FBG (mg/dL)	122 ± 7.51	$173 \pm 14.30^*$	$147 \pm 9.11^\#$	164 ± 10.12
HbA1c (%)	6.62 ± 0.51	$9.36 \pm 0.15^*$	$7.82 \pm 0.15^\#$	$7.12 \pm 0.37^\#$

All values are means ± SD. * $p < 0.05$ compared with the normal control (NC) group; # $p < 0.05$ compared with the diabetic control (DMC) group. NC, normal mice (negative control); DMC, T2DM mice (positive control); LL, T2DM mice supplemented with low dose (100 mg/kg/day) of LBE; HL, T2DM mice supplemented with high dose (250 mg/kg/day) of LBE.

3.2. Effect of LBE Supplementation on Renal Function and Renal Morphology in T2DM Mice

The ACR in the DMC group was significantly higher than that in the NC group over the whole experiment period (Figure 1A). However, the ACR in the LL group was significantly lower than that in the DMC group at the mid and late stages of the experiment. Plasma creatinine and BUN were significantly higher in the DMC group compared to the NC group. At the same time, a high dose of LBE supplementation significantly decreased the level of plasma creatinine and BUN in the diabetic mice.

In the NC group, capsular space was observed as a thin white line (Figure 1C). Capsular space of the DMC group was thickened compared to that of the NC group. However, a high dose of LBE supplementation improved corpuscular architecture and tubular necrosis compared to the DMC group.

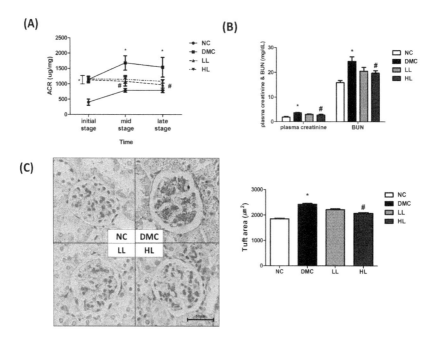

Figure 1. Effect of LBE supplementation on renal function and morphology in T2DM mice. (**A**) Urine albumin/creatinine ratio (ACR) during experiment period, (**B**) plasma creatinine and blood urea nitrogen (BUN), (**C**) kidney morphology (magnification ×400), and glomeruli size. * $p < 0.05$ compared with NC group; # $p < 0.05$ compared with the DMC group.

3.3. Effect of LBE Supplementation on Renal Receptor for Advanced Glycation end Products (RAGE) Formation in T2DM Mice

The protein level of RAGE was significantly elevated in the DMC group compared to that of the NC group (Figure 2). The protein level of RAGE was significantly reduced in the LL group compared to that of the DMC group.

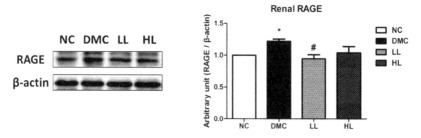

Figure 2. Effect of LBE supplementation on receptor for advanced glycation end products (RAGE) in T2DM mice. A representative band image of repeated experiments is shown in the left panel. * $p < 0.05$ compared with NC group; # $p < 0.05$ compared with the DMC group.

3.4. Effect of LBE Supplementation on Renal Inflammation in T2DM Mice

The protein levels of NLRP3, ASC, procaspase-1, caspase-1, pro IL-1β, and mature IL-1β were significantly elevated in the DMC group compared to those of the NC group (Figure 3A). However, the protein levels of NLRP3, procaspase-1, caspase-1, pro IL-1β, and mature IL-1β showed significant reduction in the HL group compared to those of the DMC group. There was no significant difference of the protein level of ASC among the DMC group and LBE-supplemented groups.

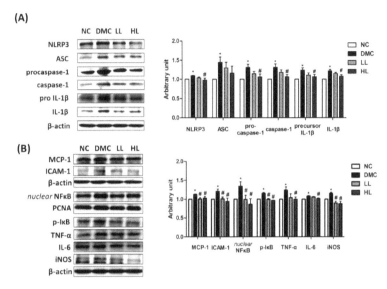

Figure 3. Effect of LBE supplementation on renal NLRP3 inflammasome and inflammation in T2DM mice. Protein levels of (**A**) nucleotide-binding oligomerization domain-like pyrin domain containing receptor 3 (NLRP3) inflammasome: nucleotide-binding oligomerization domain-like pyrin domain containing receptor 3 (NLRP-3); apoptosis-associated speck-like proteins including caspase recruitment domain (ASC), caspase-1, and interleukin (IL)-1β; and (**B**) markers of pro-inflammatory response: monocyte chemoattractant protein-1 (MCP-1) and intercellular adhesion molecule 1 (ICAM-1); and nuclear factor kappa B (NF-κB)-related inflammatory response: nuclear factor kappa B (NF-κB), phosphorylated IκB (p-IκB), tumor necrosis factor-α (TNF-α), interleukin (IL)-6, and inducible nitric oxide synthase (iNOS); representative band images of each marker are shown in the left panel. * $p < 0.05$ compared with NC group; # $p < 0.05$ compared with the DMC group.

The DMC group showed greater levels of the protein related to inflammation including MCP-1 and CRP than the NC group (Figure 3B). The DMC group also showed higher protein levels of nuclear NF-κB, phosphorylated IκB, ICAM-1, TNF-α, IL-6, and inducible nitric oxide synthase (iNOS) than the NC group. Simultaneously, the protein levels of MCP-1, nuclear NF-κB, phosphorylated IκB, ICAM-1, and iNOS significantly decreased in both LBE-supplemented groups compared to the DMC group. The protein levels of TNF-α and IL-6 were significantly lowered in the LL group compared to the DMC group.

3.5. Effect of LBE Supplementation on Renal Oxidative Stress in T2DM Mice

The renal protein level of 4-hydroxynonenal (4-HNE) was significantly higher in the DMC group than that of the NC group (Figure 4A). Simultaneously, the protein level of 4-HNE was significantly reduced in the LBE-supplemented groups compared with that in the DMC group. The level of renal protein carbonyls was significantly increased in the DMC group compared to that in the NC group. However, the level of renal protein carbonyls was significantly decreased by LBE supplementation in the DM group. The protein levels of nuclear Nrf2 (nuclear factor erythroid 2-related factor 2) and cytosolic heme oxygenase-1 (HO-1), NAD(P)H dinucleotide phosphate dehydrogenase quinone 1 (NQO1), catalase, and manganese superoxide dismutase (MnSOD) were significantly higher in the DMC group compared to those in the NC group (Figure 4B). The protein levels of Nrf2 and NQO1 in the LBE supplementation groups were significantly lowered compared to those in the DMC group. The protein levels of HO-1 and catalase in the high dose of LBE supplementation groups were significantly lowered compared to those in the DMC group. The protein level of MnSOD was significantly reduced in the LL group compared to the DMC group.

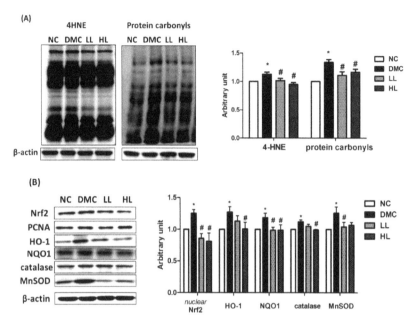

Figure 4. Effect of LBE supplementation on renal oxidative stress in T2DM mice. Representative band images of (**A**) 4-hydroxynonenal (4-HNE) and protein carbonyl groups and (**B**) nuclear factor erythroid 2-related factor 2 (Nrf2)-associated antioxidant defense markers: heme oxygenase-1 (HO-1), NAD(P)H dehydrogenase quinone 1 (NQO1), catalase, and manganese superoxide dismutase (SOD) are shown. * $p < 0.05$ compared with NC group; # $p < 0.05$ compared with the DMC group.

3.6. Effect of LBE Supplementation on AMPK Phosphorylation and SIRT1 in T2DM Mice

The protein level of AMPK was significantly decreased in the DMC group compared to the NC group and was increased in the LL and the HL groups compared to that of the DMC group (Figure 5A). At the same time, the protein level of phospho adenosine monophosphate kinase (pAMPK) was significantly higher in the LL group compared to that of the DMC group. Consequently, the AMPK phosphorylation ratio (pAMPK/AMPK) was significantly increased in the LL group compared to that of the DMC group.

The renal protein levels of SIRT1 and peroxisome proliferator-activated receptor gamma -coactivator α (PGC1α) were significantly lower in the DMC group than those of the NC group (Figure 5B). Simultaneously, the protein level of SIRT1 was significantly increased in the LL group compared to that of the DMC group. The protein levels of PGC1α were significantly decreased in the DMC group compared to those of the NC group. However, there was no significant difference of the protein levels of PGC1α in the LBE supplementation groups compared to the DMC group.

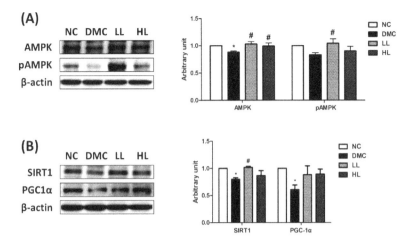

Figure 5. Effect of LBE supplementation on renal adenosine monophosphate kinase (AMPK) phosphorylation and Sirtuin (SIRT)-1/ peroxisome proliferator-activated receptor gamma coactivator-1α (PGC-1α) signaling in T2DM mice. (**A**) Renal AMPK phosphorylation and (**B**) SIRT1-PGC1 activation. Representative band images of each marker are shown in the left panel. * *p* < 0.05 compared with NC group; # *p* < 0.05 compared with the DMC group.

4. Discussion

Various medical plants and natural products have been found to be antidiabetic agents, including banaba, fenugreek, and gymnema, among others. Among these plants, LB is a perennial deciduous shrub belonging to the Leguminosae family and has been used for treatment of inflammation throughout Asia. LB as a legume family contains phenolic compounds including many different types of flavonoid derivatives. The previous study reported by our group found that LBE contained polyphenolic compounds such as quercetin (0.853 mg/g), genistein (0.053 mg/g), daidzein (0.165 mg/g), and naringenin (0.08 mg/g) [24,30,31]. These four components known as major active compounds in Leguminosae have been shown to exert antioxidant effects by inhibiting AGEs formation [24]. Furthermore, quercetin and genistein in LB increased free amine contents, resulting in the increased breakage of AGEs and inhibition of AGE formation [24]. The findings support that the ameliorative effect of LBE against diabetes might be due to synergistic or additive effects of these active ingredients. In the current study, we hypothesized that LBE supplementation could ameliorate hyperglycemia-induced renal inflammation by regulation of NLRP3-inflammasome associated hyperinflammation in an in vivo diabetic model.

First of all, it is well-known that chronic hyperglycemia contributes to renal malfunction such as progression of elevated urinary albumin excretion [34,35]. HFDs induce insulin resistance, and potentially moderate pancreatic beta-cell dysfunction [36]. HbA1c is known to reflect average blood glucose within 3 months. A recent study reported that HbA1c level is a better indicator of hyperglycemia with fewer variables compared to overnight fasting blood glucose [37]. The current study demonstrated that LBE supplementation, regardless of dose, decreased the level of HbA1c in the diabetic mice. Previous studies have shown that decreased glucotoxicity caused by hyperglycemia improved renal function [31,38,39]. In the present study, a high dose of LBE supplementation declined the level of BUN and serum creatinine, and a low dose of LBE supplementation lowered the ACR. Elevated BUN, serum creatinine, and urine ACR level are well-known markers of renal malfunction with albuminuria [40]. Furthermore, the low dose of LBE supplementation attenuated albuminuria and the high dose of LBE supplementation minimized basement membrane thickening in diabetic kidney morphology. It can be inferred that LBE attenuated renal malfunction by regulating hyperglycemia accompanied by morphological alteration of diabetic kidney.

Hyperglycemia-induced oxidative stress results in the formation of AGEs and activation of protein kinase C (PKC). These changes are accelerated by mitochondrial overproduction of ROS in prolonged exposure to hyperglycemia. Activated renal RAGE stimulated production of cytosolic ROS, leading to mitochondrial ROS [41,42]. A previous study reported that LB acts as an AGE modulator by suppressing oxidative stress [30]. Furthermore, LBE ameliorated oxidative stress by reducing RAGE expression, which subsequently reduced AGE–RAGE interaction in MGO-induced renal glucotoxicity [31]. The current study demonstrated that the high dose of LBE supplementation reduced the renal protein level of RAGE in diabetic mice. Both LBE supplementations also suppressed the protein levels of 4-HNE and protein carbonyls. 4-HNE is a representative biomarker of lipid peroxidation, and has cytotoxic and mutagenic activities in various tissues [43,44]. ROS overproduction also leads to oxidative modification of proteins and produces protein carbonyls via lipid peroxidation or glycation/glycoxidation [45]. These data suggest that LBE supplementation ameliorated AGE formation and ROS production by remarkably decreasing lipid peroxidation and protein oxidation. Furthermore, activation of Nrf2 corresponding with 4-HNE and protein carbonyls could serve as an illustration that oxidative stress induces the stimulation of Nrf2 and its related antioxidant defense systems via the compensatory activation against overproduction of ROS. Our results demonstrated that LBE supplementation regulated increased Nrf2 and its related antioxidant defense enzymes in the type 2 diabetic mice.

Moreover, ROS overproduction activates inflammatory response including NLRP3 inflammasome. NLRP3 inflammasome activates various pro-inflammatory cytokines including IL-Iβ, TNF-a, and IL-6. The pro-inflammatory cytokines can critically trigger inflammatory response in diabetic kidney [4,5]. Therefore, suppression of NLRP3 inflammasome could be a potential target of hyperglycemia-induced renal damage [4,5]. A previous study demonstrated that administration of polyphenols inhibited TNF-α-associated pro-inflammatory cytokines [6]. Genistein, quercetin, daidzein, and naringenin in LBE are known to inhibit nuclear NF-κB translocation, along with decreases in iNOS and NO productions in vitro and in vivo [27]. In particular, inhibition of NLRP3 inflammasome could prevent facilitation of the progression of hyperglycemia-induced renal failure [5]. For the first time, the current study showed that the high dose of LBE supplementation suppressed NLRP3 inflammasome along with nuclear NF-κB activation. Indeed, LBE supplementation ameliorated inflammatory responses via suppression of NLRP3 inflammasome.

AMPK has some physiological effects on mitochondrial biogenesis and glucose metabolism. AMPK also ameliorates the NF-κB related inflammatory response through activation of SIRT1 and PGC-1α [9,10]. SIRT1 suppresses NF-κB by deacetylation of p65 and decreases priming of NLRP3 protein [10]. One previous study suggested that SIRT1 decreased activation of NLRP3 inflammasome in vitro [10]. Furthermore, SIRT1 was found to preserve podocyte function by regulating claudin-1, which induces podocyte effacement and albuminuria [46,47]. Hence, the AMPK/SIRT1 signaling pathway could be a therapeutic target in diabetic kidney damage. Other studies suggest that anthocyanin and resveratrol reduce albuminuria, glomerulosclerosis, and tubulointerstitial fibrosis in diabetic nephropathy through the activation of AMPK/SIRT1 signaling [20,21]. The current study showed that LBE supplementation activated SIRT1 and AMPK in diabetic kidney. It would be inferred that LBE supplementation has protective effects on hyperglycemia-induced renal damage by activation of AMPK/SIRT1 along with reduced NLRP3 inflammasome-associated hyper-inflammation in diabetes.

Various pathways accelerate transcription of nuclear NF-κB. Oxidative stress and downregulated AMPK/SIRT1 signaling pathway can directly and indirectly activate NF-κB in hyperglycemia. As mentioned before, our results showed that LBE supplementation has protective action against oxidative stress demonstrated by RAGE, protein carbonyls, and 4-HNE. In particular, the high dose of LBE supplementation was more effective on suppression of NLRP3 inflammasome in our study. However, the low dose of LBE supplementation accelerated the activation of AMPK/SIRT1 more than did the high dose of LBE supplementation in the diabetic condition. The lower protein level of NF-κB in both doses of LBE supplementation might be influenced by various pathways, including AMPK/SIRT1 and oxidative stress as well as NLRP3 inflammasome [48]. In our previous study, LBE supplementation alleviated hepatic inflammation by suppressing the activation of NF-κB. Collectively, LBE supplementation, particularly at a high dose, ameliorates renal inflammation in diabetes according to these findings.

5. Conclusions

The current study demonstrated that LBE had protective effects on renal NLRP3 inflammasome-associated hyperinflammation in T2DM mice. Simultaneously, LBE at a high dose stimulated AMPK/SIRT1 activation and attenuated oxidative stress, although some molecular markers were selectively regulated at different treatment doses of LBE in in T2DM mice. Conclusively, the present study suggests that LB might have potential benefit to prevent and ameliorate hyperglycemia-induced renal inflammation under diabetic conditions.

Author Contributions: Conceptualization: Y.L.; data curation: J.E.P.; formal analysis: Y.L. and J.E.P.; investigation: Y.L and S.Y.K.; funding acquisition: Y.L.; methodology: Y.L., J.E.P., and H.L.; supervision: Y.L.; writing, review, and editing: J.E.P., H.L., and Y.L. All authors have read and agreed to the published version of the manuscript.

Funding: This research was supported by a grant (2018R1D1A1B07046778) funded by the Ministry of Education, Science and Technology, Republic of Korea.

Conflicts of Interest: The authors declare no conflict of interest. The funders had no role in the design of the study; in the collection, analyses, or interpretation of data; in the writing of the manuscript, or in the decision to publish the results.

Abbreviations

The following abbreviations are used in this manuscript:

ACR	Albumin/creatinine ratio
AGE	Advanced glycation end products
AMPK	AMP-activation kinase
AUC	Area under the curve
BSA	Bovine serum albumin
BUN	Blood urea nitrogen
BW	Body weight
DM	Diabetes mellitus
FBG	Fasting blood glucose
4-HNE	Four-hydroxynonenal
H&E	Hematoxylin and eosin
HO-1	Heme oxygenase-1
ICAM	Intercellular adhesion molecule
IL-1β	Interleukin-1β
IL-6	Interleukin-6
LB	*Lespedeza Bicolor*
MCP	Monocyte chemoattractant protein
NC	Normal control
NF-κB	nuclear factor kappa B
NLRP3	Nucleotide-binding oligomerization domain-like pyrin domain containing receptor 3
NQO1	NAD(P)H dehydrogenase quinone 1
Nrf2	Nuclear factor erythroid 2-related factor 2
SIRT1	Sirtuin1

SOD	Superoxide dismutase
STZ	Streptozotocin
RAGE	Advanced glycation end products receptor
ROS	Reactive oxygen species
T2DM	Type 2 diabetes mellitus
TNF-α	Tumor necrosis factor α

References

1. Stadler, K.; Goldberg, I.J.; Susztak, K. The evolving understanding of the contribution of lipid metabolism to diabetic kidney disease. *Curr. Diabetes Rep.* **2015**, *15*, 40. [CrossRef] [PubMed]

2. Alicic, R.Z.; Rooney, M.T.; Tuttle, K.R. Diabetic Kidney Disease: Challenges, Progress, and Possibilities. *Clin. J. Am. Soc. Nephrol.* **2017**, *12*, 2032–2045. [CrossRef] [PubMed]

3. Baud, L.; Ardaillou, R. Reactive oxygen species: Production and role in the kidney. *Am. J. Physiol. Physiol.* **1986**, *251*, F765–F776. [CrossRef] [PubMed]

4. Ratliff, B.B.; Abdulmahdi, W.; Pawar, R.; Wolin, M.S. Oxidant Mechanisms in Renal Injury and Disease. *Antioxid. Redox Signal.* **2016**, *25*, 119–146. [CrossRef]

5. Jha, J.C.; Banal, C.; Chow, B.S.; Cooper, M.E.; Jandeleit-Dahm, K. Diabetes and Kidney Disease: Role of Oxidative Stress. *Antioxid. Redox Signal.* **2016**, *25*, 657–684. [CrossRef]

6. Minutoli, L.; Puzzolo, D.; Rinaldi, M.; Irrera, N.; Marini, H.R.; Arcoraci, V.; Bitto, A.; Crea, G.; Pisani, A.; Squadrito, F.; et al. ROS-Mediated NLRP3 Inflammasome Activation in Brain, Heart, Kidney, and Testis Ischemia/Reperfusion Injury. *Oxidative Med. Cell. Longev.* **2016**, *2016*, 1–10. [CrossRef]

7. DeWolf, S.E.; Shigeoka, A.A.; Scheinok, A.S.; Kasimsetty, G.; Welch, A.K.; McKay, D.B. Expression of TLR2, NOD1, and NOD2 and the NLRP3 Inflammasome in Renal Tubular Epithelial Cells of Male versus Female Mice. *Nephron* **2017**, *137*, 68–76. [CrossRef]

8. Mehaffey, E.D.; Majid, S.A. Tumor necrosis factor-alpha, kidney function, and hypertension. American journal of physiology. *Renal Physiol.* **2017**, *313*, F1005–F1008. [CrossRef]

9. Mitchell, S.; Vargas, J. Signaling via the NFkappaB system. *Wiley Interdiscip Rev. Syst. Biol. Med.* **2016**, *8*, 227–241. [CrossRef]

10. Song, W.; Wei, L.; Du, Y.; Wang, Y.; Jiang, S. Protective effect of ginsenoside metabolite compound K against diabetic nephropathy by inhibiting NLRP3 inflammasome activation and NF-kappaB/p38 signaling pathway in high-fat diet/streptozotocin-induced diabetic mice. *Int Immunopharmacol.* **2018**, *63*, 227–238. [CrossRef]

11. Zheng, Z.; Zheng, F. Immune Cells and Inflammation in Diabetic Nephropathy. *J. Diabetes Res.* **2016**, *2016*, 1841690. [CrossRef] [PubMed]

12. Duran-Salgado, M.B.; Rubio-Guerra, A.F. Diabetic nephropathy and inflammation. *World J. Diabetes* **2014**, *5*, 393–398. [CrossRef] [PubMed]

13. Granata, S.; Gassa, A.D.; Bellin, G.; Lupo, A.; Zaza, G. Transcriptomics: A Step behind the Comprehension of the Polygenic Influence on Oxidative Stress, Immune Deregulation, and Mitochondrial Dysfunction in Chronic Kidney Disease. *BioMed Res. Int.* **2016**, *2016*, 1–16. [CrossRef] [PubMed]

14. Fakhruddin, S.; Alanazi, W.; Jackson, K.E. Diabetes-Induced Reactive Oxygen Species: Mechanism of Their Generation and Role in Renal Injury. *J. Diabetes Res.* **2017**, *2017*, 1–30. [CrossRef]

15. Klen, J.; Goričar, K.; Janež, A.; Dolžan, V. NLRP3 Inflammasome Polymorphism and Macrovascular Complications in Type 2 Diabetes Patients. *J. Diabetes Res.* **2015**, *2015*, 1–6. [CrossRef]

16. Rampanelli, E.; Orsó, E.; Ochodnicky, P.; Liebisch, G.; Bakker, P.J.; Claessen, N.; Butter, L.M.; Weerman, M.A.V.D.B.; Florquin, S.; Schmitz, G.; et al. Metabolic injury-induced NLRP3 inflammasome activation dampens phospholipid degradation. *Sci. Rep.* **2017**, *7*, 2861. [CrossRef]

17. Shen, J.; Wang, L.; Jiang, N.; Mou, S.; Zhang, M.; Gu, L.; Shao, X.; Wang, Q.; Qi, C.; Li, S.; et al. NLRP3 inflammasome mediates contrast media-induced acute kidney injury by regulating cell apoptosis. *Sci. Rep.* **2016**, *6*, 34682. [CrossRef]

18. Kim, S.-M.; Kim, Y.G.; Kim, N.-J.; Park, S.H.; Jeong, K.-H.; Lee, Y.H.; Lim, S.J.; Lee, S.-H.; Moon, J.-Y. Inflammasome-Independent Role of NLRP3 Mediates Mitochondrial Regulation in Renal Injury. *Front. Immunol.* **2018**, *9*, 2563. [CrossRef]

19. Park, H.S.; Lim, J.H.; Kim, M.Y.; Kim, Y.; Hong, Y.A.; Choi, S.R.; Chung, S.; Kim, H.W.; Choi, B.S.; Kim, Y.S.; et al. Resveratrol increases AdipoR1 and AdipoR2 expression in type 2 diabetic nephropathy. *J. Transl. Med.* **2016**, *14*, 176. [CrossRef]

20. Zhou, L.; Xu, D.-Y.; Sha, W.-G.; Shen, L.; Lu, G.-Y.; Yin, X.; Wang, M.-J. High glucose induces renal tubular epithelial injury via Sirt1/NF-kappaB/microR-29/Keap1 signal pathway. *J. Transl. Med.* **2015**, *13*, 352. [CrossRef]

21. Chou, X.; Ding, F.; Zhang, X.; Ding, X.; Gao, H.; Wu, Q. Sirtuin-1 ameliorates cadmium-induced endoplasmic reticulum stress and pyroptosis through XBP-1s deacetylation in human renal tubular epithelial cells. *Arch. Toxicol.* **2019**, *93*, 965–986. [CrossRef] [PubMed]

22. Cetrullo, S.; D'Adamo, S.; Tantini, B.; Borzi, R.M.; Flamigni, F. mTOR, AMPK, and Sirt1: Key Players in Metabolic Stress Management. *Crit. Rev. Eukaryot. Gene Expr.* **2015**, *25*, 59–75. [CrossRef] [PubMed]

23. Kim, S.M.; Kim, Y.G.; Kim, D.J.; Park, S.H.; Jeong, K.H.; Lee, Y.H. Resveratrol prevents renal lipotoxicity and inhibits mesangial cell glucotoxicity in a manner dependent on the AMPK-SIRT1-PGC1alpha axis in db/db mice. *Diabetologia* **2013**, *56*, 204–217. [CrossRef] [PubMed]

24. Lee, J.H.; Parveen, A.; Do, M.H.; Lim, Y.; Shim, S.H.; Kim, S.Y. Lespedeza cuneata protects the endothelial dysfunction via eNOS phosphorylation of PI3K/Akt signaling pathway in HUVECs. *Phytomedicine* **2018**, *48*, 1–9. [CrossRef] [PubMed]

25. Miyase, T.; Sano, M.; Nakai, H.; Muraoka, M.; Nakazawa, M.; Suzuki, M. Antioxidants from Lespedeza homoloba. (I). *Phytochemistry* **1999**, *52*, 303–310. [CrossRef]

26. Ko, Y.-H.; Shim, K.-Y.; Kim, S.-K.; Seo, J.-Y.; Lee, B.-R.; Hur, K.-H.; Kim, Y.-J.; Kim, S.-E.; Do, M.H.; Parveen, A.; et al. *Lespedeza bicolor* Extract Improves Amyloid Beta25—35-Induced Memory Impairments by Upregulating BDNF and Activating Akt, ERK, and CREB Signaling in Mice. *Planta Med.* **2019**, *85*, 1363–1373. [CrossRef]

27. Lee, S.J.; Hossaine, M.D.; Park, S.C. A potential anti-inflammation activity and depigmentation effect of *Lespedeza bicolor* extract and its fractions. *Saudi J. Biol. Sci.* **2016**, *23*, 9–14. [CrossRef]

28. Maximov, O.; Kulesh, N.; Stepanenko, L.; Dmitrenok, P. New prenylated isoflavanones and other constituents of *Lespedeza bicolor*. *Fitoterapia* **2004**, *75*, 96–98. [CrossRef]

29. Miyase, T. Antioxidants from Lespedeza homoloba (II). *Phytochemistry* **1999**, *52*, 311–319. [CrossRef]

30. Do, M.H.; Lee, J.H.; Wahedi, H.M.; Pak, C.; Lee, C.H.; Yeo, E.-J.; Lim, Y.; Ha, S.K.; Choi, I.; Kim, S.Y. *Lespedeza bicolor* ameliorates endothelial dysfunction induced by methylglyoxal glucotoxicity. *Phytomedicine* **2017**, *36*, 26–36. [CrossRef]

31. Do, M.H.; Lee, J.H.; Cho, K.; Kang, M.C.; Subedi, L.; Parveen, A.; Kim, S.Y. Therapeutic Potential of *Lespedeza bicolor* to Prevent Methylglyoxal-Induced Glucotoxicity in Familiar Diabetic Nephropathy. *J. Clin. Med.* **2019**, *8*, 1138. [CrossRef] [PubMed]

32. Zhang, M.; Lv, X.Y.; Li, J.; Xu, Z.G.; Chen, L. The characterization of high-fat diet and multiple low-dose streptozotocin induced type 2 diabetes rat model. *Exp Diabetes Res.* **2008**, *2008*, 704045. [CrossRef] [PubMed]

33. Jheng, H.-F.; Tsai, P.-J.; Chuang, Y.-L.; Shen, Y.-T.; Tai, T.-A.; Chen, W.-C.; Chou, C.-K.; Ho, L.-C.; Tang, M.-J.; Lai, K.-T.A.; et al. Albumin stimulates renal tubular inflammation through an HSP70-TLR4 axis in mice with early diabetic nephropathy. *Dis. Model. Mech.* **2015**, *8*, 1311–1321. [CrossRef] [PubMed]

34. Shikata, K.; Makino, H. Microinflammation in the pathogenesis of diabetic nephropathy. *J. Diabetes Investig.* **2013**, *4*, 142–149. [CrossRef] [PubMed]

35. Neumiller, J.J.; Hirsch, I.B. Management of Hyperglycemia in Diabetic Kidney Disease. *Diabetes Spectr.* **2015**, *28*, 214–219. [CrossRef]

36. Liu, Z.; Patil, I.Y.; Jiang, T.; Sancheti, H.; Walsh, J.P.; Stiles, B.L. High-Fat Diet Induces Hepatic Insulin Resistance and Impairment of Synaptic Plasticity. *PLoS ONE* **2015**, *10*, e0128274. [CrossRef]

37. Andrikopoulos, S.; Blair, A.R.; DeLuca, N.; Fam, B.C.; Proietto, J. Evaluating the glucose tolerance test in mice. *Am. J. Physiol. Metab.* **2008**, *295*, E1323–E1332. [CrossRef]

38. Álvarez-Cilleros, D.; López-Oliva, E.; Goya, L.; Martín, M. Ángeles; Ramos, S. Cocoa intake attenuates renal injury in Zucker Diabetic fatty rats by improving glucose homeostasis. *Food Chem. Toxicol.* **2019**, *127*, 101–109. [CrossRef]

39. Su, S.; Cao, M.; Wu, G.; Long, Z.; Cheng, X.; Fan, J.; Xu, Z.; Su, H.; Hao, Y.; Li, G.; et al. Hordenine protects against hyperglycemia-associated renal complications in streptozotocin-induced diabetic mice. *Biomed. Pharmacother.* **2018**, *104*, 315–324. [CrossRef]

40. Yang, W.; Luo, Y.; Yang, S.; Zeng, M.; Zhang, S.; Liu, J.; Han, Y.; Liu, Y.; Zhu, X.; Wu, H.; et al. Ectopic lipid accumulation: Potential role in tubular injury and inflammation in diabetic kidney disease. *Clin. Sci.* **2018**, *132*, 2407–2422. [CrossRef]

41. Giacco, F.; Brownlee, M. Oxidative stress and diabetic complications. *Circ. Res.* **2010**, *107*, 1058–1070. [CrossRef] [PubMed]

42. Sourris, K.C.; Morley, A.L.; Koitka, A.; Samuel, P.; Coughlan, M.T.; Penfold, S.A.; Thomas, M.C.; Bierhaus, A.; Nawroth, P.P.; Yamamoto, H.; et al. Receptor for AGEs (RAGE) blockade may exert its renoprotective effects in patients with diabetic nephropathy via induction of the angiotensin II type 2 (AT2) receptor. *Diabetologia* **2010**, *53*, 2442–2451. [CrossRef] [PubMed]

43. Xiao, M.; Zhong, H.; Xia, L.; Tao, Y.; Yin, H. Pathophysiology of mitochondrial lipid oxidation: Role of 4-hydroxynonenal (4-HNE) and other bioactive lipids in mitochondria. *Free. Radic. Boil. Med.* **2017**, *111*, 316–327. [CrossRef]

44. Kim, N.H.; Kwack, S.J.; Yoon, K.S.; Choi, J.S.; Lee, B.-M. 4-Hydroxynonenal: A Superior Oxidative Biomarker Compared to Malondialdehyde and Carbonyl Content Induced by Carbon Tetrachloride in Rats. *J. Toxicol. Environ. Health Part A* **2015**, *78*, 1051–1062. [CrossRef] [PubMed]

45. Muchová, J.; Országhová, Z.; Žitňanová, I.; Trebatický, B.; Breza, J.; Ďuračková, Z. The effect of natural polyphenols on the oxidative stress markers in patients with diabetic nephropathy. *Free Radic. Boil. Med.* **2014**, *75*, S42. [CrossRef]

46. Hong, Q.; Zhang, L.; Das, B.; Li, Z.; Liu, B.; Cai, G. ncreased podocyte Sirtuin-1 function attenuates diabetic kidney injury. *Kidney Int.* **2018**, *93*, 1330–1343. [CrossRef] [PubMed]

47. Wang, W.; Sun, W.; Cheng, Y.; Xu, Z.; Cai, L. Role of sirtuin-1 in diabetic nephropathy. *J. Mol. Med.* **2019**, *97*, 291–309. [CrossRef] [PubMed]

48. Borgohain, M.P.; Lahkar, M.; Ahmed, S.; Chowdhury, L.; Kumar, S.; Pant, R.; Choubey, A. Small Molecule Inhibiting Nuclear Factor-kB Ameliorates Oxidative Stress and Suppresses Renal Inflammation in Early Stage of Alloxan-Induced Diabetic Nephropathy in Rat. *Basic Clin. Pharmacol. Toxicol.* **2017**, *120*, 442–449. [CrossRef] [PubMed]

 *antioxidants*

Article

Phenolic Compounds and the Anti-Atherogenic Effect of Bee Bread in High-Fat Diet-Induced Obese Rats

Zaidatul Akmal Othman [1,2], Wan Syaheedah Wan Ghazali [1], Liza Noordin [1], Nurul Aiman Mohd. Yusof [3] and Mahaneem Mohamed [1,4,*]

[1] Department of Physiology, School of Medical Sciences, Universiti Sains Malaysia, Kubang Kerian 16150, Kelantan, Malaysia; zaidaakmal@unisza.edu.my (Z.A.O.); syaheeda@usm.my (W.S.W.G.); lizakck@usm.my (L.N.)
[2] Faculty of Medicine, Universiti Sultan Zainal Abidin, Kuala Terengganu 20400, Terengganu, Malaysia
[3] Department of Anatomy, School of Medical Sciences, Universiti Sains Malaysia, Kubang Kerian 16150, Kelantan, Malaysia; aimannur@usm.my
[4] Unit of Integrative Medicine, School of Medical Sciences, Universiti Sains Malaysia, Kubang Kerian 16150, Kelantan, Malaysia
* Correspondence: mahaneem@usm.my; Tel.: +60-9767-6158

Received: 4 December 2019; Accepted: 26 December 2019; Published: 30 December 2019

Abstract: This study was undertaken to determine the phenolic compounds and the anti-atherogenic effect of bee bread in high-fat diet (HFD)-induced obese rats. The presence of phenolic compounds in bee bread was determined by liquid chromatography–mass spectrometry. Thirty-two male Sprague Dawley rats were divided into four groups, (n = 8/group); i.e., Normal (N), HFD (high-fat diet), HFD + BB (high-fat diet and 0.5 g/kg/day bee bread), and HFD + O (high-fat diet and 10 mg/kg/day orlistat) groups. After 6 weeks of the experiment, rats were sacrificed. Five phenolic compounds were identified in bee bread; namely, caffeic acid, ferulic acid, kaempferol, apigenin, and isorhamnetin. Bee bread significantly reduced Lee obesity index and levels of total cholesterol (TC), low-density lipoprotein (LDL), fatty acid synthase (FAS) activity, atherogenic index, oxidised-LDL (oxLDL), and malondialdehyde (MDA), and significantly increased aortic antioxidant activities, such as those of superoxide dismutase (SOD) and glutathione peroxidase (GPx). Adipocyte sizes were found to be smaller in the HFD + BB group compared to the N group, and en face aortas showed an absence of atherosclerotic plaque in rats supplemented with bee bread. These changes might suggest an anti-atherogenic effect of bee bread in HFD-induced obese rats via its antioxidant and hypocholesterolaemic properties.

Keywords: bee bread; obese; anti-atherogenic; phenolic compounds

1. Introduction

Obesity is a major contributor to total burden of disease in developing countries. Obesity has been an important target for health professionals to reduce obesity-related cardiovascular disease (CVD), notably dyslipidaemia, hypertension, and coronary artery disease [1]. Prolonged administration of a high-fat diet (HFD) to rats has been shown to develop a status of impaired-lipid metabolism, as evidenced by higher levels of total cholesterol (TC), triglyceride (TG), and low-density lipoprotein (LDL) in rats fed with a HFD [2]. Apart from impairment of lipid metabolism, attention has also recently focused on the role of low grade chronic inflammation as one of the mechanisms of obesity related disorders. It has been speculated that an excess of adipose tissue accumulation is a precursor of pro-inflammatory cytokines' production contributing to adverse obesity-related complications, such as insulin resistance and increased blood pressure [3].

Recent decades have shown that there is increasing interest to assess the potential medicinal and therapeutic properties of natural products to prevent obesity-related CVD [4,5]. The naturally occurring products have been shown to possess anti-atherogenic effects by improving lipid profile, reducing oxidative stress status, and increasing the antioxidant enzyme defence mechanism [6,7]. Bee bread is one of the bee kingdom products formed by bees. It contains a mixture of bee pollen and bees' digestive enzymes, and is abundantly found in the beehive. After 2 weeks, anaerobic lactic acid fermentation process contributes to a greater nutritive value of bee bread [8]. Bee bread is a well-balanced diet, as it contains carbohydrate, lipid, and protein sources, and essential minerals and vitamins, such as vitamins C, B1, B2, E, iron, calcium, and magnesium [9]. It also contains phenolic compounds, such as p-coumaric acid, kaempherol, isorhamnetin [10], apigenin, chrysin, ferulic acid, caffeic acid, gallic acid, naringenin, and quercetin [11,12]. Bee bread has been shown to offer protection against tumour cells reactivity and possess other biological properties, such as antimicrobial and hepatoprotective effects [11,13,14]. Moreover, it has been shown to exert a hypocholesterolaemic property by significantly reducing 15.7% of TC and 20.5% LDL levels in overweight and obese patients [15]. Studies of antioxidant activities of bee bread have been reported in few countries, including Lithuania [16], Araucania [17], Poland [11], Ukraine [18], Romania [19], and Georgia [20]. However, no study has been reported on its possible anti-atherogenic effect in obesity so far. Hence, the present study was aimed to determine the phenolic compounds' presence in Malaysian bee bread and its anti-atherogenic effect in HFD-induced obese rats.

2. Materials and Methods

2.1. Materials

Animal ghee was purchased from Unilever Holdings Sdn. Bhd. (Kuala Lumpur, Malaysia). Calcium and vitamin D were purchased from Eurobio Sdn. Bhd. (Victoria, Australia). Orlistat was purchased from Xepa-Soul Pattinson Sdn. Bhd. (Melaka, Malaysia), cholesterol powder from Nacalai Tesque (Kyoto, Japan), Eosin Y from Sigma-Aldrich (St. Louis, MI, USA), haematoxylin from Richard-Allan Scientific (Kalamazoo, MN, USA), and oil-Red O from VWR Life-Science AMRESCO (Solon, OH, USA). All other reagents were of analytical grade.

2.2. Preparation of Bee Bread Sample

Bee bread from stingless bee (*Heterotrigona itama*) was purchased from local stingless bee farm from Selangor, Malaysia. The sample was dried using food dehydrator at 35 °C. Then, it was ground into fine powder using a mini blender and kept in a sterilised container at –20 °C until further analysis.

2.3. Liquid-Chromatography-Mass Spectrometry Analysis of Bee Bread

The presence of phenolic compounds was assessed by liquid chromatography-mass spectrometry. Based on studies conducted by Isidorov et al. [10] and Urcan et al. [21], bee bread was screened for the presence of fourteen phenolic compounds, which included apigenin, benzaldehyde, caffeic acid, chrysin, ferulic acid, gallic acid, hydroquinone, isorhamnetin, kaempferol, mangiferin, naringenin, p-coumaric acid, quercetin, and resveratrol. Briefly, ten gram of powdered bee bread was soaked in 5 mL of methanol and sonicated (Lab Companion, Model UC-20, Seoul, Korea) for 30 min. The solution was filtered and evaporated using rotovap (Buchi, Rotavapor® R-300 system, Flawil, Switzerland) to make a stock solution of 3 mg/mL. The resulting solution was filtered through a membrane filter (pore size 0.22 μm) before analysis. The sample was analysed by LTQ Orbitrap mass spectrometer (Thermo Scientific, San Jose, CA, USA). Acetonitrile and 0.1% formic acid were used as the mobile phase. The spectral *m/z* from 100–1000 was recorded in positive ionization mode. The mass spectrophotometry was performed in electrospray ionisation conditions and positive mode with the following parameter settings: source accelerating voltage = 4.0 kV; capillary temperature = 280 °C; sheath gas flow = 40 arb; auxiliary gas = 20 arb.

2.4. Animals and Diet

Thirty-two male Sprague Dawley rats of age between 8 and 10 weeks (180–230 g) were obtained from Animal and Research Centre (ARASC), Universiti Sains Malaysia, Kubang Kerian, Kelantan. Animals were housed in an individual cage with a constant temperature at 22–24 °C, given a 12 h light and dark cycle, and supplied with normal rat chow pellet with water ad libitum. Animals were handled according to guidelines provided from local Ethics Committee (USM/Animal Ethics Approval/ 2016/(98) (744)). Following an acclimatization period, rats were administered either a normal diet or high-fat diet (HFD). The normal diet is a standard Altromin pellet imported from Germany by Sterling Ascent, Malaysia. Obesity was established by feeding with a HFD using the previous method with slight modifications, consisting of 32 g of ghee (saturated fat from animal), 68 g of powdered normal rat chow, 300 mg of calcium, 100 UI of vitamin D3, and 12% cholesterol powder [22]. After a dough-like consistency formed, foods were shaped into small hand-balls and kept at 4 °C overnight to feed the rats in the next morning. Foods were prepared every two days to avoid lipid oxidation. The nutrient composition of normal and HFD is shown in Table 1.

Table 1. Content of nutrients in normal and high-fat diets.

Nutrient Composition	Normal Diet (g/100)	High-Fat Diet (g/100 g)
Carbohydrate	64	46
Protein	24	12
Fat	12	31
Ash	6.9	3.8
Energy (kcal/100 g)	318.8	516.5

2.5. Experimental Design

A pilot study was conducted with three different doses of bee bread (0.5, 1.0, and 1.5 g/kg/day) (n = 3/group) administered for 6 weeks via oral gavage to determine the best dose of bee bread in HFD-induced obese rats. According to Reagen-Shaw et al. [23], the lowest dose, i.e., 0.5 g/kg, was calculated based on the body surface area normalization method, relative to the local human consumption of bee bread, which is 5 g/day. Bee bread at the dose of 0.5 g/kg/day was chosen as the best dose and used in the present study, as it reduced Lee obesity index, TC, and LDL levels in HFD-induced obese rats (unpublished observation).

Thirty-two male Sprague Dawley rats were randomly divided into four groups (n = 8/group); i.e., normal group (N, on normal rat chow pellet and distilled water), high-fat diet (HFD, on high-fat diet and distilled water), HFD + BB (on high-fat diet and bee bread at 0.5 g/kg/day), and HFD + O (on high-fat diet and orlistat at 10 mg/kg/day). Normal rat chow pellets and the HFD were given ad libitum. Distilled water, bee bread, and orlistat were administered to rats via oral gavage for 6 weeks. Body weight and food intake were measured every other day. At the end of experimental period, Lee obesity index was calculated using a previous method [24], and a value of less than 315 was considered as normal [25]. Animals were sacrificed after being anaesthetised with ketamine 90 mg/kg and xylazine 5 mg/kg. Blood was collected from posterior vena cava for serum biological markers. Thoracic aorta was immediately excised, rinsed in ice-cold phosphate buffer solution, and homogenized for assessment on the levels of oxidant-antioxidant markers and fatty acid synthase (FAS) activity. Section of aortic arch was analysed for the presence of atherosclerotic plaque. Adipose tissue was dissected out and stored in 10% formalin for histological study.

2.6. Measurement of Lipid Profile and Atherogenic Index

Total cholesterol was determined by Architect c total cholesterol kit (ARCHITECT c cholesterol kit, Abbott, IL, USA) using an enzymatic-colorimetric method, which produced the end product quinoneimine from hydrogen peroxide (coefficient of variation, CV ≤ 3% and sensitivity 18.26 mmol/L).

TG was determined using Architect c triglyceride kit (ARCHITECT c Triglyceride Reagent kit, Abbott, IL, USA), which hydrolysed lipase to free fatty acids and glycerol (CV ≤ 5% and sensitivity 16.05 mmol/L). Reaction changes for TC and TG were measured at 500 nm (ARCHITECT c System, Abbott, IL, USA). High-density lipoprotein was measured based on elimination of chylomicrons, LDL, and very-low density lipoprotein by cholesterol esterase, cholesterol oxidase, and catalase using Biosino Direct HDL-Cholesterol reagent kit, Biosino Bio-Technology and Science Inc, Beijing, China (sensitivity up to 2.586 mmol/L). Absorbance value was determined at 600 nm (ARCHITECT c System, Abbott, IL, USA). LDL was determined by the formula described by Friedewald et al. [26]: LDL (mmol/L) = (TC − HDL − TG)/5. Atherogenic index was calculated using formula: AI = (TC − HDL-C)/HDL-C [27].

2.7. Determination of Aortic Oxidant/Antioxidant Status Markers and Fatty Acid Synthase (FAS)

Aortic tissue was homogenized using a tissue grinder (Tissue Grinder G50, Coyote Bioscience Co., Ltd., Beijing, China) in an ice-chilled 0.1 M phosphate buffer solution, pH 7.4 and centrifuged (Avanti J-HC, Beckman Coulter, IN, USA) at 4000 rpm for 15 min. Supernatant was collected and used to analyse oxidant-antioxidant markers and FAS using procedures described by respective experimental protocols. Aortic oxidised LDL (oxLDL) and MDA were determined by commercially available kits from Northwest (Vancouver, WA, USA) and Cloud-Clone (Houstan, TX, USA), respectively. Aortic antioxidant enzymes such as superoxide dismutase (SOD), glutathione peroxidase (GPx), and catalase (CAT) were determined by commercially available kits from Bioassay (San Francisco, CA, USA). Level of FAS activity was determined using a commercially available kit (Cloud-Clone, Houstan, TX, USA).

2.8. Assessment on the Presence of Atherosclerotic Plaque in Aortic Arch

The aortic arch was transversely cut at about 2 mm from, where it emerged in 2 cm length. Clean aortas were fixed with 78% methanol followed by incubation with Oil Red O solution for 50–60 min. Aortas were washed twice with 78% methanol followed by phosphate buffer solution. En face images of aortic arches were visualized under a stereomicroscope (Olympus SZ, OLYMPUS, Tokyo, Japan) at ×20 magnification [28].

2.9. Histology of Adipose Tissue

Adipose tissue was processed and embedded in paraffin. A sample block was cut into sections of 5 μm size and fixed on glass slides. After drying, all slides were stained with haematoxylin and eosin (H&E) and inspected under a light microscope (Leica DM750, LEICA, Wetzlar, Germany).

2.10. Statistical Analysis

Data analysis was carried out using Statistical Package of Social Science (SPSS) version 22. After assessment for normal distribution and homogenous variance, the one-way analysis of variance (ANOVA) test was used and followed by Tukey's post-hoc test for multiple comparisons. $p < 0.05$ was defined as statistically significant. Values are expressed as means (with standard deviations).

3. Results

3.1. Liquid Chromatography-Mass Spectrophotometry Analysis of Bee Bread

Five phenolic compounds were identified in the bee bread used in the present study. Isorhamnetin showed highest level of mass spectrum (317.07 *m/z*), followed by kaempferol (287.06 *m/z*), apigenin (271.06 *m/z*), ferulic acid (195.09 *m/z*), and caffeic acid (181.12 *m/z*) (Table 2).

Table 2. Liquid chromatography-mass spectrophotometry analysis of bee bread.

Compounds	Molecular Formula	Molecular Weight (g/mol)	Mass Spectrum (*m/z*)	Retention Time (min)
Apigenin	$C_{15}H_{10}O_5$	270.05	271.06	17.76
Caffeic acid	$C_9H_8O_4$	180.16	181.12	17.37
Ferulic acid	$C_{10}H_{10}O_4$	194.18	195.09	12.45
Isorhamnetin	$C_{16}H_{12}O_7$	316.26	317.07	17.49
Kaempferol	$C_{15}H_{10}O_6$	286.23	287.06	17.59

3.2. Lee Obesity Index, Weight Gain, Food, and Calorie Intake

After 6 weeks, all rats in HFD, HFD + BB, and HFD + O groups were obese, as their Lee obesity indices were more than 315 compared to the N group. The Lee obesity index was significantly lower in the HFD + BB group compared to HFD group. There were no significant differences in weight gain and food intake among all groups. Calorie intake was significantly higher in all groups which received the HFD compared to the N group, but it was not significantly different among all groups that received the HFD (Table 3).

Table 3. The effects of bee bread on Lee's obesity index, weight gain, food, and calorie intake.

	N	HFD	HFD + BB	HFD + O
Lee obesity index	312.37 ± 5.66	337.83 ± 13.01 [a]	316.83 ± 7.70 [b]	322.27 ± 13.97
Weight gain (g)	112.73 ± 42.22	123.20 ± 21.84	98.70 ± 35.11	104.73 ± 21.99
Food intake (g)	20.23 ± 3.61	17.94 ± 1.58	18.73 ± 2.82	20.90 ± 1.06
Calorie intake (kcal)	64.32 ± 11.47	92.41 ± 8.13 [a]	96.46 ± 14.50 [a]	107.61 ± 5.45 [a]

Data are presented as means (with standard deviations) ($n = 8$ per group). N, normal; HFD, high fat diet; HFD + BB, high-fat diet and 0.5 g/kg bee bread; HFD + O, high-fat diet and 10 mg/kg orlistat. [a] $p < 0.05$ compared with N group; [b] $p < 0.05$ compared with the HFD group (one-way ANOVA followed by Tukey's post-hoc test).

3.3. The Effects of Bee Bread on Lipid Profile and Atherogenic Index

TC and LDL levels were found to be significantly higher in HFD group compared to N group and were significantly lower in HFD + BB group compared to HFD group. No significant differences were found for TG and HDL levels among all the groups. Atherogenic index was significantly lower in the groups supplemented with bee bread (HFD + BB) and orlistat (HFD + O) compared to the HFD group. However, the indices were not significantly different between HFD + BB and HFD + O groups (Table 4).

Table 4. The effects of bee bread on serum lipid profiles and the atherogenic index.

Serum Lipid Profile and Atherogenic Index	N	HFD	HFD + BB	HFD + O
TC (mmol/L)	1.77 ± 0.18	2.29 ± 0.20 [a]	1.89 ± 0.23 [b]	1.93 ± 0.23
TG (mmol/L)	0.79 ± 0.33	1.09 ± 0.35	0.73 ± 0.23	1.03 ± 0.36
LDL (mmol/L)	0.16 ± 0.11	0.43 ± 0.20 [a]	0.14 ± 0.10 [b]	0.16 ± 0.10 [b]
HDL (mmol/L)	1.20 ± 0.15	1.29 ± 0.13	1.40 ± 0.14	1.30 ± 0.15
Atherogenic index	0.44 ± 0.02	0.55 ± 0.16	0.32 ± 0.08 [b]	0.33 ± 0.12 [b]

Data are presented as means (with standard deviations), $n = 8$ per group. N, normal; HFD, high fat diet; HFD + BB, high-fat diet and 0.5 g/kg bee bread; HFD + O, high-fat diet and 10 mg/kg orlistat. TC, total cholesterol; TG, triglyceride; LDL, low-density lipoprotein; HDL, high-density lipoprotein. [a] $p < 0.05$ compared with N group; [b] $p < 0.05$ compared with the HFD group (one-way ANOVA followed by Tukey's post-hoc test).

3.4. The Effects of Bee Bread on Aortic Oxidant-Antioxidant Status and FAS Activity

Aortic oxLDL and MDA levels were significantly higher in the HFD group compared to the N group and significantly lower HFD + BB compared to the HFD group. OxLDL was significantly lower in the HFD + O group compared to the HFD group. GPx and CAT activities were significantly lower in the HFD group compared to the N group. Meanwhile, significant increases of SOD and GPx activities were seen in HFD + BB group when compared to the HFD group. GPx activity was significantly higher in HFD + O group compared to N, HFD, and HFD + BB groups. The HFD group had significantly more FAS compared to the N group. However, in the HFD+BB group, the FAS level was significantly lower than for the HFD group (Table 5).

Table 5. The effects of bee bread on aortic oxidant/antioxidant biomarkers and fatty acid synthase.

Oxidant-Antioxidant Status	Group			
	N	HFD	HFD + BB	HFD + O
OxLDL(pg/mL)	272.08 ± 41.73	468.23 ± 113.94 [a]	287.19 ± 92.19 [b]	310.83 ± 93.59 [b]
MDA(nmol/mg protein)	0.18 ± 0.03	0.24 ± 0.05 [a]	0.16 ± 0.02 [b]	0.21 ± 0.05
SOD(Umg/ protein)	3.29 ± 0.77	2.82 ± 0.43	3.86 ± 0.46 [b]	3.48 ± 0.67
GPx(Umg/protein)	245.87 ± 12.74	232.28 ± 4.38 [a]	269.23 ± 11.45 [a,b]	311.53 ± 6.23 [a,b,c]
CAT(Umg/protein)	1.13 ± 0.15	0.76 ± 0.42 [a]	0.93 ± 0.63	1.08 ± 0.41
FAS (pg/mL)	763.07 ± 226.23	1580.47 ± 239.19 [a]	754.09 ± 183.93 [b]	831.70 ± 126.10

Data are presented as means (and standard deviation), $n = 8$ per group. N, normal; HFD, high fat diet; HFD + BB, high-fat diet and 0.5 g/kg bee bread; HFD + O, high-fat diet and 10 mg/kg orlistat. OxLDL, oxidised LDL; MDA, malondialdehyde; SOD, superoxide dismutase; GPx, glutathione peroxidase; CAT, catalase; FAS, fatty acid synthase. [a] $p < 0.05$ compared with N group; [b] $p < 0.05$ compared with HFD group; [c] $p < 0.05$ compared with HFD + BB group (one-way ANOVA followed by Tukey's post-hoc test).

3.5. The Effects of Bee Bread on the Presence of Atherosclerotic Plaque

Figure 1 shows representative pictures of aortic arch segments in Oil Red O staining. Aortic arch segments from N, HFD + BB, and HFD + O groups were intact without the presence of atherosclerotic plaque. Whereas an aortic arch segment from HFD group showed a red-stained atherosclerotic plaque within the curvature of aortic arch.

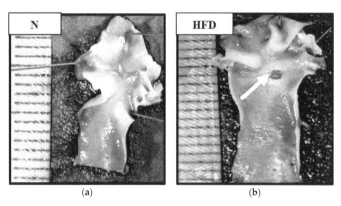

(a)   (b)

Figure 1. *Cont.*

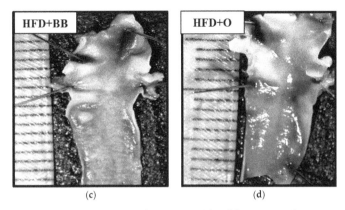

(c)   (d)

Figure 1. Macroscopic findings of aortic arch segment in Oil Red O staining under a stereomicroscope. Aortic arch segments from N (**a**), HFD + BB (**c**), and HFD + O (**d**) groups show intact aorta arch segments without atherosclerotic plaque. However, the segment from HFD group shows the presence of atherosclerotic plaques (yellow arrow) in the aortic arch (**b**). N, normal; HFD, high fat diet; HFD + BB, high-fat diet and 0.5 g/kg bee bread; HFD + O, high-fat diet and 10 mg/kg orlistat.

3.6. The Effects of Bee Bread on Histology of Adipose Tissue

Figure 2 shows the difference in adipocyte sizes of adipose tissue from each representative experimental group using H&E staining. Adipocyte size in HFD group was relatively larger compared to the N group. The sizes were observed to be smaller in HFD + BB and HFD + O groups compared to that of the HFD group.

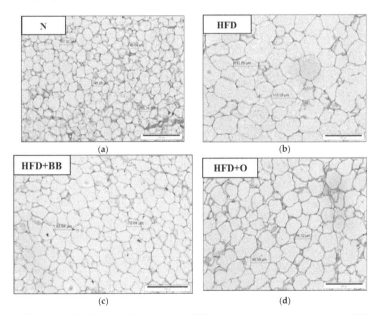

(a)   (b)

(c)   (d)

Figure 2. Histological findings of adipose tissue in H&E staining under light microscope. HFD group (**b**) has relatively larger adipocyte size compared to N group (**a**). Both HFD + BB (**c**) and HFD + O (**d**) groups had relatively smaller adipocyte size compared to the HFD group. N, normal; HFD, high fat diet; HFD + BB, high-fat diet and 0.5 g/kg bee bread; HFD + O, high-fat diet and 10 mg/kg orlistat. (Magnification ×200, Haematoxylin and Eosin staining).

4. Discussion

In the present study, the phenolic compounds and the anti-atherogenic effect of bee bread were evaluated in HFD-induced obese rats. After 6 weeks of continuous administration of HFD, Lee obesity index was significantly higher (more than 315) in the HFD group compared to N group, suggesting that the HFD used in the present study successfully induced an animal model of obesity. As compared to normal diet, the HFD contained higher caloric and fat contents, but lower carbohydrate and protein contents, as shown in Table 1. These differences were due to the mixture of 68 g normal diet with 32 g ghee, 300 mg calcium, 100 IU vitamin D, and 12% cholesterol powder based on the previous study [22] with slight modifications. Hence, the obesity in the HFD group could be due to high composition of fat component in HFD regime ingested, as significantly higher calorie intake was found in this group. HFD + BB group had a significant decrease in Lee obesity index when compared to HFD group, suggesting the anti-obesity effect of bee bread. Although Lee obesity index and weight gain in HFD + O group were observed to be lower compared to HFD group, the difference was not statistically significant. This may suggest bee bread at 0.5 g/kg/day has a better anti-obesity effect compared to orlistat at 10 mg/kg/day in this animal model.

Hypercholesterolemia is closely associated with pathogenesis of atherosclerosis. In the present study, the levels of TC and LDL were significantly higher in the HFD group compared to the N group, similarly to a previous study [29]. A previous study hypothesized that elevated TC and TG levels have been reported to be a crucial factor in lipoprotein metabolism, and its higher concentration was attributed to increased LDL formation and deposition, which is potently atherogenic [30]. Meanwhile, levels of TC and LDL were significantly decreased in the HFD + BB group compared to the HFD group, suggesting a hypocholesterolaemic property of bee bread. A similar finding was also found in a study in which there were significant decreases of TC and LDL levels in obese and overweight patients when combined with honey [15]. Significant low level of LDL was also observed in the HFD + O group, which is consistent with a previous study, due to its action towards inhibition of gastric and pancreatic lipase enzymes [31]. The atherogenic index values of HFD + BB and HFD + O groups were significantly lower (by 40%) than the HFD group's, indicating that bee bread and orlistat are able to reduce the risk of CVD as high atherogenic index is an indicator of high risk to develop CVD [32]. Hence, it is plausible to suggest that both bee bread and orlistat have LDL-lowering effects which might reduce the progression of atherosclerosis.

Growing evidence supports that increased oxidative stress is attributed by the presence of excessive free radicals which interplay between hypercholesterolemia and atherosclerosis [33]. Oxidative modification of LDL plays an immense role in the initial development of atherosclerosis and promotes further accumulation of free radicals in the arterial wall. A significant increase of aortic oxLDL and MDA levels in the HFD group might suggest an excessive formation of oxidative stress in the aortic tissue following HFD ingestion as a consequence of the lipid oxidation process [34]. Meanwhile, these oxidative stress markers demonstrated significantly lower levels in the HFD + BB group compared to the HFD group. The HFD + O group had significantly lower oxLDL level compared to the HFD group, without any changes in MDA level. This might indicate that bee bread may have a greater ability to reduce lipid oxidation compared to orlistat. Antioxidants have been shown to stabilize free radicals, thereby reducing oxidative damage within biochemical, cellular and molecular levels [35]. HFD group had significantly lower levels of aortic GPx and CAT activities compared to N group which could be due to suppression or deactivation of these enzymes by oxidative stress. Significant increase of SOD and GPx activities in the HFD + BB group could be responsible for the lower oxLDL and MDA levels found in this group, which suggest the involvement of antioxidants in reducing the increase of lipid oxidation. This antioxidant effect could partly due to the presence of phenolic compounds such as isorhamnetin, apigenin, caffeic acid, ferulic acid, and kaempferol found in the bee bread which have antioxidant properties [36]. However, it is suggested to further quantify these identified phenolic compounds in future study. In addition, previous studies have reported that bee bread also contains other compounds that have antioxidant properties, such as amino acids, vitamins, and minerals [9,37,38]. As reported in our previous study, the bee bread used in the present study consists of carbohydrate (59.55%), protein (18.37%), and fat (4.51%) [38]. Hence, the antioxidant effect of bee bread found in the present study could also partly due to the interaction among these compounds, which needs further study. Orlistat has also shown to exert an antioxidant effect by evidence of significant increase in GPx activity compared to the HFD group. The previous study has shown involvement of antioxidant activity following orlistat administration in high-fed diet rats, whereby a significant increase of testicular and brain SOD activity was demonstrated [39]. High levels of oxLDL and MDA, suggesting high oxidative stress, with concomitant high TC and LDL levels, might explain the presence of atherosclerotic plaque in HFD group. Meanwhile, both HFD + BB and HFD + O groups showed an absence of atherosclerotic plaque, suggesting that supplementation of bee bread and orlistat for 6 weeks might protect against the formation of atherosclerotic plaque. Similarly, a study has reported the protective effect of orlistat in reducing the progression of atherosclerotic changes in rats fed with HFD [40].

The above results indicate that supplementation of bee bread for 6 weeks demonstrated anti-atherogenic effect as it significantly improved Lee obesity index, TC, and LDL levels; the atherogenic index; aortic oxidant-antioxidant status; and showed an absence of atherosclerotic plaque formation. To further assess the possible underlying mechanism of anti-atherogenic effect of bee bread, we also evaluated the level of aortic FAS activity. Significant low levels of TC and LDL in HFD + BB group might be related to the presence of ferulic and caffeic acids which are reported to exert hypocholesterolemic properties by significantly reducing TC, TG, and LDL levels. This, in turn, may reduce the risk of atherosclerosis [41,42]. The abundance of oxLDL in circulatory system is permeable to subendothelial layer, which further promotes inflammatory response that subsequently affects the endothelial wall integrity and whole vascular function [39]. A previous study has reported that the increase in the levels of adhesive molecules, such as intracellular and vascular cell adhesion molecule, is mediated by platelet-activating factor, which is crucial for adhesion and migration of leucocytes into subendothelium layer [43]. As a result, more leucocytes engulf the oxLDL, and subsequently form foam cells, which further triggers higher inflammation cascades for development of an atherosclerotic plaque [44]. Kaempferol, a flavonoid derivative, has been shown to exert an anti-inflammatory effect by reducing the aortic levels of inflammatory markers, intracellular and vascular cell adhesion molecule, monocyte chemotactic protein 1, and E selectin in rabbits as the model of atherosclerosis [45]. Hence, the anti-atherogenic effect of bee bread could also be attributed to the anti-inflammatory effect of kaempferol and the hypocholesterolemic effects of ferulic and caffeic acids that are present in the bee bread. In addition, it is also suggested to determine the role of inflammatory cytokines in a future study.

Higher fatty acids in circulation are associated with higher formation of polyunsaturated fatty acids mediated by FAS [46]. In the present study, significant higher aortic FAS in the HFD group, which represents higher fatty acid formation, could be attributed to high TC and LDL levels found in this group. This is further supported by the finding of larger adipocyte size observed in this group. A significant low activity of FAS in the HFD + BB group might explain the low levels of TC and LDL, and the presence of smaller adipocyte size in this group. Taken together, these findings may indicate the potential mechanism of anti-atherogenic effects of bee bread, which needs further study to determine its exact molecular mechanism of action.

5. Conclusions

Bee bread at 0.5 g/kg/day significantly improved Lee obesity index, TC, LDL, atherogenic index, aortic oxidative stress status (oxLDL and MDA levels), aortic antioxidant enzymes (SOD and GPx activities), and FAS level in HFD-induced obese rats. These findings were in accordance with our findings on en face aortas, which showed an absence of atherosclerotic plaque and lower size of adipocyte. Hence, it is plausible to suggest that bee bread has anti-atherogenic property, possibly partly due to the presence of phenolic compounds which have high antioxidant and hypocholesterolemic properties. However, further study is needed to investigate the exact molecular mechanisms of actions that contribute to the anti-atherogenic properties of bee bread.

Author Contributions: Conceptualization, M.M.; data curation, Z.A.O. and M.M.; investigation, Z.A.O.; methodology, M.M., L.N., and W.S.W.G.; histology supervision, N.A.M.Y.; original draft preparation, Z.A.O.; writing—review and editing, M.M., L.N., W.S.W.G., and N.A.M.Y. All authors have read and agreed to the published version of the manuscript.

Funding: This work was supported by a USM Short Term Research University Grant (304/PPSP/61313189).

Acknowledgments: Authors would like to thank all staff from the Physiology Department (Aminah Che Romli, Normawati Ahmad, and Umeer Rahimi) for the technical support and the School of Dental Science for providing the stereomicroscope.

Conflicts of Interest: The authors declare no conflict of interest.

References

1. Jean, N.; Somers, V.K.; Sochor, O.; Medina-Inojosa, J.; Liano, E.M.; Lopez-Jimenez, F. Normal-weight obesity: Implications for cardiovascular health. *Curr. Atheroscler. Rep.* **2014**, *16*, 1–11. [CrossRef] [PubMed]
2. Yang, D.; Hu, C.; Deng, X.; Bai, Y.; Cao, H.; Guo, J.; Su, Z. Therapeutic effect of Chitooligosaccharide tablets on lipids in high-fat diet induced hyperlipidemic rats. *Moecules* **2019**, *24*, 514. [CrossRef] [PubMed]
3. Jiang, P.; Ma, D.; Wang, X.; Wang, Y.; Bi, Y.; Yang, J.; Wang, X.; Li, X. Astragaloside IV prevents obesity-associated hypertension by improving pro-inflammatory reaction and leptin resistance. *Mol. Cells* **2018**, *41*, 244–273.
4. Nimmi, O.S.; George, P. Antiobesity and antioxidant effects of a new polyherbal formulation (PHF) in obesity induced wistar rats. *Indian J. Tradit. Knowl.* **2017**, *16*, 297–302.
5. Bais, S.; Singh, G.S.; Sharma, R. Antiobesity and Hypolipidemic Activity of Moringa oleifera Leaves against High Fat Diet-Induced Obesity in Rats. *Adv. Biol.* **2014**, *2014*, 162914. [CrossRef]
6. Jeevangi, S.; Manjunath, S.; Sakhare, P. A study of anti-hyperlipidemia, hypolipedimic and anti-atherogenic activity of fruit of *emblica officinalis* (Amla) in high fat fed albino rats. *Int. J. Med. Res. Health Sci.* **2013**, *2*, 70–77.
7. Gasparotto, F.M.; Palozi, R.A.C.; da Silva, C.H.F.; Pauli, K.B.; Donadel, G.; Lourenço, B.H.L.B.; Nunes, B.C.; Lívero, F.A.D.R.; de Souza, L.M.; Lourenço, E.L.B.; et al. Antiatherosclerotic Properties of *Echinodorus grandiflorus* (Cham. & Schltdl.) Micheli: From Antioxidant and Lipid-Lowering Effects to an Anti-Inflammatory Role. *J. Med. Food* **2019**, *22*. [CrossRef]
8. Zuluaga, C.M.; Serrato, J.C.; Quicazan, M.C. Chemical, nutritional and bioactive characterization of Colombian bee-bread. *Chem. Eng. Trans.* **2015**, *43*, 175–180.
9. Mutsaers, M.; Blitterswijk, H.V.; Leven, L.V.; Kerkvliet, J.; Waerdt, J.V.D. *Bee Products*, 1st ed.; Agromisa Foundation: Wageningen, The Netherlands, 2005; pp. 33–35. ISBN 90-8573-028-7.
10. Isidorov, V.A.; Isidorova, A.G.; Sczczepaniak, L.; Czyzewska, U. Gas chromatographic–mass spectrometric investigation of the chemical composition of beebread. *Food Chem.* **2009**, *115*, 1056–1063. [CrossRef]
11. Sobral, F.; Calhelha, R.C.; Barros, L.; Duenas, M.; Tomas, A.; Santos-Buelga, C.; Vilas-Boas, M.; Ferreira, I.C.F.R. Flavonoid composition and antitumour activity of bee bread collected in northeast Portugal. *Molecules* **2017**, *22*, 248. [CrossRef]
12. Markiewicz-Zukowska, R.; Naliwajko, S.K.; Bartosiuk, E.; Moskwa, J.; Isidorov, V.; Soroczynska, J.; Borawska, M.H. Chemical composition and antioxidant activity of beebread, and its influence on the glioblastoma cell line (U87MG). *J. Apic. Sci.* **2013**, *57*, 147–157. [CrossRef]
13. Eswaran, V.U.; Bhargava, H.R. Chemical analysis and anti-microbial activity of Karnataka bee bread of Apis species. *World Appl. Sci. J.* **2014**, *32*, 379–385.
14. Ceksteryte, V.; Balzekas, J. The use of beebread—Honey mixture in the treatment of liver diseases in alcohol-dependent patients. *J. Chem. Technol.* **2012**, *2*, 62–66.
15. Kas'ianenko, V.I.; Komisarenko, I.A.; Dubtsova, E.A. Correction of atherogenic dyslipidemia with honey, pollen and bee bread in patients with different body mass. *Ter. Arkh.* **2011**, *83*, 58–62. [PubMed]
16. Ceksteryte, V.; Kazlauskas, S.; Racys, J. Composition of flavonoids in Lithuanian honey and beebread. *Biologija* **2006**, *2*, 28–33.
17. Duran, X.A.; Mardones, I.Q.; Gutierrez, M.M.; Ulloa, D.M. Total polyphenols in bee bread (*Apis mellifera* L.) from hives the Araucania Region. *Idesia* **2014**, *32*, 107–111.

18. Ivanisova, E.; Kacaniova, M.; Francakova, H.; Petrova, J.; Hutkova, J.; Brovarskyi, V.; Velychko, S.; Adamchuk, L.; Schubertova, Z.; Musilova, J. Bee bread—Perspective source of bioactive compounds for future. *Potravinarstvo* **2015**, *9*, 592–598.

19. Cocan, O.; Marghitas, L.A.; Dezmirean, D. Total polyphenols, flavonoids and radical scavenging activity of beepollen and bee bread collected from Transylvania area. *Bull. Univ. Agric. Sci. Vet. Med. Cluj-Napoca. Anim. Sci. Biotechnol.* **2009**, *62*, 1–5.

20. Tavdidishvili, D.; Khutsidze, T.; Pkhakadze, M.; Vanidze, M.; Kalandia, A. Flavonoids in Georgian bee bread and bee pollen. *J. Chem. Chem. Eng.* **2014**, *8*, 676–681.

21. Urcan, A.; Al-Marghitas, L.; Dezmirean, D.S.; Bobis, O.; Bonta v Murusen, C.L.; Margaoan, R. Chemical Composition and Biological Activities of Beebread—Review. *Bull. UASVM Anim. Sci. Biotechnol.* **2017**, *74*, 250–255. [CrossRef]

22. Rason, N.; Ramli, N.; Safuan, S.; Noordin, L.; Ahmad, W.A.N. Histopathological Alteration in Organ Structures of Induced-Obese Rats Fed with High-Fat Diet. *Ann. Microsc.* **2016**, *15*, 38–48.

23. Reagen-Shaw, S.; Nihal, M.; Ahmad, N. Dose translation from animal to human studies revisited. *Life Sci. Forum* **2018**, *22*, 659–661. [CrossRef] [PubMed]

24. Bellinger, L.L.; Bernardis, L.L. Effect of dorsomedial hypothalamic nuclei knife cuts on ingestive behavior. *Am. J. Physiol. Integr. Comp. Physiol.* **1999**, *276*, R1772–R1779. [CrossRef] [PubMed]

25. Malafaia, A.B.; Nassif, P.A.N.; Ribas, C.A.P.M.; Ariede, B.L.; Sue, K.N.; Cruz, M.A. Obesity induction with high fat sucrose in rats. *ABCD Arquiros Bras. Cir. Dig.* **2013**, *26*, 17–21. [CrossRef] [PubMed]

26. Friedewald, W.; Levy, R.; Fredrickson, D. Estimation of the concentration of low-density lipoprotein cholesterol in plasma, without use of the preparative ultracentrifuge. *Clin. Chem.* **1972**, *18*, 499–502.

27. Suanarunsawat, T.; Ayutthaya, W.D.N.; Songsak, T.; Thirawarapan, S.; Poungshompoo, S. Antioxidant activity and lipid-lowering effect of essential oils extracted from *Ocimum sanctum* L. leaves in rats fed with a high cholesterol diet. *Clin. Biochem.* **2009**, *46*, 52–59. [CrossRef]

28. Andrés-manzano, M.J.; Andrés, V.; Dorado, B. *Methods in Mouse Atherosclerosis in Methods in Molecular Biology*; Springer Science + Business Media: New York, NY, USA, 2015; pp. 85–99.

29. Noeman, S.A.; Hamooda, H.E.; Baalash, A.A. Biochemical Study of Oxidative Stress Markers in the Liver, Kidney and Heart of High Fat Diet Induced Obesity in Rats. *Diabetol. Metab. Syndr.* **2011**, *3*, 17. [CrossRef]

30. Sacks, F.M. The crucial roles of apolipoproteins E and C-III in apoB lipoprotein metabolism in normolipidemia and hypertriglyceridemia. *Curr. Opin. Lipidol.* **2015**, *26*, 56–63. [CrossRef]

31. Bougoulia, M.; Triantos, A.; Koliakos, G. Effect of weight loss with or without orlistat treatment on adipocytokines, inflammation, and oxidative markers in obese women. *Hormones* **2006**, *5*, 259–269. [CrossRef]

32. Nwagha, U.; Ikekpeazu, E.J.; Ejezie, F.E.; Neboh, E.E.; Maduka, I.C. Atherogenic index of plasma as useful predictor of cardiovascular risk among postmenopausal women in Enugu, Nigeria. *Afr. Health Sci.* **2010**, *10*, 248–252.

33. Lee, H.Y.; Oh, M.R.; Jung, E.S.; Lee, Y.S.; Kim, D.S.; Kang, S.S.; Chae, H.J.; Chae, S.W. Mulberry and its main components protect against oxidized low-density lipoprotein-induced endothelial nitric oxide synthase uncoupling. *J. Funct. Foods* **2017**, *29*, 295–302. [CrossRef]

34. Sunil, V.; Shree, N.; Venkataranganna, M.V.; Bhonde, R.R.; Majumdar, M. The anti-diabetic and anti-obesity effect of Memecylon umbellatum extract in high fat diet induced obese mice. *Biomed. Pharmacother.* **2017**, *89*, 880–886. [CrossRef]

35. Birben, E.; Sahiner, U.M.; Sackesen, C.; Erzurum, S.; Kalayci, O. Oxidative Stress and Antioxidant Defense. *World Allergy Organ. J.* **2012**, *5*, 1–9. [CrossRef] [PubMed]

36. Horbury, M.D.; Baker, L.A.; Quan, W.D.; Greenough, S.E.; Stavros, V.G. Photodynamics of potent antioxidants: Ferulic and caffeic acids. *Phys. Chem. Chem. Phys.* **2016**, *26*, 17691–17697. [CrossRef] [PubMed]

37. Barene, I.; Daberte, I.; Siksna, S. Investigation of bee bread and development of its dosage forms. *Proteins* **2015**, *24*, 20–30. [CrossRef]

38. Othman, Z.A.; Wan Ghazali, W.S.; Nordin, L.; Omar, N.; Mohamed, M. Nutritional, Phytochemical and Antioxidant Analysis of Bee Bread from Different Regions of Malaysia. *Indian J. Pharm. Sci.* **2019**, *81*, 955–960. [CrossRef]

39. Galaly, S.R.; Hozayen, W.G.; Amin, K.A.; Ramadan, S.M. Effects of Orlistat and herbal mixture extract on brain, testes functions and oxidative stress biomarkers in a rat model of high fat diet. *Beni-Suef Univ. J. Basic Appl. Sci.* **2014**, *3*, 93–105. [CrossRef]

40. Ueshima, K.; Akihisa-umeno, H.; Nagayoshi, A.; Takakura, S.; Matsuo, M.; Mutoh, S. A gastrointestinal lipase inhibitor reduces progression of atherosclerosis in mice fed a western-type diet. *Eur. J. Pharmacol.* **2004**, *501*, 137–142. [CrossRef]

41. Bumrungpert, A.; Pingeesakikul, T.; Tirawanchai, N.; Tuntipopipat, S.; Lilitchan, S.; Komindr, S. Effects of Ferulic Acid Supplementation on Lipid Profiles, Oxidative Stress and Inflammatory Status in Hypercholesterolemic Subjects. *FASEB J.* **2012**, *26*, 263–267.

42. Prince, S.M.P.; Senthil Kumaran, K. Preventive effects of caffeic acid on lipids, lipoproteins and glycoproteins in isoproterenol induced myocardial infarcted rats. *Food Res. Int.* **2012**, *45*, 155–160. [CrossRef]

43. Tsoupras, A.; Lordan, R.; Zabetakis, I. Inflammation, not cholesterol, is a cause of chronic disease. *Nutrients* **2018**, *10*, 604. [CrossRef] [PubMed]

44. Witztum, J.L.; Steinberg, D. Role of oxidized low density lipoprotein in atherogenesis. *J. Clin. Investig.* **1991**, *88*, 1785–1792. [CrossRef] [PubMed]

45. Kong, L.; Luo, C.; Li, X.; Zhou, Y.; He, H. The anti-inflammatory effect of kaempferol on early atherosclerosis in high cholesterol fed rabbits. *Lipids Health Dis.* **2013**, *12*, 1–12. [CrossRef] [PubMed]

46. Chirala, S.S.; Chang, H.; Matzuk, M.; Abu-Elheiga, L.; Mao, J.; Mahon, K.; Finegold, M.; Wakil, S.J. Fatty acid synthesis is essential in embryonic development: Fatty acid synthase null mutants and most of the heterozygotes die in utero. *Proc. Natl. Acad. Sci. USA* **2003**, *100*, 6358–6363. [CrossRef]

Article

Blueberry Juice Antioxidants Protect Osteogenic Activity against Oxidative Stress and Improve Long-Term Activation of the Mineralization Process in Human Osteoblast-Like SaOS-2 Cells: Involvement of SIRT1

Vladana Domazetovic [1,*], **Gemma Marcucci** [1], **Irene Falsetti** [1], **Anna Rita Bilia** [2], **Maria Teresa Vincenzini** [1,*], **Maria Luisa Brandi** [1] and **Teresa Iantomasi** [1]

[1] Department of Biomedical Experimental and Clinical Sciences "Mario Serio", University of Florence, Viale Morgagni 50, 50134 Florence, Italy; gemma.marcucci@unifi.it (G.M.); irene.falsetti@stud.unifi.it (I.F.); marialuisa.brandi@unifi.it (M.L.B.); tiantomasi@unifi.it (T.I.)

[2] Department of Chemistry "Ugo Schiff" University of Florence, Via U. Schiff, 6, 50019 Sesto Fiorentino, Italy; annarita.bilia@unifi.it

* Correspondence: vladana.domazetovic@unifi.it (V.D.); vincenzini@unifi.it (M.T.V.); Tel.: +39-347-394-2628 (V.D.); 39-55-275-1200 (M.T.V.)

Received: 17 December 2019; Accepted: 29 January 2020; Published: 1 February 2020

Abstract: Diets rich in fruits and vegetables with many antioxidants can be very important in the prevention and treatment of osteoporosis. Studies show that oxidative stress, often due to lack of antioxidants, is involved in alteration of bone remodeling and reduction in bone density. This study demonstrates in human osteoblast-like SaOS-2 cells that blueberry juice (BJ), containing 7.5 or 15 $\mu g \cdot mL^{-1}$ total soluble polyphenols (TSP), is able to prevent the inhibition of osteogenic differentiation and the mineralization process due to oxidative stress induced by glutathione depletion. This situation mimics a metabolic condition of oxidative stress that may occur during estrogen deficiency. The effect of BJ phytochemicals occurs through redox- and non-redox-regulated mechanisms. BJ protects from oxidative damage factors related to bone remodeling and bone formation, such as alkaline phosphatase and Runt-related transcription factor 2. It upregulates these factors by activation of sirtuin type 1 deacetylase expression, a possible molecular target for anti-osteoporotic drugs. Quantitative analysis of TSP in BJ shows high levels of anthocyanins with high antioxidant capacity and bioavailability. These novel data may be important to elucidate the molecular and cellular beneficial effects of blueberry polyphenols on bone regeneration, and they suggest their use as a dietary supplement for osteoporosis prevention and therapies.

Keywords: blueberry juice (BJ); total soluble polyphenols (TSP); osteoporosis; dietary antioxidants; oxidative stress; osteoblast osteogenic differentiation; alkaline phosphatase (ALP); Runt-related transcription factor 2 (RUNX-2); sirtuin type 1 deacetylase (SIRT1)

1. Introduction

Recent studies show that changes in the oxidative state and the regulation of redox homeostasis affect bone turnover and remodeling [1–3]. Excessive production of reactive oxygen species (ROS), not counterbalanced by endogenous antioxidant defense systems, induces oxidative stress with consequent abnormal osteocyte apoptosis, which activates the osteoclasts and inhibits osteoblast osteogenic activity [1,4–6]. This is related to estrogen deficiency, aging, or bone inflammatory processes in which oxidative stress induces low bone mineral density and loss of bone mass [3,7–9]. A few recent clinical studies showed that an imbalance at a cellular level between ROS and antioxidants seems to be involved in the pathophysiology of bone-related diseases [1,10–12]. Oxidative stress and a decreased reduced glutathione/oxidized glutathione (GSH/GSSG) ratio are associated with the inhibition of osteoblast differentiation and the mineralization process and alter the levels of specific osteogenic markers [13]; furthermore, the ROS increase activates osteoclast differentiation [10,14]. These events are often associated with bone metabolic diseases such as osteoporosis, the most common bone disease, in which oxidative stress is considered a significant risk factor for its development [7–9]. Increased ROS production is responsible for diverting bone precursor cell differentiation toward the formation of other cell types rather than bone tissue cells [15,16]. On the contrary, antioxidants counteract these negative effects and favor the activity of osteoblasts, the viability of bone stem cells, and the maintenance of a normal bone remodeling process [1,3,6,11,12,16].

Literature data obtained in animals or cell lines showed the antioxidant activity of various natural substances [1]. In particular, diets rich in vegetables and/or fruits with high content of active antioxidants, such as polyphenols including flavonols, isoflavones, and phytosterols/phytoestrogens, can have an important role in prevention and/or management of osteoporosis and bone inflammatory diseases related to oxidative stress [17–21]. Indeed, plasma antioxidant content was found diminished in osteoporotic women [11,22]. These antioxidant compounds scavenge ROS [1,6,16,23,24] and reduce oxidative stress in many diseases including bone diseases and, in particular, osteoporosis [17,22,24–27]. Many literature data suggest a positive relationship between antioxidant intake and prevention of bone loss often associated with increased bone fractures [18,20,24,27]. For this, osteoporosis is considered a highly debilitating and socially relevant pathology; in fact, among the elderly, the pathological consequences of osteoporosis are among the main causes of mortality [28,29]. Recently, it was shown that diets containing blueberry (BB) prevent osteoporosis in ovariectomized rats [19,26,30]; indeed, BB and, in particular, *Vaccinuim myrtillus* (VM) have a wide variety and high concentrations of well-characterized polyphenols such as anthocyanins, coumarins, flavonols, flavanols, and their phenolic derivatives [31,32], with beneficial properties in bone anabolism [17–21]. Moreover, recent studies suggest VM as a "functional food" and, as such, of benefit for dietary supplementation [31,32]; today, VM, together with *Vaccinium corymbosum*, is among the main species of BB used in the food industry. Recently, we demonstrated that blueberry juice (BJ), mainly obtained from VM, exhibits osteogenic action, through its antioxidant and antiosteoclastogenic effect, in murine osteocytes, MLO-Y4. Moreover, it shows a protective effect in bone marrow mesenchymal stromal cells (MSCs), fundamental for cell therapy in bone diseases, by preventing oxidative stress-induced toxicity [33].

The aim of this study was to evaluate the effect of BJ containing certain quantities of soluble polyphenols on the factors related to differentiation and the mineralization process of osteoblasts in the presence or absence of oxidative stress. In fact, the role of these dietary polyphenols on osteogenic activity of osteoblasts and on redox-regulated molecular processes involved in bone formation and regeneration is still little known. In particular, no data are reported on the molecular mechanisms involved in the protective action of BJ phytochemicals against oxidative stress-induced damage on osteogenic activity of osteoblasts. Moreover, it is interesting to assess effects of complex mixture of phytochemicals on osteoblast activity, considering that individuals consume fruit and vegetables rich in a variety of polyphenols. Indeed, some studies show that various polyphenols and their derivatives are bioavailable from BB and they are also absorbed in humans in intact form [34–36]. Finally, this study was performed to elucidate, at a cellular and molecular level, the beneficial effects of BJ polyphenols on bone regeneration, before suggesting their use as a dietary and pharmacological supplement for the prevention and/or management of osteoporosis and other bone diseases related to oxidative stress.

This study was performed in human osteoblast-like cell line SaOS-2 in which oxidative stress was induced by an intracellular depletion of GSH by butionine sulfoximine (BSO), a specific inhibitor of γ-glutamylcysteine synthetase that regulates GSH synthesis [13], before starting osteogenic differentiation and during the early phases of the mineralization process. We used SaOS-2 cells given that, in these cells, BSO-induced oxidative stress inhibits osteogenic factors involved in the final stage of osteoblast activity and related to differentiation and the mineralization process [13]. These cells reflect a normal phenotype of osteoblasts [37,38] and, like them, display the entire differentiation sequence and are able to form an extracellular mineralized matrix [39]. All these features contribute to the SaOS-2 cell line being considered as a cellular model to study osteoblast functions and, in particular, processes associated to late osteoblastic differentiation stage in human cells, such as the formation of bone nodules by differentiated osteoblasts [37,40,41].

2. Materials and Methods

2.1. Reagents

All common reagents were purchased from Sigma-Aldrich (Saint Louis, MO, USA), Extrasynthèse (Genay, France), GE Healthcare (Little Chalfont, Great Britain), Santa Cruz Biotechnologies (Santa Cruz, CA, USA), Millipore (Bedford, MA, USA), Abcam (Cambridge, UK), Euroclone (Milan, Italy), Thermo Scientific (Waltham, MA, USA), Bioassay Systems (Hayward, CA, USA), Promega (Madison, WI, USA), and Invitrogen (Carlsbad, CA, USA), unless differently specified in the text.

The following reagents were purchased from Sigma-Aldrich: Ham's F12 Coon's modification medium, L-glutamine, dimethyl sulfoxide (DMSO), BSO, trypsin, bovine serum albumin, Tris/HCl, Triton X100, NaCl, NaF, ethylene bis(oxyethylenenitrilo)tetraacetic acid (EGTA), β-glycerophosphate, human sirtuin type 1 (SIRT1) small interfering RNA (siRNA), Universal Negative Control #1, Alizarin Red S, phenolic reference standards ellagic acid (assay HPLC ≥ 95%) for hydroxybenzoic acids, (+)-catechin hydrate (assay HPLC ≥ 96.0%) for flavan-3-ols, acetonitrile HPLC grade (assay 99.9%), formic acid for (HPLC assay 98–100%), ascorbic acid, dexamethasone, paraformaldehyde, cetylpyridinium chloride, Folin–Ciocalteu reagent, NaCl/Pi.

The following reagents were purchased from Extrasynthèse: anthocyanin reference standard cyanidin 3-glucoside chloride (assay HPLC ≥ 96%), flavonol reference standard quercetin 3-O-glucoside (assay HPLC ≥ 99%), hydroxycinnamic acid reference standard 3-O-caffeoyl quinic acid (chlorogenic acid, assay HPLC ≥ 99%).

The following reagents were purchased from GE Healthcare: penicillin/streptomycin 100× solution, phosphate-buffered saline (PBS), polyvinylidene fluoride (PVDF) membrane, enhanced chemiluminescence (ECL) Western Blotting Detection Reagent kit.

The following reagents were purchased from Santa Cruz Biotechnologies: EX527, Protein A/G PLUS-Agarose, anti-Runt-related transcription factor 2 (RUNX-2), anti-phospho-tyrosine, anti-histone H3.

The following reagents were purchased from Milipore: Milli-Q water, Cytobuster Protein Extraction Reagent.

The following reagents were purchased from Abcam: SIRT1 ELISA kit, anti-histone H3.

The following reagent was purchased from Euroclone: fetal bovine serum South American origin.

The following reagent was purchased from Thermo Scientific: Pierce bicinchoninic acid (BCA) protein assay kit.

The following reagent was purchased from Bioassay Systems: QuantiFluo Alkaline Phosphatase Assay Kit.

The following reagent was purchased from Promega: CellTiter-Glo Luminescent Cell Viability Assay.

The following reagents were purchased from Invitrogen: lipofectamine RNAiMAX™, 2′,7′-dichlorodihydrofluorescein diacetate.

2.2. Preparation of Blueberry Juice and Determination of Total Soluble Polyphenols

BBs, harvested in August 2018/2019 in Tuscany Apennines and supplied by IL BAGGIOLO S.R.L. (Abetone, Pt, Italy) and DANTI GIAMPIERO S.R.L. (Cutigliano, Pt, Italy), were frozen freshly picked in aliquots of 100 g each and homogenized in a refrigerated Waring Blender to prepare BJ. Insoluble particles were removed by filtration under vacuum and centrifuged at 20,000× *g* for 10 min. Aliquots of BJ were stored at −20 °C until use. The total soluble polyphenol (TSP) fraction of BJ was quantified with Folin–Ciocalteu reagent using gallic acid as the standard as described in our previous work [33] and via the HPLC method reported below. TSP concentration in BJ obtained from 100 g of BB fresh weight was expressed as mg/100 mL ± SD and the values measured by Folin–Ciocalteu assay or HPLC method were 169.5 ± 19.4 and 158.8 ± 12.3, respectively.

2.3. HPLC-PDA-MS Analysis of Phenolic Compounds

The identification of phenolic compounds was performed using a Waters Alliance 2695 coupled online with a Waters 2996 photodiode array detector, and with a Quattro micro mass spectrometry detector with an electrospray interface. Separations were performed on a C18 reversed-phase Gemini Phenomenex (150 × 3 mm, 5 μm particle size) with a mobile phase flow rate of 0.4 mL·min^{-1}. The mobile phase consisted of (A) H_2O containing 5% formic acid and (B) MeCN. A gradient elution program was applied as follows: 0–1.0 min held on 8% B, 1.0–16.0 min linear gradient to 15% B, 16.0–28.0 min linear gradient 50% B, 28.0–36.0 min linear gradient to 95% B, then in 1 min to the initial (starting) condition, and held 8 min for re-equilibration. The total run time was 45 min. The sample was diluted 1:10 (*v/v*) with 8% B and 92% A, with an injection volume of 10 μL. Determination of phenolic compounds was performed using two detectors online: a photodiode array UV detector, followed by a single quadrupole mass spectrometry detector. The photodiode array scanned the samples at λ_{max} 270, 320, 360, and 520 nm. The mass spectrometer detector was optimized to the following conditions: capillary voltage 3.20 kV, source block temperature 125 °C, and desolvation temperature 350 °C, operating in electrospray positive mode, detection range 100–1000 Da with total ion count extracting acquisition. The cone voltage was 32 V, the extractor lens was 3 V, and the cone and desolvation gas flows were 20 and 320 L·h^{-1}, respectively. Phenolic compound identification in the sample was carried out by comparing UV absorption spectra and mass spectra of each compound with those reported in the literature [42]. The quantification of polyphenols was calculated using the method of an external standard. Each standard was freshly prepared up to 300 μg/mL concentration and injected three times to obtain its calibration curve. Quantification was obtained as total content of each polyphenol group. Quantification of total constituents of each class of flavonoids was carried out using single anthocyanin, flavonol, and flavan-3-ol standards, namely, cyanidin-3-glucoside, quercetin-3-glucoside, and (+)-catechin equivalents, respectively. The values were expressed as gallic acid equivalent.

2.4. Cell Cultures, Treatments, Osteogenic Differentiation, and Cellular Viability

Osteoblast-like SaOS-2 cells were cultured in Ham's F12 Coon's modification medium, supplemented with 10% fetal bovine serum, 2 mM L-glutamine, 72 mg/L penicillin, and 100 mg/mL streptomycin (growth medium, GM), and incubated at 37 °C in a 5% CO_2 humidified atmosphere with 20% oxygen. For the experiments of osteogenic differentiation, when SaOS-2 cells reached 70–80% confluence, GM was changed with osteogenic medium (OM) to induce osteogenic differentiation. OM was the growth medium supplemented with 10 nM dexamethasone, 0.2 mM ascorbic acid, and 10 mM β-glycerophosphate. Then, 40 μM BSO, or BJ containing 7.5 or 15 μg·mL^{-1} TSP, or BJ + BSO, or BJ + 10 μM EX527, or BJ + BSO + 10 μM EX527 were added or not to GM for 24 h (day 1) before exchanging it for OM, containing or not the before mentioned compounds, to stimulate the differentiation process. The OM was refreshed twice a week for the whole study period, BSO was added for only two days after the beginning of differentiation and BJ or EX527 were added to the OM at each change from the beginning of the differentiation process for the whole study period.

Cell viability was evaluated using the CellTiter-Glo Luminescent Cell Viability Assay, according to the manufacturer's instructions.

In some experiments, the cells were transiently transfected with 75 nM human SIRT1 siRNA corresponding to two DNA target sequences of human SIRT1 (5'-GUGUCAUGGUUCCUUUGCA[dT][dT]-3' accession number SASI_Hs01_00153666; 5'-

UGCAAAGGAACCAUGACAC[dT][dT]-3′, accession number SASI_Hs01_00153666 6_AS) or scrambled siRNA (Scr siRNA) (Universal Negative Control #1), using lipofectamine RNAiMAX^{TM}, according to the manufacturer's instructions. The ability of SIRT1 siRNA to silence SIRT1 expression levels of about 50% was checked in control cells transfected for 24 h in GM and for other 48 h in OM. Additionally, 0.008% DMSO was present in experiments with EX527 in all conditions.

2.5. Determination of Intracellular ROS

The cell-permeant probe, 2′,7′-dichlorodihydrofluorescein diacetate (H$_2$DCFDA), was added in the culture medium of SaOS-2 seeded in 12-well plates one hour before the end of the various treatments performed as written above. The probe after deacetylation by esterases is rapidly oxidized to a highly fluorescent compound in the presence of ROS. After PBS washing, adherent cells were lysed in radioimmunoprecipitation assay RIPA buffer (50 mM Tris/HCL pH 7.5, 1% Triton X-100, 150 mM NaCl, 100 mM NaF, 2 mM EGTA, phosphatase, and protease inhibitor cocktail), centrifuged at 20,000× g (ALC PK121R, Thermo Fisher Scientific, Waltham, MA, USA) for 10 min, and the intracellular levels of ROS were measured by florescence analysis at 510 nm. The normalization of the data was obtained by using total proteins, and the values were expressed as percentages with respect to the controls.

2.6. Alkaline Phosphatase Activity

SaOS-2 cells seeded in six-well plates during differentiation in the presence or not of the various treatments, as described above, were collected in Cytobuster Protein Extraction Reagent (Milipore, Burlington, MA, USA). After sonication twice on ice and centrifugation at 4 °C for 15 min at 1000× g, alkaline phosphatase (ALP) activity was measured in the supernatants using the QuantiFluo Alkaline Phosphatase Assay Kit following the manufacturer's instructions. The ALP activity was normalized to protein content for each well, and data were expressed as percentages relative to the control values.

2.7. Western Blot Analysis of RUNX and RUNX-2 Phosphorylation

Western blot analysis was performed in SaOS-2 cells six days after differentiation and treated or not (control) as described above. Whole-cell lysates and nuclear extracts were obtained as previously described in References [13,33], respectively. Equal amounts of nuclear proteins were then incubated with antibody against Runt-related transcription factor 2 (RUNX-2) for 1 h at 4 °C. Subsequently, the immune complexes were precipitated using Protein A/G PLUS-Agarose. The immunoprecipitates (200 μg) were mixed with Laemmli buffer for 5 min at 95 °C, subjected to SDS/PAGE, and electrotransferred to a PVDF membrane [13]. Phospho-RUNX-2 (p-RUNX-2), RUNX-2, histone H3, and β-actin were visualized using antibody anti-phospho-tyrosine proteins, anti-RUNX-2, anti-histone H3, or anti-β-actin, respectively. Antigen–antibody complexes were detected using chemiluminescence ECL Western Blotting Detection Reagent kit. Digital images of the bands were detected by Amersham Imager A600 (GE Healthcare, Chicago, IL, USA).

2.8. Alizarin Red S Assay

The deposition of calcium was measured 12 and 24 days after differentiation in cells treated as described above. Cells were fixed in 4% paraformaldehyde for 15 min after washing twice with NaCl/Pi for a few minutes; subsequently, they were washed another three times with deionized water. Calcium mineral deposits were stained by using 2% Alizarin Red S at pH 7.8 for 2 min and were destained using 10% cetylpyridinium chloride in deionized water for 60 min at 50 °C. The absorbance of Alizarin Red S extracts was measured at 560 nm. Calcium content was evaluated using a standard curve of hydroxyapatite (100 μg/mL in cetylpyridinium chloride solution) and expressed as mg hydroxyapatite (HA) per cm^2.

2.9. SIRT1 Expression Assay

SIRT1 levels were measured by using the Human SIRT1 ELISA kit in SaOS-2 cells, seeded in 12-well plates. Cell were solubilized in Cell Extraction Buffer and centrifuged at $18,000 \times g$ for 20 min at 4 °C according to manufacturer's instructions. Data, normalized on total protein content, were expressed as percentages of control levels.

2.10. Protein Assay

Protein concentrations were determined by the bicinchoninic acid solution protein reagent assay using bovine serum albumin as the standard.

2.11. Statistical Analysis

One-way ANOVA analysis with Bonferroni's multiple comparison test, using GraphPad Prism Software, or Student's *t*-test were used to determine the statistical significance. A *p*-value ≤ 0.05 was considered statistically significant.

3. Results

3.1. Polyphenolic Composition of BJ

Phenolic constituents from BJ were identified by HPLC-PDA-MS analysis as reported in Section 2. The chromatographic profile displayed a suitable separation of all the polyphenol constituents in the juice after just one run, and the data analysis is reported in Table 1.

Table 1. Identified polyphenols and total content of each class of constituents in blueberry juice.

Polyphenol Group	Identified Constituents	Total Polyphenols Expressed as Gallic Acid (mg ± SD/100 mL)
Anthocyanins	dephinidin 3-*O*-galactoside	
	delphinidin 3-*O*-glucoside	
	cyanidin 3-*O*-galactoside	
	delphinidin 3-*O*-arabinoside	
	cyanidin 3-*O*-glucoside	
	petunidin 3-*O*-galactoside	
	petunidin 3-*O*-glucoside	
	cyanidin 3-*O*-arabinoside	
	peonidin 3-*O*-galactoside	
	petunidin 3-*O*-arabinoside	
	malvidin 3-*O*-galactoside	
	peonidin 3-*O*-glucoside	
	malvidin 3-*O*-glucoside	
	malvidin 3-*O*-arabinoside	
Total anthocyanins		107.0 ± 9.3

Table 1. *Cont.*

Polyphenol Group	Identified Constituents	Total Polyphenols Expressed as Gallic Acid (mg ± SD/100 mL)
Flavonols	quercetin 3-*O*-arabinoside quercetin 3-*O*-galactoside quercetin 3-*O*-glucoside myricetin 3-*O*-glucoside myricetin 3-*O*-galactoside	
Total flavonols		2.9 ± 0.9
Flavan-3-ols	catechin epicatechin	
Total flavanols		5.8 ± 1.4
Hydroxybenzoic acids	ellagic acid	12.5 ± 2.4
Hydroxycinnamic acids	chlorogenic acid	30.6 ± 6.3

Fourteen anthocyanins were identified using UV wavelength detection at 520 nm and mass spectra in the positive ion mode, since these compounds are present as flavylium ions in the chromatographic conditions applied. Delphinidin, cyanidin, petunidin, peonidin, and malvidin were the representative aglycons, glycosylated at C-3 with the same sugars of anthocyanins, namely, glucose, galactose, and arabinose. Similarly, five flavanols were identified using UV wavelength detection at 360 nm and mass spectra in both the positive and the negative ion mode, as reported in Table 1. Aglycons were identified as quercetin and myricetin glycosylated at C-3. Two further flavonoid structures were identified, the flavan-3ols catechin and epicatechin, using the same strategy reported for the other flavonoids. Finally, ellagic acid and chlorogenic acid were unambiguously identified as simple polyphenols, by comparison of their retention times and UV and mass spectra with those of the authentic samples. Table 1 shows the total content of each group expressed as gallic acid. Anthocyanins, expressed as cyanidin-3-glucoside, represented the main constituents corresponding to about 0.63 mmol/100 mL of juice, whereas flavonol and catechin contents were about 0.017 and 0.034 mmol/100 mL, expressed as quercetin-3-glucoside and (+)-catechin equivalents, respectively. The amount of ellagic acid was ca. 0.073 mmol/100 mL juice, while that of chlorogenic acid was ca. 0.18 mmol/100 mL.

3.2. Effect of BJ on Cell Viability and in Preventing Oxidative Stress Induced by BSO Treatment in SaOS-2 Cells

Initially, we assessed cell viability during the pre-treatment (24 h in GM, day 1) before the induction of the differentiation and after two days of differentiation in the presence or not (control) of BSO and BJ (Table 2).

Table 2. Effect of butionine sulfoximine (BSO) and blueberry juice (BJ) on cell viability.

Days	1	2
Control	100 ± 8	100 ± 11
BSO	80 ± 10	83 ± 8
BJ	90 ± 8	85 ± 10
BSO + BJ	79 ± 9	80 ± 7

Viability was measured using the CellTiter-Glo Luminescent Cell Viability Assay in cells treated or not (control) with 40 μM BSO and/or BJ containing 15 μg·mL^{-1} of total soluble polyphenols. The data expressed as a percentage of the respective controls are means ± standard error of the mean (SEM) of four independent experiments.

In particular, BSO treatment was performed at the 40 μM concentration that induces oxidative stress due to significant decrease of GSH/GSSG ratio, an index of the intracellular oxidative status, as previously reported in SaOS-2 cells [13]. BJ containing two different concentrations of TSP (7.5 or 15 μg·mL^{-1}), which previously demonstrated antioxidant activity in starved osteocytes [33], was used. Table 2 shows that neither BSO nor the highest concentration of BJ, used alone or together with BSO, significantly altered cell viability as compared to control cells.

Figure 1 reports the BJ antioxidant effect on BSO-treated cells. In fact, BSO pre-treatment (24 h in GM, day 1) was able to significantly increase ROS levels as compared with the control values measured in untreated cells (Figure 1).

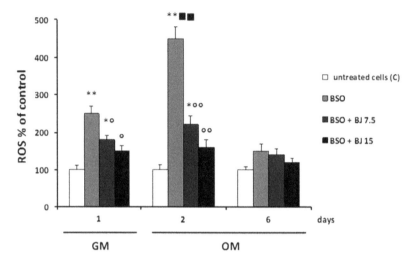

Figure 1. BJ effect on intracellular reactive oxygen species (ROS) production in BSO-treated SaOS-2 cells. Intracellular ROS, detected by measuring the fluorescence intensity of the probe 2′,7′-dichlorodihydrofluorescein diacetate (H$_2$DCFDA), were measured in SaOS-2 cells treated or untreated (C; control) with BSO or BSO + BJ containing 7.5 or 15 μg·mL^{-1} total soluble polyphenols (TSP) for one day in growth medium (GM) and subsequently treated or untreated (C; control) for two or six days in osteogenic medium (OM), as reported in Section 2. ROS data, normalized on total protein content, are expressed as a percentage of the C values, and they are the means ± SEM of four experiments repeated in triplicate; * $p \leq 0.05$, ** $p \leq 0.001$ compared to C cells; $^{\circ}$ $p \leq 0.05$, $^{\circ\circ}$ $p \leq 0.001$ compared to BSO-treated cells; ■■ $p \leq 0.001$ compared to BSO-treated cells for one day in GM.

ROS levels increased further when BSO was subsequently added for other two days in OM as compared with control (Figure 1); from this time on (two days), BSO was no longer added, and ROS content returned to the control levels after six days after the induction of differentiation (Figure 1). In order to prevent the effect of BSO, the cells were treated simultaneously with BSO and BJ containing 7.5 or 15 μg·mL^{-1} TSP. Figure 1 reports that BJ at both concentrations significantly prevented ROS increase in SaOS-2 cells after just 24 h in GM, and this effect was even more marked (by about 50–70%) after two days after the induction of differentiation. The highest concentration was able to decrease ROS levels to control values. No change in the intracellular oxidative state was observed after six days after the induction of differentiation in all conditions used (Figure 1). Similarly, no change in ROS levels was observed, when only BJ at both TSP concentrations was added before and during the differentiation at all studied times (data not shown), indicating that BJ per se does not have any effect on a normal cellular redox state.

3.3. BJ Effect on the Markers of Differentiation and Osteogenic Process in SaOS-2 Cells in the Presence or Not of BSO-Induced Oxidative Stress

In SaOS-2 cells treated or not with BSO, BJ, or BSO + BJ, as reported in Section 2, the levels of alkaline phosphatase (ALP, EC 3.1.3.1), an early biochemical marker of osteoblast differentiation and osteogenic activity, were measured [13]. This enzyme is considered an osteoblast phenotype marker in SaOS-2 cells and, therefore, an osteoblast differentiation indicator [37,43]. Figure 2 shows the time course of ALP activity in SaOS-2 cells as a percentage of the activity values measured in cells cultured in GM (controls).

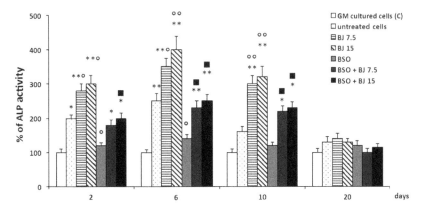

Figure 2. BJ effect on alkaline phosphatase (ALP) activity during differentiation of BSO-treated and untreated SaOS-2 cells. ALP activity, detected by the QuantiFluo Alkaline Phosphatase Assay Kit, was measured in SaOS-2 cells treated or untreated with BJ, containing 7.5 or 15 µg·mL^{-1} total soluble polyphenols (TSP), or BSO or BSO + BJ for one day in growth medium (GM). Subsequently, untreated cells were cultured in GM (C; control) for two, six, 10, or 20 days and, for the same times, treated and untreated cells were cultured in osteogenic medium (OM), as reported in Section 2. ALP activity is expressed as a percentage of the respective C values, and these are the means ± SEM of four experiments performed in triplicate; * $p \leq 0.05$, ** $p \leq 0.001$ compared to C cells; $^{\circ}$ $p \leq 0.05$, $^{\circ\circ}$ $p \leq 0.001$ compared to untreated cells; ■ $p \leq 0.05$ compared to BSO-treated cells.

ALP activity significantly increased in the early phase of differentiation process (2–6 days) in untreated cells cultured in OM as compared to the respective controls. Ten days after the induction of the differentiation, the percentage of ALP increase was no longer significantly different from the control (Figure 2). The ALP trend, in cells treated with BJ containing both concentrations of TSP, showed that its activity was higher during the initial phase of differentiation with respect to the untreated cells, and it remained high even after 10 days, unlike what happened in the untreated cells (Figure 2). It is worthy to note that the BJ effect occurred in cells with normal redox state. On the contrary, BSO significantly inhibited the upregulation of ALP activity levels (Figure 2). Finally, in BSO + BJ-treated cells, BJ was able to eliminate the effect of BSO and to maintain ALP levels at the values measured in untreated cells (Figure 2).

Subsequently, under the same experimental conditions, the expression and activation of RUNX-2 by tyrosine phosphorylation were studied six days after differentiation in SaOS-2 cell lysates and in nuclear extracts by Western blot analysis (Figure 3A–C).

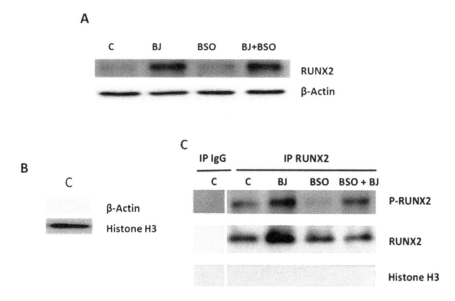

Figure 3. BJ effect on Runt-related transcription factor 2 (RUNX-2) expression and activation in BSO-treated and untreated SaOS-2 cells. RUNX-2 expression (**A**), nuclear fraction purification (**B**), and RUNX-2 activation (**C**) were detected in SaOS-2 cells treated or not with BJ at 15 µg·mL^{-1} total soluble polyphenols (TSP) or BSO or BSO + BJ for one day in growth medium (GM) and, subsequently, for six days in osteogenic medium (OM), in the presence or not of various treatments, as reported in Section 2. RUNX-2 expression was detected by Western blot analysis in whole cellular lysate (**A**), RUNX-2 activation was detected by phosphorylation in immunoprecipitates of nuclear extracts using the anti-RUNX-2 antibody (**C**), and β-actin and histone H3 were detected in nuclear extract (**B**). RUNX-2, p-RUNX-2, β-actin, and histone H3 were revealed with anti-RUNX-2, anti-p-tyrosine proteins, anti-β-actin, or anti-histone H3, respectively. The blots are representative of three experiments.

RUNX-2 is an important transcription factor for the activation of osteoblast differentiation and for regulation of bone remodeling, and it is involved in many bone diseases [44,45]. Figure 3A shows that BJ containing 15 µg·mL^{-1} TSP was able to upregulate RUNX-2 levels, whereas no change was detected in cells treated with BSO only. RUNX-2 activation was evaluated by immunoprecipitation of equal amounts of nuclear proteins using anti-RUNX-2 antibody. The purification of the nuclear fraction was observed in control cells by Western blot, which revealed the presence of the histone H3 protein and not β-actin (Figure 3B). Figure 3C shows the absence of RUNX-2 or P-RUNX-2 or histone H3 bands in Western blot analysis of immunoprecipitates performed with IgG (negative control) in control cells; unlike RUNX-2 or P-RUNX-2 bands, no Histone H3 bands were detected after immunoprecipitation with anti-RUNX-2 (Figure 3). These data demonstrate the absence of non-specific bands under these experimental conditions. Figure 3C also shows that BJ containing 15 µg·mL^{-1} TSP increased RUNX-2 nuclear levels and its phosphorylation as compared to control. On the other hand, decreases in RUNX-2 phosphorylation and no change in its nuclear levels were observed in cells treated with BSO, whereas RUNX-2 phosphorylation appeared to be restored by simultaneous treatment with BJ. Overall, these findings indicate that BJ was able to increase RUNX-2 and ALP activation, in normal redox state conditions, as well as prevent the inhibition of these factors in BSO-induced oxidative stress.

3.4. BJ Effect on the Mineralization Process in SaOS-2 Cells in the Presence or Not of BSO-Induced Oxidative Stress

The mineralization process was studied in cells treated or not (control) with BJ containing 15 µg·mL^{-1} TSP or with BSO or BJ + BSO. Calcium deposition was measured 12 and 24 days after the induction of differentiation by staining with Alizarin Red S (Figure 4A).

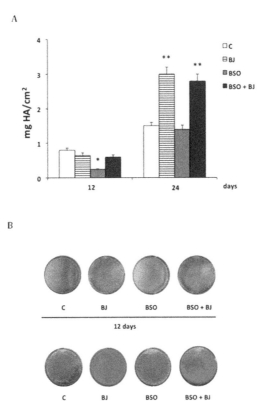

Figure 4. BJ effect on the mineralization process during differentiation of BSO-treated SaOS-2 cells. Calcium content, measured by Alizarin Red S assay, was detected in SaOS-2 cells treated or untreated with BJ, containing 15 µg·mL^{-1} total soluble polyphenols (TSP), or BSO or BSO + BJ for one day in growth medium (GM) and, subsequently, treated or untreated (C; control) for 12 or 24 days in osteogenic medium (OM), as reported in Section 2. Calcium content is expressed as mg hydroxyapatite (HA) per cm^2 and values are means ± SEM of three independent experiments (**A**); * $p \leq 0.05$, ** $p \leq 0.001$ compared to the respective C cells. Representative images of calcium content in 12-well plates (**B**).

Figure 4A,B show that BSO-induced oxidative stress in the initial phase of differentiation remarkably decreased the osteogenic activity after 12 days (by about 70%) as compared to control. This effect was prevented in BJ + BSO-treated cells, but no change in calcium deposition was observed in BJ-treated cells in this early phase as compared to control (Figure 4A,B). On the other hand, after 24 days, long-term activation of the mineralization process (of about 100%) was found in BJ- and BSO + BJ-treated cells, and no change was observed in BSO-treated cells as compared to control (Figure 4A,B). These data show that BJ phytochemicals prevent the anti-osteogenic effect of BSO-induced oxidative stress, and they are able to activate the mineralization process, even if this occurs later in time.

3.5. Involvement of SIRT1 on BJ-Induced Activation of Osteogenic Differentiation and Mineralization Process in SaOS-2 Cells

We subsequently evaluated the involvement of sirtuin type 1 (SIRT1), a class III histone deacetylase, in BJ-induced activation of osteogenic factors and the mineralization process, which occurred in the presence of a normal intracellular redox state. A possible role of SIRT1 with regard to the antioxidant activity of BJ was also studied. Indeed, SIRT1 is related to the regulation of osteogenic differentiation of tendon and mesenchymal stem cells [46,47], and it is a positive regulator of RUNX-2 [47,48]. Moreover, this enzyme is activated in mammals by dietary blueberry [49,50] and in osteocytes by BJ [33]. Initially, the BJ effect on SIRT1 levels in SaOS-2 cells in the presence or not of BSO-induced oxidative stress was studied. Figure 5A shows that BJ significantly increased SIRT1 expression as compared to control six days after differentiation, and a similar increase was also observed in BSO + BJ-treated cells, whereas no change in SIRT1 levels was detected in BSO-treated cells.

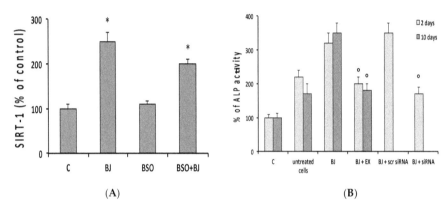

(A) (B)

Figure 5. BJ effect on sirtuin type 1 (SIRT1) expression and SIRT1 inhibition role in BJ-induced ALP activation during differentiation of SaOS-2 cells. SIRT-1 expression (**A**) and ALP activity (**B**) were detected in SaOS-2 cells treated or not with BJ at 15 μg·mL^{-1} total soluble polyphenols (TSP) or BSO, BSO + BJ, or BJ + EX527, for one day in growth medium (GM) and, subsequently, in osteogenic medium (OM), in the presence or not of various treatments, as reported in Section 2. SIRT1 expression was detected after six days in OM by ELISA kit according to the manufacturer's instructions, and levels are expressed as a percentage of the C values (A). ALP activity was also detected after two and 10 days in GM (control, C) and OM, as well as in transfected SIRT1 small interfering RNA (siRNA) or Scr RNA cells after two days in OM. SIRT1 expression and ALP activity values are expressed as a percentage of the respective C values, and they are the means ± SEM of three independent experiments; * $p \leq 0.05$ compared to C cells; $^{\circ}$ $p \leq 0.05$ compared to BJ-treated cells.

Subsequently, the role of SIRT1 in BJ activation of osteoblast differentiation and mineralization was determined. To evaluate this, SIRT1 expression and activity were reduced using cells transfected with a specific SIRT1 siRNA or treated with EX527, a specific inhibitor of SIRT1, as reported in Section 2. Figure 5B reports that the downregulation of both SIRT1 and EX527, at the concentration able to inhibit SIRT1 activity [33], removed the activating effect of BJ on ALP activity two days after differentiation, and this effect was also observed at 10 days in EX527-treated cells.

SIRT1 involvement in BJ-induced RUNX-2 expression and activation was also studied in whole cellular lysates and in nuclear immunoprecipitates (Figure 6A,B).

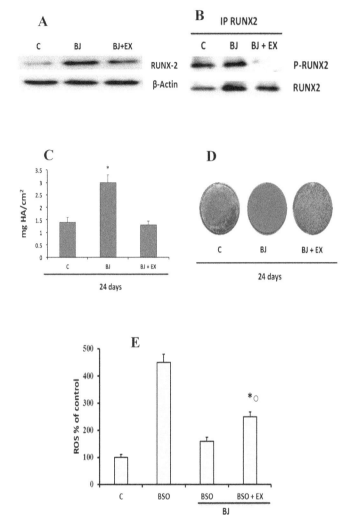

Figure 6. Effect of SIRT1 inhibition on BJ activation of RUNX-2 and the mineralization process, as well as on BJ antioxidant action during differentiation of SaOS-2 cells. RUNX-2 expression (**A**), RUNX-2 activation (**B**), calcium content (**C,D**), and ROS levels (**E**) were detected in SaOS-2 cells treated or not with BJ at 15 μg·mL^{-1} total soluble polyphenols (TSP) or BSO, BSO + BJ, BJ + EX527, or BJ + BSO + EX527, for one day in growth medium (GM) and, subsequently, in osteogenic medium (OM), in the presence or not of various treatments, as reported in Section 2. RUNX-2 expression was detected after six days in OM by Western blot analysis of whole cellular lysates (**A**), and RUNX-2 activation was detected by phosphorylation in immunoprecipitates of nuclear extracts using the anti-RUNX-2 antibody (**B**). RUNX-2, p-RUNX-2, and β-actin were revealed with anti-RUNX-2, anti-p-tyrosine proteins, and anti-β-actin, respectively. The blots are representative of three experiments. Calcium content was measured after 24 days in OM, and it is expressed as mg hydroxyapatite per cm^2 (**C**). Representative images of calcium content in 12-well plates (**D**). ROS data are expressed as a percentage of the C values (**E**). The values are means ± SEM of three independent experiments; * $p \leq 0.05$ compared to the respective C cells; $^{\bigcirc}$ $p \leq 0.05$ compared to BSO + BJ-treated cells.

EX527 treatment partially prevented RUNX-2 expression (Figure 6A), as well as RUNX-2 activation (Figure 6B) induced by BJ six days after differentiation. The possible involvement of SIRT1 in long-term activation of the mineralization process induced by BJ is shown in Figure 6C,D. Finally, we evaluated the effect of SIRT1 on ROS levels in cells treated with BSO + BJ, considering that the antioxidant action of BJ could also be mediated by SIRT1. Figure 6E shows that BJ antioxidant action may only partially be mediated by SIRT1.

4. Discussion

This study reports new data on the role of BJ phytochemicals and polyphenolic antioxidants in the activation of osteogenic factors and in the induction of the mineralization process in the presence or not of oxidative stress induced by GSH depletion. In particular, the polyphenolic content of the juice was characterized, and it was shown that BJ performs an important antioxidant action and protects from damage induced by oxidative stress, as well as upregulates factors such as ALP and RUNX-2, related to differentiation and the mineralization process, in normal intracellular redox state conditions. The involvement of SIRT1 in these events was also demonstrated.

In this study, the effect of BJ containing certain amounts of TSP was evaluated in GSH-depleted SaOS-2 cells, an in vitro condition that mimics what happens in vivo in the bone environment in the presence of oxidative stress due to microdamage and/or estrogen deficiency, [4,5,8,22,51]. Indeed, GSH is involved in osteoblast and osteoclast differentiation and, together with other thiol antioxidants, it may play a crucial role in estrogen deficiency-associated bone loss [1,22,51,52]. In fact, some data show that bone loss due to a lack of estrogen is related to the lowered thiol antioxidants in osteoclasts, and this activates osteoclastogenic signals which induce ROS-enhanced expression of cytokines promoting osteoclastic bone resorption [51].

We used BJ given that BBs are commercialized in different ways, mainly as fresh or frozen products, also in addition to juices or dry extracts. However, the drying process and treatment with solvents (i.e., for the production of dry extracts) might partially destroy anthocyanins and their antioxidant effects [53], and the anthocyanins seem to be more stable over time in a juice with acidic pH than in a dry extract [53]. The results obtained from the qualitative and quantitative analysis of TSP in BJ show that the main polyphenolic component was represented by anthocyanins belonging to the flavonoid family, which were present mainly as glucosides, galactosides, and arabinosides; these data are similar to those found in the literature [42,54]. Moreover, TSP content in BJ obtained by HPLC-PDA was very similar to the value obtained with the Folin–Ciocalteu method, indicating that quantification via this spectrometric method is feasible and realistic.

Some studies demonstrated that many BB polyphenols are bioavailable; in fact, after various processes of ingestion, they were found in the plasma [36,54,55]. It was also demonstrated that anthocyanins or cyanidins, after oral administration, can be absorbed in intact form as glycosides and/or aglycones [34,35,55]. Moreover, even if BB polyphenols undergo complex metabolic modifications, their derivatives have the same functional characteristics [34,36]. The flavonoids and anthocyanins present in BB have strong antioxidant capacity [24,31,32,54], and these, along with the other polyphenol compounds and their derivatives, favor the formation of bone mass [18–20,30,54].

The data of this study demonstrate that TSPs, together with other phytochemicals contained in BJ, are able to prevent BSO-induced oxidative stress, and the results partly correlate with what was previously obtained with thiol antioxidants, such as GSH and *N*-acetyl cysteine, in SaOS-2 cells under similar conditions of oxidative stress [13]. The BJ antioxidant effect in SaOS-2 cells was obtained with the same concentrations of TSP used in osteocytes in which oxidative stress was induced by starvation [33], and ROS reduction was achieved by BJ treatment very quickly both in osteocytes and in SaOS-2 cells [13,33], similarly to thiol antioxidants [6]. Therefore, thanks to their antioxidant action, BJ phytocompounds may effectively contribute to preventing and/or eliminating oxidative stress damage present in bone pathologies, particularly in osteoporosis, as reported in the literature for various polyphenols or their derivatives [18,24,25,30]. Our results support these data; in fact, the initial stimuli that induce osteogenic activity in SaOS-2 cells are sensitive to changes in the oxidative state. Indeed, both ALP and RUNX-2 are important markers related to the activation of the first phase of the osteoblast differentiation process and to the subsequent induction of calcium and matrix deposition by differentiated osteoblasts [13,37,43,44]. In fact, we observed a strong initial increase of ALP activity that subsequently remained high and then decreased, indicating the achievement of a high degree of differentiation, as also previously observed [13]. Both ALP activity and RUNX-2 expression and activation significantly decreased in the presence of BSO-induced oxidative stress, as well as the mineralization process. These events are efficiently prevented by BJ antioxidant action.

The results of this study also show that BJ treatment in the presence of normal ROS levels has a remarkable non-redox-regulated osteogenic action that occurs through a significant upregulation of ALP and RUNX-2 activity. It is worthy to note that BJ maintains ALP activity levels higher than those in untreated cells for a long time, and this seems to be related to the activation of the mineralization process that is evident only in the late phase of this event. Finally, the similar and high levels of calcium, obtained in cells treated with BSO + BJ or with BJ alone after 24 days, show that the elimination of the oxidative state in the initial phase of the differentiation allows BJ to perform the long-term activation of this process. Indeed, modulation of ALP and RUNX-2 activity in BJ-treated SaOS-2 cells, in the presence or not of BSO-induced oxidative stress, is similar to that previously observed in these cells treated with thiol antioxidants, even if the effect of the latter on the mineralization process became evident more quickly [13]. These differences may be due to the different chemical characteristics and action mechanisms of the antioxidants. However, in both studies, thiol and non-thiol antioxidants regulated the osteogenic activity of osteoblasts through mechanisms unrelated to their antioxidant activity. In fact, the activating effect of BJ or of thiol antioxidants on the mineralization process occurred in cells in which there was no alteration in the redox state. It is worthy to note that the BJ effects on osteogenic factors were found using TSP concentrations similar to those used to demonstrate the osteogenic activity of the polyphenolic component of dried plums [56]. In fact, these antioxidants restore the TNFα-induced suppression of ALP activity and upregulate RUNX-2 expression, influencing mineralized matrix formation under normal and inflammatory conditions [56]. Moreover, our data agree with the increased expression of RUNX-2 and ALP in pre-osteoblast cells treated with serum from BB-fed rats and with the subsequent increase in osteoblast activity and bone formation [57]. These data are also related to the ability of BB-rich diets administered in young female rats to prevent bone loss in ovariectomized adult female rats [19,20,24,30], where the effects of dietary BB appear similar to those of estrogens [57]. In fact, the polyphenols seem to interact with the estrogen receptors and induce their effects through redox-independent factors and signaling pathways related to the regulation of bone cell activity [36,57].

Moreover, many data suggest that anthocyanins, in addition to their antioxidant activity, can also have other beneficial health effects [20,24–26]. This may agree with the possible involvement of SIRT1 in ALP and RUNX-2 activation, as well as the increase in calcium deposition, due to BJ treatment in the presence or not of a normal redox state. Indeed, SIRT1 levels did not change in the presence of BSO-induced oxidative stress, indicating that SIRT1 expression does not seem to be a redox-regulated mechanism. BJ was effectively able to upregulate SIRT1 expression in BSO-treated and untreated cells, and BJ antioxidant action was partly related to SIRT1 activity. Previously, we similarly demonstrated a significant relationship between BJ phytocompounds and molecular events related to apoptosis and expression of osteoclastogenic factors induced by oxidative stress and SIRT1 activation [33]. Indeed, dietary BBs increase SIRT1 levels in mammals [49,50], and SIRT1 overexpression is also related to the inhibition of osteoclastogenic factors [58,59]. Moreover, SIRT1 activity promotes osteogenic differentiation of mesenchymal stem cells and activation of RUNX-2 [46–48]. Previously, we also demonstrated that SIRT1 activity contributes, in part, to the BJ protective effect in MSCs against cytotoxicity due to oxidative damage [33]. Therefore, the possible role of SIRT1 can explain, at the molecular level, the positive action of TSP and/or other phytocompounds contained in BJ on the osteogenic activity and the mineralization process of osteoblasts, although other experiments will have to be performed to validate SIRT1's involvement in these events.

The activation of osteogenic factors and mineralization due to BJ treatment is also in agreement with the increase in bone mass found in young subjects fed with diets rich in blueberries or fruits rich in antioxidant phytochemicals [17,20,24,60,61]. It was also shown that BBs stimulate the growth of bone in growing rats, and this appears to be due to polyphenols and their metabolic derivatives [18,62]. Indeed, phenolic acid derivatives present in the diet promote the differentiation of osteoblasts and bone growth in young mice [63]. Some studies demonstrated that daily consumption of these compounds may be important in increasing the bone mass peak [20,60,64], and this is an independent predictor of increased bone mass in early pubertal children [61].

5. Conclusions

The present study demonstrated, in GSH-depleted SaOS-2 cells, that TSPs, together with other phytocompounds contained in BJ, are able to prevent early oxidative stress-induced inhibition of osteogenic differentiation and the mineralization process. This can occur in vivo in estrogen deficiency, as well as in aging and inflammatory diseases in which the loss of antioxidants leads to accelerated bone loss and, thus, to osteoporosis or osteopenia. It was also shown that the effect of BJ is not only due to its protective antioxidant activity, but also due to its ability to modulate signals that upregulate the expression and activity of osteogenic factors which are related to bone remodeling and bone formation. In fact, the increased expression of SIRT1 seems to be related to the osteogenic action of BJ, and these findings confirm that this enzyme may be considered a possible target for anti-resorptive drugs and for anabolic treatments for osteoporosis [58,59]. Finally, qualitative and quantitative analysis of the BJ soluble polyphenolic component showed the prevalence and high presence of anthocyanins. Overall, the results of this study, together with those previously obtained on osteocytes, may contribute to explain, at a cellular and molecular level, the beneficial effects of BBs on bone metabolism. In particular, they suggest that BJ effects are mainly related to TSP; in fact, polyphenols activate osteoblast function and inhibit osteoclast differentiation, thereby promoting bone growth [18–20,26,54,62]. Indeed, data obtained in animal studies showed the anabolic effects of BB in bone, and they suggested BB as a useful supplement for the prevention and/or management of osteoporosis and osteopenia [18,19,26,30,62]. In fact, anti-resorption drugs are effective in reducing bone mass loss and osteoclast activity, while they are also associated with limitations and side effects [28,65], as they do not restore a normal bone remodeling process [1,28]. Therefore, there is a growing demand for natural substances that can support medical therapy to reduce bone loss and restore normal bone metabolism. Future researches in vivo and in vitro are needed to better elucidate the molecular mechanisms underlying the action of a complex mixture of BB polyphenols on bone repair and formation processes in osteoporosis or bone inflammatory diseases related to oxidative stress.

Author Contributions: Conceptualization, M.T.V., T.I., and M.L.B.; methodology, V.D., G.M., and I.F.; validation, V.D. and G.M.; investigation, V.D., G.M., I.F., and A.R.B.; resources, V.D., G.M., and A.R.B.; writing—original draft preparation, M.T.V. and T.I.; writing—review and editing, M.L.B., M.T.V., T.I., and V.D.; funding acquisition, M.L.B. and T.I. All authors have read and agreed to the published version of the manuscript.

Funding: This study was supported by grants from Fondazione Cassa di Risparmio di Pistoia e Pescia (IANTCRPP15) and Ministero dell'Istruzione, dell'Università e della Ricerca (RICATEN18) to T.I. and M.L.B.

Conflicts of Interest: The authors declare no conflict of interest.

References

1. Domazetovic, V.; Marcucci, G.; Iantomasi, T.; Brandi, M.L.; Vincenzini, M.T. Oxidative stress in bone remodeling: Role of antioxidants. *Clin. Cases Miner. Bone. Metab.* **2017**, *14*, 209–216. [CrossRef]
2. Ohyama, Y.; Ito, J.; Kitano, V.J.; Shimada, J.; Hakeda, Y. The polymethoxy flavonoid sudachitin suppresses inflammatory bone destruction by directly inhibiting osteoclastogenesis due to reduced ROS production and MAPK activation in osteoclast precursors. *PLoS ONE* **2018**, *13*, e0191192. [CrossRef]

3. Wauquier, F.; Leotoing, L.; Coxam, V.; Guicheux, J.; Wittrant, Y. Oxidative stress in bone remodelling and disease. *Trends Mol. Med.* **2009**, *15*, 468–477. [CrossRef] [PubMed]

4. Domazetovic, V.; Fontani, F.; Marcucci, G.; Iantomasi, T.; Brandi, M.L.; Vincenzini, M.T. Estrogen inhibits starvation-induced apoptosis in osteocytes by a redox-independent process involving association of JNK and glutathione S-transferase P1-1. *FEBS Open Bio.* **2017**, *7*, 705–718. [CrossRef] [PubMed]

5. Banfi, G.; Iorio, E.L.; Corsi, M.M. Oxidative stress, free radicals and bone remodeling. *Clin. Chem. Lab. Med.* **2008**, *46*, 1550–1555. [CrossRef] [PubMed]

6. Fontani, F.; Marcucci, G.; Iantomasi, T.; Brandi, M.L.; Vincenzini, M.T. Glutathione, N-acetylcysteine and lipoic acid down-regulate starvation-induced apoptosis, RANKL/OPG ratio and sclerostin in osteocytes: Involvement of JNK and ERK1/2 signalling. *Calcif. Tissue Int.* **2015**, *96*, 335–346. [CrossRef]

7. Almeida, M.; Martin-Millan, M.; Ambrogini, E.; Bradsher, R., 3rd; Han, L.; Chen, X.D.; Roberson, P.K.; Weinstein, R.S.; O'Brien, C.; Jilka, R.L.; et al. Estrogens attenuate oxidative stress and the differentiation and apoptosis of osteoblasts by DNA-binding-independent actions of the ERalpha. *J. Bone Miner. Res.* **2010**, *25*, 769–781.

8. Doshi, S.B.; Agarwal, A. The role of oxidative stress in menopause. *J. Midlife Health.* **2013**, *4*, 140–146.

9. Manolagas, S.C. From estrogen-centric to aging and oxidative stress: A revised perspective of the pathogenesis of osteoporosis. *Endocr. Rev.* **2010**, *31*, 266–300. [CrossRef]

10. Baek, K.H.; Oh, K.W.; Lee, W.Y.; Lee, S.S.; Kim, M.K.; Kwon, H.S.; Rhee, E.J.; Han, J.H.; Song, K.H.; Cha, B.Y.; et al. Association of oxidative stress with postmenopausal osteoporosis and the effects of hydrogen peroxide on osteoclast formation in human bone marrow cell cultures. *Calcif. Tissue Int.* **2010**, *87*, 226–235. [CrossRef]

11. Maggio, D.; Barabani, M.; Pierandrei, M.; Polidori, M.C.; Catani, M.; Mecocci, P.; Senin, U.; Pacifici, R.; Cherubini, A. Marked decrease in plasma antioxidants in aged osteoporotic women: Results of a cross-sectional study. *J. Clin. Endocrinol. Metab.* **2003**, *88*, 1523–1527. [CrossRef] [PubMed]

12. Ostman, B.; Michaëlsson, K.; Helmersson, J.; Byberg, L.; Gedeborg, R.; Melhus, H.; Basu, S. Oxidative stress and bone mineral density in elderly men: Antioxidant activity of alpha-tocopherol. *Free Radic. Biol. Med.* **2009**, *47*, 668–673. [CrossRef] [PubMed]

13. Romagnoli, C.; Marcucci, G.; Favilli, F.; Zonefrati, R.; Mavilia, C.; Galli, G.; Tanini, A.; Iantomasi, T.; Brandi, M.L.; Vincenzini, M.T. Role of GSH/GSSG redox couple in osteogenic activity and osteoclastogenic markers of human osteoblast-like SaOS-2 cells. *FEBS J.* **2013**, *280*, 867–879. [CrossRef] [PubMed]

14. Lean, J.M.; Jagger, C.J.; Kirstein, B.; Fuller, K.; Chambers, T.J. Hydrogen peroxide is essential for estrogen-deficiency bone loss and osteoclast formation. *Endocrinology* **2005**, *146*, 728–735. [CrossRef] [PubMed]

15. Oka, Y.; Iwai, S.; Amano, H.; Irie, Y.; Yatomi, K.; Ryu, K.; Yamada, S.; Inagaki, K.; Oguchi, K. Tea polyphenols inhibit rat osteoclast formation and differentiation. *J. Pharmacol. Sci.* **2012**, *118*, 55–64. [CrossRef]

16. Yagi, H.; Tan, J.; Tuan, R.S. Polyphenols suppress hydrogen peroxide-induced oxidative stress in human bone-marrow derived mesenchymal stem cells. *J. Cell. Biochem.* **2013**, *114*, 1163–1173. [CrossRef]

17. Tou, J.C. Resveratrol supplementation affects bone acquisition and osteoporosis: Pre-clinical evidence toward translational diet therapy. *Biochim. Biophys. Acta* **2015**, *1852*, 1186–1194. [CrossRef]

18. Chen, J.R.; Lazarenko, O.P.; Wu, X.; Kang, J.; Blackburn, M.L.; Shankar, K.; Badger, T.M.; Ronis, M.J. Dietary-induced serum phenolic acids promote bone growth via p38 MAPK/β-catenin canonical Wnt signaling. *J. Bone Miner. Res.* **2010**, *25*, 2399–2411. [CrossRef]

19. Li, T.; Wu, S.M.; Xu, Z.Y.; Ou-Yang, S. Rabbiteye blueberry prevents osteoporosis in ovariectomized rats. *J. Orthop. Surg. Res.* **2014**, *9*, 56.

20. Weaver, C.M.; Alekel, D.L.; Ward, W.E.; Ronis, M.J. Flavonoid intake and bone health. *J. Nutr. Gerontol. Geriatr.* **2012**, *31*, 239–253. [CrossRef]

21. Austermann, K.; Baecker, N.; Stehle, P.; Heer, M. Putative Effects of Nutritive Polyphenols on Bone Metabolism In Vivo—Evidence from Human Studies. *Nutrients* **2019**, *11*, 871. [CrossRef] [PubMed]

22. Sendur, O.F.; Turan, Y.; Tastaban, E.; Serter, M. Antioxidant status in patients with osteoporosis: A controlled study. *Jt. Bone Spine* **2009**, *76*, 514–518. [CrossRef] [PubMed]

23. Domazetovic, V.; Fontani, F.; Tanini, D.; D'Esopo, V.; Marcucci, G.; Panzella, L.; Napolitano, A.; Brandi, M.L.; Capperucci, A.; Menichetti, S.; et al. Protective role of benzoselenophene derivatives of resveratrol on the induced oxidative stress in intestinal myofibroblasts and osteocytes. *Chem. Biol. Interact.* **2017**, *275*, 13–21. [CrossRef] [PubMed]

24. Hubert, P.A.; Lee, S.G.; Lee, S.-K.; Chun, O.K. Dietary Polyphenols, Berries, and Age-Related Bone Loss: A Review Based on Human, Animal, and Cell Studies. *Antioxidants* **2014**, *3*, 144–158. [CrossRef] [PubMed]

25. Islam, M.A.; Alam, F.; Solayman, M.; Khalil, M.I.; Kamal, M.A.; Gan, S.H. Dietary Phytochemicals: Natural Swords Combating Inflammation and Oxidation-Mediated Degenerative Diseases. *Oxid. Med. Cell. Longev.* **2016**, *2016*, 5137431. [CrossRef] [PubMed]

26. Li, A.N.; Li, S.; Zhang, Y.J.; Xu, X.R.; Chen, Y.M.; Li, H.B. Resources and biological activities of natural polyphenols. *Nutrients* **2014**, *6*, 6020–6047. [CrossRef]

27. Higgs, J.; Derbyshire, E.; Styles, K. Nutrition and osteoporosis prevention for the orthopaedic surgeon: A wholefoods approach. *EFORT Open Rev.* **2017**, *2*, 300–308. [CrossRef]

28. Rachner, T.D.; Khosla, S.; Hofbauer, L.C. Osteoporosis: Now and the future. *Lancet* **2011**, *377*, 1276–1287. [CrossRef]

29. Marcucci, G.; Brandi, M.L. Rare causes of osteoporosis. *Clin. Cases Miner. Bone Metab.* **2015**, *12*, 151–156. [CrossRef]

30. Devareddy, L.; Hooshmand, S.; Collins, J.K.; Lucas, E.A.; Chai, S.C.; Arjmandi, B.H. Blueberry prevents bone loss in ovariectomized rat model of postmenopausal osteoporosis. *J. Nutr. Biochem.* **2008**, *19*, 694–699. [CrossRef]

31. Ancillotti, C.; Ciofi, L.; Pucci, D.; Sagona, E.; Giordani, E.; Biricolti, S.; Gori, M.; Petrucci, W.A.; Giardi, F.; Bartoletti, R.; et al. Polyphenolic profiles and antioxidant and antiradical activity of Italian berries from *Vaccinium myrtillus* L. and *Vaccinium uliginosum* L. subsp. *gaultherioides* (Bigelow) S.B. Young. *Food Chem.* **2016**, *204*, 176–184. [CrossRef] [PubMed]

32. Prencipe, F.P.; Bruni, R.; Guerrini, A.; Rossi, D.; Benvenuti, S.; Pellati, F. Metabolite profiling of polyphenols in Vaccinium berries and determination of their chemopreventive properties. *J Pharm. Biomed. Anal.* **2014**, *89*, 257–267. [CrossRef] [PubMed]

33. Domazetovic, V.; Marcucci, G.; Pierucci, F.; Bruno, G.; Di Cesare Mannelli, L.; Ghelardini, C.; Brandi, M.L.; Iantomasi, T.; Meacci, E.; Vincenzini, M.T. Blueberry juice protects osteocytes and bone precursor cells against oxidative stress partly through SIRT1. *FEBS Open Bio.* **2019**, *9*, 1082–1096. [PubMed]

34. Matsumoto, H.; Inaba, H.; Kishi, M.; Tominaga, S.; Hirayama, M.; Tsuda, T. Orally administered delphinidin 3-rutinoside and cyanidin 3-rutinoside are directly absorbed in rats and humans and appear in the blood as the intact forms. *J. Agric. Food Chem.* **2001**, *49*, 1546–1551. [CrossRef]

35. Cao, G.; Muccitelli, H.U.; Sánchez-Moreno, C.; Prior, R.L. Anthocyanins are absorbed in glycated forms in elderly women: A pharmacokinetic study. *Am. J. Clin. Nutr.* **2001**, *73*, 920–926. [CrossRef] [PubMed]

36. Zhong, S.; Sandhu, A.; Edirisinghe, I.; Burton-Freeman, B. Characterization of Wild Blueberry Polyphenols Bioavailability and Kinetic Profile in Plasma over 24-h Period in Human Subjects. *Mol. Nutr. Food Res.* **2017**, *61*. [CrossRef] [PubMed]

37. Rodan, S.B.; Imai, Y.; Thiede, M.A.; Wesolowski, G.; Thompson, D.; Bar-Shavit, Z.; Shull, S.; Mann, K.; Rodan, G.A. Characterization of a human osteosarcoma cell line (Saos-2) with osteoblastic properties. *Cancer Res.* **1987**, *47*, 4961–4966.

38. Boskey, A.L.; Roy, R. Cell culture systems for studies of bone and tooth mineralization. *Chem. Rev.* **2008**, *108*, 4716–4733. [CrossRef]

39. McQuillan, D.J.; Richardson, M.D.; Bateman, J.F. Matrix deposition by a calcifying human osteogenic sarcoma cell line (SAOS-2). *Bone* **1995**, *16*, 415–426. [CrossRef]

40. Gundle, R.; Beresford, J.N. The isolation and culture of cells from explants of human trabecular bone. *Calcif. Tissue. Int.* **1995**, *56*, S8–S10. [CrossRef]

41. Hausser, H.J.; Brenner, R.E. Phenotypic instability of Saos-2 cells in long-term culture. *Biochem. Biophys. Res. Commun.* **2005**, *333*, 216–222. [CrossRef] [PubMed]

42. Díaz-García, M.C.; Obón, J.M.; Castellar, M.R.; Collado, J.; Alacid, M. Quantification by UHPLC of total individual polyphenols in fruit juices. *Food Chem.* **2013**, *138*, 938–949. [CrossRef] [PubMed]

43. Kotobuki, N.; Matsushima, A.; Kato, Y.; Kubo, Y.; Hirose, M.; Ohgushi, H. Small interfering RNA of alkaline phosphatase inhibits matrix mineralization. *Cell Tissue Res.* **2008**, *332*, 279–288. [CrossRef] [PubMed]

44. Komori, T. Regulation of osteoblast differentiation by transcription factors. *J. Cell. Biochem.* **2006**, *99*, 1233–1239. [CrossRef]

45. Coffman, J.A. Runx transcription factors and the developmental balance between cell proliferation and differentiation. *Cell. Biol. Int.* **2003**, *27*, 315–324. [CrossRef]

46. Cohen-Kfir, E.; Artsi, H.; Levin, A.; Abramowitz, E.; Bajayo, A.; Gurt, I.; Zhong, L.; D'Urso, A.; Toiber, D.; Mostoslavsky, R.; et al. Sirt1 Is a Regulator of Bone Mass and a Repressor of *Sost* Encoding for Sclerostin, a Bone Formation Inhibitor. *Endocrinology* **2011**, *152*, 4514–4524. [CrossRef]

47. Liu, J.; Han, W.; Chen, L.; Tang, K. Mechanism of osteogenic and adipogenic differentiation of tendon stem cells induced by sirtuin 1. *Mol. Med. Rep.* **2016**, *14*, 1643–1648. [CrossRef]

48. Zainabadi, K.; Liu, C.J.; Guarente, L. SIRT1 is a positive regulator of the master osteoblast transcription factor, RUNX2. *PLoS ONE* **2017**, *12*, e0178520. [CrossRef]

49. Ren, T.; Huang, C.; Cheng, M. Dietary blueberry and bifidobacteria attenuate nonalcoholic fatty liver disease in rats by affecting SIRT1-mediated signaling pathway. *Oxid. Med. Cell. Longev.* **2014**, *2014*, 469059. [CrossRef]

50. Zhou, L.; Wang, S.I.; Moon, Y.J.; Kim, K.M.; Lee, K.B.; Park, B.H.; Jang, K.Y.; Kim, J.R. Overexpression of SIRT1 prevents hypoxia-induced apoptosis in osteoblast cells. *Mol. Med. Rep.* **2017**, *16*, 2969–2975. [CrossRef]

51. Lean, J.M.; Davies, J.T.; Jagger, C.J.; Kirstein, B.; Partington, G.A.; Urry, Z.L.; Chambers, T.J. A crucial role for thiol antioxidants in estrogen-deficiency bone loss. *J. Clin. Investig.* **2003**, *112*, 915–923. [CrossRef] [PubMed]

52. Sanders, K.M.; Kotowicz, M.A.; Nicholson, G.C. Potential role of the antioxidant N-acetylcysteine in slowing bone resorption in early post-menopausal women: A pilot study. *Transl. Res.* **2007**, *150*, 215. [CrossRef] [PubMed]

53. Lohachoompol, V.; Srzednicki, G.; Craske, J. The Change of Total Anthocyanins in Blueberries and Their Antioxidant Effect After Drying and Freezing. *J. Biomed. Biotechnol.* **2004**, *2004*, 248–252. [CrossRef] [PubMed]

54. Michalska, A.; Łysiak, G. Bioactive Compounds of Blueberries: Post-Harvest Factors Influencing the Nutritional Value of Products. *Int. J. Mol. Sci.* **2015**, *16*, 18642–18663. [CrossRef]

55. Kuntz, S.; Rudloff, S.; Asseburg, H.; Borsch, C.; Fröhling, B.; Unger, F.; Dold, S.; Spengler, B.; Römpp, A.; Kunz, C. Uptake and bioavailability of anthocyanins and phenolic acids from grape/blueberry juice and smoothie in vitro and in vivo. *Br. J. Nutr.* **2015**, *113*, 1044–1055. [CrossRef]

56. Bu, S.Y.; Hunt, T.S.; Smith, B.J. Dried plum polyphenols attenuate the detrimental effects of TNF-α on osteoblast function coincident with up-regulation of Runx2, Osterix and IGF-I. *J. Nutr. Biochem.* **2009**, *20*, 35–44. [CrossRef]

57. Zhang, J.; Lazarenko, O.P.; Blackburn, M.L.; Shankar, K.; Badger, T.M.; Ronis, M.J.; Chen, J.R. Feeding blueberry diets in early life prevent senescence of osteoblasts and bone loss in ovariectomized adult female rats. *PLoS ONE* **2011**, *6*, e24486. [CrossRef]

58. Artsi, H.; Cohen-Kfir, E.; Gurt, I.; Shahar, R.; Bajayo, A.; Kalish, N.; Bellido, T.M.; Gabet, Y.; Dresner-Pollak, R. The Sirtuin1 Activator SRT3025 Down-Regulates Sclerostin and Rescues Ovariectomy-Induced Bone Loss and Biomechanical Deterioration in Female Mice. *Endocrinology* **2014**, *155*, 3508–3515. [CrossRef]

59. Gurt, I.; Artsi, H.; Cohen-Kfir, E.; Hamdani, G.; Ben-Shalom, G.; Feinstein, B.; El-HAj, M.; Dresner-Pollak, R. The Sirt1 Activators SRT2183 and SRT3025 Inhibit RANKL-Induced Osteoclastogenesis in Bone Marrow-Derived Macrophages and Down-Regulate Sirt3 in Sirt1 Null Cells. *PLoS ONE* **2015**, *10*, e0134391. [CrossRef]

60. Novotny, R.; Daida, Y.G.; Grove, J.S.; Acharya, S.; Vogt, T.M.; Paperny, D. Adolescent dairy consumption and physical activity associated with bone mass. *Prev. Med.* **2004**, *39*, 355–360. [CrossRef]

61. Tylavsky, F.A.; Holliday, K.; Danish, R.; Womack, C.; Norwood, J.; Carbone, L. Fruit and vegetable intakes are an independent predictor of bone size in early pubertal children. *Am. J. Clin. Nutr.* **2004**, *79*, 311–317. [CrossRef] [PubMed]

62. Zhang, J.; Lazarenko, O.P.; Kang, J.; Blackburn, M.L.; Ronis, M.J.; Badger, T.M.; Chen, J.R. Feeding blueberry diets to young rats dose-dependently inhibits bone resorption through suppression of RANKL in stromal cells. *PLoS ONE* **2013**, *8*, e70438. [CrossRef] [PubMed]

63. Chen, J.R.; Lazarenko, O.P.; Zhang, J.; Blackburn, M.L.; Ronis, M.J.; Badger, T.M. Diet-derived phenolic acids regulate osteoblast and adipocyte lineage commitment and differentiation in young mice. *J. Bone. Miner. Res.* **2014**, *29*, 1043–1053. [CrossRef] [PubMed]

64. Gilsanz, V.; Wren, T. Assessment of bone acquisition in childhood and adolescence. *Pediatrics* **2007**, *119*, S145–S149. [CrossRef] [PubMed]
65. Tarantino, U.; Iolascon, G.; Cianferotti, L.; Masi, L.; Marcucci, G.; Giusti, F.; Marini, F.; Parri, S.; Feola, M.; Rao, C.; et al. Clinical guidelines for the prevention and treatment of osteoporosis: Summary statements and recommendations from the Italian Society for Orthopaedics and Traumatology. *J. Orthop. Traumatol.* **2017**, *18*, 3–36. [CrossRef]

 *antioxidants*

Article

BG-4 from Bitter Gourd (*Momordica charantia*) Differentially Affects Inflammation In Vitro and In Vivo

Andrea Nieto-Veloza [1], Zhihong Wang [1], Qixin Zhong [1], Hari B. Krishnan [2] and Vermont P. Dia [1,*]

[1]   Department of Food Science, University of Tennessee, Knoxville, TN 37996, USA;
       cnietove@vols.utk.edu (A.N.-V.); zwang78@vols.utk.edu (Z.W.); qzhong@utk.edu (Q.Z.)
[2]   Agricultural Research Service, United States Department of Agriculture (USDA),
       Columbia, MO 65211, USA; Hari.Krishnan@ars.usda.gov
*   Correspondence: vdia@utk.edu; Tel.: +1-865-974-7265

Received: 13 May 2019; Accepted: 11 June 2019; Published: 14 June 2019

Abstract: BG-4 isolated from bitter gourd has been reported for anti-cancer properties. The objective was to evaluate the anti-inflammatory properties of BG-4 in vitro and in vivo. Comparative study of the anti-inflammatory properties of BG-4 in vitro and in vivo was conducted on lipopolysaccharide (LPS)-activated mouse macrophages, and on dextran sodium sulfate (DSS)-induced colitis in mice. BG-4 reduced the production of pro-inflammatory markers in LPS-activated macrophages. On the other hand, intraperitoneal administration of BG-4 in DSS-induced colitis led to colon shortening, elevated neutrophils infiltration and myeloperoxidase activity, presence of blood in the stool, and loss of body weight, with differential systemic and local effects on pro-inflammatory cytokines in vivo. The results demonstrated that BG-4 differentially affected inflammation in vitro and in vivo.

Keywords: BG-4; bitter gourd; colitis; inflammation; macrophages

---

1. Introduction

Inflammatory bowel disease (IBD) is a life-long condition of chronic and relapsing inflammation of the gastrointestinal tract associated with immune-mediated disorders [1]. It has two major phenotypes: Crohn's disease, which can severely affect any part of the bowel, and ulcerative colitis (UC), which involves damage in the superficial mucosa of the colon, starting always from the anus [1,2]. IBD patients are at major risk of developing gastrointestinal and extra-intestinal carcinomas, especially those carrying UC whose probability for developing colitis-associated colorectal cancer (CACC) increases with the length and severity of inflammatory manifestation [3]. The increasing incidence of UC, especially at a younger age, has raised a global concern considering the detrimental consequences in terms of quality of life, economic loss associated with lower productivity and increased medical expenses, and the imminent risk of development of CACC [2,4]. Hence, alternative ways to manage inflammation are needed, and plant origin compounds may prevent, ameliorate and alleviate chronic inflammation, and consequently the risk of IBD and associated diseases.

Momordica charantia, commonly known as bitter gourd, is a member of the Cucurbitaceae family mainly cultivated in Asia, Africa, and South America [5]. It is traditionally consumed as a vegetable and with medicinal purposes such as treatment of inflammation, fever, rheumatism, as well as antidiabetic and anti-helmitic [6]. Several studies have addressed in vitro and/or in vivo effects of the whole edible parts or extracts with demonstrated anti-oxidant, anti-inflammatory, anti-diabetic, anti-cancer and metabolic regulatory properties [7–12].

BG-4 is a novel 4 kDa peptide isolated from bitter gourd seeds with trypsin inhibitory and in vitro anti-colon cancer and anti-inflammatory properties [13,14]. BG-4 was isolated from the seeds of *Momordica charantia* by 70% ethanol extraction. It showed very strong trypsin inhibitory activity which is at least 8x more potent than purified soybean Kunitz trypsin inhibitor [13]. Moreover, mass spectrometric analysis showed the following peptide sequence matches: SWPQLVGSTGAAAK, VGSPVTADFR, GIVARPPAIG and DSDCLAQCICVDGHCG [13]. However, the potential bioactive properties of BG-4 in animal models remain unexplored. Herein, we made a comparative in vitro and in vivo anti-inflammatory study of BG-4, by measuring the expression of pro-inflammatory markers in lipopolysaccharide (LPS)-activated mouse-derived macrophages, and in dextran sodium sulfate (DSS)-induced colitis in mice. Our results indicate that BG-4 has differential effects in inflammation within in vitro and in vivo settings.

2. Materials and Methods

2.1. Extraction of BG-4

The 4 kDa peptide BG-4 was extracted from bitter gourd seeds as described previously [13].

2.2. In Vitro Antioxidant Activity of BG-4

The antioxidant capacity of BG-4 was tested via the oxygen radical absorbance capacity assay (ORAC) as described by Vernaza and coworkers [15] with slight modifications. In brief, 150 µL of fluorescein solution prepared in phosphate buffer (75 mM, pH 7.4) were plated in a black 96-well plate. Twenty-five microliters of Trolox standard curve (100–3.125 µM in phosphate buffer), blank or sample diluted in phosphate buffer were added and incubated at 37 °C for 30 min. Then, 25 µL of 2,2'-azobis (2-amidinopropane) dihydrochloride (AAPH) (Sigma-Aldrich, St. Louis, MO, USA) solution at 41.5 mg/mL in phosphate buffer was added and fluorescence was read at 485 nm/20 nm excitation and 528 nm/20 nm emission wavelengths for 2 h every min. Each sample and standard curve point was measured in triplicate and results were expressed as µM of Trolox equivalents/g of BG-4. Radical scavenging activity was measured by quantifying the inhibition of 2,2-diphenyl-1-picrylhydrazyl free radical (DPPH•). Briefly, 100 µL of sample and blank were plated in a clear 96-well plate, then 100 µL of 100 µM DPPH• (Sigma-Aldrich, St. Louis, MO, USA) dissolved in methanol were added and incubated in dark for 30 min. Simultaneously, a combination of sample and methanol, instead DPPH•, were tested as reference for background signal. Absorbance was read at 517 nm. The absorbance of methanol reference was subtracted and the percentage of inhibition was calculated against blank. Results are presented as percentage of scavenging rate of DPPH•.

2.3. Measurement of Pro-Inflammatory Markers In Vitro

Murine RAW 264.7 macrophages were cultured in DMEM supplemented with 10% heat-inactivated fetal bovine serum (Life Tech, Carlsbad, CA, USA) and 1% penicillin/streptomycin at 37 °C in a humidified 5% CO_2 incubator. Cells were seeded at 2×10^5 cells/well in 6-well plates in 2 mL media, or 5×10^3 cells/well in 96-well plates in 200 µL media and allowed to attach overnight. Cells were treated with BG-4 (0–500 µg/mL) for 8 h and stimulated with LPS (1 µg/mL) for 16 h. After which, supernatant was collected for TNF-α and IL-6 measurement via ELISA following the manufacturer's protocol (BioLegend, San Diego, CA) and nitric oxide (NO) production by Griess reagent assay. Whole cell lysates were collected for immunoblotting of inducible nitric oxidase synthase (iNOS) and cyclooxygenase-2 (COX-2) (ProteinTech, Chicago, IL, USA) by chemiluminescence following standard protocol. Cell viability was tested by MTS assay following the manufacturer's protocol (Promega, Madison, WI, USA).

2.4. Dosage Information and In Vivo Experimental Procedure

The BG-4 dose used in the animal study (15 mg/kg body weight (bw)) is equivalent to the optimum concentration (375 µg/mL) of BG-4 in vitro producing significantly decreased expression of pro-inflammatory markers without affecting cell viability. This translation assumes an average mouse weight of 25 g and circulating blood of 1 mL. This will be equivalent to a daily intake of two 500 mg capsules as a dietary supplement for a 70-kg person. The protocol for the animal experiment was approved by the Institutional Animal Care and Use Committee of the University of Tennessee Knoxville (Approval Protocol #2591-0418) and followed guidelines of the National Institutes of Health guide for the care and use of Laboratory Animals (NIH Publications No. 8023, revised 1978). Twenty-two male C57BL/6 7-week old mice (Jackson Laboratories, Harbor, ME, USA) were randomized and housed in pairs in standard mouse cages with water and food provided ad libitum, under standard controlled conditions (23 ± 2 °C, 30–70% relative humidity with 12 h light and 12 h dark cycle). Mice were randomly divided into three groups and treated as follows: control group (CG, *n* = 6), DSS-treated group (DSS, *n* = 8), and DSS + BG-4-treated group (BG-4, *n* = 8). Mice in CG were administered with normal drinking water, while DSS and BG-4 groups received drinking water with 3% DSS (MW = 36–50 kDa, MP Biomedicals, Santa Ana, CA) to induce colitis. Two stages of DSS administration were performed allowing a recovery period in between, in order to simulate the periods of relapse and remission that IBD patients experience [16]. Daily intraperitoneal injection (IP) of 100 µL sterile water was performed over CG and DSS groups, while BG-4 received IP of 15 mg BG-4/kg bw dissolved in 100 µL sterile water. Food intake and body weight were recorded daily. Presence of visible blood (in stool or anus), as well as stool consistency, were monitored and scored daily. Stool samples were collected from the cages every three days to evaluate the presence of occult blood via quantification of hemoglobin in feces. At day 15, mice were anesthetized with isoflurane, blood collected by cardiac puncture, followed by cervical dislocation. Colon was removed, washed with PBS, length measured and cut longitudinally into two pieces: one for hematoxylin and eosin (H&E) staining, and the other frozen in liquid nitrogen for biochemical analysis.

2.5. Myeloperoxidase Assay in the Colon

Neutrophils infiltration was assessed by measuring myeloperoxidase (MPO) activity in colonic extracts as reported previously [17] with slight modifications. Colonic extracts were obtained by beads homogenization of 50 mg of colon samples with 1 mL buffer (5 g of hexadecyltrimethylammonium in 1 L of 50 mM potassium phosphate buffer at pH 6.0), followed by centrifugation at 20,000× *g* for 15 min at 4 °C. Supernatant was collected and further centrifuged to ensure total precipitation of solid tissue. Ten µL of supernatant was plated in triplicate in a 96-well plate and combined with 200 µL freshly prepared *o*-dianisidine solution (16.7 mg of o-dianisidine, 90 mL of deionized water and 10 mL of potassium phosphate buffer, combined with 50 µL of 1.2% H_2O_2). Absorbance at 450 nm was recorded every 30 s for 5 min. MPO activity was calculated as the amount needed to degrade 1 µmol H_2O_2/min at 21–22 °C per mg protein in the colonic extract.

2.6. Measurement of Hemoglobin Content in the Feces

Presence of occult blood in the feces was assessed by measuring hemoglobin content [18,19]. Twenty mg of freeze-dried pulverized samples were vortexed with 100 µL dH_2O, and boiled for 10 min. Six hundred microliters of 30% acetic acid was added, vortexed for 2 min, then 900 µL of ethyl acetate was added, and organic layer was collected in a separate microcentrifuge tube after centrifugation at 2000× *g* for 3 min. In a quartz cuvette, equal parts of the organic phase and TMB solution (14.4 mg of 3,3′,5,5′-tetramethylbenzidine in 100 mL mixture of glacial acetic acid/dH_2O/ethanol 20/30/50) were mixed and the reaction was started by adding the same amount of 3% H_2O_2. The absorbance was recorded at 660 nm at 30 s, 60 s, and 90 s. Hemoglobin content was calculated as the average for the three time points per mg of feces using bovine hemoglobin (Alfa Aesar, Ward Hill, MA, USA) standard curve.

2.7. Measurement of Cytokines by ELISA

Supernatants of treated macrophages, as well as blood serum and colonic extracts, were used to measure the expression of pro-inflammatory cytokines using ELISA kits according to manufacturer instructions (BioLegend, San Diego, CA, USA).

2.8. Statistical Analysis

All experiments were performed in triplicate. Results were reported as mean ± SD or SE. Analysis of variance (ANOVA) and Tukey's test were used to establish significant differences ($p < 0.05$) and t-student for comparison of two samples or groups, using Statgraphics Centurion ® software (Statgraphics Inc, The Plains, VA, USA).

3. Results and Discussion

3.1. BG-4 Exert Antioxidant and Antiradical Activity

Antioxidant capacity of BG-4 was estimated as 4.72 ± 0.41 µM of Trolox Equivalent per gram, being comparably higher to that reported for protocatechuic acid and protocatechuates (<3 µM of Trolox Equivalent/g) [20]. The ability of BG-4 to convert DPPH radical into it picrylhydrazine form increase about 1.6 times when doubling the concentration, as it can be seen in Figure 1, exerting up to 26% inhibition at a concentration of 0.5 mg/mL of BG-4.

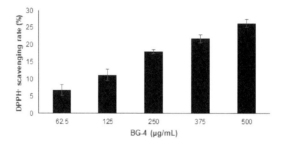

Figure 1. Radical scavenging activity of BG-4 calculated as % of inhibition of DPPH free radical for different concentrations. Results are presented as mean ± SD.

3.2. BG-4 Decreased Expression of Pro-Inflammatory Markers In Vitro

Macrophages are part of the first line of defense against injury, mediating the innate non-specific immune response via inflammation, and playing an important role not only in host defense but in tissue homeostasis, repair, and pathology development including IBD [21,22]. RAW 264.7 mouse derived macrophages have been widely used as in vitro model to study modulatory effects of several compounds using LPS for activation [23–25]. Treatment with BG-4 at concentrations up to 375 µg/mL did not affect the viability of macrophages (Figure 2A). It is known that LPS can activate NF-κB which acts as a master regulator of the inflammatory response by promoting the release of signaling and effector molecules such as pro-inflammatory cytokines (IL-6, TNF-α, IL-1β) and nitric oxide (NO) that act as mediators of inflammation during the host immune response [6]. The destruction of normal and healthy tissue as a result of chronic inflammatory condition can lead to IBD, rheumatoid arthritis and multiple sclerosis [26], hence reducing the level of these pro-inflammatory secreted molecules can lead to management and alleviation of these diseases. BG-4 dose-dependently reduced the production of NO (Figure 2B) and IL-6 (Figure 2C) in LPS-activated RAW 264.7 macrophages. Moreover, the expression of iNOS and COX-2 (Figure 2D) was reduced by BG-4.

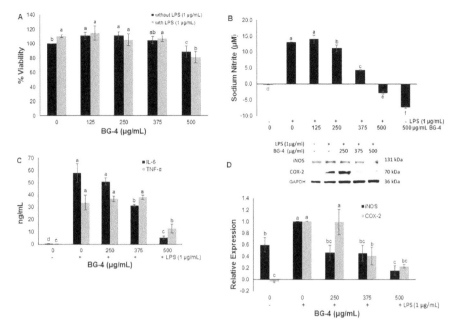

Figure 2. Effect of BG-4 on viability of activated lipopolysaccharide (LPS+) and non-activated (LPS-) macrophages (**A**), NO production (**B**), cytokine production (**C**), and iNOS and COX-2 expression (**D**), in vitro. Results are presented as mean ± SD for (**A–C**) and mean ± SE for (**D**). Different letters indicate significant differences ($p < 0.05$) among treatments.

These results suggest that the mechanistic effect of BG-4 had a major impact on molecules particularly involved in the pathway associated with the specific expression of iNOS and IL-6, and consequently over their downstream products, but affected in a lower extent the expression of COX-2 and TNF-α. Hence, we selected 375 µg/mL concentration to study the ability of BG-4 to ameliorate DSS-induced colitis in mice with a translation of IP administration of BG-4 at 15 mg/kg bw assuming an average mouse weight of 25 g and a circulating blood volume of one milliliter. Two stages of DSS administration were performed in order to induce damage to the epithelial barrier in the colon to simulate colitis, allowing a period of recovery in between as presented in Figure 3A. This experimental design mimics the periods of remission and relapse that IBD patients usually experience [16]. BG-4 administration started at three days post DSS to mimic ingestion of BG-4 as a supplement for ameliorating established IBD (versus prevention) in human as there are no known risk factors to IBD. Hence, it is highly likely that dietary supplement will be consumed for management and not for the prevention of IBD.

3.3. IP Administration of BG-4 did not Alleviate Indicators of Colitis in Vivo

The damage in the colonic mucosa that occurs in ulcerative colitis results in different symptoms and indicators such as diarrhea, presence of blood in the stool, increased frequency of bowel movements, mucus discharge, abdominal pain, weight loss, bloody diarrhea, and rectal bleeding irritation and fissures [27]. Daily monitoring of body weight, presence of visible blood and stool consistency were performed, in order to establish variation of external indicators of the disease. CG maintained a constant incremental increase in weight while the DSS group presented a significant decrease starting at day five, and minimum trough at day seven, with a 6% loss of original weight. BG-4 administration in DSS-treated mice showed a continued loss in weight until day nine and in days 14 and 15 with a 10% decrease in body weight at euthanasia as shown in Figure 3A. For CG, no visible blood in the stool or anus and normal stool consistency were observed with a disease score of zero (Figure 3B) neither DSS nor BG-4 groups presented watery or bloody diarrhea, but changed in stool consistency, becoming much softer in comparison to CG group and BG-4 administration led to stool softening earlier than DSS group as shown in Figure 3B. Presence of blood in stool was observed for DSS and BG-4 groups mostly between days 3–6 and 10–14, but the frequency of mice presenting blood in the anus was higher for BG-4 than for DSS group as presented in Figure 3C.

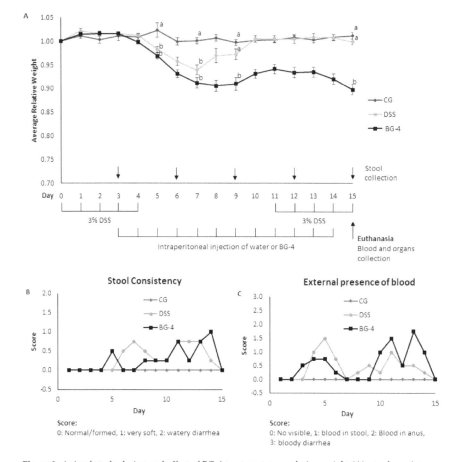

Figure 3. Animal study design and effect of BG-4 treatment over relative weight (**A**), stool consistency (**B**), and presence of visible blood (**C**) on dextran sodium sulfate (DSS)-induced colitis in mice. Scores for stool consistency and presence of visible blood for CG were 0 for every observation. Results are presented as mean ± SE. Different letters indicate significant differences ($p < 0.05$) among treatments.

Overall, external indicators of the disease suggest that DSS administration induced colitis with a mild grade of severity in this study. Since diarrhea or reduction in food intake were not observed, loss of body weight might be due to an increased frequency in bowel movements with a softened stool consistency and presence of blood, that upon removal of DSS was compensated by food intake, allowing partial or total recovery of the animals. However, the lower extent of recovery for BG-4 group, in addition to the higher frequency of animals with rectal bleeding may indicate that IP administration of BG-4 aggravated symptoms of the disease.

3.4. IP Administration of BG-4 Aggravated DSS-Induced Colitis in Mice

Colon shortening has been reported for several studies as an outcome of colitis in animal models [6,28–30]. BG-4 group presented a significant reduction in average colon length of about 2 cm in comparison with CG as shown in Figure 4A. H&E staining allows a comparison of the effects of DSS challenge and BG-4 treatment over the internal structure of colonic tissue. Micrographs of stained colonic tissue for the three groups show that animals under DSS-induced colitis exhibited immune cells infiltration (black arrows) in the lamina propria, and a distortion of crypts architecture (white arrows) accompanied by the loss of goblet cells (Figure 4B). In the case of BG-4, infiltration was extended to the muscularis region and to form crypt abscesses and reach the glandular lumen of the crypts forming abscesses as shown in Figure 4B.

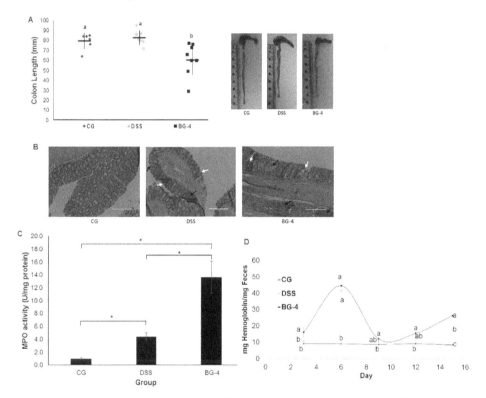

Figure 4. Colon length (**A**), H&E staining of colonic tissue (**B**), MPO activity (**C**), and fecal hemoglobin (**D**) on DSS-induced colitis in mice. Results are presented as mean ± SD (**A**) and (**C**) or SE (**D**). Different letters and * indicate significant differences ($p < 0.05$) among treatments. Immune cells infiltration and distortion of the crypt architecture are indicated by black and white arrows, respectively.

MPO is a peroxidase enzyme that plays an important role during infections by modulating the production of hypochlorous acid and other non-selective reactive species that mediate pathogens killing, and can induce host tissue damage by promoting inflammation [31]. It is mainly present in specialized granules of neutrophils hence elevated MPO levels and neutrophil infiltration have been correlated to inflammatory autoimmune disorders [32]. DSS and BG-4 groups exhibited an MPO activity four and 14 times higher, respectively, than CG (Figure 4C), corroborating observations in H&E staining micrographs where a higher infiltration of immune cells was detected for both groups with elevated severity upon BG-4 treatment.

Quantification of hemoglobin in collected feces was used to estimate fecal occult blood. Figure 4D indicates the presence of hemoglobin in feces for BG-4 and DSS groups followed the same trend as loss in weight. At the end of the study, the presence of hemoglobin in feces from BG-4 group was significantly higher than in DSS group, being consistent with the observations and scoring for the visual presence of blood in stool or rectum presented in Figure 3B,C.

3.5. IP Administration of BG-4 Exerted a Differential Systemic and Localized Effect in Pro-Inflammatory Cytokines In Vivo

Cytokines are signaling proteins that contribute to the modulation of the immune and inflammatory response during tissue damage and repair. The levels of pro-inflammatory cytokines IL-6, TNF-α, and IL-1β in colonic extracts (A) and in serum (B) are presented in Figure 5. No significant effect was observed upon DSS challenge and/or BG-4 treatment over the expression of IL-6 and TNF-α in colonic extracts, but both compounds were upregulated in serum in the DSS group and attenuated under BG-4 treatment (Figure 5A,B). IL-1β, in contrast, was upregulated in the DSS group and attenuated in the BG-4 group in colonic extracts but remained high in serum (Figure 5A,B). These results suggest that DSS and BG-4 were capable to exert a systemic (in circulating blood) but not localized (in colonic tissue) effect. A recent study has demonstrated dysregulation of pro-inflammatory cytokines in DSS-induced colitis mouse model with similar differential outcomes at the serum and colonic level observed in our study [33]. The particular differences in the systemic and localized effect over cytokines seem to indicate that IP injection allowed BG-4 to reach blood circulation, as expected for the high bioavailability reported for this administration route but post the question if the appropriate concentration was, in fact, capable to reach the intestinal barrier, where the tissue damage was induced via DSS and the inflammatory response was concentrated.

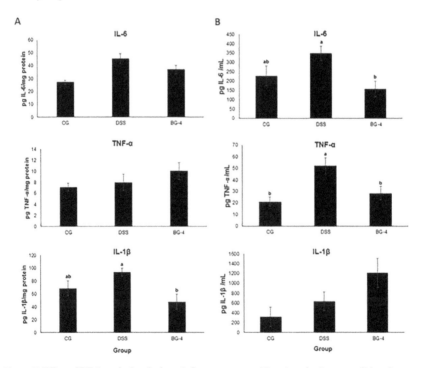

Figure 5. Effect of BG-4 on the level of pro-inflammatory cytokines in colonic extract (**A**) and serum (**B**). Results are presented as mean ± SE. Different letters indicate significant differences ($p < 0.05$) among treatments.

Our results showed that BG-4 exerted a differential effect over inflammation in vitro and in vivo. In LPS-stimulated macrophages, treatment with BG-4 showed a dose-dependent reduction of NO, IL-6, COX-2, and iNOS, suggesting 375 µg/mL as an optimal concentration for significant reduction of inflammatory markers. However, IP administration of BG-4 in a DSS-induced colitis mouse model, aggravated disease symptoms when compared with untreated mice, accompanied by the dysregulation of pro-inflammatory cytokines. The systemic circulation of BG-4 due to IP administration involved a possible effect over other immune and epithelial cells that can be more or less sensitive, in terms of cytotoxicity [34] and alteration of signaling and regulatory pathways, than the tested macrophages. For instance, it has been recently demonstrated the induction of NO metabolism in enterocytes alleviates colitis and CACC [29], suggesting a controversial role of NO in the regulation of the inflammatory response associated with its origin. According to this perspective, suppression of NO production exerted by BG-4 could result in a counteracting effect by simultaneously suppressing NO production on macrophages and enterocytes.

The outcomes observed in vivo under BG-4 treatment suggest that the mechanistic effect by which BG-4 suppresses NO production may be associated with enterocyte than macrophages. Under this circumstance, the reduced expression of NO by the enterocyte allows neutrophils infiltration, generation of cytotoxic compounds by MPO, tissue damage, and a consequently increased inflammatory response. One strength of our study is the first report on the comparative anti-inflammatory properties of BG-4 peptide from *Momordica charantia* using both in vitro and in vivo models. In addition, both mouse cell line and mouse model of colitis were utilized in the study. On the other hand, the observed contrasting result of in vitro and in vivo models on the anti-inflammatory effect of BG-4 is a potential weakness. The intraperitoneal injection of BG-4 may have resulted in the toxic effect of BG-4 in mouse model resulting in its pro-inflammatory effect which is contradictory in the observed anti-inflammatory effect in vitro. Hence the next step on the potential application of BG-4 for management of inflammatory diseases must be observed via oral route to determine if it can be used as a dietary supplement to mitigate diseases such as colitis.

4. Conclusions

In RAW 264.7 macrophages, BG-4 reduced the production of pro-inflammatory molecules NO, IL-6 and TNF-α as well as the expression of COX-2 and iNOS. On the other hand, in DSS-induced colitis mouse model intraperitoneal administration of BG-4 led to diarrhea, blood in stool and loss in weight. Our results demonstrated that IP administration of BG-4 in DSS-induced colitis mouse model led to a worsened outcome of the disease, in contrast to the reduction of the pro-inflammatory markers observed in vitro. BG-4 dose and route of administration must be further studied to realize the role of BG-4 in ameliorating IBD.

Author Contributions: A.N.-V.: performance of in vitro and in vivo analysis, and writing of the manuscript, Z.W.: performance of in vivo analysis, Q.Z.: Revision and editing of the manuscript, H.B.K.: Extraction of BG-4, and V.P.D.: Study design, guidance in the in vitro and in vivo experiments, and final editing and revision of the manuscript.

Funding: This work was partially supported by HATCH 1010230 to V.P.D. and Hatch Project TEN00487 to Q.Z. PhD for A.N.-V. is partially supported by COLCIENCIAS-FULBRIGHT cohort 2017.

Conflicts of Interest: The authors declare no conflicts of interest.

References

1. Egberg, M.D.; Kappelman, M.D.; Gulati, A.S. Improving Care in Pediatric Inflammatory Bowel Disease. *Gastroenterol. Clin. North Am.* **2018**, *47*, 909–919. [CrossRef] [PubMed]
2. Crowley, E.; Muise, A. Inflammatory Bowel Disease: What Very Early Onset Disease Teaches Us. *Gastroenterol. Clin. North Am.* **2018**, *47*, 755–772. [CrossRef] [PubMed]
3. Chang, M.; Chang, L.; Chang, H.M.; Chang, F. Intestinal and Extraintestinal Cancers Associated With Inflammatory Bowel Disease. *Clin. Colorectal Cancer* **2018**, *17*, e29–e37. [CrossRef]

4. Sairenji, T.; Collins, K.L.; Evans, D.V. An Update on Inflammatory Bowel Disease. *Prim. Care Clin. Off. Pract.* **2017**, *44*, 673–692. [CrossRef] [PubMed]

5. Palamthodi, S.; Lele, S.S. Nutraceutical applications of gourd family vegetables: Benincasa hispida, Lagenaria siceraria and Momordica charantia. *Biomed. Prev. Nutr.* **2014**, *4*, 15–21. [CrossRef]

6. Lii, C.K.; Chen, H.W.; Yun, W.T.; Liu, K.L. Suppressive effects of wild bitter gourd (*Momordica charantia* Linn. var. *abbreviata* ser.) fruit extracts on inflammatory responses in RAW 264.7 macrophages. *J. Ethnopharmacol.* **2009**, *122*, 227–233. [CrossRef] [PubMed]

7. Dandawate, P.R.; Subramaniam, D.; Padhye, S.B.; Anant, S. Bitter melon: A panacea for inflammation and cancer. *Chin. J. Nat. Med.* **2016**, *14*, 81–100. [CrossRef]

8. Xu, J.; Cao, K.; Feng, Z.; Liu, J. Benefits of the soluble and insoluble fractions of bitter gourd in mice fed a high-fat diet. *J. Funct. Foods.* **2018**, *42*, 216–223. [CrossRef]

9. Farooqi, A.A.; Khalid, S.; Tahir, F.; Sabitaliyevich, U.Y.; Yaylim, I.; Attar, R.; Xu, B. Bitter gourd (*Momordica charantia*) as a rich source of bioactive components to combat cancer naturally: Are we on the right track to fully unlock its potential as inhibitor of deregulated signaling pathways. *Food Chem. Toxicol.* **2018**, *119*, 98–105. [CrossRef]

10. Raish, M.; Ahmad, A.; Ansari, M.A.; Alkharfy, K.M.; Aljenobi, F.I.; Jan, B.L.; Al-Mohizea, A.M.; Khan, A.; Ali, N. Momordica charantia polysaccharides ameliorate oxidative stress, inflammation, and apoptosis in ethanol-induced gastritis in mucosa through NF-kB signaling pathway inhibition. *Int. J. Biol. Macromol.* **2018**, *111*, 193–199. [CrossRef]

11. Kubola, J.; Siriamornpun, S. Phenolic contents and antioxidant activities of bitter gourd (*Momordica charantia* L.) leaf, stem and fruit fraction extracts in vitro. *Food Chem.* **2008**, *110*, 881–890. [CrossRef] [PubMed]

12. Raina, K.; Kumar, D.; Agarwal, R. Promise of bitter melon (*Momordica charantia*) bioactives in cancer prevention and therapy. *Semin. Cancer Biol.* **2016**, *40–41*, 116–129. [CrossRef] [PubMed]

13. Dia, V.P.; Krishnan, H.B. BG-4, a novel anticancer peptide from bitter gourd (*Momordica charantia*), promotes apoptosis in human colon cancer cells. *Sci. Rep.* **2016**, *6*, 1–12. [CrossRef]

14. Jones, L.D.; Pangloli, P.; Krishnan, H.B.; Dia, V.P. BG-4, a novel bioactive peptide from *Momordica charantia*, inhibits lipopolysaccharide-induced inflammation in THP-1 human macrophages. *Phytomedicine* **2018**, *42*, 226–232. [CrossRef] [PubMed]

15. Vernaza, M.G.; Dia, V.P.; Gonzalez de Mejia, E.; Chang, Y.K. Antioxidant and Antiinflammatory Properties of Germinated and Hydrolysed Brazilian Soybean Flours. *Food Chem.* **2012**, *134*, 2217–2225. [CrossRef]

16. Richard-Eaglin, A.; Smallheer, B.A. Immunosuppressive/Autoimmune Disorders. *Nurs. Clin. North Am.* **2018**, *53*, 319–334. [CrossRef] [PubMed]

17. Kim, J.J.; Shajib, M.S.; Manocha, M.M.; Khan, W.I. Investigating Intestinal Inflammation in DSS-induced Model of IBD. *J. Vis. Exp.* **2012**, 1–6. [CrossRef]

18. Dai, Z.; Feng, S.; Liu, A.; Wang, H.; Zeng, X.; Yang, C.S. Anti-inflammatory effects of newly synthesized α-galacto-oligosaccharides on dextran sulfate sodium-induced colitis in C57BL/6J mice. *Food Res. Int.* **2018**, *109*, 350–357. [CrossRef]

19. Welch, C.L.; Young, D.S. Spectrophotometry of occult blood in feces. *Clin. Chem.* **1983**, *29*, 2022–2025.

20. Grajeda-Iglesias, C.; Salas, E.; Barouh, N.; Baréa, B.; Panya, A.; Figueroa-Espinoza, M.C. Antioxidant Activity of Protocatechuates Evaluated by DPPH, ORAC, and CAT Methods. *Food Chem.* **2016**, *194*, 749–757. [CrossRef]

21. Foss, C.A.; Sanchez-Bautista, J.; Jain, S.K. Imaging Macrophage-associated Inflammation. *Semin. Nucl. Med.* **2018**, *48*, 242–245. [CrossRef] [PubMed]

22. Van den Bossche, J.; Saraber, D.L. Metabolic regulation of macrophages in tissues. *Cell. Immunol.* **2018**, *330*, 54–59. [CrossRef] [PubMed]

23. Hsu, C.L.; Fang, S.C.; Liu, C.W.; Chen, Y.F. Inhibitory effects of new varieties of bitter melon on lipopolysaccharide-stimulated inflammatory response in RAW 264.7 cells. *J. Funct. Foods.* **2013**, *5*, 1829–1837. [CrossRef]

24. Dia, V.P.; Bringe, N.A.; de Mejia, E.G. Peptides in pepsin-pancreatin hydrolysates from commercially available soy products that inhibit lipopolysaccharide-induced inflammation in macrophages. *Food Chem.* **2014**, *152*, 423–431. [CrossRef] [PubMed]

25. de Mejia, E.G.; Dia, V.P. Lunasin and lunasin-like peptides inhibit inflammation through suppression of NF-κB pathway in the macrophage. *Peptides* **2009**, *30*, 2388–2398. [CrossRef] [PubMed]

26. An, J.Y.; Lee, H.H.; Shin, J.S.; Yoo, H.S.; Park, J.S.; Son, S.H.; Kim, S.W.; Yu, J.; Lee, J.; Lee, K.T.; et al. Identification and structure activity relationship of novel flavone derivatives that inhibit the production of nitric oxide and PGE2in LPS-induced RAW 264.7 cells. *Bioorganic Med. Chem. Lett.* **2017**, *27*, 2613–2616. [CrossRef] [PubMed]

27. Sinha, C.K.; Coran, A.G. Ulcerative colitis. *Handb. Pediatr. Surg.* **2010**, 201–206. [CrossRef]

28. Wu, X.; Song, M.; Cai, X.; Neto, C.; Tata, A.; Han, Y.; Wang, Q.; Tang, Z.; Xiao, H. Chemopreventive Effects of Whole Cranberry (*Vaccinium macrocarpon*) on Colitis-Associated Colon Tumorigenesis. *Mol. Nutr. Food Res.* **2018**, 1800942. [CrossRef]

29. Stettner, N.; Rosen, C.; Bernshtein, B.; Gur-Cohen, S.; Frug, J.; Silberman, A.; Sarver, A.; Carmel-Neiderman, N.N.; Eilam, R.; et al. Induction of Nitric-Oxide Metabolism in Enterocytes Alleviates Colitis and Inflammation-Associated Colon Cancer. *Cell Rep.* **2018**, *23*, 1962–1976. [CrossRef]

30. Huang, Y.; Guo, J.; Gui, S. Orally targeted galactosylated chitosan poly(lactic-co-glycolic acid) nanoparticles loaded with TNF-α siRNA provide a novel strategy for the experimental treatment of ulcerative colitis. *Eur. J. Pharm. Sci.* **2018**, *125*, 232–243. [CrossRef]

31. Strzepa, A.; Pritchard, K.A.; Dittel, B.N. Myeloperoxidase: A new player in autoimmunity. *Cell. Immunol.* **2017**, *317*, 1–8. [CrossRef] [PubMed]

32. Aratani, Y. Myeloperoxidase: Its role for host defense, inflammation, and neutrophil function. *Arch. Biochem. Biophys.* **2018**, *640*, 47–52. [CrossRef] [PubMed]

33. Hong Li, Y.; Adam, R.; Colombel, J.F.; Xiang Bian, Z. A characterization of pro-inflammatory cytokines in dextran sulfate sodium-induced chronic relapsing colitis mice model. *Int. Immunopharmacol.* **2018**, *60*, 194–201. [CrossRef]

34. Wang, Y.; Ning, Z.H.; Tai, H.W.; Long, S.; Qin, W.C.; Su, L.M.; Zhao, Y.H. Relationship between lethal toxicity in oral administration and injection to mice: Effect of exposure routes. *Regul. Toxicol. Pharmacol.* **2015**, *71*, 205–212. [CrossRef] [PubMed]

Article

Gamma Tocopherol Reduced Chemotherapeutic-Induced ROS in an Ovarian Granulosa Cell Line, But Not in Breast Cancer Cell Lines In Vitro

Daniela Figueroa Gonzalez and Fiona Young *

Medical Biotechnology, College of Medicine and Public Health, Flinders University, Adelaide 5042, Australia; daniela.figueroagonzalez@flinders.edu.au
* Correspondence: Fiona.Young@flinders.edu.au; Tel.: +618-7221-8558

Received: 25 November 2019; Accepted: 31 December 2019; Published: 7 January 2020

Abstract: Doxorubicin and cyclophosphamide are used to treat breast cancer, but they also cause infertility through off-target cytotoxicity towards proliferating granulosa cells that surround eggs. Each chemotherapeutic generates reactive oxygen species (ROS) but the effects of the combination, or the antioxidants alpha (αToc) and gamma tocopherol (γToc) on ROS in breast cancer or ovarian cells are unknown. Human breast cancer (MCF7, T47D) and ovarian cancer (OVCAR, COV434) cells were loaded with DCDFA and exposed (1, 2, 3, 24 h) to the MCF7-derived EC25 values of individual agents, or to combinations of these. ROS were quantified and viable cells enumerated using crystal violet or DAPI. Each chemotherapeutic killed ~25% of MCF7, T47D and OVCAR cells, but 57 $\pm$ 2% (doxorubicin) and 66 $\pm$ 2% (cyclophosphamide) of the COV434 granulosa cells. The combined chemotherapeutics decreased COV434 cell viability to 34 $\pm$ 5% of control whereas doxorubicin + cyclophosphamide + γToc reduced ROS within 3 h ($p < 0.01$) and reduced cytotoxicity to 54 $\pm$ 4% ($p < 0.05$). αToc was not cytotoxic, whereas γToc killed ~25% of the breast cancer but none of the ovarian cells. Adding γToc to the combined chemotherapeutics did not change ROS or cytotoxicity in MCF7, T47D or OVCAR cells. The protection γToc afforded COV434 granulosa cells against chemotherapy-induced ROS and cytotoxicity suggests potential for fertility preservation.

Keywords: breast cancer; reactive oxygen species; tocopherol; doxorubicin; cyclophosphamide; ovary; granulosa cell; infertility

---

1. Introduction

Intracellular reactive oxygen species (ROS) [1–3] are crucial for normal cell metabolism [3–6] and ROS generation is highly regulated by either enzymatic (catalases, peroxidases and dismutases) or non-enzymatic (vitamin A, C or E) reductive molecules. Disturbances in cellular redox balance can lead to an over-accumulation of ROS [1]. Cells also produce ROS after exposure to radiation or chemotherapeutics [7], many of which induce ROS to toxic levels as part of their mechanism of action [8].

The combination of doxorubicin (Dox) and cyclophosphamide is often used to treat breast cancer [9–11]. Dox is an anthracycline agent that causes apoptosis by intercalating into double-stranded DNA and inhibiting topoisomerase-II [12]. A second mechanism of action involving ROS has also been described [5,13,14].

Cyclophosphamide is an alkylating agent that requires hepatic metabolic activation [15], which generates 4-hydroxycyclophosphamide and aldophosphamide [16]. Aldophosphamide is metabolized into phosphoramide mustard and acrolein, which increases ROS production in a variety of cell lines [17,18].

Dox and cyclophosphamide are associated with a variety of adverse effects in vivo, including T-cell suppression, chronic cardiotoxicity and premature ovarian failure [19–28]. It has been proposed that chemotherapeutics cause premature ovarian failure by targeting proliferating granulosa cells in growing follicles [22,23]. Since granulosa cells synthesise anti-Müllerian hormone (AMH), the loss of follicles due to chemotherapeutic-induced cytotoxicity causes a consequent depletion in circulating AMH, which results in the activation and recruitment of dormant primordial follicles into the growing pool [23]. It is thought that the in vivo administration of repeated cycles of Dox and cyclophosphamide diminishes the cohort of active growing follicles, reduces the reserve of primordial follicles, and results in premature ovarian failure [21,23–29].

Although the toxicity of cyclophosphamide and Dox (as single agents) on the ovary is well established [21,23–29] there are no reports that describe the effect of the combination of Dox and cyclophosphamide on proliferating granulosa cells.

The tocopherols (alpha, beta, gamma and delta) and tocotrienols (alpha, beta, gamma and delta) that together form Vitamin E [30] act as free radical scavengers in cell membranes [31]. α-tocopherol (αToc) is the most abundant form in nature, while γ-Tocopherol (γToc) is the most common form in the human diet [31]. It has been proposed that Dox-induced cardiotoxicity is the result of ROS-induced membrane lipid peroxidation [32], and vitamin E deficiency results in histological features that are comparable to Dox-treated cardiac tissue [19,32]. Although the administration of αToc to breast cancer patients before chemotherapy elevated serum concentrations 8-fold, there were no other observable effects [19]. However, the effects of αToc on post-chemotherapeutic ovarian function were not examined. γToc delayed the formation of breast cancer tumours in rodent models [33], induced apoptosis in breast cancer cells in vitro [34,35] and may prevent breast cancer in vivo [36,37]. Additionally, a mixture of γ and delta tocopherol down-regulated the expression of estrogen receptor and inhibited estradiol-induced human MCF-7 breast cancer cell proliferation in vitro [36].

Both α and γ tocopherol are antioxidants with the potential to reduce chemotherapeutic-induced ROS damage, and consequently reduce premature ovarian failure. Reduced ROS, however, could also lead to decreased efficacy against breast cancer cells. γToc has both reductive power and anticancer activity [33], and this led to our hypothesis that gamma tocopherol, but not alpha tocopherol, would augment the cytotoxic activity of the combination of Dox and cyclophosphamide against breast cancer cells in vitro, whilst simultaneously reducing ROS generation.

2. Materials and Methods

2.1. Chemicals and Reagents

All chemicals and reagents used in the study were obtained from Sigma-Aldrich (Sydney, Australia), unless otherwise specified. The 2′,7′-dichlorofluorescin diacetate (DCFDA) cellular ROS detection assay kit was purchased from Abcam (Melbourne, Australia).

2.2. Preparation of Solutions

Supplemented RPMI was prepared by mixing 500 mL of phenol red-free RPMI with foetal calf serum (FCS, DKSH, Victoria, Australia) at 10% for MCF-7 and T47D, and 20% for OVCAR-3 cells, and 1% *v/v* of 10,000 unit/mL penicillin + 10 mg/mL streptomycin (pen-strep). Supplemented RPMI with 20% FCS also contained 5 µg/mL of recombinant human insulin for use with OVCAR-3 cells. Supplemented DMEM/F-12 was prepared by mixing phenol red-free DMEM/F-12, 10% FCS and 1% *v/v* of pen-strep. A total of 10 mL Hank's balanced salt solution (HBSS, provided by the DCFDA ROS assay kit manufacturer) was added to 90 mL ddH$_2$O. DCFDA was diluted in 1X HBSS to generate a solution of 10 µM. The DCFDA ROS assay positive control, ter-butyl hydrogen peroxide (TBHP), was diluted in supplemented media (RPMI or DMEM/F12) without phenol red, to give final concentrations of 12.5 and 50 µM. Stock solutions of 100 µM Dox and 1000 µM 4-hydroperoxycyclophosphamide (4-Cyc, ThermoFisher Scientific, Victoria, Australia) were prepared in supplemented media (RPMI or DMEM/F-12) and kept at 4 and −20 °C, respectively, for a maximum of three months. α and γ tocopherol were diluted in 100% dimethyl sulfoxide (DMSO) to a concentration of 1000 μM. These stock solutions were kept at 4 °C for a maximum of three months. Further dilutions were made using supplemented media, and the concentration of DMSO the cells were exposed to was lower than 0.8% DMSO. The crystal violet stain (0.5%) was prepared in a 50% methanol (99.9% pure). Destain solution for the crystal violet assay was prepared with 100% acetic acid diluted to 33% with demineralised water.

2.3. Cell Culture

The MCF-7 human epithelial breast adenocarcinoma cell line and the T47D human epithelial breast ductal carcinoma cell line were obtained from the America Type Culture Collection (ATCC, Manassas, VA, USA) and maintained in supplemented RPMI medium with 10% FCS. The OVCAR-3 human epithelial ovarian adenocarcinoma cell line (ATCC, Manassas, VA, USA) was maintained in RPMI medium supplemented with 20% FCS and 5 μg/mL insulin. The COV434 (ECACC 07071909) human ovarian granulosa cancer cell line was maintained in supplemented DMEM/F12 medium. Media in each 75 cm^2 flask of cells were replaced every 2–3 days and each cell line was subcultured twice a week. Cells that had undergone fewer than 25 passages were used for all experiments when they were 80% confluent, and in the exponential growth phase.

2.4. Determination of MCF-7 Effective Concentration (EC) Values

MCF-7 cells (20,000 cells per well) were exposed to increasing concentrations of chemotherapeutics and tocopherols for 24 h and cell viability was examined in a crystal violet assay. The effective concentration that killed 50% and 25% of MCF-7 cells was calculated by a non-linear regression analysis performed using GraphPad Prism (Version 5.00, San Diego, CA, USA). The experiment was repeated on three separate occasions.

2.5. Effect of Dox, 4-Hydroperoxycyclophosphamide (4-Cyc), α or γ Tocopherol on ROS Generation

MCF-7, T47D, OVCAR-3 or COV434 cells (20,000 cells per well) were added to dark, clear bottom 96-well microplates for 24 h to adhere before adding each test agent to triplicate wells. Cells were exposed to 100 μL 10 μM DCFDA for 45 min at 37 °C in a humidified 5% CO_2 incubator in the dark. The DCFDA solution was removed, and cells were exposed to 100 μL of chemotherapeutics or tocopherols (Table 1) for 24 h. Concentrations of chemotherapeutics and γToc were the effective concentrations that killed 25% of MCF-7 cells (EC25). Since a cytotoxic concentration of αToc was not determined, the highest concentration tested was selected for further examination.

Controls were cells in medium only (background negative control), and cells exposed to low (12.5 μM) or high (50 μM) concentrations of TBHP (positive controls) [38], or 0.8% DMSO as a vehicle control for the tocopherols. Each experiment was repeated on three separate occasions ($n = 3$).

Table 1. 24 h MCF-7-derived EC25 chemotherapeutics and tocopherols values.

Single Agents	Concentrations (μM)
Dox	1.21
4-Cyc	21.23
αToc	100
γToc	35.1
Combined Agents	**Concentrations (μM)**
Dox + 4-Cyc	1.21 (Dox) + 21.23 (4-Cyc)
Dox + 4-Cyc + αToc	1.21 (Dox) + 21.23 (4-Cyc) + 100 (αToc)
Dox + 4-Cyc + γToc	1.21 (Dox) + 21.23 (4-Cyc) + 35.1 (γToc)

Dox—Doxorubicin, 4-Cyc—4-hydroperoxycyclophosphamide, αToc—α-Tocopherol, γToc—γ-Tocopherol.

2.6. ROS Measurement by DCFDA Assay

The ROS production was detected by recording fluorescence immediately after addition of test agents (time 0), every hour for a 3 h incubation period, and after 24 h continuous incubation. Fluorescence was measured according to protocol described by Figueroa et al., [38]. Fluorescence readings were made using a plate spectrofluorometer (GloMax® Explorer, Promega, Sydney, Australia). Relative fluorescence units (RFU) for each culture well were calculated by subtracting background readings (cells in media only), from all fluorescence values obtained from DCFDA loaded cells in media + test reagents. Each concentration of DCFDA and TBHP was examined in triplicate wells. Plates were sealed to maintain sterility during fluorescence readings and kept at 37 °C in a humidified 5% CO_2 incubator in the dark between readings.

2.7. Crystal Violet (CV) Assay

After measurement of ROS, cell viability was determined using crystal violet (4-[(4-dimethylaminophenyl)-phenyl-methyl]-*N,N*-dimethyl-aniline) to stain DNA [39–42]. In short, 20,000 cells per well were cultured for 24 h to allow adherence, then loaded with DCFDA and exposed to test reagents. ROS were measured 0, 1, 2, 3 and 24 h after adding chemotherapeutics and tocopherols. Media containing test agents and non-adherent dead cells were removed, the cells were rinsed with PBS, and the PBS was replaced with 50 μL of crystal violet stain (0.5%) for 10 min. Cells were rinsed with demineralised water to remove any excess stain, then left to air-dry overnight. A total of 60 μL destain solution of 33% acetic acid was added for 10 min before absorbance was read at 570 nm with correction at 630 nm [41]. Linear correlations between optical density and cell number have been reported [41,42], therefore the numbers of viable cells remaining after exposure to test agents were determined by a comparison with a CV standard curve using densities of 0–80,000 cells per well (R^2 = 0.99) generated for the same replicate experiment. Since CV stains DNA, the optical density values included contributions from any stained and adherent DNA, such as that included in condensed nuclei in the early stages of apoptosis or other forms of cell death, and adherent apoptotic bodies characteristic of the later stages of apoptosis.

2.8. DAPI Staining and Scoring of Cell Nuclei

6-diamidino-2-phenylindole (DAPI), a blue fluorescent dye, binds A–T-rich regions in dsDNA and has been used to visualise condensed, deformed or fragmented nuclei formed during both necrosis and apoptosis [8,43]. Early apoptosis is characterised by cell shrinkage and increased membrane permeability, which facilitates uptake of nuclear dyes such as DAPI. This causes condensed chromatin to appear as 'bright' dye-dense areas, whereas during late apoptosis the nucleus fragments and forms smaller apoptotic bodies.

MCF-7, T47D, OVCAR-3 or COV434 cells (30,000 cells per well) were added to Nunc Lab-Tek II –CC2 chamber units (Promega, Sydney, Australia). After an initial 24 h adherence period to the glass microscope slide, cells were exposed to 300 μL of chemotherapeutics with or without tocopherols (Table 1) and incubated for another 24 h. The test reagents were removed, and the cells rinsed with PBS before fixation with 4% paraformaldehyde in PBS for 25 min at 4 °C. The cells were rinsed with PBS, then incubated with 1 μg/mL DAPI prepared in sterile PBS for 30 min in the dark at room temperature. After rinsing with PBS, cells were mounted in buffered glycerol and examined using an Olympus fluorescence microscope with filter Chroma 31,000 at excitation 340–380 nm, Dichroic 400 and emission 435–485 nm [44]. Four digital images of each well were taken at 20× magnification and the experiment was repeated on three separate occasions (*n* = 3) for each of the four cell types.

Scoring DAPI-stained nuclei in digital images is a subjective pastime. The scoring criteria were determined by reviewing published reports [45–47] and by observation of MCF7 images from the present study. Very small, bright (DAPI-intense) objects, that appeared as though the nucleus had fragmented into smaller apoptotic bodies (Figure 1A,D), or small very bright objects, usually with irregular shapes suggestive of condensed nuclei (Figure 1A,D,H,I), were collectively scored as condensed nuclei. Larger, relatively dull objects with regular spherical outlines (Figure 1E–G), or sometimes crescent-shaped outlines, particularly for the COV434 cells (Figure 1C), were scored as normal nuclei. Objects with irregular outlines that were smaller and brighter than normal nuclei were scored as uncertain. In some cases, they were only slightly larger than condensed nuclei, but if they had less DAPI (were duller), they were considered to have less condensed DNA and were classified as uncertain (Figure 1B,F). Groups of dull objects with a similar morphology to groups of apoptotic bodies were included in the condensed category (Figure 1A). Objects scored as uncertain were not clearly apoptotic or condensed nuclei, but neither were they unequivocally normal nuclei. Only complete nuclei or objects were included in the count and objects on the edges of the images were excluded.

Each image was allocated a code and deidentified, shuffled into a random order and scored blind. The scores were recorded onto each image before re-identifying and entering the numbers of condensed, uncertain or normal nuclei into a spreadsheet. The numbers of condensed nuclei (includes apoptotic bodies that were given a score of 1 for each group) were expressed as a percentage of the normal nuclei for each image (i.e., the uncertain nuclei were excluded from this calculation). There were three independent experiments, except for some cases (OVCAR and MCF7 medium control, MCF7 Dox + 4-Cyc + αToc, MCF7 Dox + 4-Cyc + γToc and MCF7 Dox) in which the experiment was repeated on four separate occasions. The effects of the chemotherapeutics and tocopherols on the nuclear morphology of MCF7, T47D and OVCAR cells were very similar, and hence representative examples have been shown in Figure 1. The mean ± stdev ($n = 3$ or 4) was calculated for the percentages of condensed nuclei. Data were subjected to 1Way ANOVA with Tukey post-hoc test.

2.9. Statistical Analysis

One-way ANOVA with Tukey HSD post-hoc tests were applied to the 24 h crystal violet, ROS and DAPI datasets, and a Two-way ANOVA with Bonferroni post-test was applied to the 24 h ROS control data using GraphPad Prism, GraphPad Software, San Diego, CA, USA). Two-way ANOVA with Bonferroni post-hoc tests were performed to examine the effect of 1–3 h exposure and reagent concentration on ROS production. These statistical analyses were performed using SPSS statistics software (V22.0 IBM, Armonk, NY, USA). Statistical significance was set at $p \leq 0.05$. All experiments were performed as three independent replicates, and all data expressed as mean ± standard deviation.

3. Results

The numbers of DAPI-stained nuclei with normal regular morphology in the images of cell culture medium control wells were T47D (415 ± 68, Figure 1I) > MCF7 (312 ± 18 Figure 1G) > OVCAR (173 ± 32) > COV434 (53 ± 19) and there were similar numbers of nuclei with normal morphology in the 0.8% DMSO controls. The OVCAR cells were derived from ovarian surface epithelial cells, and the T47D and MCF7 cells were derived from mammary epithelial cells. The normal DAPI-stained nuclei of these three cell lines in control wells were a similar size and morphology, with regular round or oval shapes (Figure 1E,G,I). The COV434 cells were derived from a granulosa cell tumour, and their nuclei were much smaller and often shaped like a croissant (crescent, Figure 1C). DAPI-intense 'bright' objects were observed in two forms: a relatively low number of apoptotic bodies (Figure 1A,D) and much higher numbers of what appeared to be small, irregularly shaped condensed nuclei (Figure 1A,H). Some nuclei were clearly not 'normal', but neither were they bright nor small enough to qualify as 'condensed'. These were labelled 'uncertain' and were frequently observed in the COV434 cell line (8.9%, Figure 1B), but were found less frequently in the MCF7 (2.4%), OVCAR (1.4%) and T47D cells (1.2%).

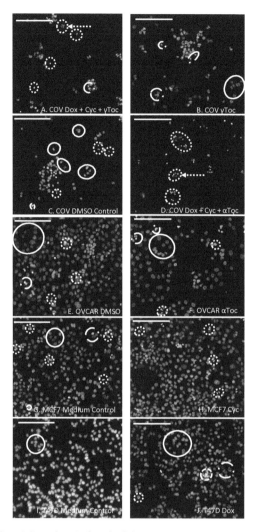

Figure 1. Cell nucleus 6-diamidino-2-phenylindole (DAPI) staining and scoring: COV434 (**A–D**),
OVCAR (**E,F**), MCF7 (**G,H**) or T47D (**I,J**) cells adhered to the glass microscope slides for 24 h before
exposure to doxorubicin (Dox, **J**) or 4-cyclophosphamide (Cyc, **H**) or α Tocopherol (αT, **F**) or γ
Tocopherol (γT, **B**) or Dox + 4-Cyc + αToc (**D**) or Dox + 4-Cyc + γToc (**A**) or cell culture medium
as a control for the chemotherapeutics (**G,I**), or 0.8% DMSO as a control for treatments containing
tocopherols (**C,E**) were stained with DAPI before a fluorescence microscope was used to obtain digital
images. The experiment was repeated on three separate occasions (*n* = 3) for each of the four cell
types. Representative examples in each image shown of nuclei with normal morphology (solid circles),
condensed DAPI-bright nuclei (dotted circles) or groups of apoptotic bodies (dotted circles and arrow)
and nuclei with uncertain status (broken dash and dot circles). Scale bars 100 μm.

Although the numbers of nuclei with normal morphology were similar in cell culture medium and
in medium containing 0.8% DMSO in all four cell lines (representative examples shown in Figure 1),
a 24 h culture in 0.8% DMSO caused significantly more condensed COV434 nuclei than medium
control (*p* < 0.05, Figure 2A), whereas the percentages of condensed nuclei were similar in media and
DMSO controls in the other three cell lines (Figure 2). 4-Cyc significantly increased the percentage

of condensed COV434 nuclei ($p < 0.05$) compared to the cell culture medium control. The COV434 cell nuclei in control cell culture media were smaller than the nuclei of the other three cell lines, but exposure to the combination of Dox + 4-Cyc + αToc (Figure 1D) caused the nuclei which most resembled 'normal' to become even smaller. Nuclei exposed to Dox + 4-Cyc + αToc were difficult to score because it was not clear if they should be placed in the condensed or uncertain categories. It was clear, however, that there were very few normal nuclei; only 9.6 ± 1.5 normal (Figure S1A) and 12.3 ± 7.8 condensed nuclei ($53 \pm 16\%$, Figure 2A) per image, as opposed to 59.5 ± 3.5 normal nuclei in the COV434 DMSO control images (Figure 1C). Although exposure to αToc alone resulted in the same proportions of condensed nuclei as in the DMSO control, the addition of αToc to the chemotherapeutics significantly increased the percentage of condensed nuclei compared to the DMSO control and to Dox + 4-Cyc ($p < 0.001$, Figure 2A). Even though the COV434 DAPI-stained nuclei were difficult to score, it was still clear that αToc increased the cytotoxic activity of Dox + 4-Cyc.

Conversely, γToc reduced the background levels of the condensed COV434 nuclei to zero (Figure 2A) and the addition of γToc to the chemotherapeutics maintained the number of normal nuclei at 48 ± 9 (Figure 1B and Figure S1A), hence there were no statistical differences between the percentages of condensed nuclei in DMSO control and Dox + 4-Cyc + γToc treated COV434 cells (Figure 2A).

Neither of the chemotherapeutics affected the percentages of condensed MCF7 nuclei (Figure 2B). MCF7 cells exposed to αToc for 24 h had 375 ± 101 normal nuclei and 21 ± 4 condensed nuclei ($6 \pm 2.7\%$, Figure 2B), whereas exposure to Dox + 4-Cyc + αToc resulted in only 90 ± 20 normal nuclei (Figure S1D) and $0.48 \pm 0.6\%$ condensed nuclei (Figure 2B). This reduction in condensed nuclei occurred in the context of cell loss indicative of cell death earlier in the 24 h exposure and was unlikely to be caused by αToc protecting MCF7 against the cytotoxic effects of Dox + 4-Cyc. MCF7 cells cultured in DMSO control conditions or exposed to Dox + 4-Cyc + γToc were like the COV434 cells in that there were no significant differences in the numbers of normal nuclei, nor the percentages of condensed nuclei.

Dox + 4-Cyc increased the number of condensed T47D nuclei ($p < 0.01$) compared to the medium control, and the addition of each of the tocopherols to Dox + 4-Cyc increased the percentages of condensed nuclei compared to the DMSO control ($p < 0.05$, Figure 2C). Addition of the tocopherols to the chemotherapeutics also increased the numbers of normal nuclei; there were 253 ± 13 normal nuclei after exposure to Dox + 4-Cyc, but 503 ± 290 and 650 ± 73 normal nuclei after exposure to the chemotherapeutics combined with αToc and γToc, respectively (Figure S1C).

The combination of Dox + 4-Cyc also increased the number of condensed OVCAR nuclei ($p < 0.01$, Figure 2D). Although γToc reduced the number of condensed nuclei compared to the DMSO control ($p < 0.05$), when the tocopherols were combined with Dox + 4-Cyc neither affected the proportions of condensed (Figure 2D) or normal nuclei (Figure S1B).

Crystal violet stains DNA. The proportion of condensed nuclei in all cases except one (COV434 Dox + 4-Cyc + αToc) was lower than 10% (Figure 2). It is therefore reasonable to assume that at least 90% of the crystal violet staining was indicative of viable cells containing nuclei with normal morphologies. Exposure to 0.8% DMSO, the vehicle for both tocopherols, did not affect the amount of crystal violet staining in any cell line, for example, there were $33,837 \pm 1642$ T47D cells after 24 h in medium control and $37,897 \pm 495$ in control medium containing 0.8% DMSO (Figure S1). Although 20,000 cells were initially seeded into the 96 well plates, after a total of 48 h in control conditions there were fewer COV434 cells than the other three cell lines—$22,948 \pm 1567$ COV434 cells per well (Figure S1).

The MCF-7 derived EC25 values for 4-Cyc reduced viable cell numbers by approximately 25% in the present study. MCF-7 viable cell numbers were reduced to $68 \pm 9\%$ of control, T47D to $71 \pm 2\%$, COV434 to $66 \pm 6\%$ and OVCAR to $61 \pm 15\%$ (Figure 3). Cell line sensitivity to the cytotoxic effects of Dox was slightly different. COV434 cells were the most sensitive ($57 \pm 2\%$), whereas the three epithelial cell lines had similar sensitivities, ranging from $67 \pm 6\%$ (T47D) to $75 \pm 5\%$ (OVCAR). The combination of the EC25 value for 4-Cyc with the EC25 value for Dox was expected to cause death of 50% of the cells, but was less cytotoxic to MCF-7 ($76 \pm 14\%$ of control) and T47D ($61 \pm 4\%$) but more cytotoxic to COV434 cells (34 ± 5% of control). For OVCAR cells, the cytotoxicity caused by the two chemotherapeutics was additive; the combination reduced viable OVCAR cell numbers to 57 ± 11% of control.

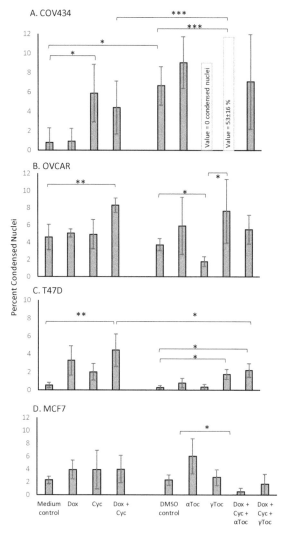

Figure 2. DAPI-stained condensed cell nuclei: COV434 (**A**), OVCAR (**B**), T47D (**C**) or MCF7 (**D**) cells adhered to glass microscope slides for 24 h before a 24 h exposure to doxorubicin (Dox) or 4-cyclophosphamide (Cyc) or α Tocopherol (αToc) or γ Tocopherol (γToc) or combinations of these. Cell culture medium was a control for the chemotherapeutics and 0.8% DMSO in culture medium was a control for tocopherols. Cells were stained with DAPI before a fluorescence microscope was used to capture digital images. The numbers of normal and condensed (includes groups of apoptotic bodies) nuclei were scored in each image, and the condensed nuclei expressed as a percentage. The experiment was repeated on three separate occasions and the mean ± stdev of percentages is shown. Data were subjected to 1 Way ANOVA with a Tukey post-test * $p < 0.05$, ** $p < 0.01$, *** $p < 0.001$.

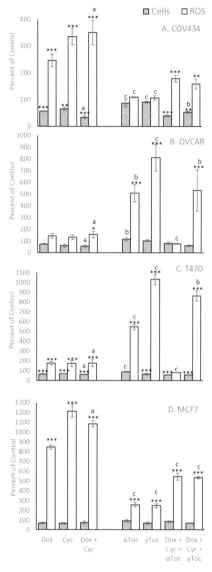

Figure 3. Effect of chemotherapeutics and tocopherols on cell viability and reactive oxygen species (ROS). Human COV434 (**A**), OVCAR (**B**), T47D (**C**) and MCF7 (**D**) cells were cultured for 24 h before being loaded with DCFDA and exposed to Doxorubicin (Dox) or 4-Cyclophosphamide (Cyc) or α Tocopherol (αToc) or γ Tocopherol (γToc), or combinations of these, for 24 h in triplicate wells. ROS were measured before measuring the number of adherent cells per well in a crystal violet assay (Cells). The average cell number, or ROS, obtained from triplicate wells, was expressed as a percentage of control for the same experimental replicate. Controls were culture medium, or culture medium containing DMSO which was the vehicle for tocopherols. Data are shown as mean ± stdev of percentages obtained in three independent experiments ($n = 3$). The original 'Cells' or 'ROS' data (i.e., not percentages) were subjected to 1 Way ANOVA with a Tukey post-test. Within either Cells or ROS, significant difference from control * $p > 0.05$, ** $p > 001$, *** $p > 0.001$, or a v b $p > 0.05$, b v c $p < 0.01$, a v c $p > 0.001$.

A cytotoxic dose of αToc was not found, and the relatively high non-cytotoxic concentration of αToc used in the present study was not cytotoxic to any cell line (Figure 3). The MCF7-derived EC25 value of γToc reduced T47D cell viability to 64 ± 9% ($p < 0.01$, Figure 3C) and MCF7 cells to 70 ± 14% of DMSO control but had no effect on the viability of COV434 or OVCAR cells (Figure 3). γToc interacted with the chemotherapeutics and COV434 cells such that Dox + 4-Cyc reduced viable COV434 cell numbers to 34 ± 5% of medium control ($p < 0.001$), but when γToc was added to the combined chemotherapeutics COV434 cell viability was reduced to 54 ± 4% of the DMSO control ($p < 0.01$). Hence, when compared to Dox + 4-Cyc, γToc conferred a significant protective effect against the cytotoxicity caused by the chemotherapeutics ($p < 0.05$). However, γToc did not affect the cytotoxicity of the combined chemotherapeutics in the other three cell lines.

Although 0.8% DMSO, the vehicle control for tocopherols, had no effect on cell viability (Figure S1), COV434, OVCAR and T47D cells cultured in 0.8% DMSO generated significantly more ROS than in culture medium ($p < 0.001$, Figure 4), whereas MCF7 cells generated similar amounts of ROS in the two control media (Figure 4).

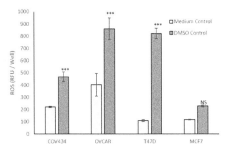

Figure 4. Reactive oxygen species (ROS) generation under in vitro control conditions. Cells were cultured for 24 h before being loaded with DCFDA, then cultured for 24 h in either cell culture medium (Medium Control) or cell culture medium containing 0.8% DMSO (DMSO Control). Relative Fluorescent Units (RFU per culture well) indicative of reactive oxygen species (ROS) generated by the cells in that well were measured using a 96-well plate spectrofluorometer. Data are shown as mean ± stdev of three independent experiments ($n = 3$). The RFU per well values were analysed by 2-Way ANOVA with Bonferroni post-test. Within each cell line, significant difference between two controls: NS not significant, *** $p > 0.001$.

After 24 h exposure, 4-Cyc caused all four cell lines to generate more ROS than Dox (Figure 3). The addition of the MCF7-derived EC25 4-Cyc to the EC25 Dox did not double ROS compared to each chemotherapeutic alone, but ROS levels after exposure to the combined chemotherapeutics were always higher than after exposure to 4-Cyc alone. Neither αToc nor γToc affected ROS production by COV434, OVCAR or T47D cells, but it was surprising that each tocopherol significantly increased ROS in MCF7 cells ($p < 0.001$ Figure 3D). The addition of tocopherols to Dox + 4-Cyc was unable to prevent ROS generation by MCF7, T47D or COV434 cells, but αToc reduced and γToc completely prevented the chemotherapeutic-stimulated increase in ROS.

Although ROS levels did not change in cell culture medium, ROS levels increased in the cell culture medium containing 0.8% DMSO during the first 3 h of culture (Figure 5). Acute, time-dependent, significant increases in ROS levels were detected in MCF-7, T47D and OVCAR-3 cells during the first 3 h exposure to the MCF-7 EC25 value (21.23 μM) of 4-Cyc (Figure 5). Dox caused a lower, but still significant increase in ROS production by the same cell lines. In COV434 granulosa cells, ROS levels increased after 1 h exposure to Dox. Unlike the other cell lines, 4-Cyc and Dox stimulated the same amount of ROS during the first 3 h; the amount of ROS generated by 4-Cyc was lower than in the other three cell lines (Figure 5). α and γToc did not stimulate ROS generation after 1, 2 or 3 h in any of the cell lines.

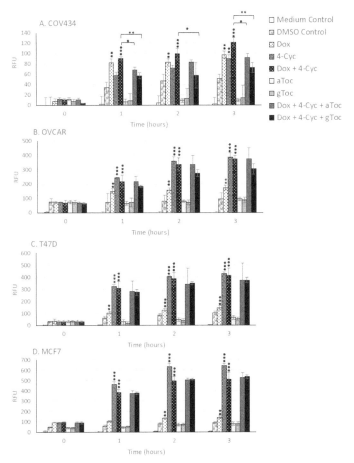

Figure 5. Effect of 3 h exposure to chemotherapeutics and tocopherols on ROS production. (**A**) COV434, (**B**) OVCAR, (**C**) T47D, and (**D**) MCF-7 cells were loaded with DCFDA then exposed to Doxorubicin (Dox), 4-Cyclophosphamide (4-Cyc), α Tocopherol (aToc) or γ Tocopherol (gToc) or combinations of these for 3 h at concentrations that reduced MCF-7 viability by 25% (EC25). Fluorescence was read every hour for 3 h. Means ± SD of three independent experiments are shown. Relative fluorescent units (RFU) were subjected to Two-way ANOVA with Bonferroni post-hoc test * $p \leq 0.05$, ** $p \leq 0.01$, *** $p \leq 0.001$ significant difference from same exposure control, bars show significant difference compared to combination of Dox and 4-Cyc at same exposure.

The combination of Dox + 4-Cyc also caused time-dependent, significant increases in ROS within the first 3 h of exposure (Figure 5). The addition of either tocopherol to the combination of chemotherapeutics had no effect on acute ROS generation by three of the cell lines, but significantly reduced ROS generation by COV434 cells. γToc was more effective than αToc at reducing Dox + 4-Cyc generated ROS in COV434 cells within the first 3 h of exposure.

4. Discussion

This is the first study to examine the effect of a clinically relevant combination of the chemotherapeutics Dox and 4-Cyc on cytotoxicity and ROS production by human breast and ovarian cell lines in vitro. Our finding that γToc reduced chemotherapeutic-generated ROS production by transformed ovarian granulosa COV434 and epithelial adenocarcinoma OVCAR cells, but not by breast cancer cells, indicates the potential to develop antioxidant γToc as an adjunct treatment to reduce the adverse effects of chemotherapeutic-stimulated ROS on proliferating ovarian granulosa cells.

DAPI and CV staining showed that there were similar numbers of viable cells in cell culture medium and culture medium containing 0.8% DMSO, but there were approximately 33% fewer viable COV434 cells in the culture medium than in the other three cell lines. The cell doubling times have been reported as COV434 24 h [48] to 36 h [49], MCF7 30 h [50], T47D 39 h [50] and OVCAR 48 h [51]. If doubling times were the explanation for the difference in viable cell numbers there should have been fewer OVCAR than COV434 cells, because OVCAR are reported as having the slowest doubling times. Although the ECACC recommends growing COV434 cells in high glucose DMEM, Tsai-Turton et al. (2007, [52]) used high glucose DMEM/F12, and we repeated their method because primary-derived human granulosa cells are commonly cultured in the same medium [53–55]. In the present study, however, the pH indicator phenol red was omitted to avoid interference with ROS quantification. Phenol red is a weak estrogen and COV434 cells respond to estrogen by proliferating. We speculate that our estrogen-depleted control culture medium resulted in lower levels of COV434 proliferation. The addition of 0.8% DMSO to this culture medium did not change the numbers of DAPI-stained COV434 nuclei with normal morphology, nor the numbers of viable cells quantified in our crystal violet assay, but significantly increased ROS and the percentages of COV434 condensed nuclei. It is likely that, if COV434 cells were cultured in 0.8% DMSO for longer periods of time (than 24 h), the numbers of viable cells would decrease to reflect the increase in ROS and condensed cell nuclei.

Breast cancer patients are commonly administered an infusion of Dox intravenously (60 mg/m^2) then an infusion of cyclophosphamide (600 mg/m^2) [56,57], and different types of breast cancer have additional agents added to their treatment regimens (e.g., addition of paclitaxel to four cycles of Dox and cyclophosphamide [58,59], but breast cancer is not treated with either agent alone. In early animal studies, the combination of Dox and cyclophosphamide was therapeutically potentiating against four different murine mammary tumour lines compared to Dox as a single agent [60] and this was attributed to different cytotoxic mechanisms of action. However, we have been unable to locate any in vitro or human in vivo studies that compared Dox + cyclophosphamide to either Dox or cyclophosphamide alone.

The chemotherapeutics (without tocopherols) stimulated ROS in all four cell lines, reduced cell viability in COV434 and T47D cells, and increased the percentage of condensed cell nuclei in COV434, OVCAR and T47D cells, hence chemotherapeutic-stimulated ROS production was associated with cell damage when measured using DAPI or CV staining. 4-Cyc induced significant ROS generation in all cell lines within 1 h, and this increased 3- to 10-fold after 24 h exposure. Our data support previous reports that increases in ROS mediate 4-Cyc-induced apoptosis in different types of cells [17,18]. Dox on the other hand, did not generate ROS as quickly as 4-Cyc, and in three of the cell lines Dox generated fewer ROS than 4-Cyc after 24 h exposure. ROS production in H9c2 cardiac muscle cells exposed for 1 h to 10 μM Dox was four times higher than in the medium control [61]. In the present study, the lower 1.21 μM concentration of Dox that killed 25% of MCF-7 cells was compared with Tan et al. (2010) [61], and this suggests that higher amounts of ROS are produced with increasing concentrations of Dox. COV434 cells exposed to 50 μM 4-Cyc for 2 h, or 1 μM for 6 h, significantly increased the production of ROS [52]. Although the concentration of DCFDA used in this study was 100 times higher than the one used in our experiments, and higher DCFDA concentrations can be toxic and contribute to ROS generation [38], the amount of ROS generated by COV434 cells after 24 h exposure to 21 μM 4-Cyc in our study was in broad agreement with the previous study [52].

The four cell lines displayed different sensitivities to the cytotoxic and ROS-inducing activities of the test agents. Several factors affect cell line responses in vitro [62]. One factor is the cell doubling time, because some chemotherapeutics are phase-specific agents, which means that only cells that are passing through the relevant cell cycle phase when the drug is present are killed [63–65]. Because cells that are in a different cell cycle phase are not targeted by the phase-specific agent, a single of dose of the drug may only kill a fixed fraction of cells and multiple doses may be needed to eradicate the tumour [66]. 'Fractional kill' predicts a strong correlation between proliferation rate and drug sensitivity. Neither Dox or cyclophosphamide are considered cell cycle phase-specific drugs, but they have been known to preferentially target more metabolically active cells [23], and Fan et al. [67] found that Dox inhibited the growth of HepG2 cells by induction of G2/M cell cycle arrest. It's therefore possible that cell lines with longer doubling times might require a longer exposure time to Dox and 4-Cyc in vitro for cytotoxic effects. However, MCF7 cells have the shortest reported doubling time (30 h, [50]) but were the least sensitive to the cytotoxic effects of the combined chemotherapeutics. Previously, MCF7 and ovarian granulosa KGN cells were exposed to 5 μM Dox or 4-Cyc for 24 h then cultured for a further 48 h or exposed for 72 h continuously in culture [68]. There was no difference in cytotoxicity between these two exposure regimens; >80% of both cell lines died within the first 24 h. In the present study, then, the differing proliferation rates of the four cell lines do not appear to explain the data.

Another factor that affects in vitro responses to test agents is the origin and phenotype of the cell line. The MCF-7 and T47D cell lines were isolated from a pleural effusion of patients with breast carcinoma [69,70]. MCF-7 cells maintain several of the functional characteristics of differentiated mammary epithelium, including the expression of estrogen receptors [71], which means that control proliferation rates may have been reduced in our phenol red-free system. Similarly, the T47D line expresses receptors for estradiol, progesterone and other steroid hormones [70]. The COV434 cell line was derived from a solid primary human ovarian granulosa cell carcinoma but is a good in vitro model for normal healthy granulosa cells because the cell line maintains many of the functional characteristics required for follicle growth and development [72]. These include the expression of estrogen receptors and a steroidogenic pathway that enables COV434 cells to synthesise steroid hormones such as estrogen and progesterone. Steroidogenesis generates ROS, and human steroidogenic ovarian cells have relatively high levels of intracellular antioxidants which include Vitamin E in humans [73,74]. The OVCAR-3 cell line also synthesizes steroid hormones and was obtained from a patient who was administered a combination of Dox, cyclophosphamide and cisplatin to treat an epithelial adenocarcinoma of the ovary. Eight months later, her ascites fluid-containing ovarian adenocarcinoma cells were injected into nude mice, and the resulting tumours were disaggregated and used to generate the OVCAR-3 cell line. These cells are resistant to clinically relevant concentrations of doxorubicin, although the effects of 4-Cyc have not been reported [57]. In the present study, the MCF7-derived EC25 value of Dox reduced viable OVCAR cells to 75 ± 5% of control, which suggests that OVCAR have a resistance to Dox comparable to MCF7 cells, whereas the same concentration of Dox reduced COV434 cell viability to 57 ± 2% of control. The combination of the EC25 Dox with the EC25 4-Cyc was additive towards OVCAR cells (57 ± 2% of control) but did not increase cytotoxicity towards MCF7 (76 ± 14%) or T47D cells. Although the combined chemotherapeutics were not more cytotoxic to the two breast cancer cell lines than either agent alone, there were marked increases in chemotherapeutic-stimulated ROS, to 1413 ± 230% (T47D) and 1085 ± 31% (MCF7) of control. If the chemotherapeutics also stimulate a 10-fold increase in ROS in vivo, perhaps it is accompanied by a more impressive increase in cytotoxicity than occurred in our in vitro system. The combined chemotherapeutics displayed synergistic cytotoxicity towards the granulosa-derived COV434 cells, and the reduction in viable cells to 34 ± 5% of control was accompanied by a 770 ± 84% increase in ROS. In this study, the viability of the granulosa tumour-derived COV434 cell line was more sensitive to the clinically relevant combination of Dox + 4-Cyc than the two breast cancer cell lines. More experiments are needed to determine if primary-derived physiologically normal granulosa cells display the same sensitivity, but since immortalised cancer-derived cell lines are generally more robust and resistant to cytotoxic agents than mortal primary-derived cells, we predict that proliferating follicular granulosa cells will be more sensitive to Dox + 4-Cyc than breast cancer cells.

Cancer-derived cell lines are different from tumours in vivo, and cell lines and tumours are different from physiologically normal, healthy cells. Tumour-derived COV434 granulosa cells, however, retain features of physiologically normal granulosa cells, and the ovarian epithelial OVCAR cells are different from the mammary epithelial cells because they, like normal granulosa and COV434 cells, retain a steroidogenic pathway. The steroidogenic pathway and associated intracellular antioxidants imply differences in redox status between the two ovarian and two breast cancer cell lines. This frames our hypothesis that antioxidant tocopherols might reduce chemotherapeutic-induced ROS and their associated damage in granulosa-like steroidogenic cells, whilst maintaining the anti-cancer cytotoxicity of the chemotherapeutics against breast cancer cells. Therefore, one of the aims of this study was to discover the effect of αToc and γToc on ROS induced by exposure to the combination of Dox + 4-Cyc.

In our earlier study, we did not find a concentration of αToc that killed MCF7 breast cancer cells, and selected the highest concentration tested. In the present study, this relatively high concentration of αToc alone did not kill any cell type compared to the DMSO control, had no significant effect on the proportions of condensed nuclei, and did not affect ROS generation in three of the four cell lines, although both tocopherols stimulated MCF7 ROS generation somewhere between 3 and 24 h of exposure. The addition of αToc to Dox + 4-Cyc for 24 h decreased T47D cell viability while increasing condensed nuclei, and significantly increased ROS in all four cell lines. The COV434 cells differed from the other three cell lines in that αToc reduced chemotherapeutic-stimulated ROS in the first 3 h of exposure, but in the subsequent 3–24 h of exposure the combination of Dox + 4-Cyc + αToc caused significantly more ROS, condensed nuclei and loss of viable COV434 cells than Dox + 4-Cyc without αToc, and additionally caused COV434 nuclei to shrink. Steroid hormones and tocopherols are lipophilic and miscible with cell membrane lipid bilayers. The chemotherapeutics Dox and 4-Cyc are soluble in water, and this caused us to speculate that if the relatively high, non-cytotoxic concentration of αToc used in this study were to affect the fluidity and plasticity of the cell membranes, it may have improved chemotherapeutics' access to the interior of the cell in some way. Another difference between COV434 cells and the other three cell lines is their size; COV434 cells are smaller and probably have a higher surface area to volume ratio, which would increase the importance of membrane changes and chemotherapeutic uptake relative to the other three cell lines. Our finding that αToc increased the cytotoxicity of Dox + 4-Cyc against the COV434 granulosa tumour cell line, in an estrogen-depleted in vitro system, provides a rationale for further investigation.

A 24 h exposure to the concentration of γToc that killed 25% of MCF7 cells in a previous study had no effect on condensed nuclei but significantly increased ROS and killed approximately 25% of the two breast cancer cell lines. In contrast, the same 24 h exposure to the MCF7 EC25 value of γToc did not kill the two ovarian cell lines and the lower percentages of condensed nuclei corresponded to the higher numbers of viable cells. Although 24 h exposure to γToc stimulated MCF7 ROS, it had no effect on ROS in any other cell line. It is interesting that, in the two ovarian cell lines, γToc alone not only prevented an increase in ROS levels but no condensed nuclei at all were observed in COV434 cells, and there were significantly fewer condensed OVCAR nuclei than in the DMSO control ($p < 0.05$). These differences between the two steroidogenic cell lines may reflect their different sizes, or the different steroid hormones they synthesise.

Twenty-four hours exposure to Dox + 4-Cyc (without γToc) increased ROS, reduced cell viability and generally increased the percentage of condensed nuclei in all four cell lines. The addition of γToc to Dox + 4-Cyc nearly halved chemotherapeutic-induced ROS in COV434 cells within 1 h and maintained this inhibition for 3 h but had no effect on ROS in the other three cell lines. This early inhibition of ROS in COV434 cells may have been the reason there was no increase in condensed nuclei after 24 h, and why there were significantly more viable cells after 24 h exposure to Dox + 4-Cyc + γToc than after exposure to Dox + 4-Cyc without γToc. The different responses to the combination of chemotherapeutics and γToc displayed by COV434 and the other three cell lines are unlikely to be explained by antioxidant or REDOX status and are more likely to be related to the interaction of γToc with apoptotic pathways within the cells. MCF7 and T47D cells have different apoptotic pathways, which may have resulted in significant increases in condensed nuclei in T47D but not MCF7 cells. OVCAR are resistant to Dox, and probably to 4-Cyc too, and this may account for the maintenance of viable cell numbers and lack of increase in condensed cell nuclei, despite significant increases in ROS.

Antioxidants **2020**, *9*, 51

Nevertheless, the finding that γToc reduced COV434 ROS for 3 h and prevented nucleus condensation and loss of cell viability for 24 h, whilst stimulating ROS and nucleus condensation and decreasing T47D breast cancer cell viability during a 24 h exposure, supports our hypothesis: γToc reduced chemotherapeutic-induced ROS and associated damage in granulosa-like steroidogenic cells, whilst maintaining the anti-cancer cytotoxicity of the chemotherapeutics against breast cancer cells.

5. Conclusions

The clinical efficacy of the combined regimen of Dox and cyclophosphamide against breast cancer in vivo is probably related to their combined cytotoxicity as well as their ability to increase ROS production. One way to improve existing anti-cancer treatments is to reduce off-target adverse effects without reducing efficacy against breast cancer. In the present study, the addition of γToc to Dox and 4-Cyc differentially and specifically reduced ROS levels after only 1 h in the ovarian granulosa cell line COV434 and maintained the percentages of condensed nuclei indicative of cell damage at the same levels as the DMSO control in the two ovarian cell lines expressing steroidogenic pathways, whereas γToc increased cell damage caused by the chemotherapeutics in the breast cancer T47D cell line. If the protective effects of γToc in the presence of Dox + 4-Cyc can be repeated in normal, non-cancerous, primary-derived granulosa cells and the chemotherapeutic enhancing effects of γToc can be demonstrated in primary-derived breast cancer tumour cells, this will confirm the potential for antioxidant γToc to be developed as an adjunct to existing breast cancer chemotherapy, which will improve fertility preservation for premenopausal breast cancer patients.

Supplementary Materials: The following are available online at http://www.mdpi.com/2076-3921/9/1/51/s1, **Figure S1**: Comparison of DAPI and Crystal Violet Datasets: The numbers of human COV434 (**A**), MCF7 (**B**), T47D (**C**) and OVCAR (**D**) cells per well that were determined using a crystal violet assay were divided by 100 to allow comparison with the DAPI dataset on the same axis. The crystal violet values show mean ± stdev (*n* = 3). The DAPI values are the sum of nuclei with 'condensed' + 'uncertain' + normal morphologies scored in images from three replicate experiments. Each group of apoptotic bodies were assumed to have been formed by the fragmentation of a single nucleus and were therefore given a score of '1'. These were added to the numbers of small, irregularly shaped DAPI-dense nuclei. Nuclei classified as 'uncertain' formed 8.9% (COV434), 2.4% (MCF7), 1.4% (OVCAR) and 1.2% (T47D) of the total numbers of nuclei in all assessed images, whereas the normal nuclei formed 85% (COV434), 95% (MCF7), 94% (OVCAR) and 97.2% (T47D). DAPI values shown as the mean ± stdev (*n* = 3). The crystal violet cell data were subjected to 1Way ANOVA with a Tukey post-test. Significant difference from control. ** $p > 001$, *** $p > 0.001$, or a v b $p > 0.05$, a v c $p > 0.001$. **Figure S2**: Images of DAPI-stained cell nuclei obtained using an Olympus AX70 fluorescence microscope at ×20 magnification after cells were exposed to chemotherapeutics and tocopherols for 24 h. Dox—doxorubicin, Cyc—cyclophosphamide, Toc—tocopherol.

Author Contributions: Conceptualization, F.Y.; methodology, F.Y., D.F.G.; formal analysis, F.Y., D.F.G., investigation, D.F.G.; resources, F.Y.; data curation, F.Y., D.F.G.; writing—original draft preparation, D.F.G.; writing—review and editing, F.Y., D.F.G.; supervision, F.Y.; project administration, F.Y. All authors have read and agreed to the published version of the manuscript.

Funding: This research received no external funding.

Acknowledgments: Yvette DeGraaf and Pat Vilimas of the Flinders Microscopy and Cell Biology Facility gave much appreciated technical support.

Conflicts of Interest: The authors declare no conflict of interest.

References

1. Fan, L.M.; Li, J.-M. Evaluation of methods of detecting cell reactive oxygen species production for drug screening and cell cycle studies. *J. Pharmacol. Toxicol. Methods* **2014**, *70*, 40–47. [CrossRef]

2. Gomes, A.; Fernandes, E.; Lima, J.L. Fluorescence probes used for detection of reactive oxygen species. *J. Biochem. Biophys. Methods* **2005**, *65*, 45–80. [CrossRef] [PubMed]

3. Valko, M.; Leibfritz, D.; Moncol, J.; Cronin, M.T.; Mazur, M.; Telser, J. Free radicals and antioxidants in normal physiological functions and human disease. *Int. J. Biochem. Cell Biol.* **2007**, *39*, 44–84. [CrossRef]

4. Droge, W. Free radicals in the physiological control of cell function. *Physiol. Rev.* **2002**, *82*, 47–95. [CrossRef] [PubMed]

5. Doroshow, J.H. Role of hydrogen peroxide and hydroxyl radical formation in the killing of Ehrlich tumor cells by anticancer quinones. *Proc. Natl. Acad. Sci. USA* **1986**, *83*, 4514–4518. [CrossRef] [PubMed]

6. Gutteridge, J.M.; Halliwell, B. Antioxidants: Molecules, medicines, and myths. *Biochem. Biophys. Res. Commun.* **2010**, *393*, 561–564. [CrossRef]

7. Halliwell, B. Drug antioxidant effects. *Drugs* **1991**, *42*, 569–605. [CrossRef] [PubMed]

8. Nogueira, V.; Hay, N. Molecular pathways: Reactive oxygen species homeostasis in cancer cells and implications for cancer therapy. *Clin. Cancer Res.* **2013**, *19*, 4309–4314. [CrossRef]

9. Bray, J.; Sludden, J.; Griffin, M.; Cole, M.; Verrill, M.; Jamieson, D.; Boddy, A. Influence of pharmacogenetics on response and toxicity in breast cancer patients treated with doxorubicin and cyclophosphamide. *Br. J. Cancer* **2010**, *102*, 1003–1009. [CrossRef]

10. Joerger, M.; Huitema, A.D.R.; Richel, D.J.; Dittrich, C.; Pavlidis, N.; Briasoulis, E.; Vermorken, J.B.; Strocchi, E.; Martoni, A.; Sorio, R.; et al. Population Pharmacokinetics and Pharmacodynamics of Doxorubicin and Cyclophosphamide in Breast Cancer Patients. *Clin. Pharmacokinet.* **2007**, *46*, 1051–1068. [CrossRef]

11. Nabholtz, J.M.; Falkson, C.; Campos, D.; Szanto, J.; Martin, M.; Chan, S.; Pienkowski, T.; Zaluski, J.; Pinter, T.; Krzakowski, M.; et al. Docetaxel and doxorubicin compared with doxorubicin and cyclophosphamide as first-line chemotherapy for metastatic breast cancer: Results of a randomized, multicenter, phase III trial. *J. Clin. Oncol.* **2003**, *21*, 968–975. [CrossRef] [PubMed]

12. Tewey, K.; Rowe, T.; Yang, L.; Halligan, B.; Liu, L.-F. Adriamycin-induced DNA damage mediated by mammalian DNA topoisomerase II. *Science* **1984**, *226*, 466–468. [CrossRef] [PubMed]

13. Gewirtz, D. A critical evaluation of the mechanisms of action proposed for the antitumor effects of the anthracycline antibiotics adriamycin and daunorubicin. *Biochem. Pharmacol.* **1999**, *57*, 727–741. [CrossRef]

14. Mizutani, H.; Tada-Oikawa, S.; Hiraku, Y.; Kojima, M.; Kawanishi, S. Mechanism of apoptosis induced by doxorubicin through the generation of hydrogen peroxide. *Life Sci.* **2005**, *76*, 1439–1453. [CrossRef]

15. Emadi, A.; Jones, R.J.; Brodsky, R.A. Cyclophosphamide and cancer: Golden anniversary. *Nat. Rev. Clin. Oncol.* **2009**, *6*, 638–647. [CrossRef]

16. Boddy, A.V.; Yule, S.M. Metabolism and Pharmacokinetics of Oxazaphosphorines. *Clin. Pharmacokinet.* **2000**, *38*, 291–304. [CrossRef]

17. Liu, F.; Li, X.-L.; Lin, T.; He, D.-W.; Wei, G.-H.; Liu, J.-H.; Li, L.-S. The cyclophosphamide metabolite, acrolein, induces cytoskeletal changes and oxidative stress in Sertoli cells. *Mol. Biol. Rep.* **2012**, *39*, 493–500. [CrossRef]

18. Mythili, Y.; Sudharsan, P.T.; Selvakumar, E.; Varalakshmi, P. Protective effect of dl-α-lipoic acid on cyclophosphamide induced oxidative cardiac injury. *Chem. Biol. Interact.* **2004**, *151*, 13–19. [CrossRef]

19. Legha, S.S.; Benjamin, R.S.; Mackay, B.; Ewer, M.; Wallace, S.; Valdivieso, M.; Rasmussen, S.L.; Blumenschein, G.R.; Freireich, E.J. Reduction of doxorubicin cardiotoxicity by prolonged continuous intravenous infusion. *Ann. Intern. Med.* **1982**, *96*, 133–139. [CrossRef]

20. Ozer, H.; Cowens, J.W.; Colvin, M.; Nussbaum-Blumenson, A.; Sheedy, D. In vitro effects of 4-hydroperoxycyclophosphamide on human immunoregulatory T subset function. I. Selective effects on lymphocyte function in TB cell collaboration. *J. Exp. Med.* **1982**, *155*, 276–290. [CrossRef]

21. Meirow, D.; Lewis, H.; Nugent, D.; Epstein, M. Subclinical depletion of primordial follicular reserve in mice treated with cyclophosphamide: Clinical importance and proposed accurate investigative tool. *Hum. Reprod.* **1999**, *14*, 1903–1907. [CrossRef] [PubMed]

22. Meirow, D.; Biederman, H.; Anderson, R.A.; Wallace, W.H.B. Toxicity of chemotherapy and radiation on female reproduction. *Clin. Obstet. Gynecol.* **2010**, *53*, 727–739. [CrossRef] [PubMed]

23. Morgan, S.; Anderson, R.; Gourley, C.; Wallace, W.; Spears, N. How do chemotherapeutic agents damage the ovary? *Hum. Reprod. Update* **2012**, *18*, 525–535. [CrossRef]

24. Petrillo, S.K.; Desmeules, P.; Truong, T.-Q.; Devine, P.J. Detection of DNA damage in oocytes of small ovarian follicles following phosphoramide mustard exposures of cultured rodent ovaries in vitro. *Toxicol. Appl. Pharmacol.* **2011**, *253*, 94–102. [CrossRef] [PubMed]

25. Oktem, O.; Oktay, K. A novel ovarian xenografting model to characterize the impact of chemotherapy agents on human primordial follicle reserve. *Cancer Res.* **2007**, *67*, 10159–10162. [CrossRef] [PubMed]

26. Oktem, O.; Oktay, K. Quantitative assessment of the impact of chemotherapy on ovarian follicle reserve and stromal function. *Cancer* **2007**, *110*, 2222–2229. [CrossRef] [PubMed]

27. Jurisicova, A.; Lee, H.; D'Estaing, S.; Tilly, J.; Perez, G. Molecular requirements for doxorubicin-mediated death in murine oocytes. *Cell Death Differ.* **2006**, *13*, 1466–1474. [CrossRef]

28. Perez, G.I.; Knudson, C.M.; Leykin, L.; Korsmeyer, S.J.; Tilly, J.L. Apoptosis-associated signaling pathways are required for chemotherapy-mediated female germ cell destruction. *Nat. Med.* **1997**, *3*, 1228–1232. [CrossRef]

29. Soleimani, R.; Heytens, E.; Darzynkiewicz, Z.; Oktay, K. Mechanisms of chemotherapy-induced human ovarian aging: Double strand DNA breaks and microvascular compromise. *Aging* **2011**, *3*, 782–793. [CrossRef]

30. Iqubal, M.A.; Khan, M.; Kumar, P.; Kumar, A.; Ajai, K. Role of Vitamin E in Prevention of Oral Cancer: A Review. *J. Clin. Diagn. Res.* **2014**, *8*, ZE05–ZE07. [CrossRef]

31. Brigelius-Flohe, R.; Kelly, F.; Salonen, J.; Neuzil, J.; Zingg, J.; Azzi, A. The European perspective on vitamin E: Current knowledge and future research. *Am. J. Clin. Nutr.* **2002**, *76*, 703–716. [CrossRef] [PubMed]

32. Myers, C.E.; McGuire, W.P.; Liss, R.H.; Ifrim, I.; Grotzinger, K.; Young, R.C. Adriamycin: The role of lipid peroxidation in cardiac toxicity and tumor response. *Science* **1977**, *197*, 165–167. [CrossRef] [PubMed]

33. Smolarek, A.; Suh, N. Chemopreventive Activity of Vitamin E in Breast Cancer: A Focus on gamma- and delta-Tocopherol. *Nutrients* **2011**, *3*, 962–986. [CrossRef] [PubMed]

34. Klein, E.A.; Thompson, I.M.; Tangen, C.M.; Crowley, J.J.; Lucia, M.S.; Goodman, P.J.; Minasian, L.; Ford, L.G.; Parnes, H.L.; Gaziano, J.M.; et al. Vitamin E and the Risk of Prostate Cancer: Updated Results of The Selenium and Vitamin E Cancer Prevention Trial (SELECT). *JAMA* **2011**, *306*, 1549–1556. [CrossRef]

35. Gopalan, A.; Yu, W.; Jiang, Q.; Jang, Y.; Sanders, B.G.; Kline, K. Involvement of de novo ceramide synthesis in gamma-tocopherol and gamma-tocotrienol-induced apoptosis in human breast cancer cells. *Mol. Nutr. Food Res.* **2012**, *56*, 1803–1811. [CrossRef] [PubMed]

36. Lee, H.J.; Ju, J.; Paul, S.; So, J.-Y.; DeCastro, A.; Smolarek, A.; Lee, M.-J.; Yang, C.S.; Newmark, H.L.; Suh, N. Mixed Tocopherols Prevent Mammary Tumorigenesis by Inhibiting Estrogen Action and Activating PPAR-γ. *Clin. Cancer Res.* **2009**, *15*, 4242–4249. [CrossRef]

37. Constantinou, C.A.; Papas, A.; Constantinou, A.I. Vitamin E and cancer: An insight into the anticancer activities of vitamin E isomers and analogs. *Int. J. Cancer* **2008**, *123*, 739–752. [CrossRef]

38. Figueroa, D.; Asaduzzaman, M.; Young, F. Real time monitoring and quantification of reactive oxygen species in breast cancer cell line MCF-7 by 2′,7′–dichlorofluorescin diacetate (DCFDA) assay. *J. Pharmacol. Toxicol. Methods* **2018**, *94*, 26–33. [CrossRef]

39. Yang, Y.-I.; Jung, D.-W.; Bai, D.-G.; Yoo, G.-S.; Choi, J.-K. Counterion-dye staining method for DNAin agarose gels using crystal violet and methyl orange. *Electrophoresis* **2001**, *22*, 855–859. [CrossRef]

40. Berry, J.M.; Huebner, E.; Butler, M. The crystal violet nuclei staining technique leads to anomalous results in monitoring mammalian cell cultures. *Cytotechnology* **1996**, *21*, 73–80. [CrossRef]

41. Vega-Avila, E.; Pugsley, M.K. An Overview of Colorimetric Assay Methods Used to Assess Survival or Proliferation of Mammalian Cells. *Proc. West. Pharmacol. Soc.* **2011**, *54*, 10–14. [PubMed]

42. Reid, K.J.; Lang, K.; Froscio, S.; Humpage, A.J.; Young, F.M. Undifferentiated murine embryonic stem cells used to model the effects of the blue–green algal toxin cylindrospermopsin on preimplantation embryonic cell proliferation. *Toxicon* **2015**, *106*, 79–88. [CrossRef] [PubMed]

43. Atale, N.; Gupta, S.; Yadav, U.C.; Rani, V. Cell-death assessment by fluorescent and nonfluorescent cytosolic and nuclear staining techniques. *J. Microsc.* **2014**, *255*, 7–19. [CrossRef] [PubMed]

44. Anderson, W.F.; Rosenberg, P.S.; Prat, A.; Perou, C.M.; Sherman, M.E. How Many Etiological Subtypes of Breast Cancer: Two, Three, Four, Or More? *JNCI J. Natl. Cancer Inst.* **2014**, *106*, dju165. [CrossRef]

45. Mathieu, C.; Jozan, S.; Mazars, P.; Come, M.G.; Moisand, A.; Valette, A. Density-Dependent Induction of Apoptosis by Transforming Growth Factor-beta1 in a Human Ovarian Carcinoma Cell Line. *Exp. Cell Res.* **1995**, *216*, 13–20. [CrossRef]

46. Kolb, R.H.; Greer, P.M.; Cao, P.T.; Cowan, K.H.; Yan, Y. ERK1/2 Signaling Plays an Important Role in Topoisomerase II Poison-Induced G2/M Checkpoint Activation. *PLoS ONE* **2012**, *7*, e50281. [CrossRef]

47. Im, J.Y.; Park, H.; Kang, K.W.; Choi, W.S.; Kim, H.S. Modulation of cell cycles and apoptosis by apicidin in estrogen receptor (ER)-positive and-negative human breast cancer cells. *Chem. Biol. Interact.* **2008**, *172*, 235–244. [CrossRef]

48. Cowley, G.S.; Weir, B.A.; Vazquez, F.; Tamayo, P.; Scott, J.A.; Rusin, S.; East-Seletsky, A.; Ali, L.D.; Gerath, W.F.; Pantel, S.E.; et al. Parallel genome-scale loss of function screens in 216 cancer cell lines for the identification of context-specific genetic dependencies. *Sci. Data* **2014**, *1*, 140035. [CrossRef]

49. Verga Falzacappa, C.; Mangialardo, C.; Patriarca, V.; Bucci, B.; Amendola, D.; Raffa, S.; Torrisi, M.R.; Silvestrini, G.; Ballanti, P.; Moriggi, G.; et al. Thyroid hormones induce cell proliferation and survival in ovarian granulosa cells COV434. *J. Cell. Physiol.* **2009**, *221*, 242–253. [CrossRef]

50. Dougherty, M.K.; Schumaker, L.M.; Jordan, V.C.; Welshons, W.V.; Curran, E.M.; Ellis, M.J.; El-Ashry, D. Estrogen receptor expression and sensitivity to paclitaxel in breast cancer. *Cancer Biol. Ther.* **2004**, *3*, 460–467. [CrossRef]

51. Hamilton, T.C.; Young, R.C.; McKoy, W.M.; Grotzinger, K.R.; Green, J.A.; Chu, E.W.; Whang-Peng, J.; Rogan, A.M.; Green, W.R.; Ozols, R.F. Characterization of a human ovarian carcinoma cell line (NIH: OVCAR-3) with androgen and estrogen receptors. *Cancer Res.* **1983**, *43*, 5379–5389. [PubMed]

52. Tsai-Turton, M.; Luong, B.T.; Tan, Y.; Luderer, U. Cyclophosphamide-Induced Apoptosis in COV434 Human Granulosa Cells Involves Oxidative Stress and Glutathione Depletion. *Toxicol. Sci.* **2007**, *98*, 216–230. [CrossRef]

53. Young, F.M.; Micklem, J.; Humpage, A.R. Effects of blue-green algal toxin cylindrospermopsin (CYN) on human granulosa cells in vitro. *Reprod. Toxicol.* **2008**, *25*, 374–380. [CrossRef] [PubMed]

54. Young, F.M.; Zebian, D.; Froscio, S.; Humpage, A. Cylindrospermopsin, a blue-green algal toxin, inhibited human luteinised granulosa cell protein synthesis in vitro. *Toxicol. In Vitro* **2012**, *26*, 656–662. [CrossRef] [PubMed]

55. Edwards, V.; Benkendorff, K.; Young, F. Novel marine compounds selectively induce apoptosis in female reproductive cancer cells but not in primary-derived human granulosa cells. *Mar. Drugs* **2012**, *10*, 64–83. [CrossRef] [PubMed]

56. Dees, E.C.; O'Reilly, S.; Goodman, S.N.; Sartorius, S.; Levine, M.A.; Jones, R.J.; Grochow, L.B.; Donehower, R.C.; Fetting, J.H. A prospective pharmacologic evaluation of age-related toxicity of adjuvant chemotherapy in women with breast cancer. *Cancer Investig.* **2000**, *18*, 521–529. [CrossRef] [PubMed]

57. Jones, S.E.; Savin, M.A.; Holmes, F.A.; O'Shaughnessy, J.A.; Blum, J.L.; Vukelja, S.; McIntyre, K.J.; Pippen, J.E.; Bordelon, J.H.; Kirby, R. Phase III trial comparing doxorubicin plus cyclophosphamide with docetaxel plus cyclophosphamide as adjuvant therapy for operable breast cancer. *J. Clin. Oncol.* **2006**, *24*, 5381–5387. [CrossRef]

58. Yardley, D.; Arrowsmith, E.; Daniel, B.; Eakle, J.; Brufsky, A.; Drosick, D.; Kudrik, F.; Bosserman, L.; Keaton, M.; Goble, S.; et al. TITAN: Phase III study of doxorubicin/cyclophosphamide followed by ixabepilone or paclitaxel in early-stage triple-negative breast cancer. *Breast Cancer Res. Treat.* **2017**, *164*, 649–658. [CrossRef]

59. Henderson, I.C.; Berry, D.A.; Demetri, G.D.; Cirrincione, C.T.; Goldstein, L.J.; Martino, S.; Ingle, J.N.; Cooper, M.R.; Hayes, D.F.; Tkaczuk, K.H. Improved outcomes from adding sequential paclitaxel but not from escalating doxorubicin dose in an adjuvant chemotherapy regimen for patients with node-positive primary breast cancer. *J. Clin. Oncol.* **2003**, *21*, 976–983. [CrossRef] [PubMed]

60. Corbett, T.; Griswold, D.; Mayo, J.; Laster, W.; Schabel, F. Cyclophosphamide-adriamycin combination chemotherapy of transplantable murine tumors. *Cancer Res.* **1975**, *35*, 1568–1573.

61. Tan, X.; Wang, D.-B.; Lu, X.; Wei, H.; Zhu, R.; Zhu, S.-S.; Jiang, H.; Yang, Z.-J. Doxorubicin induces apoptosis in H9c2 cardiomyocytes: Role of overexpressed eukaryotic translation initiation factor 5A. *Biol. Pharm. Bull.* **2010**, *33*, 1666. [CrossRef] [PubMed]

62. Nunzio, M.D.; Valli, V.; Tomás-Cobos, L.; Tomás-Chisbert, T.; Murgui-Bosch, L.; Danesi, F.; Bordoni, A. Is cytotoxicity a determinant of the different in vitro and in vivo effects of bioactives? *BMC Complement. Altern. Med.* **2017**, *17*, 453. [CrossRef] [PubMed]

63. Gascoigne, K.E.; Taylor, S.S. How do anti-mitotic drugs kill cancer cells? *J. Cell Sci.* **2009**, *122*, 2579–2585. [CrossRef]

64. Shi, J.; Orth, J.D.; Mitchison, T. Cell type variation in responses to antimitotic drugs that target microtubules and kinesin-5. *Cancer Res.* **2008**, *68*, 3269–3276. [CrossRef] [PubMed]

65. Orth, J.D.; Tang, Y.; Shi, J.; Loy, C.T.; Amendt, C.; Wilm, C.; Zenke, F.T.; Mitchison, T.J. Quantitative live imaging of cancer and normal cells treated with Kinesin-5 inhibitors indicates significant differences in phenotypic responses and cell fate. *Mol. Cancer Ther.* **2008**, *7*, 3480–3489. [CrossRef] [PubMed]

66. Berenbaum, M. In vivo determination of the fractional kill of human tumor cells by chemotherapeutic agents. *Cancer Chemother. Rep.* **1972**, *56*, 563–571. [PubMed]

67. Fan, C.; Zheng, W.; Fu, X.; Li, X.; Wong, Y.-S.; Chen, T. Strategy to enhance the therapeutic effect of doxorubicin in human hepatocellular carcinoma by selenocystine, a synergistic agent that regulates the ROS-mediated signaling. *Oncotarget* **2014**, *5*, 2853. [CrossRef]

68. Figueroa, D.; Asaduzzaman, M.; Young, F. Effect of Chemotherapeutics and Tocopherols on MCF-7 Breast Adenocarcinoma and KGN Ovarian Carcinoma Cell Lines In Vitro. *BioMed Res. Int.* **2019**, *2019*, 6146972. [CrossRef]

69. Soule, H.; Vazquez, J.; Long, A.; Albert, S.; Brennan, M. A human cell line from a pleural effusion derived from a breast carcinoma. *J. Natl. Cancer Inst.* **1973**, *51*, 1409–1416. [CrossRef]

70. Keydar, I.; Chen, L.; Karby, S.; Weiss, F.; Delarea, J.; Radu, M.; Chaitcik, S.; Brenner, H. Establishment and characterization of a cell line of human breast carcinoma origin. *Eur. J. Cancer (1965)* **1979**, *15*, 659–670. [CrossRef]

71. Huguet, E.L.; McMahon, J.A.; McMahon, A.P.; Bicknell, R.; Harris, A.L. Differential expression of human Wnt genes 2, 3, 4, and 7B in human breast cell lines and normal and disease states of human breast tissue. *Cancer Res.* **1994**, *54*, 2615–2621. [PubMed]

72. Zhang, H.; Vollmer, M.; De Geyter, M.; Litzistorf, Y.; Ladewig, A.; Dürrenberger, M.; Guggenheim, R.; Miny, P.; Holzgreve, W.; De Geyter, C. Characterization of an immortalized human granulosa cell line (COV434). *Mol. Hum. Reprod.* **2000**, *6*, 146–153. [CrossRef] [PubMed]

73. Young, F.M.; Luderer, W.B.; Rodgers, R.J. The antioxidant beta-carotene prevents covalent cross-linking between cholesterol side-chain cleavage cytochrome P450 and its electron donor, adrenodoxin, in bovine luteal cells. *Mol. Cell. Endocrinol.* **1995**, *109*, 113–118. [CrossRef]

74. Rodgers, R.J.; Lavranos, T.C.; Rodgers, H.F.; Young, F.M.; Vella, C.A. The physiology of the ovary: Maturation of ovarian granulosa cells and a novel role for antioxidants in the corpus luteum. *J. Steroid Biochem. Mol. Biol.* **1995**, *53*, 241–246. [CrossRef]

Article

Melatonin Plus Folic Acid Treatment Ameliorates Reserpine-Induced Fibromyalgia: An Evaluation of Pain, Oxidative Stress, and Inflammation

Roberta Fusco [1,†], Rosalba Siracusa [1,†], Ramona D'Amico [1,†], Alessio Filippo Peritore [1], Marika Cordaro [1], Enrico Gugliandolo [1], Rosalia Crupi [1], Daniela Impellizzeri [1,*], Salvatore Cuzzocrea [1,2,*] and Rosanna Di Paola [1]

[1] Department of Chemical, Biological, Pharmaceutical and Environmental Sciences, University of Messina, Viale Ferdinando Stagno D'Alcontres, n 31, 98166 Messina, Italy; rfusco@unime.it (R.F.); rsiracusa@unime.it (R.S.); rdamico@unime.it (R.D.A.); aperitore@unime.it (A.F.P.); cordarom@unime.it (M.C.); egugliandolo@unime.it (E.G.); rcrupi@unime.it (R.C.); dipaolar@unime.it (R.D.P.)

[2] Department of Pharmacological and Physiological Science, Saint Louis University School of Medicine, 1402 South Grand Blvd, St. Louis, MO 63104, USA

* Correspondence: dimpellizzeri@unime.it (D.I.); salvator@unime.it (S.C.); Tel.: +39-90-6765208 (D.I. & S.C.)

† These authors equally contributed to this work.

Received: 24 October 2019; Accepted: 5 December 2019; Published: 6 December 2019

Abstract: Background: Fibromyalgia is a chronic condition characterized by increased sensory perception of pain, neuropathic/neurodegenerative modifications, oxidative, and nitrosative stress. An appropriate therapy is hard to find, and the currently used treatments are able to target only one of these aspects. Methods: The aim of this study is to investigate the beneficial effects of melatonin plus folic acid administration in a rat model of reserpine-induced fibromyalgia. Sprague–Dawley male rats were injected with 1 mg/kg of reserpine for three consecutive days and later administered with melatonin, folic acid, or both for twenty-one days. Results: Administration of reserpine led to a significant decrease in the nociceptive threshold as well as a significant increase in depressive-like symptoms. These behavioral changes were accompanied by increased oxidative and nitrosative stress. Lipid peroxidation was significantly increased, as well as nitrotyrosine and PARP expression, while superoxide dismutase, nonprotein thiols, and catalase were significantly decreased. Endogenously produced oxidants species are responsible for mast cell infiltration, increased expression pro-inflammatory mediators, and microglia activation. Conclusion: Melatonin plus acid folic administration is able to ameliorate the behavioral defects, oxidative and nitrosative stress, mast cell infiltration, inflammatory mediators overexpression, and microglia activation induced by reserpine injection with more efficacy than their separate administration.

Keywords: fibromyalgia; oxidative stress; pain

1. Introduction

Fibromyalgia is a chronic clinical condition characterized by chronic widespread pain, fatigue, depression, and sleep disturbances [1–3]. It is widely distributed: 2–5.8% of the population of industrial countries are affected by it [4]. Although aspects of the pathophysiology are still unclear, evidence of involvement of neurotransmitter, genetics, autonomic nervous system (ANS) dysfunction, neuroendocrine dysfunctions, and cerebral psychophysiological abnormalities have been demonstrated [5,6]. Fibromyalgia is considered a non-inflammatory disorder stress-related with dysfunction of the hypothalamic-pituitary-adrenocortical axis [7–9]. Furthermore, changes in inflammatory actors [10,11], modified balance in anti- and pro-inflammatory cytokines [12,13], and increases in toxic metabolites of lipid peroxidation and oxidative stress [14–16] have been detected. Recent evidences have shown that fibromyalgia syndrome involves the neuropathic pain condition [17]. Hyperalgesia and allodynia are common signs in fibromyalgia [18–20]. Sleep deprivation can produce these features [21], in conjunction with inflammation, mitochondrial dysfunction, and oxidative stress, with the result of peripheral nerve damage [22]. Functional brain-imaging studies have displayed compelling evidence for changes in the pain process in fibromyalgia correlating with patients' allodynia or hyperalgesia [23]. Treatment of fibromyalgia requires a pharmacological approach focused on all symptoms with an emphasis on pain. Several pieces of evidence indicate that melatonin can be useful and suitable in fibromyalgia treatment thanks to its different properties [24–26]. It is a highly conserved indoleamine with chronobiological features [27]. Additionally, its anti-inflammatory, antidepressant, analgesic, and sedative activities have been reported [28–31]. To date, the pathophysiology of the syndrome also shows an important oxidative component [32]. It has long been shown that folic acid can improve the function of the immune system and has important antioxidant properties [33]. It exerts both indirect and direct antioxidant effects, such as protection against oxidative modification of low-density lipoproteins [34], free radical scavenging [35], and activation of cellular antioxidant defense [36,37]. Based on these findings, the aim of this study is to evaluate the effect of folic acid and melatonin administration on a fibromyalgia rat model and compare it with the single administrations of the two substances.

2. Materials and Methods

2.1. Animals

Sprague–Dawley male rats (200–230 g, Envigo, Milan, Italy) were used throughout. They received food and *water ad libitum*. The University of Messina Review Board for animal care approved the study. All in vivo experiments followed the new regulations of USA (Animal Welfare Assurance No A5594-01), Europe (EU Directive 2010/63), Italy (D.Lgs 2014/26), and the ARRIVE guidelines.

2.2. Induction of Experimental Fibromyalgia

Reserpine administration was performed by subcutaneous injection of 1 mg/kg for three consecutive days [38]. Reserpine (Sigma-Aldrich, Saint Louis, MO, USA) was dissolved in distilled water with 0.5% acetic acid (vehicle). Animals from the sham group received the same volume of vehicle, but they were administered no reserpine.

2.3. Experimental Groups

Then, rats were randomly divided into several groups ($n = 10$ for each):

Group 1. Sham + vehicle: Rats were injected subcutaneously with vehicle (distilled water with a final concentration of 0.5% acetic acid) instead of reserpine and treated orally with saline for 21 days starting from 3 days after first vehicle injection.

Group 2. Sham + melatonin: Rats were injected subcutaneously with vehicle (distilled water with a final concentration of 0.5% acetic acid) instead of reserpine and treated orally with melatonin (10 mg/kg) for 21 days starting from 3 days after first vehicle injection.

Group 3. Sham + folic acid: Rats were injected subcutaneously with vehicle (distilled water with a final concentration of 0.5% acetic acid) instead of reserpine and treated orally with folic acid (3 mg/kg) for 21 days starting from 3 days after first vehicle injection.

Group 4. Sham + melatonin + folic acid (Mel + Fol): Rats were injected subcutaneously with vehicle (distilled water with a final concentration of 0.5% acetic acid) instead of reserpine and treated orally with melatonin (10 mg/kg) and folic acid (3 mg/kg) for 21 days starting from 3 days after first vehicle injection.

Group 5. Reserpine + vehicle: Rats were subjected to injection of reserpine as previously described and treated orally with vehicle (saline) for 21 days starting from 3 days after first reserpine injection.

Group 6. Reserpine + melatonin: Rats were subjected to injection of reserpine as previously described and treated orally with melatonin (10 mg/kg) for 21 days starting from 3 days after first reserpine injection.

Group 7. Reserpine + folic acid: Rats were subjected to injection of reserpine as previously described and treated orally with folic acid (3 mg/kg) for 21 days starting from 3 days after first reserpine injection.

Group 8. Reserpine + melatonin + folic acid (Mel + Fol): Rats were subjected to injection of reserpine as previously described and treated orally with folic acid (3 mg/kg) and melatonin (10 mg/kg) for 21 days starting from 3 days after first reserpine injection.

The dose and route of administration of folic acid and melatonin were chosen based on previous studies [39,40]. Twenty-one days after reserpine injection blood was collected, animals were sacrificed and brain and sciatic nerves were harvested for histological, immunohistochemical and western blot analysis.

2.4. Von Frey Hair Test

Mechanical allodynia was evaluated using a dynamic plantar Von Frey hair aesthesiometer on day 0 and 3, 5, 7, 14, and 21 days post-injection (Bio-EVF4; Bioseb, Vitrolles, France) as previously described [41]. The device encloses a force transducer furnished with a plastic tip. When pressure is applied to the tip, the force applied is recorded. The tip was applied to the plantar area of the hind leg, and a rising upward force was exerted until the paw was withdrawn. The withdrawal threshold was defined as the force, expressed in grams, at which the mouse removed the paw.

2.5. Hot Plate Test

The hot plate test was performed on day 0 and 3, 5, 7, 14, and 21 days post-injection. The hot-plate latency was evaluated using a metal surface maintained at 53.6 °C (Ugo Basile, Milan, Italy). The rat was monitored and the licking of a hind paw was acquired as the end point. Maximal latency accepted was 45 s [42].

2.6. The Tail-Flick Warm Water Test

The tail-flick warm water test was performed on day 0 and 3, 5, 7, 14, and 21 days post-injection. The warm water tail-flick test was employed to evaluate pain threshold. 4 cm of the rat-tail was located in 50 ± 0.5 °C warm water and the time between tail input and retraction was noted (three tests were conducted and the average in units of seconds was recorded). The latency was assessed with a sensitivity of 0.01 s. A maximum tail-flick latency of 10 s was employed to minimize tissue damage to the tail [42].

2.7. Forced Swimming Test (FST)

The forced swimming test (FST) was performed on day 0 and 3, 5, 7, 14, and 21 days post-injection according to the original method by Porsolt et al. [43] and modified by Detke and Lucki [44]. Each rat was individually placed in a plexiglass cylinder for 5 min. It was considered immobile when it remained floating in the water making only essential movements to keep its head above water. The total duration of immobility was recorded as immobility time (sec/5 min).

2.8. Estimation of Lipid Peroxidation

Twenty-one days after reserpine injection brain tissues were harvested and the malondialdehyde content, an indicator of lipid peroxidation, was measured in the form of thiobarbituric acid-reactive substances by the method of Wills [45]. Briefly, 0.5 mL of cytosolic fraction of brains and 0.5 mL of Tris-HCl were incubated at 37 °C for 2 h. After incubation 1 mL of 10% trichloroacetic acid was added and centrifuged at 1000× g for 10 min. Then 1 mL of 0.67% thiobarbituric acid was added to 1 mL of supernatant and the tubes were kept in boiling water for 10 min. After cooling, 1 mL double-distilled water was added and absorbance was measured at 532 nm. Thiobarbituric acid-reactive substances were quantified using an extinction coefficient of 1.56×105 M^{-1} cm^{-1} and expressed as nmol of malondialdehyde per mg protein.

2.9. Estimation of Non Protein Thiols

Twenty-one days after reserpine injection brain tissues were harvested and non protein thiols were calculated by the method of Jollow [46]. Briefly, 1.0 mL of cytosolic fraction of brain tissues were precipitated with 1.0 mL of sulphosalicylic acid (4%). The samples were kept at 4 °C for at least 1 h and then subjected to centrifugation at $1200 \times g$ for 15 min at 4 °C. The assay mixture contained 0.1 mL supernatant, 2.7 mL phosphate buffer (0.1 M, pH 7.4) and 0.2 mL 5,5-dithiobis- (2-nitrobenzoic acid) (Ellman's reagent, 0.1 mM, pH 8.0) in a total volume of 3.0 mL. Samples was read at 412 nm and the reduced glutathione levels were reported as mmol/mg protein.

2.10. Estimation of Superoxide Dismutase

Twenty-one days after reserpine injection brain tissues were harvested and superoxide dismutase activity was assayed by the method of Kono [47]. The assay system consisted of 0.1 mM EDTA, 50 mM sodium carbonate, and 96 mM of nitro-blue tetrazolium (NBT). In a cuvette, 2 mL of the above mixture was taken and 0.05 mL of cytosolic fraction of brains and 0.05 mL of hydroxylamine hydrochloride (adjusted to pH 6.0 with NaOH) were added to it. The auto-oxidation of hydroxylamine was observed by measuring the change in optical density at 560 nm for 2 min at 30-/60-s intervals.

2.11. Estimation of Catalase

Twenty-one days after reserpine injection brain tissues were harvested and catalase activity was assayed by the method of Claiborne [48]. Briefly, the assay mixture consisted of 1.95 mL phosphate buffer (0.05 M, pH 7.0), 1.0 mL hydrogen peroxide (0.019 M), and 0.05 mL cytosolic fraction of brains in a final volume of 3.0 mL. Changes in absorbance were recorded at 240 nm. Catalase activity was assayed in terms of k min^{-1}.

2.12. Mast Cells Evaluation

Twenty-one days after reserpine injection brain and sciatic nerve were harvested. Tissues were fixed in 10% buffered formalin, and embedded in paraffin blocks. Seven-μm sections were prepared from paraffin-embedded tissues. After deparaffinization, sections were stained with toluidine blue in order to assess mast cell infiltration. The mast cells count was performed on each slide through a Leica DM6 (Milan, Italy) microscope.

2.13. TNF-α and IL-1β ELISA

The quantifications of TNF-α and IL-1β were assayed following the instructions provided by R&D Systems Quantikine Rat TNF- α and IL-1β immunoassay kit [49].

2.14. Western Blot Analysis

Western blot analysis was executed on brain and sciatic nerve harvested 21 h after reserpine injection. Cytosolic proteins were extracts as described previously [50]. Membranes were probed with specific Abs: with anti-VEGF (1:500; Santa Cruz Biotechnology, Heidelberg, Germany), or with anti-NGF (1:500; Santa Cruz Biotechnology) in 1× PBS (Phosphate buffered saline), 5% *w/v* nonfat dried milk, 0.1% Tween-20 at 4 °C, overnight. To control the equal amounts of proteins, blots also were probed with antibody against b-actin protein (cytosolic fraction 1:500; Santa Cruz Biotechnology). Signals were examined with enhanced chemiluminescence (ECL) detection system reagent according to the manufacturer's instructions (Thermo Fisher, Waltham, MA, USA). The relative expression of the protein bands was quantified by densitometry with BIORAD ChemiDocTM XRS + software and standardized to b-actin and lamin A/C levels. The blot was stripped with glycine 2% and re-incubated several times to optimize detection of proteins and to visualize other proteins minimizing the number of gels and transfers.

2.15. Immunohistochemical Analysis

Immunohistochemical analysis was performed as already described [50]. Tissues were fixed in 10% (*w/v*) PBS-buffered formaldehyde and 7 μm sections were prepared from paraffin embedded tissues. After deparaffinization, endogenous peroxidase was quenched with 0.3% (*v/v*) hydrogen peroxide in 60% (*v/v*) methanol for 30 min. The sections were permeabilized with 0.1% (*w/v*) Triton X-100 in PBS for 20 min. Non-specific adsorption was minimized by incubating the section in 2% (*v/v*) normal goat serum in PBS for 20 min. Endogenous biotin and avidin binding sites were blocked by sequential incubation for 15 min with biotin and avidin (DBA, Milan, Italy). Subsequently, the sections were incubated overnight with: anti-nitrotyrosine antibody (1:100; Millipore, Abingdon, UK) or anti-PARP antibody (1:100; Santa Cruz Biotechnology). Sections were washed with PBS and incubated with peroxidase-conjugated bovine anti-mouse IgG, secondary antibody (1:2000 Jackson Immuno Research, WestGrove, Pennsylvania, USA). Specific labeling was provided with a biotin-conjugated goat anti-mouse IgG and avidin-biotin peroxidase complex (Vector Laboratories, Burlingame, California, USA). Images were collected using a Leica DM6 (Milan, Italy) microscope. The percentage area of immunoreactivity (described by the number of positive pixels) was reported as percent of total tissue area (red staining).

2.16. Immunofluorescence Analysis

Brain sections were incubated with primary antibodies: anti-CD11b (1:100, abcam) or anti Iba-1 (1:100, Santa Cruz Biotechnology) in a humidified chamber at 37 °C overnight. Sections were washed with PBS and were incubated with secondary antibody FITC-conjugated anti-mouse Alexa Fluor-488 antibody (1:2000 *v/v* Molecular Probes, UK) for 1 h at 37 °C. Sections were laved and for nuclear staining 4′,6′-diamidino-2-phenylindole (DAPI; Hoechst, Frankfurt; Germany) 2 μg/mL in PBS was added. Sections were analysed using a Leica DM2000 microscope [51].

2.17. Materials

All compounds used in this study, except where differently specified, were purchased from Sigma-Aldrich Company Ltd.

2.18. Statistical Evaluation

All values in the figures and text are expressed as mean ± standard error of the mean (SEM) of N number of animals. In those experiments involving histology, the exhibited pictures are representative of at least three experiments performed on different days. Results were analyzed by one-way ANOVA followed by a Bonferroni post-hoc test for multiple comparisons. A *p*-value <0.05 was considered significant. * $p < 0.05$ vs. sham, ° $p < 0.05$ vs. vehicle, ** $p < 0.01$ vs. sham, °° $p < 0.01$ vs. vehicle, *** $p < 0.001$ vs. sham, °°° $p < 0.001$ vs. vehicle.

3. Results

3.1. Effect of Folic Acid and Melatonin Treatment on Behavioral Defects Induced by Reserpine Injection

Mechanical hyperalgesia was evaluated by a von Frey test. Reserpine injection produced a significant decrease in paw-withdrawal threshold in response to von-Frey hair stimulation in vehicle treated rats compared to sham groups (Figure S1). Mel + Fol treatment significantly increased the paw-withdrawal threshold in reserpine-treated rats, compared to melatonin and folic acid (Figure 1A). In addition, the effect of Mel + Fol treatment on pain sensitivity was tested by subjecting rats to hot plate and tail-flick tests. Reserpine injection produced an increased pain sensitivity in vehicle group compared to control groups (Figure S1). Mel + Fol treatment displayed an antinociceptive effect in hot plate (Figure 1B) and tail-flick tests (Figure 1C) in reserpine-treated rats, compared to melatonin and folic acid. The depressive-like behavior was evaluated by the forced swimming test. Reserpine injection increased the immobility time in reserpine-vehicle treated animals, compared to the sham groups (Figure S1). Mel + Fol treatment significantly decreased the immobility time in reserpine-treated rats, compared to melatonin and folic acid (Figure 1D).

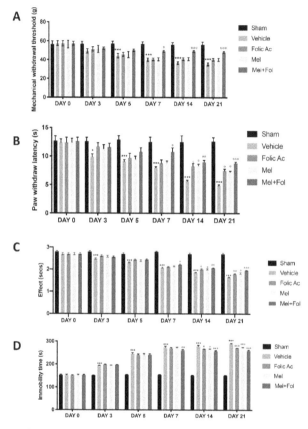

Figure 1. Efficacy of folic acid and melatonin administration on behavioral changes reserpine-induced. Behavioral tests: (**A**) Von Frey test, (**B**) hot plate test, (**C**) tail-flick test, (**D**) forced swimming test (D). A p-value < 0.05 was considered significant. * $p < 0.05$ vs. sham, ° $p < 0.05$ vs. vehicle, °° $p < 0.01$ vs. vehicle, *** $p < 0.001$ vs. sham, °°° $p < 0.001$ vs. vehicle.

3.2. Effect of Folic Acid and Melatonin Treatment on Lipid Peroxidation and Anti-Oxidant Profile Induced by Reserpine Injection

It has been shown that oxidative stress is implicated in the pathogenesis of fibromyalgia [16]. Lipid peroxide levels were increased in reserpine-vehicle treated rats compared to sham groups (Figure S2). Treatment with Mel + Fol caused a significant reduction in lipid peroxide in reserpine-treated rats, compared to melatonin and folic acid (Figure 2A). The enzymatic activity of superoxide dismutase (Figure 2B), non-protein thiols (Figure 2C), and catalase (Figure 2D) significantly decreased in the reserpine-vehicle treated rats compared to the sham groups (Figure S2). This reduction was significantly restored with in animals treated with Mel + Fol, compared to melatonin and folic acid.

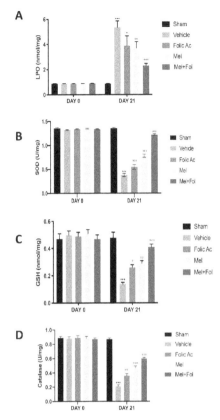

Figure 2. Efficacy of folic acid and melatonin administration on oxidative stress reserpine-induced. (**A**) Estimation of lipid peroxidation, (**B**) estimation of non protein thiols, (**C**) estimation of superoxide dismutase, (**D**) estimation of catalase. A p-value < 0.05 was considered significant. $^{\circ} p < 0.05$ vs. vehicle, $^{\circ\circ} p < 0.01$ vs. vehicle, $^{***} p < 0.001$ vs. sham, $^{\circ\circ\circ} p < 0.001$ vs. vehicle.

3.3. Effect of Folic Acid and Melatonin Treatment on Nitrosative Stress and PARP Expression Induced by Reserpine Injection

Twenty-one days after reserpine injection, we also investigated nitrotyrosine and PARP expression associated with oxidative stress by immunohistochemistry. Increased nitrotyrosine and PARP expression was found in brain tissue sections of reserpine-vehicle treated (Figure 3B,F,H,N) rats compared with the sham groups (Figure 3A,F,G,N and Figure S3). Treatment with Mel + Fol caused a significant reduction in nitrotyrosine (Figure 3E,F) and PARP expression (Figure 3M,N) in reserpine-treated rats, compared to melatonin (Figure 3D,F,L,N) and folic acid (Figure 3C,F,I,N).

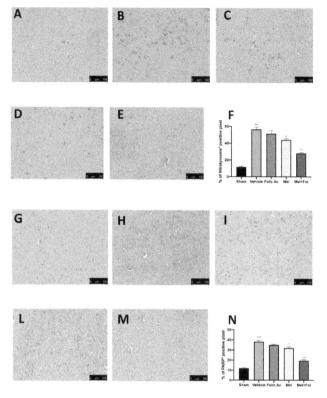

Figure 3. Efficacy of folic acid and melatonin administration on nitrityrosine and PARP expression reserpine-induced. Immunohistochemistry evaluation of nitrityrosine expression in (**A**) sham, (**B**) vehicle, (**C**) folic acid, (**D**) melatonin, (**E**) melatonin plus folic acid and (**F**) graphical quantification. Immunohistochemistry evaluation of PARP expression in (**G**) sham, (**H**) vehicle, (**I**) folic acid, (**L**) melatonin, (**M**) melatonin plus folic acid, and (**N**) graphical quantification. A *p*-value < 0.05 was considered significant, $^{\circ\circ}$ $p < 0.01$ vs. vehicle, *** $p < 0.001$ vs. sham, $^{\circ\circ\circ}$ $p < 0.001$ vs. vehicle.

3.4. Effect of Folic Acid and Melatonin Treatment on Mast Cells Infiltration induced by Reserpine Injection

Twenty-one days after reserpine injection, mast cells infiltration and degranulation were assessed by toluidine blue staining. There was a significant up-regulation in mast cell number, which performs a key role in the development of hyperalgesia and in the inflammatory process, both in brain (Figure 4B) and sciatic nerve (Figure 4G) in reserpine-vehicle treated rats, compared to the sham groups (Figure 4A,F and Figure S4). Mel + Fol treatment reduced the number of mast cells both in brain (Figure 4E) and sciatic nerve (Figure 4L) in reserpine-treated rats, more than melatonin (Figure 4D,I) and folic acid (Figure 4C,H).

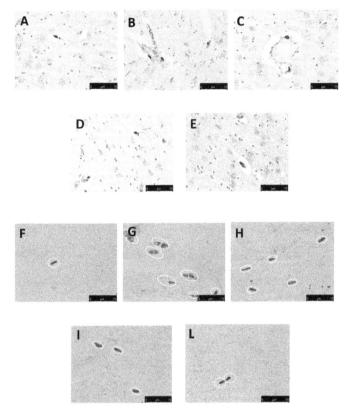

Figure 4. Efficacy of folic acid and melatonin administration on mast cells activation reserpine-induced. Evaluation of mast cell degranulation by toluidine blue in brain: (**A**) sham, (**B**) vehicle, (**C**) folic acid, (**D**) melatonin, (**E**) melatonin plus folic acid. Evaluation of mast cell degranulation by toluidine blue in sciatic nerve: (**F**) sham, (**G**) vehicle, (**H**) folic acid, (**I**) melatonin, (**L**) melatonin plus folic acid. 40× magnification is shown.

3.5. Effect of Folic acid and Melatonin Treatment on Changes in Pro-Inflammatory, Vasoactive and Neuro-Sensitizing Mediators Induced by Reserpine Injection

Twenty-one days after reserpine injection, IL-1β and TNF-α levels were increased in reserpine-vehicle treated rats, compared to the sham groups (Figure S5). Treatment with Mel + Fol produced a significant reduction in IL-1β (Figure 5A) and TNF-α (Figure 5B) levels in reserpine-treated rats, compared to melatonin and folic acid. Western blot analysis showed NGF and VEGF increased expression in both brain and nerve tissues harvested from reserpine-vehicle treated animals, compared to the sham groups (Figure 5C,D and Figure S5). Mel + Fol administration significantly reduced NGF and VEGF expression in reserpine-treated rats with more efficacy than melatonin and folic acid (Figure 5C,D).

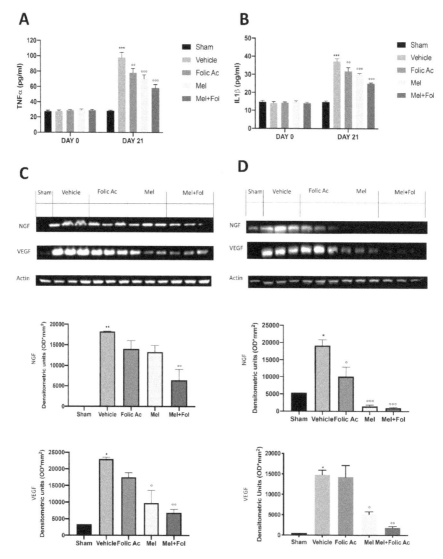

Figure 5. Efficacy of folic acid and melatonin administration on IL-1β, TNF-α, VEGF, and NGF expression reserpine-induced. Elisa kit of (**A**) IL-1β and (**B**) TNF-α levels. Western blots and respectively quantification of VEGF and NGF in (**C**) brain and (**D**) sciatic nerve. A p-value < 0.05 was considered significant. * $p < 0.05$ vs. sham, ° $p < 0.05$ vs. vehicle, ** $p < 0.01$ vs. sham, °° $p < 0.01$ vs. vehicle, *** $p < 0.001$ vs. sham, °°° $p < 0.001$ vs. vehicle.

3.6. Effect of Folic Acid and Melatonin Treatment on Microglia Activation Induced by Reserpine Injection

Twenty-one days after reserpine injection, we also investigated microglial activation by immunofluorescence. Increased Iba1 and CD11b positive cells were found in brain tissue sections of reserpine-vehicle treated (Figure 6B,G) rats compared with the sham groups (Figure 6A,F and Figure S6). Treatment with Mel + Fol caused a significant reduction in Iba1 (Figure 6E) and Cd11b positive cells (Figure 6L) in reserpine-treated rats, compared to melatonin (Figure 6D,I) and folic acid (Figure 6C,H).

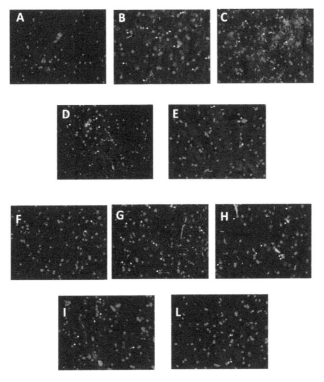

Figure 6. Efficacy of folic acid and melatonin administration on Iba1 and CD11b expression reserpine-induced. Immunofluorescence of brain Iba1 in (**A**) sham, (**B**) vehicle, (**C**) folic acid, (**D**) melatonin, (**E**) melatonin plus folic acid. Immunofluorescence of brain CD11b in (**F**) sham, (**G**) vehicle, (**H**) folic acid, (**I**) melatonin, (**L**) melatonin plus folic acid. 40× magnification is shown.

4. Discussion

Fibromyalgia is a multisymptomatic and multifactorial disease [20]. The pathophysiological mechanisms by which the disease is characterize include, among others, changes in sensory perception of pain [52], oxidative stress and inflammation [18] with damage to myelinated and nonmyelinated nerve fibers [16]. In our study, animals subjected to fibromyalgia showed increased pain sensitivity in mechanical allodynia and thermal hyperalgesia. Moreover, this enhanced sensibility was coupled with depression symptoms, as indicated by the rat behaviour in the forced swim test. Several evidence, in fact, indicates that the depression-like symptoms in rats increased allodynia and hyperalgesia under the condition of fibromyalgia [3]. A concomitant treatment of melatonin and folic acid was able to reduce the increased pain sensibility and the depression-like behaviour with more efficacy than them single administration. Increasing evidence suggests that enhanced oxidative stress and nitric oxide are involved in the fibromyalgia pathophysiology and increase the severity of the symptoms [53,54]. We are in line with literature [55,56]; our data also underlines that the oxidative and nitrosative stress induces neurogenic inflammation which is responsible for the perpetuation of pain [16]. The oxidants and antioxidants equilibrium is unbalanced in this pathology [32]: increased lipid peroxidation was detected in rats subjected to fibromyalgia, while superoxide dismutase, nonprotein thiols and catalase were significantly decreased [49]. Thanks to its antioxidant properties, a combined treatment of melatonin and folic acid was also able to reduce these parameters better than the single administration. While free oxygen radicals oxidize membrane phospholipids amplifying lipid peroxidation, nitric oxide excessively produced by iNOS reacts with superoxide anions yielding the toxic oxidizing agent peroxynitrite. It nitrates tyrosine residues, causing changes in protein function and structure that induce tissue damage. Peroxynitrite in turn activates PARP, a single-strand break DNA repair enzyme that acts by synthesizing chains of ADP-ribose [50]. To product ADP-ribose monomers, the obligate substrate is NAD+. PARP hyper-activation depletes NAD+ cellular reserves of leading to ATP depletion, cellular dysfunction, and death. Melatonin plus folic acid administration decreased nitrotyrosine and PARP staining induced by fibromyalgia better than the single administration of the two substances. This increased oxidative stress is able to induce mast cells activation [57]. Systemic mastocytosis [58] is commonly experience in patients affected by fibromyalgia [59,60]. Several pieces of evidence show the importance of mast cells activation in this disease and [61,62] comorbid disorders [63] such as neuroimmune interactions [64] and painful conditions, [65,66]. Mast cells reside near the nerve fibers, which give them the possibility to migrate for modulating nociception and neural activity [59,67–69]. As result of their migration and degranulation, there is an important release of pro-inflammatory, vasoactive and neuro-sensitizing mediators [70]. In particular, an increased expression of cytokines (IL-1β and TNF-α) [71,72] and growth factors (NGF and VEGF) [73–75] that contribute to the maintenance of inflammation and pain have been detected in both nerve and brain [76–79]. An associate administration of melatonin and folic acid was able to decrease mast cells infiltration and the related increased expression of pro-inflammatory cytokines and vasoactive and neuro-sensitizing mediators with more efficacy than them single administration. Mast cells also communicate with microglia [60,80,81]. In the contests of pain, microglia in the thalamus is responsible for maintaining the pain sensation even after the original stimulus is over [82,83]. The concomitant treatment of melatonin and folic acid was able to reduce the increased microglia activation, assessed by Iba1 and CD11b expression, with more efficacy than their single administration.

5. Conclusions

Our results provide evidence that a combined treatment of melatonin and folic acid may be useful in the treatment of fibromyalgia, thanks to its ability to target all mediators that contribute to the perpetuation of pain, from the mastocytosis and related pro-inflammatory, vasoactive and neuro-sensitizing mediators to the oxidative stress processes.

Supplementary Materials: The following are available online at http://www.mdpi.com/2076-3921/8/12/628/s1, Figure S1: Efficacy of folic acid and melatonin administration on behavioral changes of sham groups, Figure S2: Efficacy of folic acid and melatonin administration on oxidative stress of sham groups, Figure S3: Efficacy of folic acid and melatonin administration on nitrityrosine and PARP expression of sham groups, Figure S4: Efficacy of folic acid and melatonin administration on mast cells activation of sham groups, Figure S5: Efficacy of folic acid and melatonin administration on IL-1β, TNF-α, VEGF and NGF expression of sham groups, Figure S6: Efficacy of folic acid and melatonin administration on Iba1 and CD11b expression of sham groups.

Author Contributions: Conceptualization, S.C. and R.D.P.; Methodology, D.I.; Software, M.C.; Validation, M.C., R.S. and E.G.; Formal Analysis, R.C.; Investigation, A.F.P.; Resources, R.F.; data curation, R.D.; writing original draft preparation, R.F.; writing—review and editing, R.D.P.; visualization, E.G.; supervision, R.D.P.; project administration, S.C.; funding acquisition, S.C.

Funding: This research received no external funding.

Conflicts of Interest: The authors declare no conflict of interest.

References

1. Wolfe, F.; Smythe, H.A.; Yunus, M.B.; Bennett, R.M.; Bombardier, C.; Goldenberg, D.L.; Tugwell, P.; Campbell, S.M.; Abeles, M.; Clark, P.; et al. The American College of Rheumatology 1990 Criteria for the Classification of Fibromyalgia. Report of the Multicenter Criteria Committee. *Arthritis Rheum* **1990**, *33*, 160–172. [CrossRef] [PubMed]

2. Arnold, L.M.; Clauw, D.J.; McCarberg, B.H. FibroCollaborative, Improving the recognition and diagnosis of fibromyalgia. *Mayo Clin. Proc.* **2011**, *86*, 457–464. [CrossRef] [PubMed]

3. Eich, W.; Häuser, W.; Arnold, B.; Jäckel, W.; Offenbächer, M.; Petzke, F.; Schiltenwolf, M.; Settan, M.; Sommer, C.; Tölle, T. Das Fibromyalgiesyndrom. *Der Schmerz* **2012**, *26*, 247–258. [CrossRef] [PubMed]

4.   Wolfe, F.; Clauw, D.J.; Fitzcharles, M.A.; Goldenberg, D.L.; Hauser, W.; Katz, R.S.; Mease, P.; Russell, A.S.; Russell, I.J.; Winfield, J.B. Fibromyalgia criteria and severity scales for clinical and epidemiological studies: A modification of the ACR Preliminary Diagnostic Criteria for Fibromyalgia. *J. Rheumatol.* **2011**, *38*, 1113–1122. [CrossRef]

5.   Yunus, M.B. Central sensitivity syndromes: A new paradigm and group nosology for fibromyalgia and overlapping conditions, and the related issue of disease versus illness. *Semin. Arthritis Rheum.* **2008**, *37*, 339–352. [CrossRef]

6.   Glass, J.M. Fibromyalgia and cognition. *J. Clin. Psychiatry* **2008**, *69* (Suppl. 2), 20–24.

7.   Menzies, V.; Lyon, D.E.; Elswick, R.K., Jr.; Montpetit, A.J.; McCain, N.L. Psychoneuroimmunological relationships in women with fibromyalgia. *Biol. Res. Nurs.* **2013**, *15*, 219–225. [CrossRef]

8.   Bradley, L.A. Pathophysiology of fibromyalgia. *Am. J. Med.* **2009**, *122* (Suppl. 12), S22–S30. [CrossRef]

9.   Tak, L.M.; Cleare, A.J.; Ormel, J.; Manoharan, A.; Kok, I.C.; Wessely, S.; Rosmalen, J.G. Meta-analysis and meta-regression of hypothalamic-pituitary-adrenal axis activity in functional somatic disorders. *Biol. Psychol.* **2011**, *87*, 183–194. [CrossRef]

10. Garcia, J.J.; Cidoncha, A.; Bote, M.E.; Hinchado, M.D.; Ortega, E. Altered profile of chemokines in fibromyalgia patients. *Ann. Clin. Biochem.* **2014**, *51 Pt 5*, 576–581. [CrossRef]

11. Behm, F.G.; Gavin, I.M.; Karpenko, O.; Lindgren, V.; Gaitonde, S.; Gashkoff, P.A.; Gillis, B.S. Unique immunologic patterns in fibromyalgia. *BMC Clin. Pathol.* **2012**, *12*, 25. [CrossRef]

12. Uceyler, N.; Hauser, W.; Sommer, C. Systematic review with meta-analysis: Cytokines in fibromyalgia syndrome. *BMC Musculoskelet. Disord.* **2011**, *12*, 245. [CrossRef]

13. Rodriguez-Pinto, I.; Agmon-Levin, N.; Howard, A.; Shoenfeld, Y. Fibromyalgia and cytokines. *Immunol. Lett.* **2014**, *161*, 200–203. [CrossRef]

14. Toker, A.; Kucuksen, S.; Kucuk, A.; Cicekler, H. Serum ischemia-modified albumin and malondialdehyde levels and superoxide dismutase activity in patients with fibromyalgia. *Clin. Lab.* **2014**, *60*, 1609–1615. [CrossRef]

15. Akbas, A.; Inanir, A.; Benli, I.; Onder, Y.; Aydogan, L. Evaluation of some antioxidant enzyme activities (SOD and GPX) and their polymorphisms (MnSOD2 Ala9Val, GPX1 Pro198Leu) in fibromyalgia. *Eur. Rev. Med. Pharmacol. Sci.* **2014**, *18*, 1199–1203.

16. Bagis, S.; Tamer, L.; Sahin, G.; Bilgin, R.; Guler, H.; Ercan, B.; Erdogan, C. Free radicals and antioxidants in primary fibromyalgia: An oxidative stress disorder? *Rheumatol. Int.* **2005**, *25*, 188–190. [CrossRef]

17. Martinez-Lavin, M. Fibromyalgia: When Distress Becomes (Un) sympathetic Pain. *Pain Res. Treat.* **2012**, *2012*, 981565. [CrossRef]

18. Littlejohn, G. Neuroinflammation in fibromyalgia and CRPS: Top-down or bottomup? *Nat. Rev. Rheumatol.* **2016**, *12*, 242. [CrossRef]

19. Cassisi, G.; Sarzi-Puttini, P.; Casale, R.; Cazzola, M.; Boccassini, L.; Atzeni, F.; Stisi, S. Pain in fibromyalgia and related conditions. *Reumatismo* **2014**, *66*, 72–86. [CrossRef]

20. Sumpton, J.E.; Moulin, D.E. Fibromyalgia. In *Handbook of Clinical Neurology*; Elsevier: Amsterdam, The Netherlands, 2014; Volume 119, pp. 513–527.

21. Choy, E.H. The role of sleep in pain and fibromyalgia. *Nat. Rev. Rheumatol.* **2015**, *11*, 513–520. [CrossRef]

22. Sanchez-Dominguez, B.; Bullon, P.; Roman-Malo, L.; Marin-Aguilar, F.; Alcocer-Gomez, E.; Carrion, A.M.; Sanchez-Alcazar, J.A.; Cordero, M.D. Oxidative stress, mitochondrial dysfunction and, inflammation common events in skin of patients with Fibromyalgia. *Mitochondrion* **2015**, *21*, 69–75. [CrossRef]

23. Staud, R. Brain imaging in fibromyalgia syndrome. *Clin. Exp. Rheumatol.* **2011**, *29* (Suppl. 69), S109–S117.

24. Blumenthal, D.E.; Malemud, C.J. Recent strategies for drug development in fibromyalgia syndrome. *Expert Rev. Neurother.* **2016**, *16*, 1407–1411. [CrossRef]

25. Danilov, A.; Kurganova, J. Melatonin in Chronic Pain Syndromes. *Pain Ther.* **2016**, *5*, 1–17. [CrossRef]

26. Pernambuco, A.P.; Schetino, L.P.; Viana, R.S.; Carvalho, L.S.; d'Avila Reis, D. The involvement of melatonin in the clinical status of patients with fibromyalgia syndrome. *Clin. Exp. Rheumatol.* **2015**, *33* (Suppl. 88), S14–S19.

27. Johnston, J.D.; Skene, D.J. 60 YEARS OF NEUROENDOCRINOLOGY: Regulation of mammalian neuroendocrine physiology and rhythms by melatonin. *J. Endocrinol.* **2015**, *226*, T187–T198. [CrossRef]

28. Reiter, R.J.; Tan, D.X.; Galano, A. Melatonin: Exceeding expectations. *Physiology* **2014**, *29*, 325–333. [CrossRef]

29. Manchester, L.C.; Coto-Montes, A.; Boga, J.A.; Andersen, L.P.; Zhou, Z.; Galano, A.; Vriend, J.; Tan, D.X.; Reiter, R.J. Melatonin: An ancient molecule that makes oxygen metabolically tolerable. *J. Pineal Res.* **2015**, *59*, 403–419. [CrossRef]

30. Ambriz-Tututi, M.; Granados-Soto, V. Oral and spinal melatonin reduces tactile allodynia in rats via activation of MT2 and opioid receptors. *Pain* **2007**, *132*, 273–280. [CrossRef]

31. Andersen, L.P. The analgesic effects of exogenous melatonin in humans. *Acta Anaesthesiol. Scand.* **2016**, *60*, 1024–1025. [CrossRef]

32. Ozgocmen, S.; Ozyurt, H.; Sogut, S.; Akyol, O.; Ardicoglu, O.; Yildizhan, H. Antioxidant status, lipid peroxidation and nitric oxide in fibromyalgia: Etiologic and therapeutic concerns. *Rheumatol. Int.* **2006**, *26*, 598–603. [CrossRef]

33. Stanhewicz, A.E.; Kenney, W.L. Role of folic acid in nitric oxide bioavailability and vascular endothelial function. *Nutr. Rev.* **2017**, *75*, 61–70. [CrossRef]

34. Nakano, E.; Higgins, J.A.; Powers, H.J. Folate protects against oxidative modification of human LDL. *Br. J. Nutr.* **2001**, *86*, 637–639. [CrossRef]

35. Joshi, R.; Adhikari, S.; Patro, B.S.; Chattopadhyay, S.; Mukherjee, T. Free radical scavenging behavior of folic acid: Evidence for possible antioxidant activity. *Free Radic. Biol. Med.* **2001**, *30*, 1390–1399. [CrossRef]

36. Henning, S.M.; Swendseid, M.E.; Ivandic, B.T.; Liao, F. Vitamins C, E and A and heme oxygenase in rats fed methyl/folate-deficient diets. *Free Radic. Biol. Med.* **1997**, *23*, 936–942. [CrossRef]

37. Durand, P.; Prost, M.; Blache, D. Pro-thrombotic effects of a folic acid deficient diet in rat platelets and macrophages related to elevated homocysteine and decreased n-3 polyunsaturated fatty acids. *Atherosclerosis* **1996**, *121*, 231–243. [CrossRef]

38. Nagakura, Y.; Oe, T.; Aoki, T.; Matsuoka, N. Biogenic amine depletion causes chronic muscular pain and tactile allodynia accompanied by depression: A putative animal model of fibromyalgia. *Pain* **2009**, *146*, 26–33. [CrossRef]

39. Achon, M.; Alonso-Aperte, E.; Reyes, L.; Ubeda, N.; Varela-Moreiras, G. High-dose folic acid supplementation in rats: Effects on gestation and the methionine cycle. *Br. J. Nutr.* **2000**, *83*, 177–183. [CrossRef]

40. Favero, G.; Trapletti, V.; Bonomini, F.; Stacchiotti, A.; Lavazza, A.; Rodella, L.F.; Rezzani, R. Oral Supplementation of Melatonin Protects against Fibromyalgia-Related Skeletal Muscle Alterations in Reserpine-Induced Myalgia Rats. *Int. J. Mol. Sci.* **2017**, *18*, 1389. [CrossRef]

41. Bhalala, O.G.; de Morree, A. Assessment of Mechanical Allodynia in Rats Using the Electronic Von Frey Test. *J. Neurosci.* **2016**. [CrossRef]

42. Di Paola, R.; Fusco, R.; Gugliandolo, E.; Crupi, R.; Evangelista, M.; Granese, R.; Cuzzocrea, S. Co-micronized palmitoylethanolamide/polydatin treatment causes endometriotic lesion regression in a rodent model of surgically induced endometriosis. *Front. Pharmacol.* **2016**, *7*, 382. [CrossRef]

43. Porsolt, R.D.; Anton, G.; Blavet, N.; Jalfre, M. Behavioural despair in rats: A new model sensitive to antidepressant treatments. *Eur. J. Pharmacol.* **1978**, *47*, 379–391. [CrossRef]

44. Detke, M.J.; Lucki, I. Detection of serotonergic and noradrenergic antidepressants in the rat forced swimming test: The effects of water depth. *Behav. Brain Res.* **1996**, *73*, 43–46. [CrossRef]

45. Wills, E.D. Mechanisms of Lipid Peroxide Formation in Tissues. Role of Metals and Haematin Proteins in the Catalysis of the Oxidation Unsaturated Fatty Acids. *Biochim. Biophys. Acta* **1965**, *98*, 238–251. [CrossRef]

46. Jollow, D.J.; Mitchell, J.R.; Zampaglione, N.; Gillette, J.R. Bromobenzene-induced liver necrosis. Protective role of glutathione and evidence for 3,4-bromobenzene oxide as the hepatotoxic metabolite. *Pharmacology* **1974**, *11*, 151–169. [CrossRef]

47. Kono, Y. Generation of superoxide radical during autoxidation of hydroxylamine and an assay for superoxide dismutase. *Arch. Biochem. Biophys.* **1978**, *186*, 189–195. [CrossRef]

48. Claiborne, A. *Handbook of Methods for Oxygen Radical Research*; CRC Press: Boca Raton, FL, USA, 1985.

49. Arora, V.; Kuhad, A.; Tiwari, V.; Chopra, K. Curcumin ameliorates reserpine-induced pain-depression dyad: Behavioural, biochemical, neurochemical and molecular evidences. *Psychoneuroendocrinology* **2011**, *36*, 1570–1581. [CrossRef]

50. Fusco, R.; Cirmi, S.; Gugliandolo, E.; Di Paola, R.; Cuzzocrea, S.; Navarra, M. Anti-oxidant and anti-inflammatory effects of a flavonoid-rich extract from orange juice in experimental colitis. *Free Radic. Biol. Med.* **2017**, *108*, S37. [CrossRef]

51. Di Paola, R.; Fusco, R.; Gugliandolo, E.; D'Amico, R.; Cordaro, M.; Impellizzeri, D.; Perretti, M.; Cuzzocrea, S. Formyl peptide receptor 1 signalling promotes experimental colitis in mice. *Pharmacol. Res.* **2019**, *141*, 591–601. [CrossRef]

52. Jensen, K.B.; Loitoile, R.; Kosek, E.; Petzke, F.; Carville, S.; Fransson, P.; Marcus, H.; Williams, S.C.; Choy, E.; Mainguy, Y.; et al. Patients with fibromyalgia display less functional connectivity in the brain's pain inhibitory network. *Mol. Pain* **2012**, *8*, 32. [CrossRef]

53. Fatima, G.; Das, S.K.; Mahdi, A.A. Some oxidative and antioxidative parameters and their relationship with clinical symptoms in women with fibromyalgia syndrome. *Int. J. Rheum. Dis.* **2017**, *20*, 39–45. [CrossRef]

54. Fatima, G.; Das, S.; Mahdi, A. Oxidative stress and antioxidative parameters and metal ion content in patients with fibromyalgia syndrome: Implications in the pathogenesis of the disease. *Clin. Exp. Rheumatol.* **2013**, *31* (Suppl. 79), S128–S133.

55. La Rubia, M.; Rus, A.; Molina, F.; Del Moral, M.L. Is fibromyalgia-related oxidative stress implicated in the decline of physical and mental health status. *Clin. Exp. Rheumatol.* **2013**, *31* (Suppl. 79), S121–S127.

56. Meeus, M.; Nijs, J.; Hermans, L.; Goubert, D.; Calders, P. The role of mitochondrial dysfunctions due to oxidative and nitrosative stress in the chronic pain or chronic fatigue syndromes and fibromyalgia patients: Peripheral and central mechanisms as therapeutic targets? *Expert Opin. Ther. Targets* **2013**, *17*, 1081–1089. [CrossRef]

57. Saito, H. Mast cells. *Nihon Rinsho* **2005**, *63* (Suppl. 4), 166–170.

58. Jennings, S.; Russell, N.; Jennings, B.; Slee, V.; Sterling, L.; Castells, M.; Valent, P.; Akin, C. The Mastocytosis Society survey on mast cell disorders: Patient experiences and perceptions. *J. Allergy Clin. Immunol. Pract.* **2014**, *2*, 70–76. [CrossRef]

59. Theoharides, T.C.; Valent, P.; Akin, C. Mast Cells, Mastocytosis, and Related Disorders. *N. Engl. J. Med.* **2015**, *373*, 1885–1886. [CrossRef]

60. Theoharides, T.C.; Tsilioni, I.; Bawazeer, M. Mast Cells, Neuroinflammation and Pain in Fibromyalgia Syndrome. *Front. Cell. Neurosci.* **2019**, *13*, 353. [CrossRef]

61. Lucas, H.J.; Brauch, C.M.; Settas, L.; Theoharides, T.C. Fibromyalgia—New concepts of pathogenesis and treatment. *Int. J. Immunopathol. Pharmacol.* **2006**, *19*, 5–10. [CrossRef]

62. Pollack, S. Mast cells in fibromyalgia. *Clin. Exp. Rheumatol.* **2015**, *33* (Suppl. 88), S140.

63. Theoharides, T.C. Atopic conditions in search of pathogenesis and therapy. *Clin. Ther.* **2013**, *35*, 544–547. [CrossRef]

64. Skaper, S.D.; Facci, L.; Zusso, M.; Giusti, P. Neuroinflammation, Mast Cells, and Glia: Dangerous Liaisons. *Neuroscientist* **2017**, *23*, 478–498. [CrossRef]

65. Heron, A.; Dubayle, D. A focus on mast cells and pain. *J. Neuroimmunol.* **2013**, *264*, 1–7. [CrossRef]

66. Chatterjea, D.; Martinov, T. Mast cells: Versatile gatekeepers of pain. *Mol. Immunol.* **2015**, *63*, 38–44. [CrossRef]

67. Aich, A.; Afrin, L.B.; Gupta, K. Mast Cell-Mediated Mechanisms of Nociception. *Int. J. Mol. Sci.* **2015**, *16*, 29069–29092. [CrossRef]

68. Edvinsson, L.; Owman, C.; Sjoberg, N.O. Autonomic nerves, mast cells, and amine receptors in human brain vessels. A histochemical and pharmacological study. *Brain Res.* **1976**, *115*, 377–393. [CrossRef]

69. Lambracht-Hall, M.; Dimitriadou, V.; Theoharides, T.C. Migration of mast cells in the developing rat brain. *Brain Res. Dev. Brain Res.* **1990**, *56*, 151–159. [CrossRef]

70. Galli, S.J.; Tsai, M. Mast cells: Versatile regulators of inflammation, tissue remodeling, host defense and homeostasis. *J. Dermatol. Sci.* **2008**, *49*, 7–19. [CrossRef]

71. Huang, Q.-J.; Jiang, H.; Hao, X.-L.; Minor, T.R. Brain IL-1beta was involved in reserpine-induced behavioral depression in rats. *Acta Pharmacol. Sin.* **2004**, *25*, 293–296.

72. Szelenyi, J.; Kiss, J.P.; Puskas, E.; Szelenyi, M.; Vizi, E.S. Contribution of differently localized alpha (2)- and beta-adrenoceptors in the modulation of TNF-alpha and IL-10 production in endotoxemic. *Ann. N. Y. Acad. Sci.* **2000**, *917*, 145–153. [CrossRef]

73. Maren, S. Synapse-Specific Encoding of Fear Memory in the Amygdala. *Neuron* **2017**, *95*, 988–990. [CrossRef] [PubMed]

74. Abdel-Majid, R.M.; Marshall, J.S. Prostaglandin E-2 induces degranulation-independent production of vascular endothelial growth factor by human mast cells. *J. Immunol.* **2004**, *172*, 1227–1236. [CrossRef] [PubMed]

75. Chelombitko, M.A.; Fedorov, A.V.; Ilyinskaya, O.P.; Zinovkin, R.A.; Chernyak, B.V. Role of reactive oxygen species in mast cell degranulation. *Biochemistry* **2016**, *81*, 1564–1577. [CrossRef] [PubMed]
76. Watson, J.J.; Allen, S.J.; Dawbarn, D. Targeting Nerve Growth Factor in Pain What is the Therapeutic Potential. *Biodrugs* **2008**, *22*, 349–359. [CrossRef] [PubMed]
77. Vincent, L.; Vang, D.; Nguyen, J.; Gupta, M.; Luk, K.; Ericson, M.E.; Simone, D.A.; Gupta, K. Mast cell activation contributes to sickle cell pathobiology and pain in mice. *Blood* **2013**, *122*, 1853–1862. [CrossRef]
78. Kainz, V.; Levy, D.; Strassman, A.M. Mast cell degranulation activates a pain pathway underlying migraine headache. *Cephalalgia* **2007**, *27*, 598.
79. Taiwo, O.B.; Kovacs, K.J.; Sun, Y.X.; Larson, A.A. Unilateral spinal nerve ligation leads to an asymmetrical distribution of mast cells in the thalamus of female but not male mice. *Pain* **2005**, *114*, 131–140. [CrossRef]
80. Skaper, S.D.; Giusti, P.; Facci, L. Microglia and mast cells: Two tracks on the road to neuroinflammation. *Faseb J.* **2012**, *26*, 3103–3117. [CrossRef]
81. Skaper, S.D.; Facci, L.; Giusti, P. Neuroinflammation, Microglia and Mast Cells in the Pathophysiology of Neurocognitive Disorders: A Review. *CNS Neurol. Disord. Drug Targets* **2014**, *13*, 1654–1666. [CrossRef]
82. Banati, R.B. Brain plasticity and microglia: Is transsynaptic glial activation in the thalamus after limb denervation linked to cortical plasticity and central sensitisation? *J. Physiol. Paris* **2002**, *96*, 289–299. [CrossRef]
83. Hansson, E. Long-term pain, neuroinflammation and glial activation. *Scand. J. Pain* **2010**, *1*, 67–72. [CrossRef] [PubMed]

Article

Dried Yeast Extracts Curtails Pulmonary Oxidative Stress, Inflammation and Tissue Destruction in a Model of Experimental Emphysema

Yun-Ho Kim [1], Min-Kyung Kang [1], Eun-Jung Lee [1], Dong Yeon Kim [1], Hyeongjoo Oh [1], Soo-Il Kim [1], Su Yeon Oh [1], Kyung-Hee Kim [2], Sang-Jae Park [2], Yean-Jung Choi [3] and Young-Hee Kang [1],*

[1] The Korean Institute of Nutrition, Department of Food and Nutrition, Hallym University, Chuncheon 24252, Korea
[2] Mediense Co. Ltd., Chuncheon 24232, Korea
[3] Department of Bio-Food Science & Technology, Far East University, Eumseong 27601, Korea
* Correspondence: yhkang@hallym.ac.kr; Tel.: +82-33-248-2132

Received: 31 July 2019; Accepted: 22 August 2019; Published: 1 September 2019

Abstract: Pulmonary emphysema is characterized by a loss of alveolar integrity due to prolonged cigarette smoking and inhaled irritants. Dried yeast extracts (YE) are employed as food additives, savory flavorings, or creation of umami taste sensations. Despite being rich in nutrition, their application as nutraceuticals and functional foods is not investigated much and little is known about the inhibition of pulmonary emphysema. This study examined whether YE ameliorated pulmonary emphysema in mice is evoked by cigarette smoke (CS) and ovalbumin (OVA). Mice were orally administrated with 25–100 mg/kg YE for 8 weeks. Alveolar epithelial A549 cells exposed to lipopolysaccharide or CS extracts (CSE) were supplemented with 10–100 µg/mL YE. Oral YE administration reduced bronchoalveolar lavage fluid leukocytosis in CS-/OVA-exposed mice. YE reduced induction of inflammatory mediators and MMP-12, and diminished reactive oxygen species production and emphysematous alterations in CS-challenged airways. The YE treatment blunted bax/bcl-2 ratio and activation of p53 and caspases in CS-exposed lungs. Apoptotic death was dampened in CSE-loaded YE-supplemented A549 cells. YE curtailed tissue levels of MMP-12 in inflammatory OVA-exposed lungs. YE abrogated the secretion of TNF-α and MCP-1 through blocking NF-κB signaling in endotoxin-loaded A549 cells. Thus, the antioxidant YE may therapeutically ameliorate oxidative stress and inflammatory tissue destruction in emphysematous diseases.

Keywords: airway inflammation; cigarette smoke; dried yeast extracts; ovalbumin; oxidative stress; pulmonary emphysema

1. Introduction

Chronic obstructive pulmonary disease (COPD) is a chronic inflammatory lung disease with the resultant airflow obstruction from the lungs [1,2]. Its symptoms include breathing difficulty, cough, mucus (sputum) production, and wheezing [3,4]. Chronic bronchitis and emphysema are the most common disorders responsible for COPD, being caused by long-term exposure to irritating noxious gases, most often from cigarette smoke (CS) [5]. Chronic bronchitis is inflammation of the lining of the bronchial tubes, and emphysema is a condition in which the alveoli of the lungs are destroyed [6]. In fact, pathological alterations in bronchioles and alveoli lead to a loss of alveolar integrity through activating aberrant inflammatory pathways [5]. Bronchiolar and alveolar epithelial cells can display direct immune and anti-inflammatory responses against lung tissue damage [6,7]. Pulmonary mesenchymal cells such as airway smooth muscle cells and lung fibroblasts can also respond to inflammatory mediators [6,8]. In COPD, chronic inflammation mainly entails the infiltration of neutrophils, macrophages, CD8+ T lymphocytes, and other inflammatory cells into the small airways [1,6]. Bronchiolar epithelium-derived monocyte chemoattractant protein (MCP)-1 and interleukin (IL)-8 can be responsible for the chemotactic activity of neutrophils [7,9]. However, the underlying mechanisms for bronchiolar and alveolar inflammation of COPD remain to be solved. Promising mechanisms involved in small airway/alveolar destruction and structural changes may provide major therapeutic targets in COPD [10,11].

Numerous studies have identified diverse therapeutic targets in chronic bronchitis and COPD [11,12]. The major therapeutic option for these diseases is to combat airway inflammation [12,13]. Exposure to CS provokes the recruitment of inflammatory cells into the airways and prompts immune response mechanisms [14]. Thus, the immunomodulatory therapies in airways may effectively alleviate pulmonary diseases [15]. The pathogenesis of emphysema refers to alveolar destruction with airspace enlargement and loss of alveolar integrity by the interaction of apoptosis, oxidative stress, and protease/antiprotease imbalance [14,16]. Oxidative stress is a purported contributor for emphysema through activating pro-inflammatory cytokine transcription [13,17]. The protease/antiprotease imbalance impairs tissues in COPD and emphysema, which is involved in inflammatory processes [17,18]. There are major novel anti-inflammatory agents in COPD targeting lung and systemic inflammation including inhaled corticosteroids and β-adrenergic receptor agonists, phosphodiesterase-4 inhibitors, macrolides, and statins [14,19,20]. These approaches can affect more intimately COPD-specific mechanisms of inflammation, mucin production, and tissue destruction and repair [14,16,19]. Currently, such treatments in COPD are not yet justified. Therefore, new therapeutic strategies with natural agents have mostly proven to be safe, and are currently under development for treating airway inflammation [21].

Several studies show potential roles of natural plant extracts and compounds for the treatment of asthma and COPD [22,23]. Anti-inflammatory and antioxidant polyphenols including resveratrol, curcumin, quercetin, sulforaphane, lycopene, mangiferin, and dihydroquercetin suppress experimental pulmonary fibrosis and modulate various biochemical features of COPD [24,25]. A MORGEN study suggests a beneficial effect of a high intake of catechins and solid fruits with flavonols and flavones against COPD [26]. Our previous studies revealed that several compounds such astragalin, kaempferol, and oleuropein antagonized airway epithelial apoptosis and fibrosis, Inflammation and airway thickening in ovalbumin (OVA)-challenged mice [27–29]. Additionally, oleuropein rich in olives exhibits favorable effects on pulmonary inflammation in CS-challenged mice through blocking recruitment of inflammatory and allergic cells and blunting alveolar destruction [29]. A recent study has reported that dried yeast extracts (YE) may effectively inhibit oxidative stress-responsive epithelial eosinophilia and mucus-secreting goblet cell hyperplasia in asthma [30]. However, the beneficial effects of YE on smoking-induced inflammation and emphysema in bronchioles and alveoli have not been reported. This study examined whether YE abrogated airway inflammation and apoptotic emphysema in CS- and OVA-challenged mouse models. Pulmonary inflammation and emphysema were also examined in alveolar epithelial cells exposed to cigarette smoke extract (CSE) and lipopolysaccharide (LPS).

2. Materials and Methods

2.1. Chemicals

RPMI, chicken egg white albumin, and LPS were obtained from the Sigma-Aldrich Chemical (St. Louis, MO, USA), as were all other reagents, unless specifically stated elsewhere. Fetal bovine serum (FBS), penicillin-streptomycin, and trypsin-EDTA were purchased from the Lonza (Walkersville, MD, USA). Rabbit polyclonal antibodies of matrix metalloproteinase (MMP)-12 and intracellular adhesion molecule (ICAM)-1, goat polyclonal cyclooxygenase (COX)-2 antibody, and mouse monoclonal inducible NOS (iNOS) antibody were purchased from the Santa Cruz Biotechnology (Dallas, TX,

USA). Mouse monoclonal antibodies of bcl-2 and bax were provided by BD Transduction Laboratories (Franklin Lakes, NJ, USA). Rabbit polyclonal antibodies of cleaved caspase-3, cleaved caspase-9, phospho-p53, inhibitory κB (IκB), and phospho-IκB were obtained from Cell Signaling Technology (Beverly, MA, USA). Horseradish peroxidase (HRP)-conjugated goat anti-rabbit IgG, donkey anti-goat IgG, and goat anti-mouse IgG were purchased from Jackson Immuno-Research Laboratories (West Grove, PA, USA). Mouse monoclonal β-actin antibody was obtained from Sigma-Aldrich Chemicals. Essential fatty acid free bovine serum albumin (BSA) and skim milk were supplied by Becton Dickinson Company (Sparks, MD, USA). 4′,6-Diamidino-2-phenylindole (DAPI) was obtained from Santa Cruz Biotechnology.

2.2. Preparation of YE

YE used in the current study was provided by the Mediense Co. Ltd (Chuncheon, Korea). Dried yeast was extracted in boiled distilled water (10% *w/v*) at 40–60 °C for 24 h, followed by centrifugation at 3000 rpm for 10 min. The resulted supernatants were harvested after filtration with 0.45 μm. YE was dissolved in dimethyl sulfoxide (DMSO) for live culture with cells; a final culture concentration of DMSO was <0.5%.

2.3. Animal Experiments

Six week-old male BALB/c mice (Hallym University Breeding Center for Laboratory Animals) were used in this study. Female mice were excluded because of concerns that female hormone cycles would affect experiments. Mice were kept on a 12 h light/12 h dark cycle at 23 ± 1 °C with 50% ± 10% relative humidity under specific pathogen-free circumstances, fed a non-purified diet, and provided with water ad libitum at the animal facility of Hallym University. The present study was approved by the Hallym University Institutional Review Board and Committee on Animal Experimentation (Hallym 2017-56). This study was conducted in compliance with the University's Guidelines for the Care and Use of Laboratory Animals.

Mice were acclimatized for 1 week before beginning the experiments. All mice were distributed among five subgroups (*n* = 9–10 for each subgroup).

Passive smoking models: Mice receiving the smoke challenge were further divided into four subgroups. One subgroup (no CS) did not receive the smoke challenge. YE solution (containing 25–100 mg/kg BW) was orally administrated to mice 1 h via oral gavage once a day (5 days/week) for 8 weeks before. Subsequently, mice were exposed to smoke of research cigarettes (11 mg tar and 0.7 mg nicotine/cigarette) for 30 min in a specially designed chamber once a day for 8 weeks. Research cigarettes (3R4F, 11 mg tar and 0.7 mg nicotine per cigarette) were obtained from the University of Kentucky (Lexington, KY, USA).

Mouse asthma model: Mice receiving the OVA challenge were further divided into five subgroups. One subgroup (no OVA) did not receive the OVA challenge. Mice were sensitized with 20 μg OVA dissolved in 30 μL phosphate buffered saline (PBS) with 50 μL Imject Alum (Thermo Fisher Scientific, Rockford, IL, USA) through subcutaneous injections on the days 0 and 14. Subsequently, 0.1 mL YE solution (containing 25–100 mg/kg BW) was administered via oral gavage to OVA-sensitized mice 1 h before challenge. On the days of 28–30, 5% OVA inhalation to mice was carried out for 20 min in a plastic chamber linked to an ultrasonic nebulizer (Clenny2 Aerosol, Medel, Italy). Control mice were sensitized and challenged with PBS as the OVA vehicle. All mice were sacrificed 24 h after the latest provocation (day 30).

All the mice were killed with an anesthetic dose of 0.3 g/kg avertin and 8 μg/kg *tert*-amyl alcohol. The trachea was cannulated, and both lungs and airways were rinsed in 1 ml PBS for the collection of bronchoalveolar lavage fluid (BALF). The numbers of inflammatory cells including neutrophils and eosinophils in BALF were determined using a Hemavet HV950 Multispecies Hematologic Analyzer (Drew Scientific, Oxford, CT, USA). The right lungs were collected, frozen in liquid nitrogen, and kept at −80 °C until used for Western blotting. Left lungs were preserved and fixed in 4% paraformaldehyde and then used for immunohistochemical analyses.

2.4. Preparation of CSE for Cell Culture

The research cigarettes were consecutively smoked through an experimental apparatus with a constant airflow driven by an air vacuum pump. The collected CS was bubbled in 10 mL PBS. The resulting smoke suspension was filtered through a 0.22 μm pore filter in order to eliminate bacteria and large particles. The filtrates referred to a 100% CSE.

2.5. A549 Cell Culture and Viability

Human alveolar basal epithelial cells A549 cells were provided by the American Type Culture Collection (Manassas, VA, USA). A549 cells were cultured in RPMI 1640 supplemented with 10% FBS, 2 mM L-glutamine, 100 U/mL penicillin, and 100 μg/mL streptomycin. A549 cells were sustained in 90–95% confluence at 37 °C in an atmosphere of 5% CO_2. A549 cells were treated with 10–100 μg/mL YE and then stimulated with 2 μg/mL LPS or 5% CSE for up to 24 h to induce expression of target gene proteins.

The cytotoxicity of YE was determined using 3-(4,5-dimetylthiazol-yl)-diphenyl tetrazolium bromide (MTT, Duchefa Biochemie, Haarlem, Netherlands) after culture of A549 cells. These cells were incubated in a fresh medium containing 1 mg/mL MTT for 3 h at 37 °C. The purple formazan product was dissolved in 0.5 mL isopropanol with gentle shaking. Absorbance of formazan was measured at $\lambda = 570$ nm using a microplate reader (Bio-Rad Model 550, Hercules, CA, USA).

2.6. Staining with Hematoxylin and Eosin (H&E)

For the histological analyses of airways, small airway and alveolar specimens provided at the end of the experiments were fixed in 10% paraformaldehyde. The paraffin-embedded specimens were sectioned at 5 μm thickness, deparaffinized and stained with hematoxylin and eosin (H&E) stain for 2 min, and quickly dehydrated in 95% absolute alcohol. The H&E-stained tissue sections were observed using an optical microscope Axioimager system equipped for fluorescence illumination (Zeiss, Gottingen, Germany). Five images were taken from each tissue section.

2.7. Western Blot Analysis

Mouse lung tissue extracts and A549 cell lysates were prepared in 1 mM Tris-HCl (pH 6.8) lysis buffer containing 10% sodium dodecyl sulfate (SDS), 1% glycerophosphate, 0.1 mM Na_3VO_4, 0.5 mM NaF, and a protease inhibitor cocktail. Tissue extracts and cell lysates containing equal amounts of proteins were electrophoresed on 8%–15% SDS-PAGE and transferred onto a nitrocellulose membrane. Blocking a nonspecific binding was performed using either 3% fatty acid-free BSA or 5% non-fat dry skim milk for 3 h. The membrane was incubated overnight at 4 °C with a specific primary antibody of COX-2, iNOS or ICAM-1, bcl-2, bax, cleaved caspases, MMP-12, or IκB. The membrane was then applied to a secondary antibody conjugated to HRP for 1 h. Following triple washing, the target proteins were determined using the Immobilon Western Chemiluminescent HRP substrate (Millipore Corp., Billerica, MA, USA) and the Agfa medical X-ray film blue (Agfa HealthCare NV, Mortsel, Belgium). Incubation with β-actin antibody was conducted for the comparative control.

2.8. Immunohistochemical Staining

Paraffin-embedded tissue sections (5 μm thick) of small airways and alveoli were deparaffinized and hydrated in order to conduct immunofluorescent histochemical analyses. The sections were preincubated in a boiling sodium citrate buffer (10 mM sodium citrate, 0.05% Tween 20, pH 6.0) for the antigen retrieval. The tissues were blocked with 5% BSA in PBS for 1 h. A specific primary antibody against MMP-12 was incubated overnight with the sectioned tissues. Subsequently, the tissue sections were incubated for 1 h with fluorescein isothiocyanate-conjugated or Cy3-conjugated anti-rabbit IgG. For identification of nuclei, the fluorescent nucleic acid dye of DAPI was applied for 10 min. Stained tissues were mounted on slides using mounting medium (Vector Laboratories, Burlingame, CA, USA). Images of each slide were obtained with an optical microscope Axioimager system (Zeiss).

2.9. Dihydroethidium (DHE) Staining for Reactive Oxygen Species (ROS) Production

Paraffin-embedded tissue sections (5 μm thickness) of airways were deparaffinized and hydrated for the DHE staining. Airway tissues were stained by incubating for 1 h in 20 μM DHE (Invitrogen, Carlsbad, CA, USA). For the identification of nuclei, DAPI was given for 10 min. Stained tissues on slides were mounted in mounting solution. Images of each slide were taken using an optical microscope Axioimager system.

2.10. Hoechst 33258 Staining

The A549 cells were plated on a 24-well glass slide and incubated for 24 h in media containing 5% CSE in the absence or presence of 10–100 μg/mL YE. After the fixation of A549 cells with ice-cold 4% formaldehyde for 1 h on a glass slides, the nuclear stain Hoechst 33258 (Promega Co., Madison, WI, USA) was added at a final concentration of 10 μg/mL for 15 min to allow uptake and equilibration before microscopic observation. The slides were mounted while wet in aqueous VectaMount mounting solution. Cells containing fragmented or condensed nuclei were considered apoptotic. Images of each slide were taken using an optical microscope system.

2.11. Terminal Deoxynucleotidyl Transferase dUTP Nick End Labeling (TUNEL) Assay

The transferase dUTP nick end labeling (TUNEL) assay is a common method for detecting DNA fragments. The TUNEL assay was conducted using a commercial fluorometric TUNEL kit (Promega Co., Madison, WI, USA). The A549 cells were plated on a 24-well glass slide and incubated for 24 h in media containing 5% CSE in the absence or presence of 10–100 μg/mL YE. Cells fixed with ice-cold 4% formaldehyde for 20 min were permeabilized with 0.2% Triton X-100, and fragmented DNA was labeled with fluorescein-dUTP at 37 °C for 1 h. DAPI was used for counterstaining nuclei, and cells were visualized with an Axiomager optical microscope system.

2.12. Enzyme-Linked Immunosorbent Assay (ELISA)

Following culture protocols, the secretion of tumor necrosis factor (TNF)-α and MCP-1 in A549 cells was determined in collected culture medium supernatants by using ELISA kits (R&D Systems, Minneapolis, MN, USA), according to the manufacturer's instructions.

2.13. Immunocytochemical Staining

A549 (7×10^4 cells) grown on 24-well glass slides were exposed to LPS in the absence and presence of 10–100 μg/mL YE. A549 cells were fixed with 4% formaldehyde for 10 min and permeated with 0.1% Triton X-100 for 5 min on ice. Cells were blocked using a 4% FBS for 1 h. Immunofluorescent cytochemical staining of A549 cells was performed using NF-κB p50 antibody and Cy3-conjugated anti-rabbit IgG. Nuclear staining was performed with DAPI. Each slide was mounted in a VectaMount mounting medium and images were taken using an optical Axiomager microscope system.

2.14. Statistical Analysis

The results were expressed as mean ± SEM for each treatment group in each experiment. Statistical analyses were performed using the Statistical Analysis Systems statistical software package (SAS Institute, Cary, NC, USA). Significance was determined by a one-way analysis of variance, followed by a Duncan range test for multiple comparisons. Differences were considered significant at $p < 0.05$.

3. Results

3.1. Inhibition of Airway Inflammation of CS-Exposed Airways by YE

This study examined how YE inhibited CS-evoked inflammation in mouse airways. Exposure of mice to CS increased total leukocyte number in the BALF by ≈1.5-fold (Figure 1A). Surprisingly, the challenge of CS promoted the influx of neutrophils and eosinophils in the BALF, indicating that CS resulted in neutrophilic and eosinophilic inflammation (Figure 1A). Oral administration of ≥25 mg/kg YE reduced CS-induced leukocytosis of neutrophils and eosinophils, which was incomparable to that of control mice (Figure 1A). In addition, YE curtailed the number of lymphocytes and monocytes in the BALF elevated in CS-exposed mice.

It was examined whether CS-stimulated airway inflammation was attenuated in YE-supplemented mice. The tissue level of COX-2 responsible for prostaglandin biosynthesis and inflammation was elevated in CS-exposed mouse lungs (Figure 1B). In addition, the airway tissue levels of iNOS and ICAM-1 directly involved in inflammatory responses were enhanced in CS-challenged mice (Figure 1C,D). However, orally-administrated YE reduced the induction of these inflammatory proteins promoted by exposure of airways to CS (Figure 1B–D).

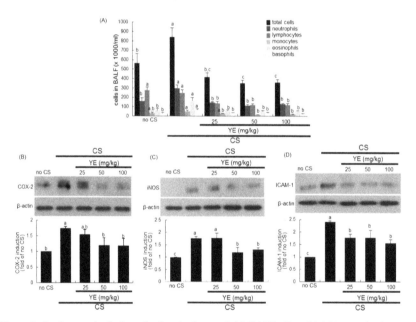

Figure 1. Leukocytes in the bronchoalveolar lavage fluid (BALF; **A**) and inhibition of pulmonary inflammation (**B–D**) in cigarette smoke (CS)-challenged mouse lungs treated with dried yeast extracts (YE). Mice were orally administrated with 25–100 mg/kg YE and exposed to CS for 30 min. Cells in BALF were counted using a Hemavet HV950 Multispecies Hematologic Analyzer (**A**). Tissue extracts were subject to Western blot analysis with a primary antibody against COX-2, iNOS, or ICAM-1. β-Actin protein was used as an internal control. The bottom bar graphs represent quantitative results of the upper bands obtained from a densitometer. Values (mean ± SEM, n = 3–4) in respective bar graphs not sharing a same small letter indicate a significant difference at $p < 0.05$.

3.2. Blockade of Emphysematous Injury of CS-Challenged Airways by YE

The histological examination was conducted in the lung tissues stained with H&E. The CS exposure induced the airway wall damage in mice (Figure 2). However, oral administration of 25–100 mg/kg YE highly attenuated the pathological alterations observed in bronchiolar and alveolar tissues of CS-challenged mice. In addition, MMP-12 was highly expressed in mouse airways exposed to CS, evidenced by FITC-immunostaining (Figure 3). In contrast, the treatment with 25–100 mg/kg YE reduced its induction in CS-exposed bronchioles (Figure 2). Moreover, the H&E histological staining revealed that the CS challenge to mice evoked destruction in pulmonary alveoli (Figure 2). Consistently, the MMP-12 induction was markedly enhanced. However, 25–100 mg/kg YE diminished the emphysematous damage in pulmonary alveoli and curtailed the FITC-staining of MMP-12 (Figure 3). Therefore, YE may inhibit emphysema and alveolar cell loss in CS-exposed small airways and alveoli.

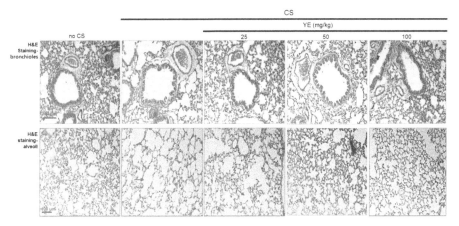

Figure 2. Blockade of airway destruction by dried yeast extracts (YE) in cigarette smoke (CS)-challenged mouse bronchioles and alveoli. Mice were orally administrated with 25–100 mg/kg YE and exposed to CS for 30 min. Airway tissue sections were stained by using a hematoxylin and eosin (H&E) reagent. Each photograph is representative of four mice. The arrows indicate damaged bronchioles and alveolar air sacs. Scale bars = 100 μm.

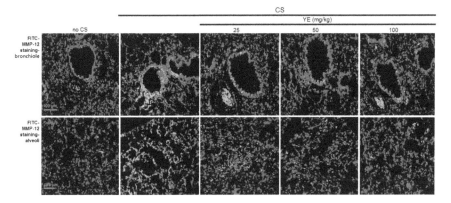

Figure 3. Inhibition of alveolar emphysema by dried yeast extracts (YE) in cigarette smoke (CS)-challenged mouse alveoli. Immunohistofluorescence analysis was done in tissues of small airways and alveoli of CS-challenged mice. The MMP-12 localization was identified as FITC-green staining in mouse airways exposed to CS. Nuclear staining was done with DAPI (blue). Each photograph is representative of four mice. Scale bars = 100 μm.

3.3. Inhibitory Effects of YE on CS-Induced Pulmonary Apoptosis and Oxidative Stress

This study attempted to examine whether YE inhibited emphysematous airway damage through blocking pulmonary apoptosis and oxidative stress induced by CS. Western blot analysis showed that

CS diminished the lung tissue level of anti-apoptotic bcl-2 and increased the level of pro-apoptotic bax, consequently elevating the bax/bcl-2 ratio (Figure 4A). Oral treatment of YE reduced the bax/bcl-2 ratio in CS-exposed mouse alveolar tissues. The tumor suppressor p53 is known to directly activate bax and mediate mitochondrial membrane permeabilization and apoptosis [31]. As expected, the activation of p53 was enhanced in CS-loaded lung tissues, which was retarded by supplementing 25–100 mg/kg YE to mice (Figure 4B). In addition, caspase-9 and its downstream executioner caspase-3 responsible for executing cell death were upregulated in lung tissues by exposure to CS (Figure 4C). In contrast, YE highly attenuated the activation of these caspases in lung tissues.

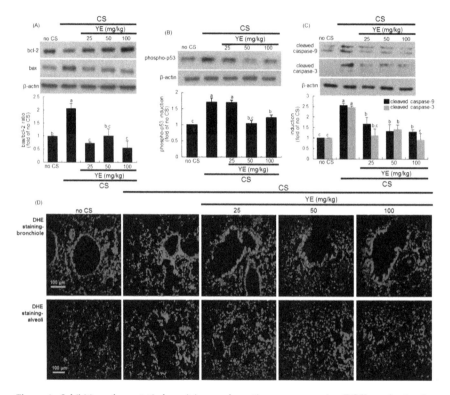

Figure 4. Inhibition of apoptotic lung injury and reactive oxygen species (ROS) production by 25–100 mg/kg yeast extracts (YE) in cigarette smoke (CS)-challenged mouse lungs. Tissue extracts were subject to Western blot with a primary antibody against bcl-2, bax, phospho-p53, cleaved caspase-9, or cleaved caspase-3 (**A–C**). β-Actin protein was used as an internal control. The bar graphs (mean ± SEM, $n = 3$) represent quantitative results of the upper bands obtained from a densitometer. Values in respective bar graphs not sharing a same small letter indicate a significant difference at $p < 0.05$. Dihydroethidium (DHE) staining showing pulmonary ROS production (**D**). Tissue sections of small airways and alveoli were stained with DHE, and nuclear staining was done with DAPI (blue). Each photograph is representative of four mice. Scale bars = 100 μm.

The reciprocal interactions among ROS, airway inflammation, and alveolar cell death play crucial role in the pathogenesis of COPD [32]. This study introduced DHE staining for ROS production in airways exposed to CS. DHE exhibits blue-fluorescence in the cytosol until oxidized, where it intercalates within the cell DNA, with subsequent staining of nuclei as a bright fluorescent red. There was a strong DHE staining in CS-loaded bronchioles and alveoli, indicating marked superoxide production by CS (Figure 4D). However, oral administration of 25–100 mg/kg YE highly attenuated ROS production in bronchiolar and alveolar tissues of CS-challenged mice.

3.4. Suppressive Effects of YE on CSE-Loaded Alveolar Apoptotic Injury

This study further explored how CS evoked alveolar damage in mice and how YE protected alveoli from CS. The treatment of A549 cells with 10–100 µg/mL YE did not cause cytotoxicity for 24 h (Figure 5A). When 5% CSE was applied to alveolar epithelial A549 cells for 24 h, the viability dropped to below 20% (Figure 5B). When 5% CSE-loaded A549 cells were supplemented with ≥10 µg/mL YE for 24 h, the viability was highly boosted (Figure 5B). On the other hand, Hoechst 33258 nuclear staining and TUNEL staining showed that 5% CSE resulted in nuclear condensation and DNA fragmentation of A549 cells in an apoptotic manner (Figure 5C). The apoptotic cell death by CSE was significantly curtailed in YE-added alveolar cells. Accordingly, CS-induced alveolar emphysema may be ascribed to its apoptotic death of alveolar cells.

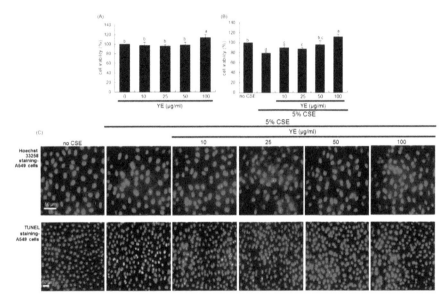

Figure 5. Viability of alveolar epithelial A549 cells and effects of dried yeast extracts (YE) on alveolar apoptosis. Alveolar epithelial cells were incubated in media containing 5% cigarette smoke extract (CSE) in the absence and presence of 10–100 µg/mL YE for up to 24 h. A549 cell viability (mean ± SEM, $n = 5$) was measured by using MTT assay and expressed as percent cell survival relative to untreated controls (**A,B**). Values in respective bar graphs not sharing a same small letter indicate a significant difference at $p < 0.05$. Nuclear staining was done with Hoechst 33258 dye for the detection of apoptotic cells (**C**). A transferase dUTP nick end labeling (TUNEL) assay was conducted to detect DNA fragmentation of apoptotic A549 cells and nuclear staining was accomplished with DAPI (**C**). Representative microphotographs were obtained by fluorescence microscopy. Scale bars = 50 µm.

3.5. Inhibition of Airway Inflammation of OVA-Exposed Airways by YE

This study investigated that YE inhibited allergic airway inflammation evoked by OVA in mouse airways. When mice underwent OVA inhalation, total leukocyte number in BALF was highly elevated by ≈2.5-fold (Figure 6A). The OVA inhalation prompted neutrophilic and eosinophilic inflammation in BALF, while oral administration of 25–100 mg/kg YE reduced OVA-induced leukocytosis of neutrophils and lymphocytes (Figure 6A). In addition, YE diminished eosinophilic inflammation elevated in OVA-exposed mice (Figure 6A).

The tissue levels of inflammatory COX-2 and iNOS were enhanced in OVA inhalation-experienced mouse lungs in a similar manner to the CS challenge (Figure 6B). However, the YE supply attenuated the lung tissue induction of these proteins promoted by OVA (Figure 6B). Accordingly, YE may alleviate OVA inhalation-induced allergic inflammation in airways. In addition, this study examined whether OVA induced pulmonary emphysema in mice. The Cy3-immunostaining revealed that OVA promoted the MMP-12 expression in mouse bronchioles and alveoli (Figure 6C). It should be noted that the MMP-12 induction by OVA inhalation was less than that of CS challenge. Nevertheless, YE curtailed the Cy3-MMP-12 staining in airways, indicating that YE abrogated pulmonary emphysema due to OVA (Figure 6C).

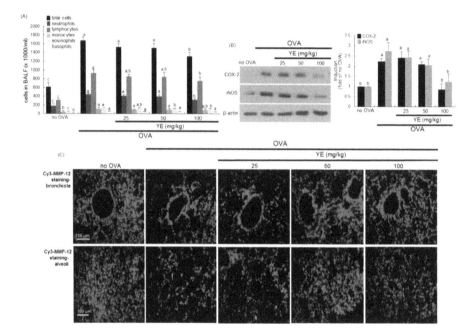

Figure 6. Suppressive effects of dried yeast extract (YE) on airway inflammation and induction of airway target proteins in ovalbumin (OVA) inhalation-challenged mouse lungs. OVA-sensitized mice were orally administered with 25–100 mg/kg YE. Cells in BALF were counted using a Hemavet HV950 Multispecies Hematologic Analyzer (**A**). Lung tissue extracts were subject to Western blot with a primary antibody against COX-2 and iNOS (**B**). β-Actin protein was used as an internal control. The bar graphs (mean ± SEM, $n = 3$) represent quantitative results of the left bands obtained from a densitometer. Values in respective bar graphs not sharing a same small letter indicate a significant difference at $p < 0.05$ Immunohistofluorescence analysis was done in tissues of small airways and alveoli of OA-challenged mice (**C**). The MMP-12 localization was identified as Cy3-red staining in mouse airways exposed to OVA. Nuclear staining was done with DAPI (blue). Each photograph is representative of four mice. Scale bars = 100 μm.

3.6. Blockade of LPS-Triggered Airway Inflammation by YE

The endotoxin LPS stimulated alveolar inflammation through the induction of COX-2, iNOS, and ICAM-1 in A549 cells (Figure 7A–C). In addition, LPS prompted the secretion of pro-inflammatory cytokines of TNF-α and MCP-1 from alveolar epithelial cells (Figure 7D,E). When LPS-loaded alveolar cells were treated with 10–100 μg/mL YE, such induction and secretion of these inflammatory proteins were reduced (Figure 7A–E).

This study further examined whether pro-inflammatory TNF-α produced by alveolar cells might be involved in evoking alveolar emphysema by pathological stimuli. When TNF-α was treated to A549 cells, the MMP-12 protein was highly induced (Figure 7F). In contrast, ≥10 μg/mL YE blunted its induction in TNF-α-experienced alveolar cells. Thus, one can speculate that airway inflammation may be a contributor to pulmonary emphysema.

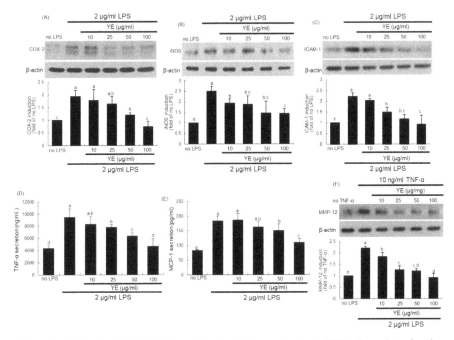

Figure 7. Blockade of alveolar inflammation by dried yeast extracts (YE) in lipopolysaccharide (LPS)-exposed A549 cells. Alveolar epithelial cells were incubated in media containing 2 μg/mL LPS or 10 ng/ml TNF-α in the absence and presence of 10–100 μg/mL YE for up to 24 h. Cell lysates were prepared for Western blot analysis with a primary antibody against COX-2, iNOS, ICAM-1, or MMP-12 (**A–C,F**). β-Actin protein was used as an internal control. The bar graphs (mean ± SEM, *n* = 3) represent quantitative results of the upper bands obtained from a densitometer. Alveolar secretion of TNF-α and MCP-1 was measured by using ELISA kits (**D,E**). Values in respective bar graphs not sharing a same small letter indicate a significant difference at *p* < 0.05.

It has been reported that sustained activation of NF-κB pathway links airway inflammation and COPD, which provides its potential as target for treatment of asthma and COPD [33]. LPS highly increased IκB phosphorylation of A549 cells, leading to induction of nuclear translocation of NF-κB (Figure 8A). The treatment of ≥10 μg/mL YE retarded its phosphorylation. Consistently, the Cy3-NF-κB staining supported the Western blot data showing nuclear translocation of NF-κB that was inhibited by YE (Figure 8B).

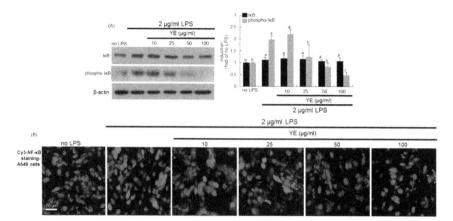

Figure 8. Involvement of NF-κB signaling in lipopolysaccharide (LPS)-induced alveolar inflammation and blockade by dried yeast extracts (YE). Alveolar epithelial cells were incubated in media containing 2 µg/mL LPS in the absence and presence of 10–100 µg/mL YE for up to 24 h. Cell lysates were prepared for Western blot analysis with a primary antibody against IκB and phospho-IκB (**A**). β-Actin protein was used as an internal control. The bar graphs (mean ± SEM, *n* = 3) represent quantitative results of the left bands obtained from a densitometer. Values in respective bar graphs not sharing a same small letter indicate a significant difference at *P* < 0.05. Immunocytofluorescence analysis was done in LPS-treated A549 alveolar epithelial cells (**B**). The NF-κB localization was identified as Cy3-red staining in cells exposed to LPS. Nuclear staining was done with DAPI (blue). Each photograph is representative of stained cells (*n* = 4). Scale bar = 50 µm.

4. Discussion

Eight major findings were extracted from this study. (1) Oral administration of ≥25 mg/kg YE markedly reduced leukocytosis of neutrophils and eosinophils as well as lymphocytes and monocytes in the BALF of CS-exposed mice. (2) YE reduced the induction of these inflammatory proteins of COX-2, iNOS, and ICAM-1 together with reduction of the pathological alterations and oxidative stress in small airways and alveoli of CS-challenged mice. (3) The treatment with 25–100 mg/kg YE blunted the MMP-12 expression and emphysematous damage of airways through diminution of bax/bcl-2 ratio and inactivation of p53 and caspases in CS-exposed mouse lungs. (4) In 5% CSE-loaded A549 cells supplemented with 10–100 µg/mL YE the apoptotic cell death was significantly attenuated. (5) The OVA inhalation highly elevated total leukocyte number in BALF, while the YE treatment diminished OVA-triggered neutrophilic and eosinophilic inflammation. (6) The tissue levels of COX-2, iNOS, and MMP-12 were enhanced in OVA-exposed mouse lungs, which was curtailed by the supply of 25–100 mg/kg YE. (7) Treatment of 10–100 g/mL YE abrogated the induction of COX-2, iNOS, and ICAM-1 and the secretion of TNF-α and MCP-1 with blockade of NF-κB signaling in LPS-loaded alveolar cells. (8) The MMP-12 induction by pro-inflammatory TNF-α was blunted in YE-treated alveolar cells. Accordingly, CS- and OVA inhalation-induced pulmonary oxidative stress and inflammation may contribute to airway tissue destruction and emphysema. YE may inhibit emphysema and alveolar cell loss in airways and alveoli encountered in the oxidative and inflammatory milieu. Therefore, anti-inflammatory and antioxidant YE had a potential benefit in treating pulmonary diseases of COPD and asthma.

COPD is a chronic inflammatory lung disease with bronchial airflow impairment and obstruction caused by long-term exposure to irritating risk factors such as cigarette smoking and biomass fuel dust exposure [1,2]. The most common disorders involved in COPD are chronic bronchitis inflamed in the lining of the bronchial tubes and emphysema liable to the alveoli [5,6]. As expected, this study showed that CS and allergic OVA enhanced the lung induction of COX-2, iNOS, and ICAM-1 responsible for lung inflammation along with marked leukocytosis in BALF. Chronic lung inflammation involves the infiltration of inflammatory cells such as neutrophils, macrophages, and lymphocytes into the small airways of COPD [1,6]. Similarly, the exposure to CS stimulates the recruitment of inflammatory cells into the airways and elicits immune responses [14]. This study revealed that the exposure of both CS and OVA to mice evoked eosinophilic allergic inflammation in airways. The challenge of LPS to alveolar cells induced lung inflammation entailing the secretion of MCP-1 and TNF-α through activating NF-κB-responsive mechanism(s). Several studies highlight the role of NF-κB signaling in these two important inflammatory lung diseases of asthma and COPD [33,34]. The definite mechanisms underlying bronchiolar and alveolar inflammation are yet unsolved in COPD. However, to alleviate airway inflammation would be a primary therapeutic option for chronic bronchitis and COPD [12,13].

Emphysema is characterized by alveolar destruction with a loss of alveolar integrity and marked airspace enlargement [14,16]. This study showed that CS enhanced the MMP-12 induction in bronchiolar airways and alveoli, indicating that CS resulted in pulmonary emphysematous injury. Several promising mechanisms including oxidative stress and protease/anti-protease imbalance have been suggested for the small airway/alveolar destruction and structural changes, which may provide major therapeutic targets in COPD [10,11]. An activation of aberrant inflammation in bronchioles and alveoli lead to pathological alterations including loss of alveolar integrity [4]. Consistently, the pro-inflammatory TNF-α released by LPS promoted alveolar MMP-12 expression. Accordingly, airway inflammation due to OVA and CS may be a major contributor in the pathogenesis of emphysema. Oxidative stress contributes to cause alveolar emphysema through activating transcription of pro-inflammatory cytokines [13,17]. Several antioxidant natural compounds of epigallocatechin gallate and glycyrrhizin ameliorate oxidative renal injury and experimental acute pancreatitis in rats [35,36]. A growing body of evidence reports that CS as a risk factor in COPD is closely associated with increased oxidative stress [37,38]. Smoke may accelerate apoptosis of structural cells in the lung by means of oxidative stress, which might possibly be an important upstream event involved in the development of COPD and pulmonary emphysema [39,40]. In this study the exposure of CS to mice markedly enhanced apoptotic mediators of lung tissues as well as the ROS formation in alveoli. Another mechanism involved in the development of COPD is imbalance between proteolytic and anti-proteolytic activity [17,18,39]. This study found that inflammatory CS and OVA elicited proteolytic MMP-12 expression, resulting in the destruction of lung tissues. However, the emphasis on alveolar matrix destruction by the combination of inflammation, oxidative stress, and excessive proteolysis has failed to fully account for the COPD-specific mechanisms [40].

There is a need for safe and effective treatments that prevent these pulmonary diseases and have beneficial impacts on the course of COPD and asthma. Diverse molecular therapeutic targets for emphysema have been proposed from the identification of cellular and molecular mechanisms of the pathogenesis of COPD and asthma [12,16,39]. The pharmacological use of inflammatory mediator-targeted therapeutic agents in patients of COPD and asthma depends on clinical phenotypes and pathophysiological mechanisms [41]. Novel anti-inflammatory agents targeting lung inflammation include inhaled corticosteroids and β-adrenergic receptor agonists, phosphodiesterase-4 inhibitors, macrolides, and statins [14,19,20]. These agents can alter COPD-specific mechanisms involved in inflammation, mucin hypersecretion, and tissue destruction [14,19]. Asthmatics with eosinophilic inflammation but not with neutrophilic inflammation respond better to corticosteroids [41]. The choice of the optimal treatment In COPD and asthma should be based on the underlying immunopathology [15]. Although therapeutic approaches aim to target the chronic neutrophilic inflammation in COPD, targeting the underlying causes of the pulmonary neutrophilia such as smoking and oxidative stress might be more promising strategies. Due to the unique interplay between oxidative stress and pathogenesis of COPD, oxidative stress represents a novel target for the treatment of COPD and therapeutic opportunity with antioxidants arising [42].

Numerous therapeutic strategies with naturally occurring bioactive compounds that have mostly proven to be safe are currently under development for treating COPD and asthma [21]. Evidence suggests that the anti-inflammatory and anti-oxidative roles of some of the existing natural agents have potential values in the treatment of inflammatory lung diseases [21,43]. The dietary natural polyphenolic compounds of kaempferol and astragalin antagonized airway epithelial apoptosis and fibrosis and airway thickening along with pulmonary inflammation in OVA-inhaled mice [27,28]. Flavonoids rich in fruits and vegetables show their beneficial effects in asthmatic animal models [44]. Several studies demonstrate potential roles of natural compounds for the treatment of COPD [22,26]. Dietary polyphenols of curcumin, resveratrol, green tea catechins, quercetin, sulforaphane, and lycopene that possess anti-oxidative activities can influence various COPD-specific mechanistic aspects for the treatment and management of COPD [25]. Our recent study showed that dietary oleuropein rich in olive blunted pulmonary inflammation and alveolar destruction led to emphysema [29]. Oleuropein also blocked the infiltration of inflammatory and allergic cells into airways in CS-challenged mice. Our recent study found that YE inhibited bronchial epithelial eosinophilia and mucus-secreting goblet cell hyperplasia in OVA-exposed mice [30]. The present study revealed that YE blocked bronchiolar and alveolar inflammation and subsequent pulmonary emphysema in CS- and OVA-challenged COPD models, in which YE abrogated chronic inflammation, MMP-12 proteolytic activity, oxidative stress, and apoptosis of structural alveolar cells in the airways that might possibly be an important upstream event in the pathogenesis of COPD.

5. Conclusions

This study investigated that YE counteracted pulmonary emphysema due to the CS challenge and OVA inhalation through blocking pulmonary inflammation. Oral administration of YE diminished CS-elicited induction of pro-inflammatory COX-2, iNOS, and ICAM-1 in airways and leukocytosis in BALF. YE antagonized CS exposure-induced lung tissue damage and emphysematous destruction of proteolytic MMP-12 through inhibiting ROS-triggered apoptosis of alveolar cells due to CSE. In addition, oral supplementation of YE inhibited OVA-prompted pulmonary asthmatic inflammation and alveolar destruction concomitantly with reduced leukocytosis in BALF. Furthermore, YE suppressed LPS-induced alveolar inflammation of TNF-α and MCP-1 via activation of NF-κB signaling. Thus, YE may have a potential benefit in treating pulmonary diseases of COPD and asthma through inhibiting oxidative stress, pulmonary inflammation, and subsequent emphysematous damage. Although YE may serve as an antioxidant and modulator against airway inflammation and alveolar emphysema due to CS and OVA, its dietary role in COPD and asthma remains unclear. Further validation is required to clarify whether an appropriate intake of YE may constitute a dietary treatment for a therapeutically preventive strategy for COPD.

Author Contributions: Y.-H.K. (Yun-Ho Kim), Y.-J.C., S.-J.P. and Y.-H.K. (Young-Hee Kang) designed research; Y.-H.K. (Yun-Ho Kim), E.-J.L., M.-K.K., D.Y.K., H.O., S.-I.K., S.Y.O. and K.-H.K., conducted research; Y.-H.K. (Yun-Ho Kim) and Y.-J.C. analyzed data; Y.-H.K. (Yun-Ho Kim) and Y.-H.K. (Young-Hee Kang) wrote the paper; and Y.-H.K. (Young-Hee Kang) had primary responsibility for final content. All authors read and approved the final manuscript.

Funding: This work was supported by the Ministry of Small and Medium-sized Enterprises (SMEs) and Startups, Korea (C050162).

Conflicts of Interest: The authors declare no conflict of interest.

Abbreviations

COPD	chronic obstructive pulmonary disease
COX-2	cyclooxygenase-2
CS	cigarette smoke
CSE	cigarette smoke extracts
YE	yeast extracts
IL	interleukin
iNOS	inducible nitric oxide synthase
LPS	lipopolysaccharide
MCP-1	monocyte chemoattractant protein-1
MMP-12	matrix metalloproteinase-12
NF-κB	nuclear factor-κB
OVA	ovalbumin
ROS	reactive oxygen species
TNF-α	tumor necrosis factor-α

References

1. O'Donnell, R.; Breen, D.; Wilson, S.; Djukanovic, R. Inflammatory cells in the airways in COPD. *Thorax* **2006**, *61*, 448–454. [CrossRef] [PubMed]
2. Rovina, N.; Koutsoukou, A.; Koulouri, N.G. Inflammation and immune response in COPD: Where do we stand? *Mediat. Inflamm.* **2013**, *2013*, 413735. [CrossRef] [PubMed]
3. Angelis, N.; Porpodis, K.; Zarogoulidis, P.; Spyratos, D.; Kioumis, I.; Papaiwannou, A.; Pitsiou, G.; Tsakiridis, K.; Mpakas, A.; Arikas, S.; et al. Airway inflammation in chronic obstructive pulmonary disease. *J. Thorac. Dis.* **2014**, *6*, S167–S172. [PubMed]
4. Yao, H.; Rahman, I. Current concepts on oxidative/carbonyl stress, inflammation and epigenetics in pathogenesis of chronic obstructive pulmonary disease. *Toxicol. Appl. Pharmacol.* **2011**, *254*, 72–85. [CrossRef] [PubMed]
5. Laniado-Laborín, R. Smoking and chronic obstructive pulmonary disease (COPD). Parallel epidemics of the 21st century. *Int. J. Environ. Res. Public Health* **2009**, *6*, 209–224. [CrossRef] [PubMed]
6. Wang, Y.; Xu, J.; Meng, Y.; Adcock, I.M.; Yao, X. Role of inflammatory cells in airway remodeling in COPD. *Int. J. Chron. Obstr. Pulm. Dis.* **2018**, *13*, 3341–3348. [CrossRef] [PubMed]
7. Huang, G.; Xu, X.C.; Zhou, J.S.; Li, Z.Y.; Chen, H.P.; Wang, Y.; Li, W.; Shen, H.H.; Chen, Z.H. Neutrophilic inflammation in the immune responses of chronic obstructive pulmonary disease: Lessons from animal models. *J. Immunol. Res.* **2017**, *2017*, 7915975. [CrossRef]
8. Alkhouri, H.; Poppinga, W.J.; Tania, N.P.; Ammit, A.; Schuliga, M. Regulation of pulmonary inflammation by mesenchymal cells. *Pulm. Pharmacol. Ther.* **2014**, *29*, 156–165. [CrossRef]
9. Meijer, M.; Rijkers, G.T.; van Overveld, F.J. Neutrophils and emerging targets for treatment in chronic obstructive pulmonary disease. *Expert Rev. Clin. Immunol.* **2013**, *9*, 1055–1068. [CrossRef]
10. Fu, P.; Natarajan, V.; Harijith, A. The role of nicotinamide adenine dinucleotide phosphate oxidases in lung architecture remodeling. *Antioxidants* **2017**, *6*, 104.
11. Barnes, P.J. Cellular and molecular mechanisms of chronic obstructive pulmonary disease. *Clin. Chest Med.* **2014**, *35*, 71–86. [CrossRef]
12. Tuder, R.M.; Yoshida, T.; Arap, W.; Pasqualini, R.; Petrache, I. Cellular and molecular mechanisms of alveolar destruction in emphysema. An evolutionary perspective. *Proc. Am. Thorac. Soc.* **2006**, *3*, 503–510. [CrossRef]
13. Kim, V.; Criner, G.J. Chronic bronchitis and chronic obstructive pulmonary disease. *Am. J. Respir. Crit. Care Med.* **2013**, *187*, 228–237. [CrossRef]
14. Roche, N.; Marthan, R.; Berger, P.; Chambellan, A.; Chanez, P.; Aguilaniu, B.; Brillet, P.Y.; Burgel, P.R.; Chaouat, A.; Devillier, P.; et al. Beyond corticosteroids: Future prospects in the management of inflammation in COPD. *Eur. Respir. Rev.* **2011**, *20*, 175–182. [CrossRef]
15. Brusselle, G.; Bracke, K. Targeting immune pathways for therapy in asthma and chronic obstructive pulmonary disease. *Ann. Am. Thorac. Soc.* **2014**, *11* (Suppl. 5), S322–S328. [CrossRef]

16. Fischer, B.M.; Pavlisko, E.; Voynow, J.A. Pathogenic triad in COPD: Oxidative stress, protease-antiprotease imbalance, and inflammation. *Int. J. Chron. Obstr. Pulm. Dis.* **2011**, *6*, 413–421. [CrossRef]

17. Kirkham, P.A.; Barnes, P.J. Oxidative stress in COPD. *Chest* **2013**, *144*, 266–273. [CrossRef]

18. Lomas, D.A. Does protease-antiprotease imbalance explain chronic obstructive pulmonary disease? *Ann. Am. Thorac. Soc.* **2016**, *13* (Suppl. 2), S130–S137.

19. Loukides, S.; Bartziokas, K.; Vestbo, J.; Singh, D. Novel anti-inflammatory agents in COPD: Targeting lung and systemic inflammation. *Curr. Drug Targets* **2013**, *14*, 235–245. [CrossRef]

20. Mapel, D.W.; Roberts, M.H. Management of asthma and chronic obstructive pulmonary disease with combination inhaled corticosteroids and long-acting β-agonists: A review of comparative effectiveness research. *Drugs* **2014**, *74*, 737–755. [CrossRef]

21. Sharafkhaneh, A.; Velamuri, S.; Badmaev, V.; Lan, C.; Hanania, N. The potential role of natural agents in treatment of airway inflammation. *Ther. Adv. Respir. Dis.* **2007**, *1*, 105–120. [CrossRef]

22. Liu, X.J.; Bao, H.R.; Zeng, X.L.; Wei, J.M. Effects of resveratrol and genistein on nuclear factor-κB, tumor necrosis factor-α and matrix metalloproteinase-9 in patients with chronic obstructive pulmonary disease. *Mol. Med. Reports.* **2016**, *13*, 4266–4272. [CrossRef]

23. Yang, Y.L.; Hsu, H.T.; Wang, K.H.; Wang, C.S.; Chen, C.M.; Ko, W.C. Hesperidin-3'-o-methylether is more potent than hesperidin in phosphodiesterase inhibition and suppression of ovalbumin-induced airway hyperresponsiveness. *Evid. Based Complement. Alternat. Med.* **2012**, *2012*, 908562. [CrossRef]

24. Impellizzeri, D.; Talero, E.; Siracusa, R.; Alcaide, A.; Cordaro, M.; Zubelia, J.; Bruschetta, G.; Crupi, R.; Esposito, E.; Cuzzocrea, S.; et al. Protective effect of polyphenols in an inflammatory process associated with experimental pulmonary fibrosis in mice. *Br. J. Nutr.* **2015**, *114*, 853–865. [CrossRef]

25. Biswas, S.; Hwang, J.W.; Kirkham, P.A.; Rahman, I. Pharmacological and dietary antioxidant therapies for chronic obstructive pulmonary disease. *Curr. Med. Chem.* **2013**, *20*, 1496–1530. [CrossRef]

26. Tabak, C.; Arts, I.C.; Smit, H.A.; Heederik, D.; Kromhout, D. Chronic obstructive pulmonary disease and intake of catechins, flavonols, and flavones: The MORGEN Study. *Am. J. Respir. Crit. Care Med.* **2001**, *164*, 61–64. [CrossRef]

27. Kim, Y.H.; Choi, Y.J.; Kang, M.K.; Park, S.H.; Antika, L.D.; Lee, E.J.; Kim, D.Y.; Kang, Y.H. Astragalin inhibits allergic inflammation and airway thickening in ovalbumin-challenged mice. *J. Agric. Food Chem.* **2017**, *65*, 836–845. [CrossRef]

28. Gong, J.H.; Cho, I.H.; Shin, D.; Han, S.Y.; Park, S.H.; Kang, Y.H. Inhibition of airway epithelial-to-mesenchymal transition and fibrosis by kaempferol in endotoxin-induced epithelial cells and ovalbumin-sensitized mice. *Lab. Investig.* **2014**, *94*, 297–308. [CrossRef]

29. Kim, Y.H.; Choi, Y.J.; Kang, M.K.; Lee, E.J.; Kim, D.Y.; Oh, H.; Kang, Y.H. Oleuropein curtails pulmonary inflammation and tissue destruction in models of experimental asthma and emphysema. *J. Agric. Food Chem.* **2018**, *66*, 7643–7654. [CrossRef]

30. Kim, Y.H.; Choi, Y.J.; Lee, E.J.; Kang, M.K.; Park, S.H.; Kim, D.Y.; Oh, H.; Park, S.J.; Kang, Y.H. Novel glutathione-containing yeast extracts inhibit eosinophilia and mucus overproduction in a murine model of asthma. *Nutr. Res. Pract.* **2017**, *11*, 461–469. [CrossRef]

31. Chipuk, J.E.; Kuwana, T.; Bouchier-Hayes, L.; Droin, N.M.; Newmeyer, D.D.; Schuler, M.; Green, D.R. Direct activation of Bax by p53 mediates mitochondrial membrane permeabilization and apoptosis. *Science* **2004**, *303*, 1010–1014. [CrossRef]

32. Han, W.; Dong, Z.; Dimitropoulou, C.; Su, Y. Hydrogen Sulfide Ameliorates Tobacco Smoke-Induced Oxidative Stress and Emphysema in Mice. *Antioxid. Redox Signal.* **2011**, *15*, 2121–2134. [CrossRef]

33. Schuliga, M. NF-κB signaling in chronic inflammatory airway disease. *Biomolecules* **2015**, *5*, 1266–1283. [CrossRef]

34. Edwards, M.R.; Bartlett, N.W.; Clarke, D.; Birrell, M.; Belvisi, M.; Johnston, S.L. Targeting the NF-κB pathway in asthma and chronic obstructive pulmonary disease. *Pharmacol. Ther.* **2009**, *121*, 1–13. [CrossRef]

35. Thangapandiyan, S.; Miltonprabu, S. Epigallocatechin gallate supplementation protects against renal injury induced by fluoride intoxication in rats: Role of Nrf2/HO-1 signaling. *Toxicol. Rep.* **2014**, *1*, 12–30. [CrossRef]

36. Yildirim, A.O.; Ince, M.; Eyi, Y.E.; Tuncer, S.K.; Kaldirim, U.; Eroglu, M.; Oztas, E.; Cayci, T.; Kilic, A.; Inal, V.; et al. The effects of glycyrrhizin on experimental acute pancreatitis in rats. *Eur. Rev. Med. Pharmacol. Sci.* **2013**, *17*, 2981–2987.

37. Zuo, L.; He, F.; Sergakis, G.G.; Koozehchian, M.S.; Stimpfl, J.N.; Rong, Y.; Diaz, P.T.; Best, T.M. Interrelated role of cigarette smoking, oxidative stress, and immune response in COPD and corresponding treatments. *Am. J. Physiol. Cell. Mol. Physiol.* **2014**, *307*, L205–L218. [CrossRef]
38. Barreiro, E.; Peinado, V.I.; Galdiz, J.B.; Ferrer, E.; Marin-Corral, J.; Sánchez, F.; Gea, J.; Barberà, J.A. Enigma in COPD project. Cigarette smoke-induced oxidative stress: A role in chronic obstructive pulmonary disease skeletal muscle dysfunction. *Am. J. Respir. Crit. Care Med.* **2010**, *182*, 477–488. [CrossRef]
39. Demedts, I.K.; Demoor, T.; Bracke, K.R.; Joos, G.F.; Brusselle, G.G. Role of apoptosis in the pathogenesis of COPD and pulmonary emphysema. *Respir. Res.* **2006**, *7*, 53. [CrossRef]
40. Tuder, R.M.; Petrache, I.; Elias, J.A.; Voelkel, N.F.; Henson, P.M. Apoptosis and emphysema: The missing link. *Am. J. Respir. Cell. Mol. Biol.* **2003**, *28*, 551–554. [CrossRef]
41. Durham, A.L.; Caramori, G.; Chung, K.F.; Adcock, I.M. Targeted anti-inflammatory therapeutics in asthma and chronic obstructive lung disease. *Transl. Res.* **2016**, *167*, 192–203. [CrossRef]
42. Bernardo, I.; Bozinovski, S.; Vlahos, R. Targeting oxidant-dependent mechanisms for the treatment of COPD and its comorbidities. *Pharmacol. Ther.* **2015**, *155*, 60–79. [CrossRef]
43. Gonçalves, P.B.; Romeiro, N.C. Multi-target natural products as alternatives against oxidative stress in chronic obstructive pulmonary disease (COPD). *Eur. J. Med. Chem.* **2019**, *163*, 911–931. [CrossRef]
44. Tanaka, T.; Takahashi, R. Flavonoids and asthma. *Nutrients* **2013**, *5*, 2128–2143. [CrossRef]

MDPI

St. Alban-Anlage 66

4052 Basel

Switzerland

Tel. +41 61 683 77 34

Fax +41 61 302 89 18

www.mdpi.com

Antioxidants Editorial Office

E-mail: antioxidants@mdpi.com

www.mdpi.com/journal/antioxidants

Lightning Source UK Ltd.
Milton Keynes UK
UKHW050319090722
405524UK00006B/87